Dynamics of

FLUIDS and PLASMAS

JOHANNES M. BURGERS

Dynamics of
FLUIDS and PLASMAS

Proceedings of the Symposium held in honor of
Professor Johannes M. Burgers sponsored by
the Air Force Office of Scientific Research and
the Institute for Fluid Dynamics and Applied
Mathematics, University of Maryland,
October 7–9, 1965

Edited by

S. I. Pai, CHAIRMAN
A. J. Faller
T. L. Lincoln
D. A. Tidman
G. N. Trytten
T. D. Wilkerson

Institute for Fluid Dynamics and Applied Mathematics
University of Maryland
College Park, Maryland

1966

ACADEMIC PRESS   NEW YORK • LONDON

ACADEMIC PRESS INC.
111 Fifth Avenue, New York, New York 10003

United Kingdom Edition published by
ACADEMIC PRESS INC. (LONDON) LTD.
Berkeley Square House, London W.1

LIBRARY OF CONGRESS CATALOG CARD NUMBER: 66-29728

PRINTED IN THE UNITED STATES OF AMERICA

This volume is cordially dedicated to

JOHANNES MARTINUS BURGERS

on the occasion of his seventieth birthday

List of Contributors

Numbers in parentheses indicate the pages on which the authors' contributions begin.

ROBERT D. ALLEN, *Department of Biology, Princeton University, Princeton, New Jersey* (3)

A. BAJER, *Department of Biology, University of Oregon, Eugene, Oregon* (59)

R. BETCHOV, *Aerospace Corporation, El Segundo, California* (215)

S. CORRSIN, *The Johns Hopkins University, Baltimore, Maryland* (275)

J. R. DORFMAN, *University of Maryland, College Park, Maryland* (199)

ALAN J. FALLER, *Institute for Fluid Dynamics and Applied Mathematics, University of Maryland, College Park, Maryland* (309)

FRANÇOIS N. FRENKIEL, *Applied Mathematics Laboratory, David Taylor Model Basin, Washington, D. C.* (257)

ROBERT E. KAYLOR, *Institute for Fluid Dynamics and Applied Mathematics, University of Maryland, College Park, Maryland* (309)

PHILIP S. KLEBANOFF, *National Bureau of Standards, Washington, D. C.* (257)

ALAN C. KOLB, *United States Naval Research Laboratory, Washington, D. C.* (505)

ROBERT H. KRAICHNAN, *Petersborough, New Hampshire* (239)

RUSSELL M. KULSRUD, *Princeton Plasma Physics Laboratory, Princeton University, Princeton, New Jersey* (333)

HERBERT LASHINSKY, *Institute for Fluid Dynamics and Applied Mathematics, University of Maryland, College Park, Maryland* (473)

TING YI LI, *Department of Aeronautical and Astronautical Engineering, Ohio State University, Columbus, Ohio* (155)

C. C. LIN, *Massachusetts Institute of Technology, Cambridge, Massachusetts* (127)

NORMAN F. NESS, *Laboratory for Space Sciences, Goddard Space Flight Center, Greenbelt, Maryland* (451)

WILLIAM A. NEWCOMB, *Lawrence Radiation Laboratory, University of California, Livermore, California* (405)

S. I. PAI,[1] *Institute for Fluid Dynamics and Applied Mathematics, University of Maryland, College Park, Maryland* (179)

[1] PRESENT ADDRESS: *Institute of Space and Aeronautical Science, University of Tokyo, Tokyo, Japan.*

G. S. PATTERSON, JR., *The Johns Hopkins University, Baltimore, Maryland* (275)

JOHN O. POWERS,[1] *Institute for Fluid Dynamics and Applied Mathematics, University of Maryland, College Park, Maryland* (179)

ROBERT P. RHEA.[2] *Rockefeller University, New York, New York* (35)

E. L. RESLER, JR., *Graduate School of Aerospace Engineering, Cornell University, Ithaca, New York* (135)

ROBERT RIKMENSPOEL, *The Population Council, Rockefeller University, New York, New York* (9)

R. S. RIVLIN, *Division of Applied Mathematics, Brown University, Providence, Rhode Island* (83)

G. SANDRI, *Aeronautical Research Associates of Princeton, Inc., Princeton, New Jersey* (341)

D. A. TIDMAN, *Institute for Fluid Dynamics and Applied Mathematics, University of Maryland, College Park, Maryland* (399)

JOHN M. WILCOX, *Space Sciences Laboratory, University of California, Berkeley, California* (433)

T. D. WILKERSON, *Institute for Fluid Dynamics and Applied Mathematics, University of Maryland, College Park, Maryland* (487)

[1] PRESENT ADDRESS: *Aerophysics Division, Naval Ordnance Laboratory, White Oak, Maryland.*

[2] PRESENT ADDRESS: *Department of Zoology, University of Minnesota, Minneapolis, Minnesota.*

List of Participants

Richard Abrams
Robert D. Allen
G. Astarita

Andrew Bajer
Bohdan Balko
Karl F. Barth
Frederick D. Bennett
Edward R. Benton
B. S. Berger
Robert Berger
R. Betchov
Alan Brandt
Ronald Brown
Dimitri S. Bugnolo
Paul Burgan
J. M. Burgers
Mrs. J. M. Burgers
J. William Byrd

Peter Cable
William S. Campbell
C. R. Cassity
C. C. Chang
Mrs. C. C. Chang
George Charatis
Eugene J. Clothiaux
Erwin V. Cohen
G. Comte-Bellot
Morton Cooper
S. Corrsin
Jorge F. Cossio
W. D. Criminale
William J. Crowe

Harry J. Davis
William P. Davis, Jr.
Howard J. Deacon
P. C. T. deBoer
Gary S. Deem
Alan DeSilva
J. Diaz
Mrs. J. Diaz
A. Dolinsky

J. R. Dorfman
Mrs. J. R. Dorfman
Michael Doria

Joachim B. Ehrman
Mrs. L. Einschlag
Chaim Elata
Gerrard Emch
J. L. Ericksen
M. Ernst
Harry Ess
Garret J. Etgen
Ahron Eviator

Alan J. Faller
Mrs. Alan J. Faller
Gaetano Fichera
Mrs. Gaetano Fichera
William S. Filler
Lee N. Foster
Mark P. Freeman
Francois N. Frenkiel
Jerry Fu
Francis Fung

George Gal
M. A. Garstens
John H. Gerrard
Alfred Gessow
A. Ghaffari
John Gilmore
N. S. Goel
Michael Goldberg
Arnold Goldburg
Robert Goldman
Sydney Goldstein
Paul S. Granville
Ernest P. Gray
Hans R. Griem
Mrs. Hans R. Griem
Eugene Guth

Michael J. Haggerty
Howard J. M. Hanley

Fred T. Harris
M. S. Harris
Paul Harris
Stewart Harris
Vascar G. Harris
Mrs. J. Haugen
John M. Hedgepeth
R. M. Helms
David Hill
Adolf Hochstim
Horace E. Hoffman
Ronald R. Holder
Samuel Horn
R. Lee Hornbake
Ian O. Huebsch
Yu Kao Hsu
Paul Hyer

A. Iberall

Gerald Janowitz
Norman C. Jen
E. W. Jerger

George K. Kahl
Robert E. Kaylor
Mrs. Robert E. Kaylor
Valdis Kibens
Phillip S. Klebanoff
W. T. Koiter
Alan C. Kolb
David W. Koopman
Samuel Korman
Dimitri Kozakoff
Robert H. Kraichnan
Paul L. Kronick
Martin Kruskal
Mrs. Martin Kruskal
Russel Kulsrud
Val Kucher
Ulrich H. Kurzweg

Frank Lane
Herbert Lashinsky

ix

Howard Laster
Mrs. Howard Laster
Maurice Levy
Jerzy J. Lewak
Ting Yi Li
C. C. Lin
Miss H. Lincke
Thomas L. Lincoln
Mrs. Thomas L. Lincoln
Bernard S. Loeb
R. S. Lowder

Kaichi Madea
J. M. Marchello
David Margolis
Monroe H. Martin
Mrs. Monroe H. Martin
S. Martin
R. S. Marvin
C. Masaitis
E. A. Mason
F. N. Mastrup
William Mayer
Mrs. William Mayer
W. L. Melnik
G. N. Mercer
D. C. Milulecky
Myron Miller
H. K. Moffatt
Louis Monchick
Elliott W. Montroll
Mrs. Elliott W. Montroll
Mark V. Morkovin
Harold S. Morton, Jr.
Jeffry Morton
T. F. Morse
Peter J. Murphy

Y. Nakagawa
Norman F. Ness
William A. Newcomb
Ralph J. Nossal

Vivian O'Brien
Binyork Ouyang
Jerzy A. Owzarek

D. C. Pack
S. I. Pai
Mrs. S. I. Pai
Coda H. T. Pan
Henry R. Pantek
Yih-Ho Pao

Aristotle Papayoanou
G. Stuart Patterson, Jr.
Gary A. Pearson
Robert H. Pearson
E. A. Pinson
Mrs. E. A. Pinson
Carl C. Pitts
Harry Polachek
Irvin Pollin
Mrs. Irvin Pollin
John O. Powers
William J. Price
Mrs. William J. Price

Carlos Quevedo

A. Radichevich
E. L. Resler
Robert P. Rhea
Robert Rikmenspoel
R. S. Rivlin
James R. Roberts
Milton Rogers
Mrs. Milton Rogers
Sidney Rothberg
Robert J. Rubin

Edward Saibel
Guido Sandri
J. M. Santiago
W. J. Schaffers
G. B. Schubauer
C. Schubert
Fritz Schultz-Grunow
Ira R. Schwartz
Harvey Scott
Raymond Sedney
F. A. Seyer
Ramy Shanny
Charles Sheer
S. F. Shen
Walter Shropshire
Donald R. Simon
R. Bruce Simpson
Raymond A. Sjodin
Milton M. Slawsky
Mrs. Milton M. Slawsky
Z. Slawsky
Allie M. Smith
Joseph H. Spurk
Robert M. St. John
Howard M. Stainer
Milomir M. Stanisic

Andrew A. Sterk
K. Suchy
Leo D. Sullivan
A. A. Szewczyk

I. G. Tadjbakhsh
John Tangeman
Charles C. Taylor
Phrixos J. Theodories
Mrs. Phrixos J. Theodories
Paul Thurston
Mrs. Paul Thurston
Derek A. Tidman
Mrs. Derek A. Tidman
Arthur N. Tifford
Nils Tongring
Kenell J. Touryan
S. C. Traugott
Arthur Travers
C. K. Tsao
P. S. Tschang
Marshall P. Tulin
George N. Trytten
Mrs. George N. Trytten

Ronald E. Walker
John P. Wallace
K. C. Wang
Kenneth Wang
Myron Wecker
Erich H. Wedemeyer
George Weiss
Michael J. Werle
John R. Weske
John M. Wilcox
M. W. Wilcox
Thomas D. Wilkerson
Mrs. Thomas D. Wilkerson
H. K. Wiskind
Calvin J. Wolf
Jerry A. Wolfe
Bernard T. Wolfson
C. S. Wu

E. A. Yadlowsky
James T. Yen
E. D. Young

Norman J. Zabusny
Robert Zwanzig
Jay Zwally

Foreword

On October 7–9 1965 the University of Maryland and the Air Force Office of Scientific Research held a Symposium on the Dynamics of Fluids and Plasmas to mark the occasion of Professor Burgers, official retirement from his post as Research Professor in the Institute for Fluid Dynamics and Applied Mathematics.

His wide range of interests are reflected in the sessions of the Symposium which dealt with Biomechanics, Rheology, Kinetic Theory, Turbulence, and Plasma Physics. To all these Professor Burgers has made significant contributions; unfortunately his philosophical interests could not be represented.

More than anyone else that I know Professor Burgers is a scientist's scientist and many of us in this Institute have at one time or another sought his advice, scientific or otherwise. Recognizing his unique capacities, the University of Maryland will maintain his appointment on a part-time basis so that we may look forward to a continuing association with him.

This volume is a record of the Proceedings of the Symposium. With it we hope Professor Burgers will relive some of his scientific victories of the past, and that younger members of the scientific community may find in its pages inspiration to extend the frontiers of these areas which in many cases owe their vigor to his pioneering studies.

December, 1966
$\qquad$ M. H. MARTIN, *Director*
Institute for Fluid Dynamics
and Applied Mathematics

Preface

The organization of the Symposium on the Dynamics of Fluids and Plasmas, held in honor of Professor Johannes M. Burgers was a great pleasure and honor for those who served on the Steering Committee; they were S. I. Pai (Chairman), A. J. Faller, T. L. Lincoln, D. A. Tidman, G. N. Trytten, and T. D. Wilkerson, with the able assistance of Mrs. Joan A. Haugen.

The general aim of the Symposium was to review the current status and present some of the newer research results in several branches of the dynamics of fluids and plasmas in which Professor Burgers has made valuable contributions.

Many persons working together contributed to the success of the Symposium. We are grateful for the encouragement and financial support provided by the Air Force Office of Scientific Research which has sustained Professor Burgers' investigations here at the University of Maryland. Particularly we greatly appreciate the sympathetic counseling of Messrs. Milton Rogers and Paul Thurston of the Air Force Office of Scientific Research. We would like to extend thanks to all the invited speakers, the chairmen of the various sessions, the participants, and guests. Special thanks are owed to Professor W. T. Koiter who represented Professor Burgers' colleagues at the Technical University of Delft, where he had taught for 37 years before coming to the University of Maryland.

Last, but by no means least, the presence of Professor and Mrs. Burgers during the Symposium helped create a milieu that became at once a scientifically stimulating forum and a relaxed and enjoyable gathering of friends.

We like to consider this Symposium as another high point in our continuing close association with Professor Burgers now and for years to come.

December, 1966

S. I. Pai, *Chairman*
Steering Committee

A Short Biography of
PROFESSOR JOHANNES MARTINUS BURGERS

Professor Johannes Martinus Burgers was born on January 13, 1895, in Arnhem, in the Netherlands. He attended primary and secondary schools at Arnhem from 1901 to 1912 and took supplementary courses in Latin and Greek from 1912 to 1914, during which period he also studied advanced mathematics and subjects relating to theoretical physics.

Professor Burgers studied at the University of Leiden, Netherlands, from 1914 to 1918 under many world famous professors such as: P. Ehrenfest, H. A. Lorentz, and H. Kamerlingh Onnes. He obtained his Doctoral degree in the Mathematical and Physical Sciences on December 12, 1918, with a thesis entitled, "Het Atoommodel van Rutherford-Bohr" (The Model of the Atom according to Rutherford and Bohr, as based on the older form of quantum theory.) His thesis advisor was Professor P. Ehrenfest.

He was appointed Professor of Aerodynamics and Hydrodynamics at the Technical University of Delft, Netherlands, in the Department of Mechanical Engineering and Shipbuilding at the age of 23. He taught at the Technical University of Delft from 1918 to 1955.

In 1955, Professor Burgers resigned from his position in Delft and accepted a position as Research Professor in the Institute for Fluid Dynamics and Applied Mathematics of the University of Maryland. At the University of Maryland Professor Burgers has been leading a strong group of scientists in the investigation of many modern aspects of fluid and plasma dynamics. Some of these subjects were reviewed in this symposium. Professor Burgers received his official retirement on June 30, 1965. Recognizing his signal achievements in science, the University will continue Professor Burgers in his position as Research Professor in a part-time capacity in the Institute for Fluid Dynamics and Applied Mathematics.

Professor Burgers is not only a great scientist but also an excellent organizer who has promoted international cooperation in the investigation and advancement of our knowledge of theoretical and applied mechanics and other related subjects.   On a suggestion made by Dr. Theodore von Karman, Professor Burgers and Professor C. B. Biezeno organized the First International Congress for Applied Mechanics in Delft, Netherlands, in April 1924.   Since then he has been a member of the International Committee for the Congresses and took part in many of the subsequent ones.   In 1946 Professor Burgers took the preparatory steps for the foundation of the International Union of Theoretical and Applied Mechanics (IUTAM) which was admitted to the International Council of Scientific Unions in 1947.   He served as general secretary of IUTAM from 1946 to 1952 and is a member of its General Assembly. He was secretary of the "Committee on Science and Its Social Relations" of the International Council of Scientific Unions from its foundation in 1937 to its termination in 1952.   He also served as secretary of the "Joint Commission on Viscosity and Plasticity" of the International Council from its creation in 1947 until its termination in 1952.   Together with Dr. G. W. Scott Blair and other members of this Committee, he took part in the organization of two international congresses on Rheology, one in Scheveningen, Netherlands, in 1948 and one in Oxford, England, in 1953. Professor Burgers also took an important part in the organization of the first three International Symposia on Cosmical Gasdynamics, 1949, 1953, 1957, and was an editor of the proceedings of these symposia.   He was active in many other international meetings.

Professor Burgers has been a member of many professional and academic societies including the Royal Netherlands Academy of Sciences, the Royal Institute of Engineers in the Netherlands, the Netherlands Physical Society (being president of this society from 1922–23); Fellow of the American Institute of Physics; member of the American Geophysical Union; Fellow of the Institute of Aeronautical Sciences in the United States of America (now the American Institute of Aeronautics and Astronautics) and Fellow of the Royal Aeronautical Society in Great Britain (the last two until his retirement in 1965); the American Academy of Arts and Sciences; the New York Academy of Sciences.

Professor Burgers has received many honors and awards during his long scientific career, including honorary degrees from the Universite Libre de Bruxelles, Belgium, February 28, 1948, and from the Université de Poitiers, France, April 29, 1950.   He was awarded the Modesto Panetti Medal and the prize from the Accademia delle Scienze di Torino, Italy, on May 10, 1961, and he was elected a foreign member of that Academy in 1964.   He received the Bingham Medal of the Society of Rheology in

October, 1964. On November 2, 1955 he had been awarded the Decoration: "Ridder in the Orde van de Nederlandse Leeuw."

During his entire scientific career, Professor Burgers has been one of the world's leading authorities on fluid dynamics, developing our knowledge of fluid dynamics from hydraulics and theoretical hydrodynamics to our present-day scientific and technical understanding of this subject. To him we gratefully dedicate this Symposium on the Dynamics of Fluids and Plasmas.

A LIST OF PUBLICATIONS BY PROFESSOR J. M. BURGERS

[EDITOR'S NOTE: *Because of the limits of space it is not possible to give a complete list of publications by Professor J. M. Burgers. The following list contains a selection and mentions most of those written since he came to the United States.*]

1. Het atoommodel van Rutherford-Bohr. (The model of the atom according to Rutherford and Bohr, as based on the older form of quantum theory.) Doctoral thesis at University of Leiden, 1918.

2. Some publications on the older form of the quantum theory in 1916 and 1917 in the Proceedings of the Royal Netherlands Academy of Sciences.

3. Stationary streaming caused by a body in a fluid with friction, Proc. Roy. Neth. Acad. Sci. *23*, 1082–1107, 1920/21.

4. On the resistance experienced by a fluid in turbulent motion, Proc. Roy. Neth. Acad. Sci. *26*, 582–604, 1923.

5. Experiments on the fluctuations of the velocity in a current of air, Proc. Roy. Neth. Acad. Sci. *29*, 547–558, 1926.

6. On Oseen's theory for the approximate determination of the flow of a fluid with very small friction along a body, Proc. Roy. Neth. Acad. Sci. *31*, 433–453, 1928.

7. On the application of Oseen's hydrodynamical equations to the problem of the slipstream from ideal propeller, Proc. Roy. Neth. Acad. Sci. *32*, 1278–1290, 1929.

8. A remark on a formula for the resistance experienced by a body in a fluid, given by Oseen and Zeilon, Proc. Roy. Neth. Acad. Sci. *33*, 504–513, 1930.

9. On the application of Oseen's theory to the determination of the friction experienced by an infinitely thin flat plate, Proc. Roy. Neth. Acad. Sci. *33*, 605–613, 1930.

10. On the motion of a fluid under the action of external forces (with an application to the theory of the lifting surface), Comptes Rendus V-ième Congrès Intern. Navig. Aérienne, La Haye 1930, Vol. I, 497–508.

11. Hitzdrahtmessungen, in "Handbuch der Experimentalphysik," Vol. IV-1, 637–667, Leipzig, 1931.

12. General aerodynamic theory—perfect fluids (with Dr. Th. von Kármán), Vol. II of W. F. Durand's "Aerodynamic Theory," Springer Verlag, Berlin, 1935.

13. Editor of the first and second reports on viscosity and plasticity, Verhand. Roy. Neth. Acad. Sci., Amsterdam, 1935 and 1958, and contributor of various chapters to these reports.

14. Some considerations on the fields of stress connected with dislocations in a regular crystal lattice, Proc. Roy. Neth. Acad. Sci. *42*, 293–325, 378–399, 1939.

15. Mathematical examples illustrating relations occurring in the theory of turbulent fluid motion, Verhand. Roy. Neth. Acad. Sci. Sec. 1. *17*, No. 2, 1–53, 1939.

16. Geometrical considerations concerning the structural irregularities to be assumed in a crystal, Proc. Phys. Soc. London *52*, 23–33, 1940.

17. On the transmission of sound waves through a shock wave, Proc. Roy. Neth. Acad. Sci. *49*, 273–281, 1946.

18. On the influence of gravity upon the expansion of a gas, Proc. Roy. Neth. Acad. Sci. *51*, 145–154, 525–532, 1948.

19. A mathematical model illustrating the theory of turbulence, Adv. in Appl. Mech. *1*, 171–199, 1948.

20. Solutions of the equations for the non-uniform propagation of a very strong shock wave (with W. P. Robbertse), Proc. Roy. Neth. Acad. Sci. *52*, 958–965, 1067–1074, 1949.

21. Correlation problems in a one-dimensional model of turbulence, Proc. Roy. Neth. Acad. Sci. *53*, 247–260, 393–406, 718–742, 1950.

22. On the coalescence of wave-like solutions of a simple non-linear partial differential equation, Proc. Roy. Neth. Acad. Sci. *B57*, 45–72, 1954.

23. Further statistical problems connected with the solution of a simple non-linear partial differential equation, Proc. Roy. Neth. Acad. Sci. *B57*, 159–169, 1954.

24. Statistical problems connected with the solution of a simple non-linear partial differential equation—Continuation, Proc. Roy. Neth. Acad. Sci. *B57*, 403–433, 1954.

25. A model for one dimensional compressible turbulence with two sets of characteristics, Proc. Roy. Neth. Acad. Sci. *B58*, 1–18, 1955.

26. Rotational motion of a sphere subject to visco-elastic deformation, Proc. Roy. Neth. Acad. Sci. *B58*, 219–237, 1955.

27. The effect of stretching of a vortex core, U. of Md. Tech. Note BN-80, 1956.

28. Selected topics from the theory of gas flow at high temperature (I)–(VI), U. of Md. Tech. Note BN-83, BN-84, 1956; BN-99, BN-103, 1957; BN-124a/b, 1958; BN-176, 1959.

29. Dislocations in crystal lattices (with W. G. Burgers), in "Rheology," Vol. I, ed. by F. R. Eirich, Academic Press, Ch. 6, 141–199, 1956.

30. On steady flow patterns appearing when a sink is combined with boundary layer flow, U. of Md. Tech. Note BN-91, 1957.

31. The penetration of a shock wave into a magnetic field, U. of Md. Tech. Note BN-102, 1957.

32. Penetration of a shock wave into a magnetic field, in "Magnetohydrodynamics," ed. by R. K. M. Landshoff, Stanford Univ. Press, 36–56, 1957.

33. On the problem of the postglacial uplift of fennoscandia, (with B. J. Collette), Proc. Roy. Neth. Acad. Sci. *B61*, 221–241, 1958.

34. Some problems of magnetogasdynamics, in S. Goldstein "Lectures in Fluid Dynamics," Wiley (Interscience), 271–299, 1960.

35. Statistical plasma mechanics, in "Plasma Dynamics," ed. by F. H. Clauser, Addison-Wesley, Ch. 5, 119–186, 1960.

36. Magnetogasdynamic problems from the point of view of particle dynamics, in "Aeronautics and Astronautics," ed. by N. J. Hoff and W. G. Vincenti, Pergamon Press, 288–304, 1960.

37. The Boltzmann equation for flows with chemical reactions, in "Physical Chemistry in Aerodynamics and Space Flight," ed. by A. L. Myerson and A. C. Harrison, Pergamon Press, 4–11, 1961.

38. Motion of a completely ionized gas across a magnetic field in the presence of an electric field, Rev. Mod. Phys. *32*, 868–880, 1960.

39. On the application of two-particle distribution functions, in "Electromagnetics and Fluid Dynamics of Gaseous Plasma," Symposium Proceedings, Brooklyn Polytechnic Press, 81–98, 1961.

40. A functional equation related to the Boltzmann equation and to the equations of gas dynamics, in "Partial Differential Equations and Continuum Mechanics," ed. by R. E. Langer, 289–317, U. of Wisc. Press, 1961.

41. On Landau damping in a fully ionized plasma and its combination with collisional damping, in "Fluid Dynamics and Applied Mathematics," ed. by J. B. Diaz and S. I. Pai, Gordon and Breach, New York, 79–103, 1962.

42. On the emergence of patterns of order, 32nd Josiah Willard Gibbs Lecture before the Amer. Math. Soc., Jan. 20, 1959, Bull. Amer. Math. Soc. *69*, 1–25, 1963.

43. The measuring process in quantum theory, Rev. Mod. Phys. *35*, 145–150, and 1032, 1963.

44. Application of the two-particle distribution function to estimate the collisional damping of plasma oscillations, Phys. Fluids *6*, 889–896, 1963.

45. Statistical problems connected with the solution of a nonlinear partial differential equation, in "Nonlinear Problems of Engineering," Proceedings Advanced Sci. Seminar, ed. by W. F. Ames, Academic Press, 123–137, 1964.

46. The transportation of magnetic lines of force by a highly conducting fluid, presented at the von Kármán sessions of the SIAM National Meeting in Washington, May 1964, published in the Proceedings of these sessions, J. Soc. Ind. App. Math. *13*, 184–205, 1965.

47. "Experience and Conceptual Activity," M. I. T. Press, 1965.

48. Functions and integrals connected with the solutions of the diffusion or heat flow equation, U. of Md. Tech. Note BN-398, 1965.

After Dinner Speech Given by Professor J. M. Burgers
October 7, 1965 during the Course of the
Symposium on the Dynamics of Fluids and Plasmas

Ladies and gentlemen, Professor Montroll, Dr. Hornbake, General Pinson, Professor Martin, Professor Pai, Professor Koiter, and most emphatically to all who are here: dear friends—I have been overwhelmed by what has been done and said here. Let me begin by expressing my deep gratitude and permit me to come back later to some of the feelings which are connected with it.

I have been scheduled on the program as a speaker, but there has already been such an array of excellent speakers that I will not take up too much of your time.

One of the things which has been very pleasant for me during the period of preparation for this Symposium was that I did not have to bother with these preparations. From time to time I heard about them, but I could always think: it is up to you to decide, I am just a guest. The excellent program which has been brought together, of which we have been enjoying the first part today, is proof that the organizers of the Symposium were of the highest caliber and that it was right not to meddle with their work. What has been arranged by the Committee in such a thoughtful way encompasses all that one can describe as flow of "structured media," whether the structure is due to electromagnetic effects as in the "plasma" of magnetogasdynamics and space science; or to molecular structures of polymers as found in substances which exhibit curious forms of rheological behavior; or finally to the presence and the activity of organic structures as are exhibited by the living protoplasma in cells.

I therefore congratulate the Symposium Committee, and its Chairman Professor Pai in particular, for the great success they have had in their work. You will be aware that the program and the contributions from the speakers in the scientific sessions are a reflection of the quality of the work carried out at the Institute for Fluid Dynamics and Applied Mathematics itself. It is to the Institute that the honor goes as well.

In connection with this I must express our gratitude to the Air Force Office of Scientific Research which has sponsored this Symposium, and

which for many years has been supporting free scientific investigation in a way such that the Institute has greatly benefited. I very much appreciate the presence here of General E. A. Pinson and that of several members of the staff of AFOSR with whom we have had many dealings, Dr. Mitch Slawsky, Mr. Milton Rogers, and Mr. Paul Thurston.

With regard to science I feel myself in a curious situation, as I am bridging a period of great expansion in which many things have moved. It is a period of development in all branches of knowledge and in particular in fluid dynamics. My contact with this subject began after I had studied physics and mathematics at the University of Leiden. When I was a student there, hydrodynamics was not a subject which commanded particular attention. At that time there existed a wide separation between theoretical hydrodynamics of the ideal fluid and hydraulics as a subject of engineering. Rheology had not yet been born. The barriers, however, were breaking down. The first indication for me was a little book by Professor Grammel on the hydrodynamical principles of flight, which appeared in 1917 and gave an account of the Kutta-Joukowsky theory of flow with circulation around wing profiles. My professor of theoretical physics, Ehrenfest, who was always keen to direct our attention to new books, had this book on show and gave some lectures on it. When in 1918 I was asked to come to the Technical University of Delft to occupy a newly created chair for aerodynamics and hydrodynamics, this was my only asset. I soon found that I had to acquaint myself with an extensive new world. Of some help were the interesting photographs of vortex motion behind bodies taken in a towing tank by Ahlborn in Hamburg; they brought the subject of vortex motion out of the domain of mathematical physics into that of practical experimentation. Then word came concerning the theory developed by Prandtl, Max Munk, and Betz for lifting systems of finite span. Prandtl's boundary layer theory had to be studied. Soon various series of scientific publications became available: the Reports and Memoranda of the British "Advisory Committee for Aeronautics"; the Reports of the American "National Advisory Committee for Aeronautics" (NACA—now NASA); the publications from Göttingen; the Zeitschrift für angewandte Mathematik und Mechanik. From France there were the publications by Eiffel; from Russia those of Dr. Riabouchinsky's laboratory in Koutchino (written in French). Of course I read Osborne Reynolds' papers on turbulence and Lorentz' comments and extension of this work.

In July 1921 Professor von Kármán invited me to visit his laboratory in Aachen. That was an initiation into the new views on boundary layer theory and on turbulence which von Kármán had just developed; and

it was also the beginning of a long friendship, from which I have profited both personally and scientifically.

When I was appointed to the Department of Mechanical Engineering and Shipbuilding of the Technical University at Delft, the presence of Professor Biezeno whose field is the theory of elasticity, was of far-reaching importance to me. He is by nature and inclination a first rate mathematician whose aim it was to keep our courses on a scientific level with prime attention to good mathematics and good reasoning. It is a cause of great concern to me that Professor Biezeno is not feeling as well as one would desire these days. I very much appreciate having Professor Koiter, Professor Biezeno's successor, here; apart from our friendship I see in him the representative of Biezeno, and I hope he will tell Biezeno that in these days of remembrance, Biezeno's personality, his friendship and help, and his influence are not forgotten.

In those days it was a big jump to go from theoretical physics to hydrodynamics, but I have never regretted entering the domain of fluid mechanics and I believe that many scientists who have become acquainted with the phenomena of flow have felt this as a welcome widening of their outlook. I have also appreciated the contact I had with the world of engineering and its problems. In the long run, physics has regained part of my love and I am happy that I could move into a domain of gasdynamics which is nearly a part of physics. Over the years other subjects have also held parts of my interest, as, for instance, astronomy, geology, biology, history, art. I came from my parental home with a large diversity of appetites. Much of my work has been directed towards interpretation and towards synthesis. I have always attempted to see phenomena and their interrelations as parts of a wider scheme, in the hope of arriving at better understanding and greater clarity; and in what I have written as well as in my teaching I have attempted to help others with these wider views.

I am deeply impressed by the advances of science in all domains, in particular by those in physics and biology. I enjoy these advances as increasing our insight and our understanding of relations existing in the universe. To have knowledge of these relations adds to the richness of life, in a way comparable to the richness which we derive from works of art. Vistas of forms of relationships of which we had not been aware are continually being opened. However, we must not forget that science is at its strongest when there is the possibility of separating a problem into separate details and isolating some of these, so that one can concentrate on such features as are amenable to exact treatment. Scientific analysis can then focus strong spotlights on particular points and call our full

attention to them.   In this respect science is again related to art; art also directs a spotlight on some idea, some relation, of which we had not been aware.   In both cases the successes are obtained at the expense of looking away from many other relations which are left unexplored as mere side effects.   Moreover, science deals most conveniently with questions which can be stated in quantitative terms.   Let us not forget that the manipulation of quantitative relations is only a tool and that real decisions may require evaluations quite different from what can be measured on a quantitative scale.   The economic relations, which carry such important effects in our society, give a poignant example of such a situation: one can calculate how much financial gain can be derived from automatization, but the important fact that human work is the basis for the dignity of the life of each person and that work ought to be distributed and arranged from this point of view cannot be expressed in such a way that it commands primary attention in economic planning.

With the expansion of the biological sciences and their growing importance for our outlook and for the structure of society, we may have to face a similar situation.   At times there seems to be a trend of expecting exclusive success from the investigation of quantitative relations and from the reliance on models taken over from physics and chemistry.   We are told that life probably soon will be made in the laboratory and that its mystery will then be solved.   It seems to be taken for granted that when self-reproducing systems shall have been obtained, the creation of life can be considered as a fact.   People who reason this way lose sight of the fact that life has features other than those which can be described in terms of the behavior of molecules and atoms.   Already the concept of an organism, the distinction between an organism and that which forms its environment, even the distinction between life and death—these concepts require notions which do not fit into the terminology of physics; they involve a reference to expectations and purposes.   The latter notions do not appear in the analysis of the behavior of nonliving matter and they cannot be measured by methods of physical experimentation. There exists therefore a tendency to deny to expectations and purposes any status as active agents in biological phenomena.   I contend that this is wrong, and I similarly contend that it is wrong to assume that thinking is a property of matter and can be taken over by computers.   Evidently life needs matter for its functioning and for its protection, as all living organisms we know of possess an elaborate material apparatus.   But this should not induce us to say that life "arises from matter."   It is the other way round: life creates matter.

I ask you to forgive me this digression, which may seem to be outside the domain which concerns us at the Symposium.   My own feeling is

that it does not; all sciences are connected, today more than ever, and interpretations helpful in one domain often can give light in other domains. This is the more important since science does not stand isolated in society: everywhere we are facing its applications. Even the work done in the space sciences, which is such a tremendous combination of physics, astronomy, and technology, poses various problems regarding life:

(a) What does space exploration mean for human life? What are we going to do with this extension of power? What will be our psychological reactions to it? and

(b) Is there a possibility that we shall encounter other forms of life? How shall we react to them, and how will they react to us? What may happen if we do not recognize that they have intentions?

In expanding and in planning our scientific work we must be aware of the fact that every result can lead to social reactions. We must be careful that our outlook and our decisions retain the freedom which is needed to ensure fullness of life. There is a danger that they may be overrun by technological tendencies which are considered as all-powerful and which we do not know how to master. Attention to the meaning of purposes and expectations as features of all forms of life can help us in the study of problems involved in the application of science and in the adjustment of society to new forms of technology. It can help us to bridge the gap between science and other forms of culture. It can lead to a deeper understanding of the creative possibilities before us and it will bring a better awareness of our responsibilities.

I now return to the starting point of this talk: my gratitude for what has been done and presented to give my wife and I pleasure and happiness. The way in which we were received at the University of Maryland ten years ago surpassed anything which we could have imagined when we came to America with the hope of settling here. We felt at home immediately and a deep love for this country has grown in us. The friendship which one can find in the United States and in particular in its scientific circles is a source of everlasting joy, which pervades all phases of one's life and one's work. It is a source of deep gratitude that I may count as personal friends not only the organizers of this Symposium, but also the majority of those present here, while the others are very close to that status. That you, Dr. Hornbake, have found time to be here and to honor this occasion in the name of President Elkins has great meaning for me and I thank you very much for your kind words. You will know how great an honor it has been for me to be a part of the University of Maryland ever since I came here, and although I have seen several other

universities in this country, I have never felt the desire to move away from Maryland.

I have already said how much I am moved by the presence of Professor Koiter and by the greetings he brought from Holland.

Again I would mention the cooperation of the Air Force Office of Scientific Research. Their understanding for the importance of the Institute for Fluid Dynamics and Applied Mathematics as a center of free scientific inquiry and free discussion has been of immense help. The Institute receives this help also from other scientific agencies, but it is AFOSR which is with us here tonight. AFOSR in this way is contributing to the protection and the diffusion of culture and we are fortunate that the notion of defense can be extended in this way. Perhaps, although I am an outsider, I may be allowed to express the wish that this extension of the notion of defense may go still further, and that it shall come to embrace also the protection of nature and wildlife and the preservation of the beauty of this great country, for all these features are part of an important cultural heritage which supports the zest for life, for free thinking, and for creative aspirations.

If it looks as if I am honored by this Symposium I can accept this only by stating that in reality I am no more than a point of reference. I could not have earned this personally without being a member of a group, and the real honor must go to the Institute, which is the pivot for the work of so many of us here. It is the wisdom of Monroe Martin which has made the Institute into what it has become: a center for research and for fruitful contact between scientists from a variety of disciplines. All members of the Institute have worked together to keep this feature alive and strong. This good understanding and sense of devoted cooperation is also a feature of the secretarial staff, whose work and whose care count for so much in our productivity.

Let my last words therefore be for the Institute and for the University; to both of them go my best wishes and I do not doubt that everyone of you will join in them.

Contents

Section I. Biomechanics and Other Problems of Living Organisms

Edited by T. L. Lincoln

Section II. Special Lectures on Rheology and Stellar Dynamics

Edited by G. N. Trytten

Section III. Kinetic Theory and Flow with Chemical Reaction

Edited by S. I. Pai

Section IV. Turbulence and Stability

Edited by Alan J. Faller

Section V. Theoretical Plasma Physics

Edited by D. A. Tidman

Section VI. Experimental Plasma Physics

Edited by T. D. Wilkerson

The Nature of Biological Movement

ROBERT D. ALLEN

DEPARTMENT OF BIOLOGY
PRINCETON UNIVERSITY
PRINCETON, NEW JERSEY

Motility, defined as the capacity of biological objects to exhibit gross movement or internal motion, is an important feature of life. The articles in Section I provide some penetrating insights into research on motility. My task is to present some kind of framework for these later contributions. Within the limitations of space, I believe that the best way to do this is to provide some indication of the scope of biological movement phenomena and to illustrate several examples by means of films.[1]

There should be no difficulty in grasping the significance of motility from animals that depend on swiftness for their survival. A deeper significance is seen, however, if one considers animals that to outward appearances are sessile, for example, the tunicates and clams. These sessile marine invertebrates have motile larvae that use their movement not only to capture food but also to find their way into ocean currents for dispersal to new environments. Adult tunicates and clams appear to have retired from such an active life; neither move bodily through the environment. Instead, they do the reverse: cilia beating within their gill chambers cause a continuous flow of sea water bearing food and oxygen through the gill chambers of the organisms. In fact, within the seemingly inert bodies of these sessile animals, there are highly active

---

[1] Motion pictures shown at the Symposium were single-concept educational color films (silent) published by the Ealing Corporation, Cambridge, Massachusetts, both in 16-mm reels and 8-mm cartridged loops. The authors, titles, and publication dates are listed below:

1. Allen, R. D. and Allen, M. D., *Amoeba proteus* (1964).
2. Allen, R. D. and Allen, M. D., *Difflugia corona* (1964).
3. Allen, R. D. and Allen, M. D., *Allogromia sp.* (1964).
4. Allen, R. D. and Allen, M. D., *Euglena gracilis* (1964).
5. Allen, R. D. and Allen, M. D., *Cytoplasmic streaming in plant cells* (1965).
6. Allen, R. D., Jones, R. F., and Allen, M. D., *Chlamydomonas rheinhardi* (1964).
7. Allen, R. D., Taub, S. R., and Allen, M. D., *Paramecium aurelia I* (1964).

cells equipped not only with cilia (gill epithelium) but also with flagella (sperm) and with pseudopodia (various amebocytes).

Higher plants also are not so motionless as they at first appear. Time-lapse pictures of leafy plants often show daily rhythms of leaf and stem movements, and cells removed from a wide variety of plant materials exhibit an astonishingly variable repertory of patterns of internal cyto-plasmic streaming and sometimes even locomotion (Kamiya, 1959). On the other hand, plants more than animals rely heavily on physical and biological factors in the environment to disperse their reproductive prod-ucts, and thus depend somewhat less on motility. The importance of the wind, legs of insects, and the digestive tracts of berry-eating mammals is so well known as not to require further comment here.

The widespread occurrence of motility in plants and animals from the simplest protists to the most complex chordates, arthropods, and higher plants suggests strongly that natural selection has placed a high premium on the ability to move. The "horsepower race" must have originated in the primeval seas, where microscopic predator and prey alike "struggled to remain alive" long enough to reproduce. Movement not only aids both the predator and prey, but it facilitates the union of gametes and effects the dispersal of reproductive products in a way that is, in principle at least, more economical than the somewhat random dispersal by wind or water currents. Most important, perhaps, is the fact that motile organisms can frequently respond "tropistically" to light, food, temper-ature, ions, and other physical and chemical environmental factors that may affect their survival.

In the large animals with which we are most familiar, movements are effected almost entirely by muscles of a wide variety of types. In this article, we shall assume some familiarity with muscular movement and go on to consider some of the more diverse mechanisms by which single cells and acellular organisms move.

Aside from muscles, probably the most efficient locomotor structures are the cilia and the flagella of single cells. Until the electron microscope revealed the basically similar ultrastructure of nine pairs of peripheral filaments surrounding two central filaments, these structures had been assigned different names and treated separately. The best source of information about the structure and function of these highly organized and efficient structures is a book by Sleigh (1962).

Two of the forementioned films show how these structures are used in cell locomotion among the protists. In the ciliate, *Paramecium aurelia*, for example, the metachronal beating of spiral rows of cilia and the oblique scoop-shaded oral groove combine to give this cell a spiral motion and helical path as it swims through pond water. A variety of stimuli can

induce reversal of ciliary beating which results in a reversal in the direction of locomotion and rotation. It is noteworthy that *Paramecium* also exhibits two functions that are related to motility, or at least perform mechanical work: contractile vacuole action, which maintains a relatively uniform intracellular osmotic pressure, and subcortical cyclosis, i.e., rotation of the inner cytoplasm adjacent to the cortex.

A film of *Euglena gracilis* shows movement typical of some flagellates; two flagella (only one of which is functional) can be seen extending from the anterior surface of the cell. The whip-like action of this structure produces locomotion in the direction toward which the flagellum extends. In spermatozoa, locomotion is away from the flagellum. In *Chlamydomonas rheinhardti*, the two functional flagella not only can be used for swimming through the fluid medium, but somehow also are able to glide without visible deformation along solid surfaces.

Another important organelle of cell locomotion is the pseudopod or "false foot," a protrusion of the surface of ameboid cells into which cytoplasm streams. Nearly all permanent bodies of water abound with ameboid cells; each species forms pseudopods with a restricted range of size and shape and a characteristic manner of movement (Bovee, 1964). Even pseudopods of the same shape, such as the cylindrical "lopopodia," vary a hundredfold in diameter, from a few microns up to a few hundred (Allen, 1961). In addition to this size variation, a spectrum of shapes is found from sheet-like "pharopodia" to filamentous "filopodia," some of which can bend and wave freely and shorten actively to perform physical work. However, another kind of filamentous pseudopod, the "actinopodium" found in Heliozoa, is supported by rigid array of "microtubules" visible only with the electron microscope. In the Foraminifera and Radiolaria (often called "the garbage collectors of the sea"), filopodia branch and fuse to form a "reticulopodial network." Each strand in this web has several streams of cytoplasm passing in each direction within it. Some of the salient features of lobopodial movement are shown in the forementioned published films of *Amoeba proteus* and *Difflugia corona*, and the reticulopodial type is shown in a film on *Allogromia sp.* Close study in recent years has shown that "ameboid movement" is a collection of surprisingly diverse movement processes. Progress has so far been made in understanding only a few of these.

Cilia, flagella, and pseudopodia are probably not the only locomotor organelles of cells. Among the bacteria, flagella are found which are basically different in both physical makeup and chemical constitution from the so-called "9 + 2 flagella" of protistan and metazoan cells (Kobayashi *et al.*, 1959). It is not even known for sure that the motive force is developed *within* the bacterial flagella, as opposed to at their base.

In spirochaets, planar and helical waves pass over the entire body of the microbe, along which extend fibrils that may play a role in this kind of motion. In myxobacteria, a type of cell locomotion occurs which involves changes in cell shape reminiscent of ameboid movement; however, the details are so poorly seen with the light microscope that it is difficult to know whether to classify this type of locomotion as "ameboid movement" (Weibull, 1960).

Some cells locomote without any visible locomotor organelles. Some bacteria, blue-green algae, diatoms, and gregarine protists "glide." "Gliding" is a term used for lack of more accurate information, for the truth is that we have no clear indications as to how these cells move. In some forms, slime secretion may be the propellant; in others, a thin peripheral layer of cytoplasm may be moving over the surface like a tractor-tread (Jarosch, 1962, and Weibull, 1960).

The movements that take place within cells are perhaps even more intriguing than the movements of whole cells. We lack an adequate explanation of most subcellular movements, such as the slow rotation of nuclei in tissue culture cells and the sudden excursion of particles previously engaged only in thermally induced Brownian motion. Rebhun (1964) has given the name "saltatory (jumping) motion" to this phenomenon and has discussed its occurrence in a wide variety of cell types.

It is probably accurate to claim that some kind of motion other than Brownian motion occurs at some time or other in all cells. This is certainly true if we include the process of mitotis, from which all cells arise (except certain cases of less precise distribution of genetic material called "amitosis"). In dividing cells, the mitotic spindle appears to "crystallize out" of the cytoplasm from fibrous proteins manufactured by the cell prior to the need for them (Mazia, 1963). Dr. Bajer will discuss several aspects of mitotic movements in his paper.

Almost as ubiquitous as mitotic movements are various types of cytoplasmic streaming. In some cells, e.g., *Euglena*, cytoplasm streams in response to pressure applied by an outer, contractile pellicle. The same is apparently true of the streaming in the acellular slime mold, *Physarum polycephalum*, which Dr. Rhea will discuss (cf. Kamiya, 1959). In this organism, polarized light has revealed the presence of circular, longitudinal, and spiral fibrils in the outer layer (ectoplasm) which form and disappear with a half-life of only a few minutes. These become deformed and simultaneously undergo changes in birefringence in a coordinated manner, suggesting strongly that they are the elements producing the motive force for streaming and torsional movements (Nakajima and Allen, 1965).

In most plant cells, however, the cytoplasm streams, despite the fact

that the cell itself is kept from changing shape by a rigid cell wall.   In the giant cells of the stonewart, *Nitella*, for example, a belt of cytoplasm with almost no internal shear revolves about the inner surface of the rigid and stationary cortex, apparently propelled by some kind of force-producing interaction between the stationary cortex and the endoplasm (Kamiya, 1959, Hayashi, 1964, and Kuroda, 1964).   In leaf cells of the common aquarium plant, *Elodea*, the endoplasm does not flow as a plug; instead, some of the chloroplasts are free to move about, but smaller particles (probably mitochondria, the "powerhouses of the cell") glide by, seemingly swept by "gusts" of activity in restricted regions of the cortex.   Not all of the activity is in the cortex; for piercing the large central vacuole are transvacuolar strands in which the cytoplasm streams in both directions.   In stamen-hair cells of *Tradescantia*, this kind of bidirectional streaming is observed not only in transvacuolar strands but also in the cortical layer.   These patterns are shown in a published film, but they are only partly representative of the geometrically varied patterns of cytoplasmic streaming found within the plant and animal kingdoms.

For a long time, the mechanisms of cell movement, cytoplasmic streaming and other motile systems appeared to be very mysterious indeed. They were very resistant to experimental attack, because nearly every experimental procedure brought motion to a halt and destroyed the process under investigation.   Within recent years, however, the electron microscope has begun to inform us about the ultrastructure of various motile cells, and there has been a rebirth of interest in more penetrating studies of living cells, for example, with new types of physical instruments, especially special light microscopes.

Progress in the study of motility has depended to a large extent not only on the hardware but also on the concepts of the physical sciences. It was difficult to comprehend, for example, bidirectional streaming in a transvacuolar strand or reticulopodial network in terms of pressure acting on ordinary Newtonian fluids.   However, enough is now known about viscoelastic, fiber-forming polymers that we can now envisage mechanisms of streaming which would not involve pressure.   Models have been developed along these lines which offer reasonably satisfactory working hypotheses for lobopodial and reticulopodial movement (Allen *et al.*, 1965, and Allen, 1964).

The study of biological movement poses many intriguing problems requiring physical, chemical, and mathematical approaches.   Biologists beset by the awesome complexity of living processes can profit enormously from some form of collaboration with physical scientists and applied mathematicians, whose relatively uncluttered minds can frequently devise

astonishingly simple models. Such models may (or may not) later explain biological realities. The realities and complexities of biological processes must not be disregarded, however. Some of the earlier attempts at analysis of cell division, cell movement, cytoplasmic streaming, etc., as exercises in "mathematical biophysics" began with unnecessarily simple and inaccurate factual information and can be said to have contributed little of lasting biological interest.

Limitations of time have not allowed me to discuss in any depth what is known about the mechanisms of motility. It is probably fair to say that diversity has been found in many situations where unity was expected. For example, there appears to be no "master molecule" found in all moving cells. For those of us working on biological movement, exciting times appear to lie ahead, for many of the problems to be solved are within the realm of what is now possible with physical and chemical techniques. It appears likely that a couple of billion years of evolution have provided us with many variations on several main themes of biological movement. As the molecules responsible for movement become better known to us, we may come to understand more fully some of the mechanisms both of movement and of organic evolution.

REFERENCES

ALLEN, R. D. (1961). *In* "The Cell" (J. Brachet and A. E. Mirsky, eds.), Vol. II, pp. 135–216. Academic Press, New York.

ALLEN, R. D. (1964). *In* "Primitive Motile Systems in Cell Biology" (R. D. Allen and N. Kamiya, eds.), pp. 407–431. Academic Press, New York.

ALLEN, R. D., FRANCIS, D. W., and NAKAJIMA, H. (1965). *Proc. Natl. Acad. Sci.* **54**, 1153–1161.

BOVEE, E. (1964). *In* "Primitive Motile Systems in Cell Biology" (R. D. Allen and N. Kamiya, eds.), pp. 189–219. Academic Press, New York.

HAYASHI, T. (1964). *In* "Primitive Motile Systems in Cell Biology" (R. D. Allen and N. Kamiya, eds.), pp. 19–29. Academic Press, New York.

JAROSCH, R. (1962). *In* "Physiology and Biochemistry of Algae" (R. Lewin, ed.), pp. 573–581. Academic Press, New York.

KAMIYA, N. (1965). *Protoplasmatologia* **8**, No. 3a, 1–199.

KOBAYASHI, T., RINKER, J. N., and KOFFLER, H., (1959). *Arch. Biochem. Biophys.* **84**, 342–362.

KURODA, K. (1964). *In* "Primitive Motile Systems in Cell Biology" (R. D. Allen and N. Kamiya, eds.), pp. 31–40. Academic Press, New York.

MAZIA, D. (1961). *In* "The Cell" (J. Brachet and A. E. Mirsky, eds.), Vol. III, pp. 77–412. Academic Press, New York.

NAKAJIMA, H. and ALLEN, R. D., (1965). *J. Cell Biol.* **25**, 361–374.

REBHUN, L. I. (1964). *In* "Primitive Motile Systems in Cell Biology" (R. D. Allen and N. Kamiya, eds.), pp. 503–525. Academic Press, New York.

SLEIGH, M. A. (1962). "The Biology of Cilia and Flagella." MacMillan, New York.

WEIBULL, C. (1960). *In* "The Bacteria" (R. Y. Stanier and I. C. Gunsalus, eds.), Vol. I, pp. 153–205. Academic Press, New York.

Physical Principles of Flagellar Motion

ROBERT RIKMENSPOEL

THE POPULATION COUNCIL
ROCKEFELLER UNIVERSITY
NEW YORK, NEW YORK

Experimental observation of flagellar motion shows that the achievement of a forward velocity is a second-order effect in the amplitude of the wave travelling in the flagellum. Helical waves in a flagellum cause a torque to be exerted on it, which makes the whole cell rotate with a frequency roughly proportional to the forward velocity. The theory of elastic bending of thin rods can be applied to simulate waveforms in flagella. From the theoretical model values are obtained for the Young's moduli of materials of which a flagellum is made, and for the forces produced by contractile elements in it. Hydrodynamic theory is successful in showing that a travelling wave in a flagellum produces, in second-order approximation, a forward velocity and, in case the waves are helical in nature, a rotation of the cell.

I. INTRODUCTION

Flagellar movement has been made accessible to detailed observation in recent years by the application of high-speed cinemicrography. The combination of this technique with the use of xenon flashlamps [1, 2] as source of illumination makes it possible to "freeze" the flagellum on each cineframe. Sufficient spatial and time resolution can thus be obtained to ensure adequate description of the motion.

The experimental results have stimulated work on the theoretical aspects of flagellar motion too. It has been recognized that the exact *form* of the wave that travels down a flagellum is dependent on the elastic properties of the materials of which it is built and also on the way active contractile elements are distributed along it [3, 4]. Furthermore, it is desirable to show from hydrodynamic considerations that the observed flagellar wave does indeed give a propulsion to the organism, in accordance with the observations.

In this article, the experimental results of observations of flagellar movement will be reviewed briefly. Spermatozoa are the most widely studied objects in this respect. The data presented here are almost all obtained from sperm flagella of different species. The forward velocity

9

of a spermatozoon is constant during periods of observation of many seconds. This greatly simplifies a quantitative description. An exhaustive presentation has not been attempted; only the data important for the physical interpretation have been related.

The elastic properties of flagella and the hydrodynamic aspects of their movement are considered in the third and fourth sections. It will be seen that a considerable understanding of the physical problems involved in flagellar motion has indeed been achieved.

II. DESCRIPTION OF FLAGELLAR MOTION

The most detailed observations available have been made of spermatozoa of the bull. The experimental technique consisted of cinemicrography at 50 and 200 frames/sec. Dark field illumination was used with a xenon flash lamp as light source [1, 5].

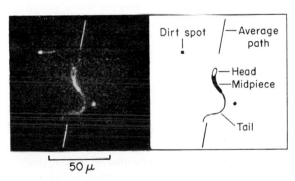

Fig. 1. Enlarged reproduction of a part of a frame of a cinemicrograph of bull sperm, taken at 200 frames/sec. Exposure time ≈ 150 μsec. The average path along which the cell was moving is shown in the figure. The diagram at the right indicates the location of the head, midpiece, and tail of the sperm. The little dirt spots visible on the photograph are fixed to the object slides and can be used as frame of reference. (Courtesy of the *Biophysical Journal*.)

Figure 1 shows an enlarged reproduction of a part of a film frame thus obtained. The main morphological features of a bull sperm are shown in this picture: the head, which contains the genetic material, is a flat elliptical disk of dimensions $8 \times 4 \times 1$ μ. The midpiece contains a single layer of mitochondria (which produce part of the energy needed by the sperm) surrounding the central structure of the flagellum [6]. The approximate dimensions of the midpiece are: length 10 μ, diameter 0.5 μ; of the tail: length 50 μ, diameter 0.4 μ.

When viewing a cinemicrograph of bull sperm, one notices that the intensity of the light scattered by the head of a sperm varies periodically with time. This is because the whole cell rotates along its longitudinal axis. Twice during each period of rotation the disk-like head passes through a position such that the light beam of the dark-field illumination is specularly reflected into the microscope objective. An intense flash of light is the result. In all other positions, light only scatters off the rim of the head as shown in Fig. 1.

A second feature apparent on viewing the films is the helical nature of the wave that progresses along the tail of the sperm. The vertical component of the helical wave can be observed qualitatively as parts of the

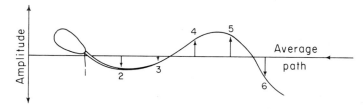

Fig. 2. Diagram showing the way wave patterns are measured. At the six numbered points, which are to be thought of as fixed to the tail, the deviation from the average path is measured as a function of time. (Courtesy of the *Biophysical Journal*.)

flagellum move in and out of the plane of focus of the microscope objective. The rotation of a sperm always occurs in conjunction with a helical wave, just as was predicted long ago by Gray [7].

In abnormal cells, a flat (planar) wave is often observed in the flagellum [5, 8], and this flat wave is never accompanied by rotation. This paper will not deal with this abnormal type of movement, however.

For quantitative measurement, the images of a cell as they occurred on 50 to 70 consecutive frames of the film were projected and drawn on paper. The average path along which the cell was moving was determined and inserted on each drawing. On each cell, six points were selected: the junction of the head and the midpiece, and five points representing successive 10 μ displacements along the tail. For each of these six points, the deviation from the average path was measured and plotted as a function of time. The procedure is illustrated in Figs. 1 and 2. In this way, six wavy curves are obtained, each showing the transverse movement of a point on the tail as a function of time.

Figure 3 shows an example of the data for a rotating sperm obtained from a film taken at 200 frames/sec. It can be seen that each point has an apparent movement around the equilibrium position which is the sum of two vibrations. If the frequency of the slow component of vibration

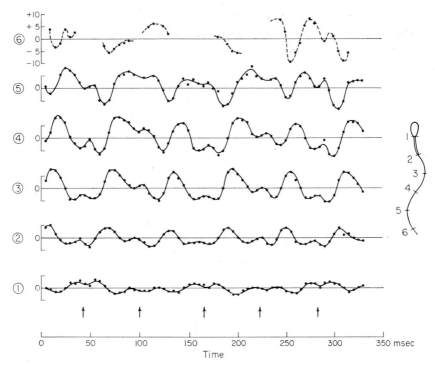

Fig. 3. Wave patterns at six points on the tail of a rotating sperm. Each point has an apparent movement around the equilibrium position which is the sum of two vibrations. The arrows indicate the moments that a light flash off the head was observed, indicating that the head was in a position perpendicular to the plane of the slide. From these light flashes, an independent measurement of the rotation frequency is obtained. (Courtesy of the New York Academy of Sciences.)

TABLE I

Frequencies ν_1 and ν_2 Occurring in the Wave Patterns of Seven Rotating Cells (Forward Velocity v and Rotation Frequency Are Shown Also)[a]

Cell no.	v (μ/sec)	ν_1 (cps)	ν_2 (cps)	$\frac{1}{2}(\nu_1 + \nu_2)$ (cps)	$\frac{1}{2}(\nu_2 - \nu_1)$ (cps)	f_{rot} (cps)
1	77	9.2	25.5	17.3	8.2	9.2
2	96	15.0	29.9	22.0	7.0	7.7
3	99	15.3	34.6	24.0	9.6	8.5
4	102	12.8	33.0	22.9	10.1	9.5
5	106	12.5	29.7	21.1	8.6	8.4
6	108	11.5	29.6	20.8	9.1	10.2
7	111	16.5	31.3	23.9	7.4	8.3

[a] Courtesy of the *Biophysical Journal*.

in Fig. 3 is called ν_1 and that of the faster component ν_2, it is found that $(\nu_2 - \nu_1)/2$ has a close correlation with the rotation frequency f_{rot} [9]. Table I presents the data for seven rotating cells. These observations make clear that the patterns of Fig. 3 are the result of a vibrational motion that is modulated by the rotation. The frequency of the vibration, f, is thus found to be $f = (\nu_2 + \nu_1)/2$.

The traveling of the wave along the flagellum is shown in Fig. 3 by the progressive phase shift of the pattern toward the distal end. The two mutually perpendicular components of the helical wave can be written as

$$U_1(x, t) = A_1(x) \sin [\omega t + \alpha(x)] \tag{1}$$
$$U_2(x, t) = A_2(x) \cos [\omega t + \alpha(x)] \tag{1a}$$

where the index 1 indicates deviation in the plane of the head, and the index 2 deviation perpendicular to it, and where $\omega = 2\pi f$.

By proper analysis of the wave patterns as shown in Fig. 3, the functions $A_1(x)$, $A_2(x)$ and $\alpha(x)$ can be obtained [4]. The results for seven cells are shown in Figs. 4 and 5. It can be seen that the amplitude in the plane of the head is approximately three times bigger than that perpendicular to it. The "main" amplitude increases as the wave travels along the tail. This will prove to be an important fact in the analysis of the elastic properties of the flagellum.

For hydrodynamic considerations, a description of the flagellar movement in terms of a characteristic frequency, an average amplitude, and an average wavelength is sufficient, as shown by Gray and Hancock [10].

The characteristic amplitude b for a wave, taken as the value of the "main" component (see Fig. 4) at the middle of the tail, can be measured in a simple way from films with only 50 frames/sec [8]. The forward velocity, v, of spermatozoa was thus found to be quadratically related to b:

$$v = \epsilon b^2 \tag{2}$$

with $\epsilon = 1.2 \pm 0.3 \ \mu^{-1} \sec^{-1}$ (mean $\pm$ S.D.)[1] [4, 8]. Figure 6 illustrates this relation.

The interference of the rotation with the vibrational motion, as shown in Fig. 3, precludes the measurement of the wave frequency f from the "slow" films. For the abnormal, nonrotating cells mentioned before, measurement of f was possible, however. For the abnormal cells it was found [5] that f does not correlate with the forward velocity. The average value of f for normal cells, 22 cps (Table II), is the same as that found for abnormal cells, 22 ± 4 cps. It is, therefore, assumed that f and the forward velocity are not correlated either.

[1] S.D. is the Standard Deviation.

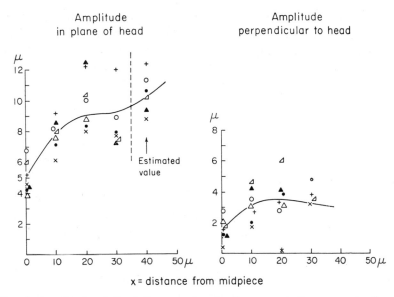

Fig. 4. Amplitude of the tail wave of each of seven rotating sperm in the plane of the head (left) and perpendicular to the plane of the head (right). (x = distance from midpiece.) (Courtesy of the *Biophysical Journal*.)

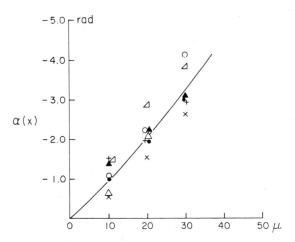

Fig. 5. Phase angle $a(x)$ of the vibration of the tail of a rotating sperm, as a function of the distance to the midpiece (x = distance from midpiece). (Courtesy of the *Biophysical Journal*.)

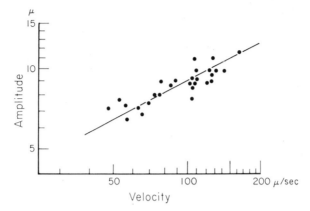

FIG. 6. Quadratic relation between forward velocities of spermatozoa and amplitudes of the tail wave.   (Courtesy of *Physics in Medicine and Biology*.)

TABLE II

OBSERVED VALUES FOR THE AVERAGE OF FREQUENCY, AMPLITUDE, AND WAVE-
LENGTH AND OF AVERAGE FORWARD VELOCITY FOR SOME SPECIES OF
SPERMATOZOA

Species	$\langle v \rangle$ (μ/sec)	$\langle b \rangle$ (μ)	$\langle \lambda \rangle$ (μ)	$\langle f \rangle$ (cps)	Reference
Bull	94	9.5	35–40	22	[4, 5]
	97				[11]
Sea urchin					
Psammachinus miliaris	191	4	24	35	[2]
Lytechanus pictus	158	4.6	22.6	30	[20]
Tunicate					
Ciona intestinalis	165	4.3	22	35	[20]
Annelid					
Chaetopterus variopedatus	105	3.8	19.5	26.5	[20]

The wavelength λ is not correlated with forward velocity [5, 11].   A representative value for λ is $\approx 40\ \mu$.

The frequency with which the normal cells rotate, f_{rot}, is proportional to the forward velocity.   This is illustrated in Fig. 7.   One can write

$$v = d\, f_{\text{rot}} \tag{3}$$

with $d = 12\ \mu$ [5].

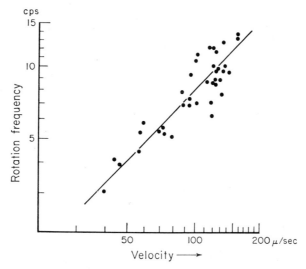

FIG. 7. Linear relation between velocity and rotation frequency of bull spermatozoa. (Courtesy of *Physics in Medicine and Biology.*)

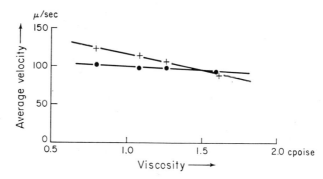

FIG. 8. Dependence of the average velocity of the sperm in two semen samples on the viscosity of the medium.

For measurement of the dependence of the forward velocity of sperm on the viscosity of the medium, cinemicrography is too tedious. A photoelectric method was developed, however, by the author and co-workers [12] by means of which the average velocity of the sperm in a given sample can be measured. It was found [8] that the average velocity $\langle v \rangle$ depends only weakly on the viscosity η. Figure 8 shows $\langle v \rangle$ of two sperm samples as a function of η. It can be seen that doubling of the viscosity causes a decrease of $\langle v \rangle$ of only $\approx 20\%$.

Other measurements of the parameters of the wave motion of sperm flagella have mainly resulted in reports on the average value of frequency, amplitude, wavelength, and forward velocity. As the velocity distributions found in sperm samples are rather narrow, bell-shaped functions, centered around the average [8, 11, 13, 14], this is not an invalid procedure. Table II summarizes data reported for sperm of the bull, the sea urchin, the annelid (a sea worm), and for tunicate sperm. Observations of Holwill [15] on flagellar movement of protozoa, in which the flagellum is attached to a large body with appreciable fluid drag, are mentioned briefly at the end of the section on hydrodynamics aspects.

III. ELASTIC PROPERTIES OF FLAGELLA

A flagellum can be considered to be a thin rod in which flexural vibrations are induced. For the bending moment M, due to the elastic resistance of the rod to bending one can write

$$M = IE \ \partial^2 U / \partial x^2 \tag{4}$$

where U is the deviation from the equilibrium position, x the distance from the proximal end, I the moment of the cross section of the rod,[2] and E the Young's modulus of the material of the rod. The counteracting moment is caused by the fluid drag only. (Inertia forces can be neglected as the Reynolds number is $\ll 1$.) For the second derivative of this moment can be written [16]

$$\partial^2 M / \partial x^2 = -k \ \partial U / \partial t \tag{5}$$

where k is the drag coefficient of the rod. Equations (4) and (5) combine to give the differential equation for a passive flagellum:

$$\frac{\partial^2}{\partial x^2} \left[IE \ \frac{\partial^2 U}{\partial x^2} \right] = -k \ \frac{\partial U}{\partial t} \ . \tag{6}$$

As flagella are tapered [6, 17], I is a function of x. For our model, the tail is taken as a truncated cone, illustrated in Fig. 9. In the notation of Fig. 9,

$$I = I_0 \frac{(L - x)^4}{L^4} \ . \tag{7}$$

In an actual flagellum, the amplitude b is not small compared to the

---

[2] The moment I is the quantity occurring in the theory of bending of beams and is defined as $I = \int y^2 \ ds$, where ds is a surface element in the cross section, and y the distance of ds to the median plane.

wavelength λ. Therefore, the drag force is not normal to the flagellum. As the ratio b/λ increases as the wave travels distally, the effective drag coefficient is accordingly reduced. It has been shown [4] that it is satis-

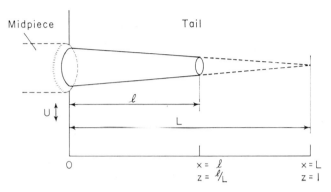

FIG. 9. Diagram illustrating the model of the sperm tail used in the calculations. The dimensions in the direction of U are greatly exaggerated. (Courtesy of the *Biophysical Journal*.)

factory to represent k by

$$k(x) = k_0 \frac{(L - x)^2}{L^2}.$$

(8)

Equations (6)–(8) combine to give

$$\frac{\partial^2}{\partial x^2}\left[(L - x)^4 \frac{\partial^2 U}{\partial x^2}\right] = -\frac{k_0 L^2}{I_0 E}(L - x)^2 \frac{\partial U}{\partial t}.$$

(9)

Equation (9) can be made dimensionless by introducing $z = x/L$ and $\tau = \omega t$:

$$\frac{\partial^2}{\partial z^2}\left[(1 - z)^4 \frac{\partial^2 U}{\partial z^2}\right] = -c\left(\frac{L}{l}\right)^4 (1 - z)^2 \frac{\partial U}{\partial \tau}$$

(10)

with

$$c = k_0 \omega l^4 / I_0 E.$$

(11)

Equation (10) describes the motion of a passive flagellum. It can be noticed that only two parameters occur in it: c, the ratio between viscous drag and the stiffness of the flagellum, and (l/L), the truncation factor.

The value of (l/L) for bull sperm was given by Bretschneider [17] as 0.45. For other flagella, a value in the neighborhood of 0.5 is an acceptable average (compare Fawcett [6] and Afzelius [18]). It has been found [4] that solutions for Eq. (10) are not very sensitive to the actual value of (l/L), if $0.35 < l/L < 0.65$. Comparison of solutions of Eq. (10) with

experimental data can therefore be expected to give information about the value of c.

A. Stiffness of Sperm Flagella

For the case of bull sperm, a complete set of boundary conditions is available. At the distal end, $\partial^2 U/\partial z^2 = \partial^3 U/\partial z^3 = 0$. At the proximal end ($z = 0$), the movement forced on the rod can be represented by $U = A(0) \sin \tau$, $\partial U/\partial z = B(0)L \cos (\tau + \beta)$. $A(0)$, $B(0)$, and β can be evaluated from Figs. 4 and 5.

Solutions for Eq. (10) were computed on an IBM 7094 computer for various values of c. The solutions necessarily have the form $U(z,\tau) = A(z) \sin [\tau + \alpha(z)]$. However, $A(z)$, the way the amplutude changes as the wave travels distally, cannot be used to find that value of c which gives the best fit. The form of $A(z)$ will, in fact, strongly depend on the presence of active contractile elements in the flagellum which enhance the wave amplitude. The effects of such contractile elements have not been introduced as yet into Eq. (10).

However, Machin [19] has shown that, in case nonlinear elements are present in the flagellum, "mode locking" will occur. This means that the initiating wave will be enhanced by the contractile elements, but that the phase $\alpha(z)$ of the passive wave should be preserved in an "active" tail. Evidence for the existence of nonlinearities has been presented by Brokaw [20] and Machin [19]. The function $\alpha(z)$ has therefore been used to derive a value of c.

The computed form of α, transformed back to be expressed as a function of x, is shown in Fig. 10 for various values of c. It will be observed in Fig. 10 that the slope $d\alpha/dx_{(x=0)}$ is the same for all solutions. It can be readily shown that

$$\frac{d\alpha}{dx_{(x=0)}} = \frac{B(0) \cos \beta}{A(0)}$$

independent of the stiffness of the flagellum.

For all values of c, the function $\alpha(x)$ as shown in Fig. 10 is monotonous. This means that no appreciable reflexion of the wave at the distal end occurs. Only for $c = 35.7$ does the curve for $\alpha(x)$ bend toward horizontal at the distal end, indicating for this (very stiff) tail a noticeable reflexion of the wave at the distal end.

For $c = 1125$, the computed form of $\alpha(x)$ agrees closely with the average of the experimental data. Of the constants that make up c [Eq. (11)], $l = 50$ μ and the average of ω, $\langle \omega \rangle = 135$ cps. With the radius of the tail $\rho = 0.2$ μ [21] and the viscosity of the fluid $\eta = 10^{-2}$ poise, the drag coefficient $k_0 = 2.1 \times 10^{-2}$ dyne-cm^{-2}-sec. This gives, for I_0E, the bend-

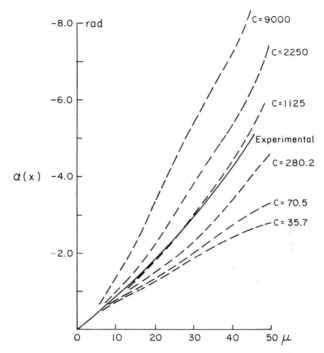

Fig. 10. Value of $\alpha(x)$ for bull sperm computed for various values of the constant c (x = distance from midpiece). (Courtesy of the *Biophysical Journal*.)

ing resistance at the proximal junction:

$$I_0 E - 1.8 \times 10^{12} \quad \text{dynes cm}^2. \tag{12}$$

The inner structure of the sperm tail is well known from electron microscopy, as illustrated in Fig. 11. The tail contains nine longitudinal fibers, embedded in matrix and surrounded by a fibrous sheath. From electron micrographs from various sources [6, 21–23], a cross section of the tail of a bull sperm at the proximal junction can be composed as shown in Fig. 12.

For the three different structures in Fig. 12, the value of I_0 can be calculated as: fibrous sheath $I_0 \approx 6 \times 10^{-20}$ cm⁴, longitudinal fibers $I_0 \approx 4 \times 10^{-21}$ cm⁴, matrix $I_0 \approx 4 \times 10^{-21}$ cm⁴. If the rigidity of the tail were caused by any one of these structures alone, the value for the Young's modulus would be

sheath alone $E \approx 3 \times 10^7$ dynes/cm²
fibers alone $E \approx 4.5 \times 10^8$ dynes/cm²
matrix alone $E \approx 4.5 \times 10^8$ dynes/cm².

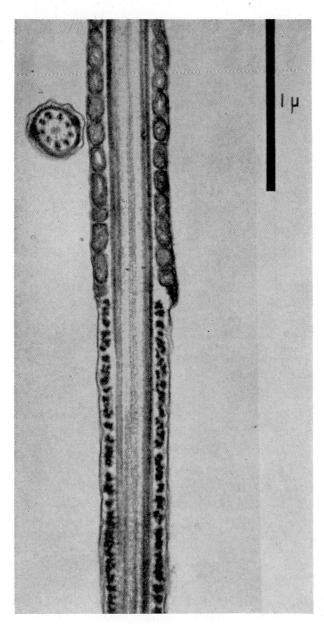

Fig. 11. Longitudinal section through the area of the midpiece-tail junction of a bull sperm flagellum. The longitudinal fibers are visible. The upper part (midpiece) shows mitochondria surrounding the fibers. Around the tail, the fibrous sheath can be seen. The left-hand corner shows a cross section of a tail with the nine fibers and the fibrous sheath. The function of the doublet central fiber is not known. (Courtesy of Lord Rothschild.)

Table III presents values for Young's modulus of some biological tissues. It can be seen that, in order to make an appreciable contribution to the stiffness, the fibers or the matrix would have to possess unrealistically high values of E. We can conclude that the stiffness of the tail is caused by the sheath, which is probably a collagen-like material with $E \approx 3 \times 10^7$ dynes/cm^2. The fibrous nature of the sheath supports this conclusion.

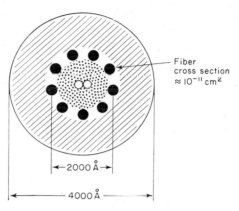

Fiber cross section $\approx 10^{-11}$ cm^2

←2000 Å→

← 4000 Å →

FIG. 12. Diagram of a cross section of a bull sperm tail at the proximal junction. The cross-hatched area represents the fibrous sheath, the dotted area the matrix. The nine peripheral fibers are shown as the black circles.

TABLE III

YOUNG'S MODULUS E OF SOME BIOLOGICAL TISSUES

Tissue	E (dyne/cm^2)	Reference
Collagen (3% strain)	3×10^7	[34]
Elastin	1×10^7	[34]
Extracted muscle fibers	6×10^7	[35]

Sea-urchin sperm flagella are an interesting counterpart of bull sperm, because electron microscopy has shown that the fibrous sheath is absent [18]. Figure 13 shows a cross section of a sea-urchin sperm tail, in which the nine fibers are visible, embedded in matrix.

Unfortunately, in the case of sea-urchin sperm, the boundary conditions at $z = 0$ for Eq. (10) are not known. It can be shown, however [24], that, if the tail is flexible enough, the influence of the boundary conditions

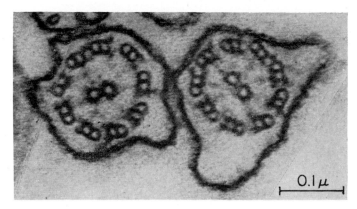

FIG. 13. Electron micrograph of a cross section through two sea-urchin sperm flagella. The nine hollow fibers are clearly visible. The cross section of each fiber is approximately 250×150 Å². The distance of the fibers to the center is 700 Å. (Courtesy of Dr. Afzelius.)

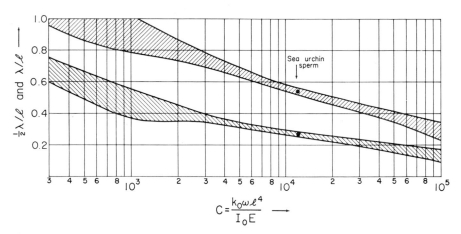

FIG. 14. Values of $\frac{1}{2}\lambda/l$ and λ/l for flagella as a function of c. The cross-hatched bands indicate the variation of $\frac{1}{2}\lambda/l$ and λ/l due to uncertainty in the boundary conditions at the proximal junction. The dots indicate values of $\frac{1}{2}\lambda/l$ and λ/l observed on sea-urchin sperm by Brokaw.

on the slope of $\alpha(z)$ decays as the wave travels distally in the tail. This means that the slope of $\alpha(z)$ in the last three-quarters of the tail is mainly determined by the stiffness. In that case, the values of Δz corresponding to $\Delta\alpha = \pi$ and $\Delta\alpha = 2\pi$ represent, respectively, one half and one full wavelength. These latter quantities are known from the measurements of Brokaw [20] and Gray [2].

Figure 14 shows the computed values for $\lambda/2$ and λ as a function of c.

The cross-hatched bands in Fig. 14 represent the dependence of $\lambda/2$ and λ on variation of the boundary conditions at $z = 0$. The variation used was such that the value of $d\alpha/dz_{(z=0)}$ ranged from $-\infty$ to 30. It can be seen from Fig. 14 that the influence of the boundary conditions becomes small for $c > 3 \times 10^3$.

The values of $\lambda/2$ and λ for sea-urchin sperm [20] give a value for c of 1.2×10^4. By an analysis similar to that applied to the bull sperm, the value for $I_0 E$ for sea-urchin sperm is found:

$$I_0 E = 6 \times 10^{-14} \quad \text{dynes cm}^2. \tag{13}$$

The value of I_0 for the fibers and for the matrix in the sea-urchin tail can be calculated: fibers $I_0 = 6 \times 10^{-22}$ cm^4, matrix $I_0 = 3 \times 10^{-21}$ cm^4. If the stiffness of the tail were caused by the fibers alone, their Young's modulus would accordingly have to be $E \approx 10^8$ dynes/cm^2. However, the matrix material need have a value of E of little more than 10^6 dynes/cm^2 in order to contribute to the stiffness of the rod. For tissue substance in which no structure can be seen, this latter figure is not unreasonably high. In that case, the value of E for the fibers would be even closer to that of muscle shown in Table III. We shall see later that other muscle-like properties are indeed associated with the longitudinal fibers in flagella.

B. Bending Moments and Forces in the Flagellum

The passive wave described in the previous section is heavily damped as it travels distally in the flagellum. The computed amplitude of a passive wave at a point $\frac{2}{3}$ along the flagellum is reduced to less than 0.3 the value at the proximal end, in striking contrast with the actual observations on bull sperm (Fig. 4) and sea-urchin sperm [2, 20]. Machin [3], from general considerations of Eq. (6), also reached the conclusion that, in a rod that is flexible enough to exhibit at least one full wave, the amplitude of the wave cannot be maintained against the fluid drag.

It is thus necessary to assume the existence of active contractile elements distributed all along the tail. An *active* bending moment $m_{\text{act}}(z,\tau)$ can be inserted in the left-hand side of Eq. (10). Since the form of $m_{\text{act}}(z,\tau)$ is not known Eq. (10) cannot be solved. As a crude approximation, one can use

$$m_{\text{act}}(z, \tau) = p \, \partial^2 U / \partial z^2. \tag{14}$$

The constant p should be understood to be the amount with which the elastically induced bending moment is amplified by the contractile elements.

When Eq. (14) is properly inserted into (10), the modified equation can be solved, using the value for the stiffness (c) as found before. The

result of computations of the function $A(x)$ for bull sperm, using different values of p, is shown in Fig. 15.   It can be seen in Fig. 15 that, for $p \approx 15$ to 20, the amplitude of the wave is maintained approximately as was observed.   It can also be concluded that in the distal part of the tail the

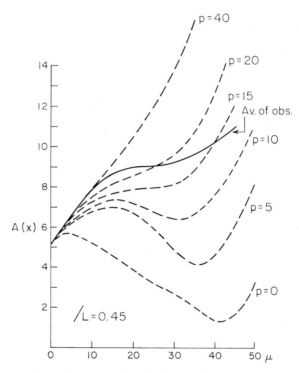

Fig. 15. Values of $A(x)$ in an "active" bull sperm flagellum computed for different values of the constant p (x = distance to midpiece).

appropriate value of p is smaller than that appropriate at the proximal part.   This calculation shows that almost all of the bending moment is produced by active contractile elements.   The same results can be obtained for sea-urchin sperm [24].

The bending moment can be readily calculated with the aid of Eq. (4). The value of $\partial^2 U/\partial x^2_{(x=0)}$ is evaluated for bull sperm from the data in Figs. 4 and 5, and the maximum of M, M_{max}, at the proximal junction is found:

$$M_{max} = 12 \times 10^{-10} \quad \text{dyne cm.} \tag{15}$$

Assuming that the moment is produced by the longitudinal fibers (Figs)

11 and 12), the force P needed is

$$P = 4 \times 10^{-5} \quad \text{dynes/fiber.}$$

At a cross section S of 10^{-11} cm^2, the tension P/S that has to be developed in each fiber is

$$P/S \approx 4 \times 10^6 \text{ dyne/cm}^2. \tag{16}$$

For sea-urchin sperm, a value for $\partial^2 U/\partial x^2$ of 2×10^3 cm^{-1} was reported by Brokaw [20]. With $I_0 E = 6 \times 10^{-14}$ dyne cm^2 as found before in Eq. (13), the bending moment at the time of maximum curvature $M_{\max}$ is

$$M_{\max} \approx 1.2 \times 10^{-10} \quad \text{dyne cm.}$$

By considering the viscous drag forces on the sea-urchin sperm flagellum, Brokaw found the maximum bending moment to be 2.9×10^{-10} dyne-cm. In view of the approximate nature of the analysis applied in our case, these two figures cannot be taken as in disagreement.

The longitudinal fibers in the sea-urchin sperm flagellum are smaller than those in bull sperm and are closer to the center (compare Figs. 11 and 13). The tension needed in each fiber for a bending moment of 1.2×10^{-10} dyne cm is

$$P/S \approx 1.6 \times 10^6 \quad \text{dynes/cm}^2. \tag{17}$$

The values cited in Eqs. (16) and (17) are well in the range of values for P/S reported for muscle, 1 to 5×10^6 dyne/cm^2 [25].

Biochemical evidence for ascribing muscle-like properties to the longitudinal fibers has been reported. Burnasheva [26] has extracted from bull sperm a protein, spermosin, that shows upon addition of adenosine triphosphate (ATP) changes of viscosity like those of myosin, a contractile protein from muscle. ATP, as will be remembered, is the key molecule for energy transfer in biological systems. Nelson [27] found in rat sperm that myosin antibodies attach specifically to the longitudinal fibers in the flagella. The biochemical and mechanical similarities of the longitudinal fibers and muscle make the identification of the longitudinal fibers as contractile elements virtually certain.

IV. HYDRODYNAMIC ASPECTS OF FLAGELLAR MOTION

It was recognized early by Gray [7] that only traveling waves in a flagellum can produce propulsion. In the case of standing waves, the forces in one-half of the cycle are exactly balanced by those in the second half-cycle, with a vanishing average as the result. We have seen, how-

ever, in the previous section that no noticeable reflexion of the waves at the distal end of a flagellum occurs, which means that traveling waves are always present.

When the wave amplitude, b, is very small compared to the wavelength, λ, the movement of each part of the flagellum is normal to the equilibrium axis. Thus, no resultant force along this axis can be present. Only for larger amplitudes, in which second-order terms have to be taken into account, is a propulsive force to be expected. This leads to a forward velocity, v, proportional to b^2. In order to arrive at a formula that relates v and b, a characteristic frequency (f) and length (λ) have to be inserted for dimensional reasons,[3] and the resulting expression is

$$v = \xi \frac{fb^2}{\lambda} \tag{18}$$

where ξ is a dimensionless constant of the order of 1.

The experimental results on bull sperm indicate that a relation of the type (18) is indeed present (Fig. 6). The value of ξ evaluated from the observations on sperm of bull, sea urchin, tunicate, and annelid are inserted in Table V.

Two different approaches to the problem of deriving Eq. (18) have been made, one by G. I. Taylor [28] and one by Gray and Hancock [10]. The two lines of approach will be sketched briefly, and the results will be compared with the experimental data.

A. Theory of G. I. Taylor

As the Reynolds number of flagellar movement is $\ll 1$, only viscous forces have to be taken into account. The equations for the fluid velocity $\mathbf{V}$ can be written as

$$\eta \text{ curl curl } \mathbf{V} = -\text{grad } p \tag{19}$$

where p is the pressure. The equation of continuity gives, with Eq. (19),

$$\nabla^2 p = 0. \tag{20}$$

A flagellum can be represented as a cylinder with radius ρ in which waves of amplitude b, wave number $\kappa = 2\pi/\lambda$, and angular frequency $\omega = 2\pi f$ are traveling. In cylindrical coordinates, as illustrated in Fig. 16, the surface of the cylinder can be written for $b \ll \rho$ as

$$r = \rho + b \cos \theta \sin (\kappa x + \omega t). \tag{21}$$

The procedure of Taylor consists of searching for solutions of Eq. (19) which conform to the boundary conditions of no slip at the surface

[3] This argument is due to Dr. N. G. van Kampen.

described by Eq. (21) and of vanishing disturbance of the fluid at infinity. In first-order approximation, solutions for $\mathbf{V}$ and p from Eqs. (19) and (20) can be found in the form

$$p = \tfrac{1}{2}\eta\kappa BK_1(\kappa r) \cos \theta \cos s \qquad (22)$$
$$V_r = v_r(r) \cos \theta \cos s \qquad (23)$$
$$V_\theta = v_\theta(r) \sin \theta \cos s \qquad (24)$$
$$V_x = v_x(r) \cos \theta \sin s \qquad (25)$$

where $s = \kappa x + \omega t$, and where v_r, v_θ, and v_x are functions of r only.

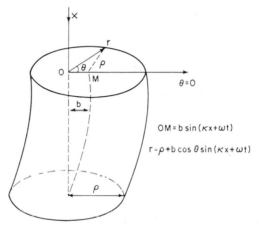

FIG. 16. Diagram showing planar wave in a cylinder of radius ρ. The wave is oriented in the plane $\theta = 0$. Cylindrical coordinates (r, θ, x).

By substituting Eqs. (22)–(25) in Eqs. (19) and (20), it is found that

$$v_r = AK_0(\kappa r) + B\kappa rK_1(\kappa r) + CK_2(\kappa r) \qquad (26)$$
$$v_\theta = -AK_0(\kappa r) + CK_2(\kappa r) \qquad (27)$$
$$v_x = B\kappa rK_0(\kappa r) + (A + C - B)K_1(\kappa r) \qquad (28)$$

where K_0, K_1, and K_2 are Bessel functions of imaginary argument in the notation of Watson [29]. The occurrence of this type of function guarantees that at $r = \infty$ the fluid velocities do indeed vanish.

The velocities of a point of the surface of the cylinder can be written as

$$V_r = \omega b \cos \theta \cos s \qquad (29)$$
$$V_\theta = -\omega b \sin \theta \sin s \qquad (30)$$
$$V_x = 0. \qquad (31)$$

From Eqs. (29)–(31), the values of the integration constants A, B, and C

are uniquely determined, and thus also the complete first-order velocity field of the fluid. The fact that the boundary condition given by Eq. (31) is fulfilled by the first-order field implies that, in this approximation, no propulsive effect on the flagellum exists. For the case $\kappa\rho \ll 1$, the constants A, B, and C reduce to

$$A = B = \omega b/\{K_0(\kappa\rho) + \tfrac{1}{2}\}, \qquad C = -\tfrac{1}{4}\omega b\kappa^2\rho^2/\{K_0(\kappa\rho) + \tfrac{1}{2}\}. \quad (32)$$

Second-order effects are taken into account by Taylor by evaluating the first-order velocity field, not at $r = \rho$, but at the boundary of the actual cylinder. For v_r at the actual boundary, one can write

$$v_r = v_r(r = \rho) + \frac{dv_r(r = \rho)}{dr}\,\delta r$$

or

$$v_r = v_r(r = \rho) + v_r'(r = \rho)\,b\,\cos\theta\,\sin s$$

and similarly for v_θ and v_x.

For the first-order velocity field at the surface of the cylinder, one thus finds (all first-order functions evaluated at $r = \rho$)

$$V_r = v_r \cos\theta \cos s + bv_r' \cos^2\theta \cos s \sin s$$

or

$$V_r = v_r \cos\theta \cos s + \tfrac{1}{4}bv_r' \sin 2s + \tfrac{1}{4}bv_r' \cos 2\theta \sin 2s. \quad (33)$$

In the same way, one obtains

$$V_\theta = v_\theta \sin\theta \cos s + \tfrac{1}{4}bv_\theta' \sin 2\theta \sin 2s \quad (34)$$

$$V_x = v_x \cos\theta \sin s - \tfrac{1}{4}bv_x' \cos 2s + \tfrac{1}{4}bv_x' \cos 2\theta$$
$$- \tfrac{1}{4}bv_x' \cos 2\theta \cos 2s - \tfrac{1}{4}bv_x'. \quad (35)$$

The velocities of Eqs. (33)–(35) have to be reconciled with those of the surface of the cylinder given in Eqs. (29)–(31), and apparently the first-order velocity field cannot accomplish this. Second-order solutions, involving dependence on $\sin 2\theta$, $\sin 2s$, etc., have to be introduced. It can be verified that the three solutions shown in Table IV do satisfy

TABLE IV

SECOND-ORDER SOLUTIONS FOR THE FLUID VELOCITY FIELD
AROUND A FLAGELLUM

	Solution No.		
	02	20	22
V_r	$v_r(02) \sin 2s$	0	$v_r(22) \cos 2\theta \sin 2s$
V_θ	0	0	$v_\theta(22) \sin 2\theta \sin 2s$
V_x	$v_x(02) \cos 2s$	$v_x(20) \cos 2\theta$	$v_x(22) \cos 2\theta \cos 2s$

Eq. (19). The functions $v(m,n)$ in Table IV are dependent on r only and can be expressed in terms of the Bessel functions K_1, K_2, and K_3.

Taylor proved that it is uniquely possible to choose the integration constants for the second-order solution such that, at $r = \rho$, $v_r(02) = -\frac{1}{4}bv_r'$, $v_r(22) = -\frac{1}{4}bv_x'$, $v_\theta(22) = -\frac{1}{4}bv_\theta'$, $v_x(02) = \frac{1}{4}bv_x'$, $v_x(20) = -\frac{1}{4}bv_x'$, and $v_x(22) = \frac{1}{4}bv_x'$. This means that, by adding the solutions of Table IV, the boundary conditions for V_r and V_θ [Eqs. (29)–(30)] can be fulfilled. It will be noticed, however, that a finite value for the fluid velocity V_x at the cylinder remains:

$$V_x = -\tfrac{1}{4}bv_x' . \tag{36}$$

The condition of no slip at the surface means that the cylinder has to move in the x-direction with a velocity given by Eq. (36). The value of v_x' at $r = \rho$ can be evaluated from Eq. (28). For a flagellum in which $\kappa\rho \ll 1$, as is actually the case, the forward velocity v is thus found, with the aid of Eq. (32):

$$v = 2\pi^2\varphi(\kappa\rho)\,\frac{fb^2}{\lambda} \tag{37}$$

where $\varphi(\kappa\rho) = \{K_0(\kappa\rho) - \tfrac{1}{2}\}/\{K_0(\kappa\rho) + \tfrac{1}{2}\}$.

Thus far, only planar waves have been considered. In the case of helical waves, it is found that the propulsive effect of the two mutually perpendicular components of a helical wave can be summed, if each is taken according to Eq. (37). Quite analogously to the way the forward velocity was found before, a fluid velocity V_θ now remains at the surface of the cylinder $V_\theta - \frac{1}{2}bv_x'$. From this follows that the flagellum has to rotate with a frequency $f_{\rm rot} = V_\theta/2\pi\rho$, or

$$f_{\rm rot} = \frac{2\pi\varphi(\kappa\rho)}{\rho}\,\frac{fb^2}{\lambda} . \tag{38}$$

The theory of Taylor has been presented in some detail because it shows that is possible from *first principles of hydrodynamics* to derive the observed properties of flagellar motion:

(1) The forward velocity is independent of the viscosity of the medium.

(2) The forward velocity is quadratically dependent on the amplitude of the wave.

(3) There is a rotation proportional to the forward velocity.

For quantitative description of the forward velocity of a flagellum, Eq. (37) is not sufficient, probably because of the original assumption $b \ll \rho$, which is in contradiction with the actual values. Table V shows a comparison of ξ from Eq. (18), as obtained from the experimental data, with the value of $2\pi^2\varphi(\kappa\rho)$ from Eq. (37) for several species. It can be seen that the latter values are about a factor 3 to 8 too high.

For bull sperm the value of $2\pi^2\varphi(\kappa\rho)$ can be made to agree with ξ_{obs} by taking $\rho = 3.5 \mu$. Quite independently, the author has previously found evidence for a virtual "thickening" of a flagellum. By observing the time intervals between passages of spermatozoa at a given location in a sperm sample, it was found that a repulsive interaction exists between the cells [30]. This interaction shows as a decrease in the number of small time intervals compared to the number expected when no interaction is present. When the spermatozoon is represented as a "hard cylinder," estimates of the radius ρ of this cylinder gave $\rho = 3.5 \mu$. It would be

TABLE V

OBSERVED VALUE OF ξ, VALUE OF $2\pi^2\varphi(\kappa\rho)$ OF EQ. (37), AND
COMPUTED VALUE ξ_{cal} FROM EQ. (40) FOR FLAGELLA
OF VARIOUS SPECIES OF SPERM

Species	ξ	$2\pi^2\varphi(\kappa\rho)$	ξ_{cal}	Reference for observations
Bull	2.1	16	4.1	[4, 5]
Sea urchin	8.3	18	8.3	[2]
Sea urchin	5.3	18	6.3	[20]
Tunicate	5.6	17	6.5	[20]
Annelid	5.6	17	6.8	[20]

interesting to find from direct observations of the fluid field around a flagellum, if indeed a "pseudo boundary layer" of fluid exists, which is carried with the flagellum.

The ratio between velocity and rotation frequency for bull sperm follows from Eqs. (37) and (38). Taking into account that only the smaller amplitude component b_2 (Fig 4) contributes to the rotation, it is found that

$$d = \frac{v}{f_{rot}} = \pi\rho \frac{b_1^2 + b_2^2}{b_2^2} \tag{39}$$

or $d \approx 7.5 \mu$ which is not very far from the observed value of $d = 12 \mu$. In Eq. (39), the function $\varphi(\kappa\rho)$ is eliminated. The value for ρ used to evaluate d was therefore taken as the actual value $\rho = 0.2 \mu$.

B. Phenomenological Theory of Flagellar Propulsion

The treatment of Taylor, discussed in the previous section, is limited by the assumption that the amplitude of the flagellar wave is small, and by the fact that the fluid drag of the body to which the flagellum is attached is not taken into account. In the case of spermatozoa, where

the head is small, the latter consideration is not serious, but for protozoa the drag of the main body of the cell may be large compared to that of the flagellum.

In order to overcome these difficulties, a different approach has been followed by Gray and Hancock [10] and by Hollwill and Burge [31]. The drag force on an element of a flagellum can be resolved into two components, one normal and one tangential to the flagellum. Each of the two components can again be resolved into two components in the direction of motion and perpendicular to it. By integrating the resultant

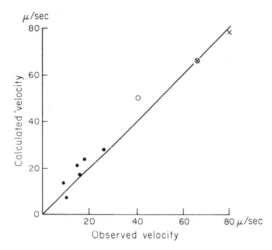

Fɪɢ. 17. Comparison of observed velocities for a variety of protozoa, and velocities calculated with the aid of Eq. (40). ✕ *Euglena,* ○ *Clamydomonas T,* ⊗ *Bodo saltans,* ● *Trypanoso matidae.* (Courtesy of Dr. M. E. J. Holwill.)

force in the direction of motion over the length of the flagellum and averaging over a complete cycle, the total propulsive force is obtained. This force is counteracted by the fluid drag of the main body. With the values for normal and tangential drag force given by Hancock [32], Eq. (16) is again obtained in this way, with the value of ξ:

$$\xi_{\mathrm{cal}} = 2\pi^2 / \{1 + (4\pi^2 b^2/\lambda^2) + [1 + (2\pi^2 b^2/\lambda^2)]^{1/2}(C_B/C_L)\} \qquad (40)$$

where C_B is the drag coefficient for the main body and C_L the tangential drag coefficient of the whole flagellum. Since the terms in Eq. (40) are known from experiment, values for ξ_{cal} may be calculated and compared with the observed data for spermatozoa and for protozoa.

In Table V are listed the values calculated for ξ with Eq. (40) for the various kinds of spermatozoon considered in this paper, using the averages shown in Table II. Figure 17 shows a comparison of observed velocities and velocities calculated by Holwill [15] with the aid of Eqs. (16) and (40). Even though the calculated values ξ_{cal} in Table V and the calculated velocities in Fig. 17 still generally come out somewhat higher than the observed ones, it can be said that the phenomenological theory is indeed successful in predicting the forward velocity due to flagellar motion.

V. DISCUSSION

In the foregoing sections, we have seen that the purely physical aspects of flagellar motion are now well understood. The observed waves can be satisfactorily related to the inner structure of the flagellum. The propulsive effects of the wave can be explained hydrodynamically.

The nature of the oscillatory mechanism that generates the wave is not understood, however. In the section on elastic properties, it was found that the two primary quantities of the oscillation are the frequency f and amplitude b. The wavelength of the wave is set mainly by the elastic constants of the flagellum.

The rate of energy dissipation in flagellar motion W is proportional to f^2b^2. It has been shown [33] that, under normal circumstances, flagellar motion is limited by the amount of energy made available at each moment by the energy producing metabolism. This leaves a flagellum with only one independent degree of freedom, f or b, whereas the other is limited via the relation $W \propto f^2b^2$.

Oscillatory systems, or "biological clocks," are widespread in nature. In general, they are based on a chain of chemical reactions with autocatalytical properties, which results in positive feedback. In flagella of spermatozoa, such a system is present in the chain of reactions producing energy, which is coupled to the contractile elements, the users of the energy. The autocatalytical elements are most probably to be sought in the contractile system, as can be inferred from the section on bending moments.

Elucidation of this oscillatory process in flagellar motion is still a most interesting problem in biophysics, and may contribute to the general understanding of biological clocks and contractile systems in nature.

Acknowledgment

This work was supported in part by the National Institute of Child Health and Human Development through Grant HD-1042.

REFERENCES

1. Eykhout, P. and Rikmenspoel, R., *Res. Film* **3,** 304 (1960).
2. Gray, J., *J. Exptl. Biol.* **32,** 775 (1955).
3. Machin, K. E., *J. Exptl. Biol.* **35,** 796 (1958).
4. Rikmenspoel, R., *Biophys. J.* **5,** 365 (1965).
5. Rikmenspoel, R., van Herpen, G., and Eykhout, P., *Phys. Med. Biol.* **5,** 167 (1960).
6. Fawcett, D. W., *Intern. Rev. Cytol.* **7,** 195 (1958).
7. Gray, J., "Ciliary Movement." Cambridge Univ. Press, London, 1928.
8. Rikmenspoel, R., "Photoelectric and Cinematographic Measurements of the Motility of Bull Sperm Cells." Smit, Utrecht, 1957.
9. Rikmenspoel, R., *Trans. N.Y. Acad. Sci.* **26,** 1072 (1964).
10. Gray, J. and Hancock, G. J., *J. Exptl. Biol.* **32,** 802 (1955).
11. Gray, J., *J. Exptl. Biol.* **35,** 96 (1958).
12. Rikmenspoel, R. and van Herpen, G., *Phys. Med. Biol.* **2,** 54 (1957).
13. Rothschild, Lord, *J. Exptl. Biol.* **30,** 128 (1953).
14. Van Duyn, C., *J. Reprod. Fertility* **4,** 277 (1962).
15. Holwill, M. E. J., *in* "Second International Congress on Protozoology, London," *Excerpta Medica*, Amsterdam (1965).
16. Sommerfeld, A., "Theoretische Physik," vol. 2. Dieterlich'sche Verlag, Weisbaden, 1947.
17. Bretschneider, L. H. and Van Iterson, W., *Proc. Koninkl. Ned. Akad. Wetenschap.* **50,** 88 (1947).
18. Afzelius, B., *J. Biophys. Biochem. Cytol.* **5,** 269 (1959).
19. Machin, K. E., *Proc. Roy. Soc. (London)*, **B158,** 88 (1963).
20. Brokaw, C. J., *J. Exptl. Biol.* **43,** 155 (1965).
21. Bahr, G. F. and Zeitler, E., *J. Cell Biol.* **21,** 175 (1964).
22. Lindahl, P. E. and Drevius, L. O., *Exptl. Cell Res.* **36,** 632 (1964).
23. Rothschild, Lord, *in* "Spermatozoan Motility" (D. W. Bishop, ed.). Am. Assoc. Advan. Sci., Washington, D.C., 1962.
24. Rikmenspoel, R., *Biophys. J.* **6,** 471 (1966).
25. Spector, W. S. (ed.), "Handbook of Biological Data." Saunders, Philadelphia, Pennsylvania, 1956.
26. Burnasheva, S. A., *Biokhimiya* **23,** 558 (1958).
27. Nelson, L., *Ann. Histochim. Suppl.* **2,** 283 (1962).
28. Taylor, G. I., *Proc. Roy. Soc. (London)*, **A211,** 225 (1952).
29. Watson, G. N., "Bessel Functions." Macmillan, New York, 1945.
30. Rikmenspoel, R., *in* "Spermatozoan Motility" (D. W. Bishop, ed.). Am. Assoc. Advan. Sci., Washington, D.C., 1962.
31. Holwill, M. E. J. and Burge, R. E., *Arch. Biochem. Biophys.* **101,** 249 (1963).
32. Hancock, G. J., *Proc. Roy. Soc. (London)*, **A217,** 96 (1953).
33. Rikmenspoel, R., *Exptl. Cell Res.* **37,** 312 (1965).
34. Meyer, K. H. and Ferri, C., *Pfluegers Arch. Ges. Physiol.* **238,** 78 (1936).
35. Bozler, E., *in* "Tissue Elasticity" (J. W. Remington, ed.). Am. Physiol. Soc., Washington, D.C., 1957.

Microcinematographic, Electron Microscopic, and Electrophysiological Studies on Shuttle Streaming in the Slime Mold Physarum polycephalum

ROBERT P. RHEA[1]

LABORATORY OF DEVELOPMENTAL BIOLOGY
ROCKEFELLER UNIVERSITY
NEW YORK, NEW YORK

Evidence is presented in support of the pressure-flow or contraction-hydraulic theory for shuttle streaming of protoplasm in the myxomycete *Physarum polycephalum*. Time-lapse movies of rhythmical changes in diameter and in the direction of streaming in plasmodial strands strongly suggest to the viewer that streaming is a passive response to pressure gradients generated in the plasmodial wall by a contractile system. Electron micrographs of strands reveal circularly and longitudinally arrayed fibrils consisting of filaments 55 Å in diameter. If contractile, these fibrils are so positioned as to bring about the changes in diameter and length associated with streaming and motility. A fibrillar network closely associated with the plasma membrane encapsulates the plasmodium and is shed by retracting strands. The possibility that this network provides restoring forces during streaming is suggested by morphological similarities between it and the internal fibrillar network. A technique is described for recording transmembrane potentials. Preliminary work on the relationship between cyclic changes in transmembrane potential and the streaming cycle indicates that membrane depolarization occurs simultaneously with strand constriction and the efflux of protoplasm, whereas its polarization accompanies relaxation and influx. A similar depolarization-contraction coupling occurs in muscle fibers.

Protoplasmic streaming in the myxomycete *Physarum polycephalum* provides a dramatic example of the flow of non-Newtonian fluids in biological systems. In this species of the "true slime molds," streaming not only reaches velocities in excess of 1 mm/sec (Kamiya, 1950), but it also cyclically reverses direction every 30 to 90 or more sec. This maneuver, designated "shuttle streaming" by Seifriz (1943, 1952), is characterized by a net flow of protoplasm in one direction and consequently in locomotion. *P. polycephalum* has been a popular subject for studies

---

[1] *Present address:* Department of Zoology, University of Minnesota, Minneapolis, Minnesota.

on streaming and related kinetic phenomena for several reasons, among
which are (a) its unusual streaming characteristics, (b) the advantage of
working with large masses of protoplasm, and (c) the relative ease of
culturing ample quantities on organic media such as rolled oats (Camp,
1936; Howard, 1931b) or on partially or completely defined media (Daniel
and Rusch, 1961, 1962; Daniel *et al.*, 1962, 1963).

Several models for the mechanism of streaming in the myxomycetes
have been proposed. The current concensus of a large number of investigators is that streaming is a passive response to pressure gradients
generated in the plasmodial walls by a contractile system. The following
summarizes some of the supporting evidence for this model, which has
been termed the "pressure-flow" or "contraction-hydraulic" theory of
streaming:

(1) Hydrostatic pressure exists within plasmodial strands, as evidenced
by the copious outflow of protoplasm following mechanical or chemical
injury to the plasmodial wall (Andresen and Pollock, 1952; Jahn *et al.*,
1964; Stewart, 1964; others).

(2) ATP (adenosine triphosphate, the immediate energy source for
muscle contraction and other biological processes), when applied to
plasmodial strands, effects an increase in the motive force of streaming
(Kamiya *et al.*, 1957; Takata, 1957) and causes constriction and flow in
both directions away from the point of contact (Jahn *et al.*, 1964).

(3) A contractile protein named "myxomyosin" or "plasmodial myo-
sin-B" and having physical-chemical properties similar to muscle acto-
myosin has been extracted from plasmodia (Loewy, 1952; Ts'o *et al.*,
1956a,b, 1957a,b; Nakajima, 1960, 1964).

(4) Wohlfarth-Bottermann (1962, 1964) has shown by electron microscopy that plasmodial strands have peripherally located fibers composed
of filaments with dimensions similar to myxomyosin filaments (Ts'o *et al.*,
1957b). McManus (1965) and McManus and Roth (1965) have reported
finding similar filaments in other myxomycetes.

(5) Allen *et al.* (1963) found that greater heat production is synchronized
with constriction and efflux of cytoplasm.

(6) Birefringent fibrils have been found in fixed (Wohlfarth-Bottermann, 1964) and live plasmodia (Nakajima and Allen, 1965). In the
latter case, circularly oriented fibrils shorten and decrease in birefringence
during constriction.

I wish to present additional evidence in support of the pressure-flow
theory by interrelating three diverse approaches to the study of cytoplasmic streaming: time lapse microcinematography, electron microscopy,
and electrophysiology.

Cinematography was employed by Seifriz (1937) to study rhythmical

changes in diameter and streaming, by Kamiya and Seifriz (1954) to demonstrate torsion in suspended strands, by Stewart and Stewart (1959a; Stewart, 1964) for streaming patterns, and by Nakajima and Allen (1964) for showing changes in birefringence in live plasmodia. The gross morphology and light microscopy of *P. polycephalum* have been described by Howard (1931a,b, 1932), Camp (1937), Jump (1954), and Guttes *et al.* (1961), and its fine structure by Stewart and Stewart (1959b, 1960, 1961), Dugas and Bath (1962), Terada (1962), Wohlfarth-Bottermann (1962, 1964), and Rhea (1966). In electrophysiological studies, Iwamura (1949), Kamiya and Abe (1950), and Kishimoto (1958) correlated certain aspects of the streaming cycle with rhythmical changes in potential measured between the two ends of plasmodial strands. Attempts at measuring transmembrane potential changes over long periods have led to little success (Kamiya and Abe, 1950; Tauc, 1953, 1954; Anderson, 1964).

My chief concern in the time-lapse microcinematographic study is to relate rhythmical changes in strand diameter to the streaming cycle. Evidence from electron micrographs presented here and more extensively elsewhere (Rhea, 1966) confirms the presence of internal fibrils, and an attempt is made to implicate them and the external fibrillar network in streaming and motility by virtue of their orientation with respect to other structural features. In the electrophysiology study, a method is described for maintaining the transmembrane potential and recording its rhythmical changes simultaneously with changes in diameter and the direction of streaming.

I. MATERIALS AND METHODS

Three forms of *Physarum polycephalum*[2] were employed: (a) motile surface plasmodia grown on a starvation medium (Fig. 1), (b) microplasmodia grown submerged and agitated in a complete growth medium (Fig. 2), and (c) spherules derived from aged and refrigerated microplasmodia (Fig. 3).

A. Culture Techniques

Stock cultures were maintained aseptically as microplasmodia (Daniel and Rusch, 1961) in a growth medium containing hematin (Daniel *et al.*, 1962). To prepare motile plasmodia, 10 ml of suspended microplasmodia from 3-day stock cultures were centrifuged at 250 g for 5 min and the sedimented plasmodia placed in a 500 ml Erlenmeyer flask onto 2 gm of moistened rolled oats. After 4 to 6 days of incubation at 18°C, plasmodial

[2] Original cultures (sclerotia) kindly furnished by Dr. J. W. Daniel, McArdle Memorial Laboratory, University of Wisconsin, Madison, Wisconsin.

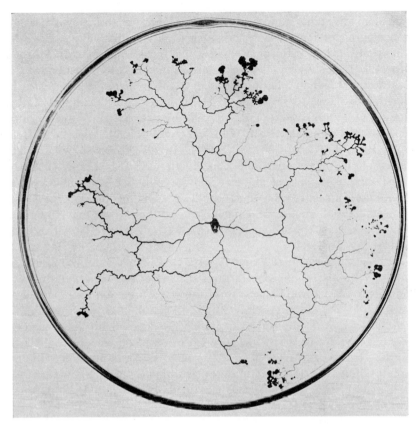

Fig. 1. Motile plasmodium grown on starvation agar in a petri dish. It consists of bulbous and fan-shaped advancing ends, less prominent retracting ends, and a network of interconnecting strands (actual size).

fragments were transferred to a petri dish containing 2% agar in a starvation medium, the sporulation medium of Daniel and Rusch (1962) less CaCO₃, niacin, and niacinamide. Spherules were prepared by refrigerating 7-day cultures of microplasmodia at 4°C for 4 to 16 days.

B. Time-Lapse Microcinematography

Small fragments of motile plasmodia were placed on a no. 1 cover glass and incubated in a moist chamber. Microplasmodia and spherules were positioned between two no. 1 cover glasses separated by 0.1 to 0.2 mm. All cultures were photographed under bright field using an inverted microscope. Exposures ranged from 0.1 to 0.25 sec. Intervals were selected so that movements were speeded up from 10 to 100 times normal when the film is projected at 24 frames/sec.

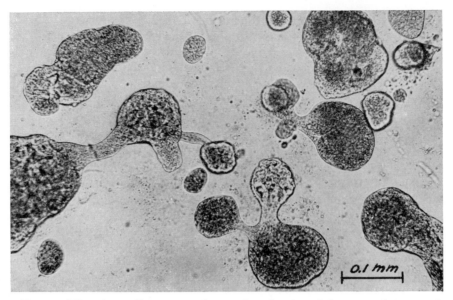

FIG. 2. Microplasmodia grown submerged and agitated in a complete growth medium. Note the nodular ends and the interconnecting strands (×160).

FIG. 3. Spherules from aged and refrigerated culture of microplasmodia. Each is encapsulated in a dense, fibrillar network (×2,000).

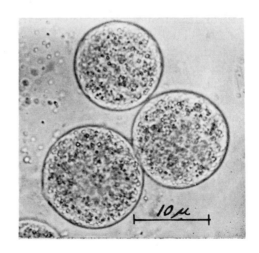

C. Electron Microscopy

Most plasmodia were fixed for 15 to 30 min in 6.25% glutaraldehyde in 0.1 M phosphate buffer (pH 7.2), rinsed in the buffer, postfixed 20 min in 1% OsO_4 in the same buffer, and dehydrated through an ethyl alcohol series containing 1% phosphotungstic acid and 0.5% uranyl acetate.

Following rinses in propylene oxide or methyl cellosolve, plasmodia were embedded in Epon 812. Where other fixatives or treatments were employed, mention is made in the figure legends. Sections were cut with a diamond knife on an LKB Ultratome and examined in an RCA (EMU-3F) electron microscope. Some sections were stained in a saturated aqueous solution of uranyl acetate.

D. Electrophysiology

Transmembrane potentials of motile plasmodia were measured with a 3 M KCl-filled glass microelectrode having a tip diameter between 1 and 2 μ and a resistance of 5 to 10 meg. For maintaining transmembrane potentials, the chelating agent ethylene-diamine-tetra acetic acid (Versene or EDTA) was added (1%) to the 3M KCl. Other additives effective in preventing membrane formation at the tip of the electrode were the detergents Na-Lauryl sulfate (1%) and lauric diethanolamide (0.5%). These were used alone and in combination with Versene. The microelectrode was attached by a polyethylene sleeve to the tip of a Beckman no. 41239 fiber junction calomel electrode. An identical calomel electrode was used as the indifferent electrode in contact with the agar. Both electrodes were connected to the input of a Keithley Model 603 direct coupled electrometer, which, in turn, drove a Heiland Model 1406 Visicorder galvanometer. Three channels on the galvanometer were used for the simultaneous recording of rhythmical changes in membrane potential, strand diameter, and the direction of streaming. For diameter changes, one ocular of a binocular microscope was fitted with a mask that cut the field to a rectangle slightly longer than the diameter of the strand at the electrode. A battery-operated photomultiplier tube (RCA 1P21) placed over the ocular was connected via a low-pass filter ($\tau = 0.05$ sec) to another Keithley 603 amplifier and thence to the galvanometer. Changes in diameter were inversely related to the current leaving the photomultiplier tube. For these measurements, plasmodial strands 1 cm long and approximately 0.1 mm in diameter were employed.

II. RESULTS

A. Time-Lapse Microcinematography

Time-lapse microcinematography shows that apposing nodules of dumbbell-shaped microplasmodia constrict and dilate reciprocally. When one nodule constricts, cytoplasm flows outward through the interconnecting strand and into the opposite and expanding nodule. Similarly, a high correlation between constriction and efflux of cytoplasm and between

relaxation and influx is seen in the advancing ends of motile plasmodia. In many instances, peristaltic-like waves begin at the tip of the advancing end and move posteriorly, a phenomenon resembling the waves of contraction which propel the contents of the alimentary canal and other tubes provided with circular and longitudinal muscle fibers. The same relationships between diameter changes and the direction of flow hold for retracting ends as well, but peristaltic-like waves are not in evidence. Contrary to all the preceding cases, the reversal of flow along the plasmodial strands that connect advancing and retracting ends does not always occur at maximum and minimum diameters.

Nearly all strands are marked by surface indentations that encircle them without passing through their centers. These irregularly spaced plicae, indentations, or "invaginations" divide strands into short sections, with each section considerably shorter than its diameter. Time-lapse films of plasmodial strands often reveal streaming channels lateral to the central, longitudinal channel and perpendicular to it. Cytoplasm from the circumferential regions of each section demarcated by indentations streams into the central channel during constriction and is replaced, presumably by different cytoplasm, during relaxation.

Although streaming does not occur in spherules, considerable activity is observed within their cytoplasm. Time-lapse studies show that this activity has a definite rhythmicity—alternate slowing and speeding up of organelle movements. Calculations for one group of spherules gave a period of 38 seconds, well within the limits of the streaming cycle of plasmodia. When spherules are left at room temperature for several hours, increasing internal activity is accompanied by undulations on the surface. Under these conditions, two adjacent spherules will fuse, undergo several streaming cycles, and then assume a more or less spherical form, whereupon streaming ceases.

Plasmodia of *P. polycephalum* secrete an encapsulating slime coat, a clear, viscous substance that remains as a visible slime track after the mold migrates to a new area. Once vacated, the tracks are often retraced and reoccupied by the same plasmodium that produced them. Another phenomenon associated with the slime is the "streaming" of debris or of foreign particles placed beside plasmodial strands. The particles "stream" with a period equal to that of the parallel cytoplasmic stream but usually out of phase with it. Whether the slime itself or fluid associated with it is streaming along with the particles is not certain.

B. Electron Microscopy

1. *Motile Plasmodia*. The circumferential region of most strands is indented by "invaginations" that extend longitudinally (Fig. 4) and

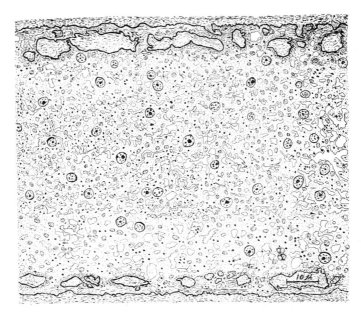

Fig. 4. Drawing of a longitudinal section of a strand. The lateral, invaginated areas contain the same filamentous material that encapsulates the strand. Internal fibrils are restricted to the peripheral region. Organelles and vacuoles are evenly distributed (×800) (Rhea, 1966).

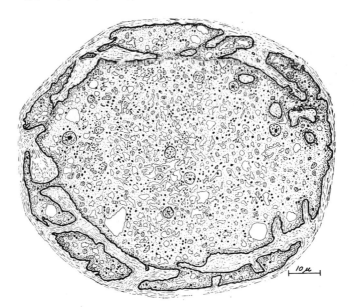

Fig. 5. Drawing of a transverse section of a plasmodial strand. Some internal filaments are seen but fewer than in longitudinal sections. The cytoplasm of the circumferential pockets resembles that of the central streaming channel (×800) (Rhea, 1966).

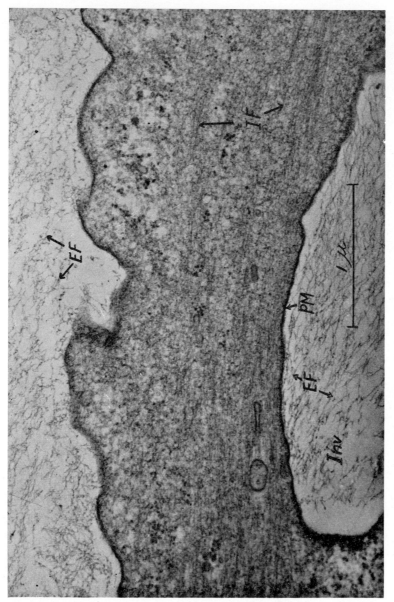

Fig. 6. Longitudinal section through the cortical cytoplasm of a strand. Internal filaments (IF) lie tangential to the membrane of an invagination (PM). Invagination (Inv); external filaments (EF). Preparation rinsed in Hasselbach-Schneider solution (Hanson and Huxley, 1953) before postfixation (×37,000) (Rhea, 1966).

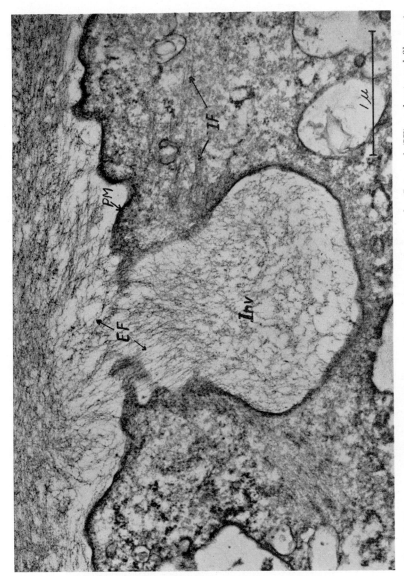

FIG. 7. Transverse section through the cortical cytoplasm of a strand. Internal (IF) and external filaments (EF) meet the plasma membrane (PM) of an invagination (Inv). Same fixation as in Fig. 6 (×32,000) (Rhea, 1966).

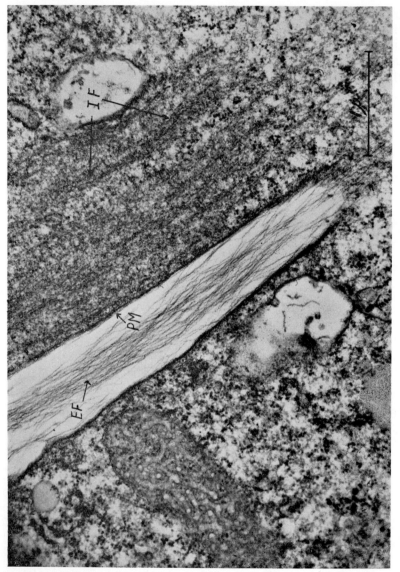

Fig. 8. Transverse section of a strand near the surface. Internal (IF) and external filaments (EF) lie tangential to the invaginated plasma membrane (PM). Same fixation as in Figs. 6 and 7 (×27,000) (Rhea, 1966).

circularly (Fig. 5) into the strand. ("Invaginations" may be a misnomer, for little is known about their origin.) Although the cytoplasm within the circumferential pockets or compartments between these invaginations bears no structural dissimilarities to the deeper cytoplasm, that which lies immediately subjacent to the plasma membrane is devoid of organelles

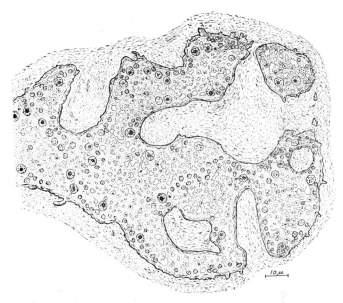

Fig. 9. Drawing of a longitudinal section through a nodule of a microplasmodium. External filaments fill the numerous invaginations, and internal filaments form a continuous network subjacent to the plasma membrane. Mitochondria are concentrated near the surface (×600) (Rhea, 1966).

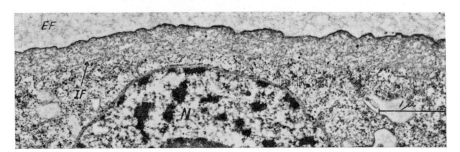

Fig. 10. Section of a microplasmodium. Internal filaments (IF) lie tangential to the plasma membrane of an invagination. External filaments (EF); nucleus (N) (×17,000) (Rhea, 1966).

and is often associated with longitudinally and circularly oriented fibrils[3] (Figs. 4–8). These fibrils measure to 1 μ or more in diameter and consist of parallel filaments approximately 55 Å in diameter. They associate freely with the invaginated plasma membrane but are usually separated

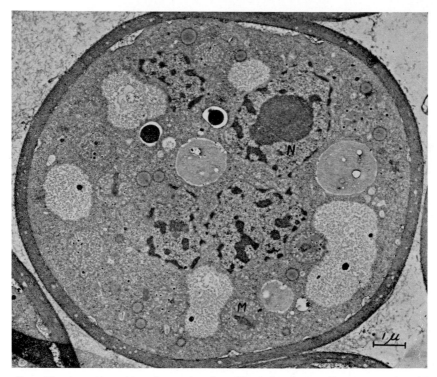

FIG. 11. A section through a spherule. Note the dense, fibrous capsule. The plasma membrane does not conform perfectly to the smooth, inner surface of the capsule. Nucleus (N); mitochondrion (M) ($\times$8,000) (Rhea, 1966).

from the noninvaginated plasma membrane by a layer of hyaline cytoplasm 1 μ or more in thickness.

External to the plasmodium is a network of curved and branched filaments 30 to 75 Å in diameter which encapsulates the plasmodium. It fills the lumens of the membranous invaginations and appears to make direct external attachments to the plasma membrane (Figs. 7 and 8). Fibrils composed of loose, parallel arrays of these filaments are oriented longitudinally and circularly to the long axis of the strand in a fashion

[3] As used in this paper, a "fibril" is resolvable in the light microscope and consists of unit "filaments" resolvable only in the electron microscope.

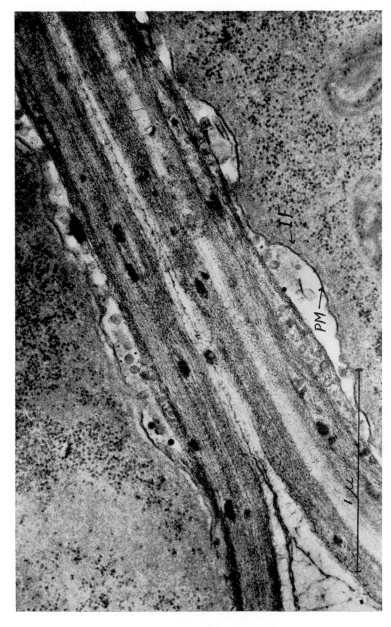

Fig. 12. Portions of two adjoining spherules, showing the lamellated fibrous capsule, the irregular border of the protoplasm, and cortical cytoplasm that contains some filamentous material. Plasma membrane (PM); internal filaments (IF). Fixed first in 2% glutaraldehyde plus 2% formaldehyde in 0.1 M phosphate buffer. Post-fixation same as other preparations (×54,000) (Rhea, 1966).

similar to the internal fibrils. Electron micrographs of slime tracks (not illustrated) indicate that part or all of the fibrillar coat is shed by retracting strands.

2. *Microplasmodia.* The nodular ends of microplasmodia are divided by invaginations of the plasma membrane into a labyrinth of irregularly

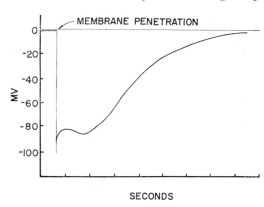

Fig. 13. Transmembrane potential "spike" recorded from a strand of motile plasmodium. Measured with a glass microelectrode filled with 3 M KCl (tip diameter 1μ; resistance 5–10 meg). The inside of the strand is negative to the outside. Note rapid decrease of potential.

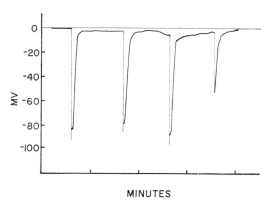

Fig. 14. A series of transmembrane potential "spikes" obtained by advancing a 3 M KCl-filled glass microelectrode into a plasmodial strand. Each drop in potential is probably due to membrane formation at the tip of the electrode.

shaped lobules and strands (Fig. 9). Internal fibrils are contiguous to the invaginated plasma membrane (Fig. 10), but they are usually separated from the noninvaginated membrane by a thin layer of cortical cytoplasm. Mitochondria are more numerous near the plasma membrane than in deeper cytoplasm. A fibrillar network like that observed around motile plasmodia encapsulates the microplasmodium and fills the lumens of the invaginations.

3. *Spherules.* Spherules are devoid of invaginations (Figs. 11 and 12). They are encapsulated by a very dense, fibrous coat consisting of filaments similar to the external filaments of motile plasmodia and microplasmodia. The thin (0.1 μ) cortical cytoplasm contains scattered filaments, some of

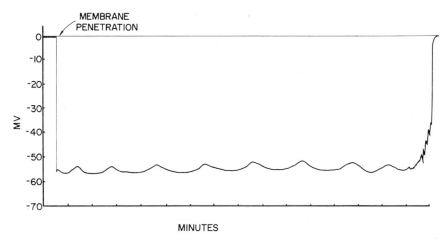

FIG. 15. A 15-min recording of the transmembrane potential of a plasmodial strand. Obtained by adding 1% Versene to the 3 M KCl of the glass microelectrode. Note the rhythmic rise and fall of potential.

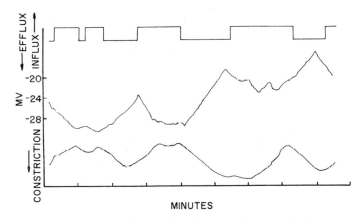

FIG. 16. Simultaneous recordings of changes in diameter (bottom), transmembrane potential (middle), and the direction of streaming (top) from one end of a plasmodial strand 1 cm long. The glass microelectrode contained 3 M KCl plus 0.25% each of Versene, Na-Lauryl sulfate, and lauric diethanolamide. Membrane depolarization, strand constriction, and the outflow of protoplasm occur together, as do membrane polarization, strand relaxation, and the influx of protoplasm.

which are oriented parallel to the plasma membrane, but few if any are organized into distinguishable fibrils.

C. Electrophysiology

When a glass microelectrode filled with 3 M KCl is inserted into a plasmodial strand, a transmembrane potential of 30 to 120 mV (inside

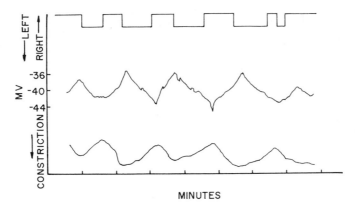

FIG. 17. Recordings similar to those of Fig. 16 but from the center of a 1-cm strand. The electrode contained 1% lauric diethanolamide. Membrane depolarization, strand constriction, and the efflux of protoplasm occur nearly together, but some phase differences are evident.

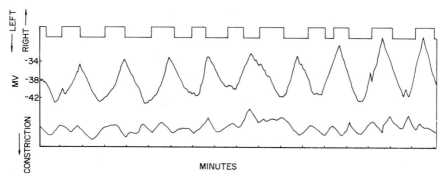

FIG. 18. Recordings similar to those of Fig. 17. The frequency or repetition rate of diameter changes is twice the frequency of either of the other two variables. Minimum potentials repeat at regular intervals, 120 ± 3 sec, but are out of phase with changes in direction and diameter.

negative to the outside) is recorded and then returns within a few seconds to zero potential (Fig. 13). If the electrode is advanced deeper into the plasmodium, similar "spikes" are obtained as the plasma membrane is repeatedly ruptured and reformed (Fig. 14). Augmenting the 3 M KCl with Versene or any one of a number of detergents permits the recording of cyclic changes in transmembrane potentials for extended periods. One recording (Fig. 15) made in this manner shows a membrane potential of approximately 52 mV and lasting 15 min before falling off. During this time, there occur nine cycles with peak-to-peak amplitudes from 4 to 6 mV and an average period of 100 sec.

Changes in diameter, transmembrane potential, and the direction of streaming were recorded simultaneously at the end of a 1-cm strand (Fig. 16) and at the center (Figs. 17 and 18). At the end, the three variables change simultaneously: constriction, membrane depolarization (decreasing potential difference), and the efflux of cytoplasm occur together, as do relaxation, membrane polarization (increasing potential difference), and the influx of cytoplasm. Seven recordings show that efflex and influx of cytoplasm begin 83% of the time at or near the beginning of constriction and relaxation, respectively.

At the center of 1-cm strands, the frequency or repetition rate of diameter change either is nearly equal to the frequency of the other two variables (Fig. 17) or is twice as fast (Fig. 18). When the three variables are nearly equal in frequency, membrane depolarization accompanies strand constriction approximately 60% of the time; when not equal, only 32% of the time. At the center, 58% of the changes in the direction of streaming occur at maximum or minimum diameters.

In recording from ends or centers of 1-cm strands, changes in membrane potential appear to occur at more regular intervals than do changes in diameter or the direction of streaming. In one recording (Fig. 18), each of nine cycles had a period of 120 ± 3 sec. Another characteristic of potential changes is the more sudden reversal of potential at minimum potential than at maximum potential.

III. DISCUSSION

The concomitance of diameter decrease and the efflux of cytoplasm does not necessarily indicate that a contractile wall mechanism is the direct cause of the outflow. Conceivably, the channel wall could be responding passively to any one of a number of mechanisms: (a) One residing within the streaming cytoplasm, for example, a diffusion drag force as proposed by Rashevsky (1940, 1948) and later suggested for *P. polycephalum* by Stewart and Stewart (1959a). Jahn (1964) has criticized this theory on grounds that it fails to explain such phenomena as "origins" (Jahn *et al.*, 1964), torsional movement, and the mechanism of retraction. That streaming of the endoplasm is a passive rather than an active phenomenon has been proposed by Kamiya (1950, 1959) and Kamiya and Kuroda (1958) on the basis of velocity profile studies. The form of the velocity profile of natural or induced streaming is that of a truncated parabola and resembles the velocity profiles of fluids with structural viscosity flowing in capillary tubes. (b) An active shearing between the strand wall and the endoplasm (Loewy, 1949; Kamiya, 1959). Kamiya and Kuroda (1958) also ruled this out on the basis of their velocity profile studies, but

Kamiya (1959) suggested that such a driving force could be operative in minute channels. (c) A frontal contraction system as proposed for ameboid motion by Allen (1961), i.e., a pulling rather than a pushing mechanism. If this theory is valid, greater heat production would be expected at the filling rather than the emptying end of a strand. By employing thermistors at opposite ends of short strands, Allen *et al.* (1963) demonstrated that greater heat production is, in fact, at the source of the stream, i.e., the constricting end.

Associated with the rhythmical changes in diameter and streaming are the peristaltic-like waves that spread posteriorly from advancing ends of strands. In a time-lapse study, Stewart (1964) observed similar waves traveling at 10 μ/sec but having no constant patterns or source. They consisted of an expanded area of strand with streaming on either side directed toward that area (afferent reversal) followed by a narrower region with streaming on either side directed outward (efferent reversal). In the present study, the waves were not observed over the entire plasmodium. However, in support of Stewart's findings, changes in the direction of streaming did occur more frequently at maximum and minimum diameters. If the peristaltic-like waves and the local changes in strand diameter represent active contraction and relaxation, then the motive force is not limited to the ends of strands but functions at all points along the channel walls. Besides being the probable locus of the motive force for streaming, the channel walls contribute materially to the central stream, as evidenced by the cyclic emptying and filling of the circumferential pockets or compartments of cytoplasm.

That spherules contain the essentials for the streaming process is suggested by the rhythmical changes in organelle motility, and demonstrated by the streaming cycles that immediately follow the union of two spherules. Because streaming ceases when the fused spherules again assume a spherical form, it seems likely that an asymmetrical and nonspherical form is essential for the expression of mechanochemical forces residing within the spherule.

A phenomenon not too unlike the streaming of particles lying on or in the slime coat is found in Ameba. In Ameba, particles placed on the surface move forward (Mast, 1926; Griffin and Allen, 1960), and some evidence indicates that a fibrillar coat moves forward also (Wolpert *et al.*, 1964). The significance of these similarities is not known.

A. Electron Microscopy

Wohlfarth-Bottermann (1962) was the first to demonstrate by electron microscopy the presence of "plasma filaments" organized into a fibrillar network in the channel walls. On the basis of their diameter (70 Å) matching that of myxomyosin filaments (Ts'o *et al.*, 1957b), their bire-

fringence, greater number during efflux than influx, and their ATP-ase activity, he concluded that they form at least one site of the motive force of streaming (Wohlfarth-Bottermann, 1964). The internal filaments and fibrils described briefly in this report and more extensively elsewhere (Rhea, 1966) resemble those observed by Wohlfarth-Bottermann, and the type I and II fibrils observed in other myxomycetes by McManus (1965) and McManus and Roth (1965). In all these cases, the fibrils were found near the surface of strands, and associated more with the membranes of "vacuoles" (the plasma membrane of invaginations in this paper) than with the noninvaginated plasma membrane. If the filaments are contractile, their arrangement in circular and longitudinal arrays as described here could bring about the kinds of motions associated with streaming and motility in *P. polycephalum*. Nakajima (1964) and Nakajima and Allen (1965) found in strands of live plasmodia positively birefringent fibrils arranged circularly, longitudinally, and spirally. During strand constriction, the circular fibrils shortened and decreased in birefringence. This, the authors cautioned, could occur in either active contraction or in passive elastic changes in length.

Of particular interest in electron micrographs of microplasmodia is the observation that mitochondria are more numerous near the fibrillar network lying subjacent to the plasma membrane than they are in the deeper cytoplasm. It is believed that the ATP for streaming comes from glycolysis rather than respiration (reviewed by Kamiya, 1960), and it is generally agreed that respiration is primarily a function of mitochondria. Their abundance near the surface may bear no direct relationship to the streaming mechanism. A more uniform distribution was the rule in motile plasmodia.

Whether the external fibrillar coat is actually part or all of the secreted slime is not known. Electron micrographs of slime tracks show nothing but the empty, fibrous coat and recognizable debris. Because of its apparent attachment to the plasma membrane, the circular and longitudinal arrays of its fibrils, and its ultimate discard by retracting ends, the coat could be considered a type of "exoskeleton" that contains the plasmodium, gives it protection, provides for its attachment, and possibly aids in streaming and locomotion. Concerning this last possibility, Seifriz (1953) commented that "a fiber is of no use for doing mechanical work if there is no place to attach it." Perhaps the external coat affords just such an attachment for the internal fibrils, thus providing restoring force during streaming and motility.

B. Electrophysiology

In seeking the cause of streaming in *P. polycephalum*, investigators have looked for clues in the relationships between cyclic electrical phenomena

and the streaming cycle. Iwamura (1949), Kamiya and Abe (1950), and Kishimoto (1958) found high correlations but no clear-cut, causal relationships between the streaming cycle and cyclic changes in potential measured between the ends of short strands. Their electrodes were positioned on the plasma membrane, not across it. In a similar experiment with longer strands (18 mm), Tauc (1954) reported little if any correlation between the streaming cycle and potential changes. Until now, attempts at relating local changes in transmembrane potential with the streaming cycle have met with little success (Kamiya and Abe, 1950; Tauc, 1953, 1954; Anderson, 1964). When the electrode—usually a glass microelectrode—penetrates the plasma membrane, a potential difference of from 20 to over 100 mV (inside negative to the outside) is recorded and then falls rapidly and disappears within seconds. Because similar "spikes" are obtained upon advancing the electrodes deeper into the plasmodium (Fig. 14), the formation of new membrane at the electrode tip is suspected. Tauc (1954) observed cyclic changes in transmembrane potentials by recording and plotting against time the maxima of a long series of potentials obtained by repeatedly penetrating the plasma membrane.

In the present study, the chelating agent ethylene-diamine-tetra-acetic acid (Versene or EDTA) was added to the 3 M KCl of the electrode to delay membrane formation, presumably by binding calcium ions that are normally required in the biochemistry of membranes. Although detergents were added to interfere with the lipid moiety of membranes, their actual role in delaying membrane formation is not known to the author. The eventual disappearance of the transmembrane potential could be due to the depletion of the chelating agent or detergent from the tip of the electrode, for, once the potential falls, the electrode is ineffectual if used again.

Evidence gathered thus far indicates that membrane depolarization occurs simultaneously with strand constriction and the outflow of cytoplasm, especially at the ends. In studies on muscle, it is recognized that membrane depolarization accompanies contraction, and that the degree of tension is proportional to the degree of depolarization (Fleckenstein, et al., 1951). This similarity in electrophysiological behavior between muscle and slime mold plasmodia together with other shared physical-chemical properties mentioned earlier (see Introduction) adds support to the contraction-hydraulic theory of streaming.

Little is known about the origin of rhythmicity in shuttle streaming. Kamiya and Nakajima (1955) found that the control mechanism as well as the potential rhythm continue during the temporary cessation of streaming which follows the gelation of cytoplasm by CO_2. In the present study, membrane potential changes have the most regular periodicity or repetition rate of the three cyclic phenomena recorded, but the

significance of this may be unrelated to a control mechanism. If constriction depends upon membrane depolarization, both should occur close together, as appears to be the case for the ends of strands. However, Kamiya and Abe (1950) found that potential changes measured externally actually lag behind the motive force by about a quarter of a period.

IV. SUMMARY

Evidence from time-lapse microcinematography, electron microscopy, and electrophysiology was presented in support of the pressure-flow or contraction-hydraulic theory of shuttle streaming in the slime mold *Physarum polycephalum*. The following is a summary of these and related findings:

(1) Evidence indicates that the flow of cytoplasm results from a contractile wall mechanism that moves in a rhythmical, peristaltic-like fashion along plasmodial strands.

(2) Cytoplasm adjacent to the central streaming channel cyclically flows in and out of circumferentially positioned pockets or compartments that are demarcated along the strand by "invaginations" of the plasma membrane.

(3) If contractile, circularly and logitudinally oriented fibrils are so positioned in the walls of strands as to bring about the kinds of movements associated with streaming and motility.

(4) An external fibrillar coat encapsulates all plasmodia. Its role could be that of an exoskeleton that contains the plasmodium, affords attachment to the substratum, and, if elastic, provides restoring forces to the contractile wall system during streaming and migration. It is shed by retracting strands and is occasionally reoccupied.

(5) The difficulty in maintaining transmembrane potentials is presumably due to the formation of new membrane over the tip of the electrode. This can be overcome by adding the chelating agent Versene or a detergent to the 3 M KCl of the glass microelectrode.

(6) From simultaneous recordings of local changes in transmembrane potential, strand diameter, and the direction of streaming, it appears that membrane depolarization accompanies strand constriction and the outflow of cytoplasm, whereas its polarization accompanies relaxation and influx. This is especially noticeable at the ends of strands. Muscle fibers also undergo membrane depolarization during contraction.

(7) The possibility that changes in transmembrane potential are related to the control mechanism for shuttle streaming was discussed.

(8) Spherules appear to have the capacity for streaming but lack the asymmetry for it. This is based upon the simultaneous and rhythmical changes in the motility of their organelles, and upon the observation that streaming cycles immediately follow the union of two spherules.

ACKNOWLEDGMENT

This investigation was carried out in the Laboratory of Developmental Biology (Professor Paul Weiss, Head). It was supported in part by Public Health Service Fellowship No. 5-F2-GM-7142-02 from the National Institute of General Medical Sciences and by Grant No. CA-06375 from the National Cancer Institute (National Institutes of Health) to Dr. Paul Weiss as Principal Investigator.

REFERENCES

ALLEN, R. D. (1961). *Exptl. Cell Res. Suppl.* **8,** 17.

ALLEN, R. D., PITTS, W. R., SPEIR, D., and BRAULT, J. (1963). *Science* **142,** 1485.

ANDERSON, J. D. (1964). *In* "Primitive Motile Systems in Cell Biology" (R. D. Allen and N. Kamiya, eds.), pp. 125–134. Academic Press, New York,

ANDRESEN, N. and POLLOCK, B. M. (1952). *Compt. Rend. Trav. Lab. Carlsberg* **28,** 247.

CAMP, W. G. (1936). *Bull. Torrey Botan. Club* **63,** 205.

CAMP, W. G. (1937). *Bull. Torrey Botan. Club* **64,** 307.

DANIEL, J. W., BABCOCK, K. L., SIEVERT, A. H., and RUSCH, H. (1963). *J. Bacteriol.* **86,** 324.

DANIEL, J. W., KELLEY, J., and RUSCH, H. P. (1962). *J. Bacteriol.* **84,** 1104.

DANIEL, J. W. and RUSCH, H. P. (1961). *J. Gen. Microbiol.* **25,** 47.

DANIEL, J. W. and RUSCH, H. P. (1962). *J. Bacteriol.* **83,** 234.

DUGAS, D. J. and BATH, J. D. (1962). *Protoplasma* **54,** 421.

FLECKENSTEIN, A., HILLE, H., and ADAM, W. E. (1951). *Pfluegers Arch. Ges. Physiol.* **253,** 264.

GRIFFIN, J. L. and ALLEN, R. D. (1960). *Exptl. Cell Res.* **20,** 619.

GUTTES, E., GUTTES, S., and RUSCH, H. P. (1961). *Develop. Biol.* **3,** 588.

HANSON, J. and HUXLEY, H. E. (1953). *Nature* **172,** 530.

HOWARD, F. L. (1931a). *Am. J. Botany* **18,** 116.

HOWARD, F. L. (1931b). *Am. J. Botany* **18,** 624.

HOWARD, F. L. (1932). *Ann. Botany (London)* **46,** 461.

IWAMURA, T. (1949). *Botan. Mag. (Tokyo)* **62,** 126.

JAHN, T. L. (1964). *Biorheology* **2,** 133.

JAHN, T. L., RINALDI, R. A., and BROWN, M. (1964). *Biorheology* **2,** 123.

JUMP, J. A. (1954). *Am. J. Botany* **41,** 561.

KAMIYA, N. (1950). *Cytologia* **15,** 183.

KAMIYA, N. (1959). *Protoplasmatologia* **8**(3a), 1.

KAMIYA, N. (1960). *Ann. Rev. Plant Physiol.* **11,** 323.

KAMIYA, N. and ABE, S. (1950). *Colloid Sci.,* **5,** 149.

KAMIYA, N. and KURODA, K. (1958). *Protoplasma* **49,** 1.

KAMIYA, N. and NAKAJIMA, H. (1955). *Japan J. Botany* **15,** 49.

KAMIYA, N., NAKAJIMA, H., and ABE, S. (1957). *Protoplasma* **48,** 94.

KAMIYA, N. and SEIFRIZ, W. (1954). *Exptl. Cell Res.* **6,** 1.

KISHIMOTO, U. (1958). *J. Gen. Physiol.* **41,**, 1205.

LOEWY, A. G. (1949). *Proc. Am. Phil. Soc.* **93,** 326.

Loewy, A. G. (1952).   J. Cellular Comp. Physiol. **40,** 127.

Mast, S. O. (1926).   J. Morphol. **41,** 347.

McManus, M. A. (1965).   Am. J. Botany **52,** 15.

McManus, M. A. and Roth, L. E. (1965).   J. Cell Biol. **25,** 305.

Nakajima, H. (1960).   Protoplasma **52,** 413.

Nakajima, H. (1964).   In "Primitive Motile Systems in Cell Biology" (R. D. Allen and N. Kamiya, eds.), pp. 111–123.   Academic Press, New York.

Nakajima, H. and Allen, R. D. (1964).   Research film, New York Cinemagnetics Corporation.

Nakajima, H. and Allen, R. D. (1965).   J. Cell Biol. **25,** 361.

Rashevsky, N. (1940).   "Advances and Applications of Mathematical Biology." Univ. of Chicago Press, Chicago, Illinois.

Rashevsky, N. (1948).   "Mathematical Biophysics."   Univ. of Chicago Press, Chicago, Illinois.

Rhea, R. P. (1966).   J. Ultrastructure Res. **15,** 349.

Seifriz, W. (1937).   Science **86,** 397.

Seifriz, W. (1943).   Botan. Rev. **9,** 49.

Seifriz, W. (1952).   In "Deformation and Flow in Biological Systems" (A. Frey-Wyssling, ed.), pp. 3–156.   Wiley (Interscience), New York.

Seifriz, W. (1953).   Nature **171,** 1136.

Stewart, B. T. and Stewart, P. A. (1960).   Norelco Reptr. **7,** 21.

Stewart, P. A. (1964).   In "Primitive Motile Systems in Cell Biology" (R. D. Allen and N. Kamiya, eds.), pp. 69–78.   Academic Press, New York.

Stewart, P. A. and Stewart, B. T. (1959a).   Exptl. Cell Res. **17,** 44.

Stewart, P. A. and Stewart, B. T. (1959b).   Exptl. Cell Res. **18,** 374.

Stewart, P. A. and Stewart, B. T. (1961).   Exptl. Cell Res. **23,** 471.

Takata, M. (1957).   22nd Ann. Meeting Botan. Soc. Japan.

Tauc, L. (1953).   J. Physiol. (Paris) **45,** 232.

Tauc, L. (1954).   J. Physiol. (Paris) **46,** 659.

Terada, T. (1962).   Osaka Univ. Faculty Sci., Osaka, Japan **1962,** 47.

Ts'o, P. O. P., Bonner, J., Eggman, L., and Vinograd, J. (1956a).   J. Gen. Physiol. **39,** 325.

Ts'o, P. O. P., Eggman, L., and Vinograd, J. (1956b).   J. Gen. Physiol. **39,** 801.

Ts'o, P. O. P., Eggman, L., and Vinograd, J. (1957a).   Arch. Biochem. Biophys. **66,** 64.

Ts'o, P. O. P., Eggman, L., and Vinograd, J. (1957b).   Biochim. Biophys. Acta **25,** 532.

Wohlfarth-Bottermann, K. E. (1962).   Protoplasma **54,** 514.

Wohlfarth-Bottermann, K. E. (1964).   In "Primitive Motile Systems in Cell Biology" (R. D. Allen and N. Kamiya, eds.), pp. 79–109.   Academic Press, New York.

Wolpert, L., Thompson, C. M., and O'Neill, C. H. (1964).   In "Primitive Motile Systems in Cell Biology" (R. D. Allen and N. Kamiya, eds.), pp. 143–171.   Academic Press, New York.

Movements within the Mitotic Spindle

A. BAJER

DEPARTMENT OF BIOLOGY
UNIVERSITY OF OREGON
EUGENE, OREGON

Difficulties involved in investigating cell division have prevented many important details, especially those of chromosome movements, from being described until the past few years. In studies on fixed material, it is often difficult to understand the sequence of events, and favorable material for studies in the living state is scarce. Attempts to study important deviant types of mitosis in the living state, such as chromosome movement with diffuse kinetochore (Luzula [1, 2]), monocentric divisions (Sciara [3]), or puzzling meiotic divisions (in some coccids [4]), have been unsuccessful. These studies have, however, contributed to an accumulation of vast amounts of valuable information which are the basis of present interpretations.

Studies concerning both structure and morphology have been carried out at the light microscopic and ultrastructural levels. In this paper, only one mechanism will be discussed—that of movement of chromosomes and other bodies within the spindle. Also, some remarks concerning the structure of the spindle will be made.

Many data and observations reported here refer directly to mitosis in plant endosperm. In the author's opinion, the general conclusions concerning movements, with slight modifications, may probably be applied to any type of division in plants and animals.

I. THE SPINDLE

The importance of the spindle during mitosis cannot be overemphasized. Many important data on structure and behavior of the spindle have been accumulated [5, 6]. Generally, it is assumed that the spindle is formed *de novo* before each division and disintegrates at the end of anaphase or beginning of telophase. Contrary views, such as that suggesting the elements of the spindle persist throughout interphase, have been presented [7]. It is likely that some basic elements from which the spindle is built are present inside the cell long before the spindle is formed [6]. Robbins and Gonatas [8] have found some elements inside the telophase nucleus. It is conceivable that these elements are present inside the

59

prophase or interphase nucleus and may be responsible for some types of chromosome movements during early prophase or late telophase [9]. The living spindle is composed of regularly arranged elements, as shown by studies in polarized light by Schmidt in 1937 [10]. Details concerning birefringence have been furnished by Inoué [11], and the connection of stronger birefringent zones with kinetochores has been demonstrated by Inoué and Bajer [12]. In electron microscope studies, several workers [13–16] have found the spindle to be composed of numerous microtubules from 150 to 270 Å thick (Figs. 1 and 2), and there seems to be no doubt that the denser arrangement of microtubules represents zones of stronger birefringence.

In endosperm, the formation of the spindle begins in prophase and is seen as a clear zone around the prophase nucleus [39]. The clear zone has the appearance of cytoplasm from which all inclusions such as mitochondria and small granules are removed. However, there are no data concerning the nature of the material in the clear zone in endosperm. Mazia and co-workers [6] have proved in a series of elegant experiments with sea-urchin eggs that the material from which the mitotic spindle forms is present inside the cell before it enters into mitosis.

On the ultrastructural level, the first stages of the spindle formation (clear zone in endosperm) may be a migration of the scattered microtubules to the neighborhood of the nucleus (Fig. 9a). This suggestion seems to be supported by observations from other material. Microtubules have been found in the cytoplasm and around the centrioles before the disappearance of the nuclear membrane in fibroblasts by Krishan and Buck [17]. Also, microtubules around the prophase nucleus in flagellates have been reported by Manton [18]. There are no comprehensive data, however, on the formation of the spindle at the ultrastructural level.

The entire clear zone in endosperm is uniformly birefringent. The arrangement of the ultrastructural elements from which the clear zone is built, probably microtubules, is uncertain. One possibility is shown schematically in Fig. 9a (cf. Section III). Zonation of the clear zone in polarized light appears after the disappearance of the nuclear membrane and after the direct contact of kinetochores with the spindle material. The zones radiate from kinetochores, indicating that the kinetochores contribute to the secondary differentiation of the spindle. Thus the spindle in polarized light during late prometaphase and metaphase appears to be composed of weaker and stronger birefringent zones that have no interconnection at the spindle poles [11, 12]. Other techniques show that bundles from adjacent kinetochores seem to be loosely intermingled and irregularly arranged at the poles. Further observations come from fragmentary electron microscope data and are based mostly on

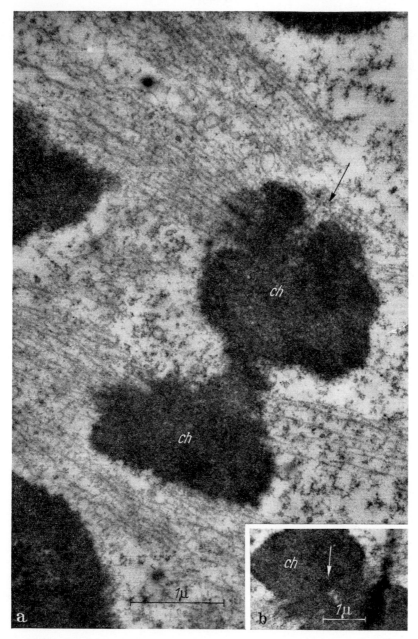

FIG. 1. Electron micrograph of flattened metaphase cell of *Haemanthus katherinae*. Parts of two chromosomes (ch) are seen with their kinetochore pairs or spindle fiber attachment regions. One of these kinetochore pairs has obviously split (arrow). Inset shows another chromosome from the same cell at a lower magnification. Glutaraldehyde postfixed with osmium (from Harris and Bajer [37]).

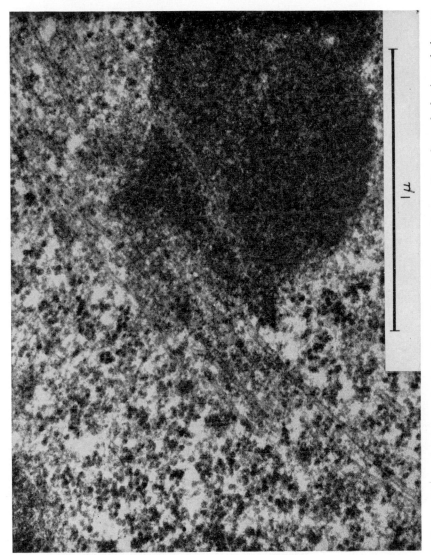

FIG. 2. Microtubules in metaphase of root tip of *Phleum pratense*. Densely packed microtubules are close to the chromosomes. Glutaraldehyde postfixed with osmium. Unpublished micrograph from Ledbetter and Porter (1965).

studies of endosperm *in vitro* with the Nomarski interference contrast system (abbreviated as the Nomarski system) and the phase contrast microscope. The Nomarski system, applied for the first time to the large, living mitotic spindle [19], demonstrates clearly details of fibrillar structure and permits a study of its change during mitosis (Figs. 3 and 4). Probably the great accumulation of microtubules is viewed as a single fibril with the Nomarski system. Single fibrils are between 0.2 and 0.3 μ, which is the limit of the resolving power of the light microscope. No conclusions concerning the exact thickness can be made. In the Nomarski system, a beaded appearance of the fibrils is noted. Presently, the significance of it is not understood. Both the electron microscope and the Nomarski system demonstrate bundles of thin fibrils connected to kinetochores during metaphase and anaphase. Individual filaments of the bundles diverge slightly as they approach the poles. However, the bundles themselves converge toward the poles. In the analysis of movement in the living cells, it is possible to observe that the bundles of chromosomal fibers close to the kinetochores appear not to change during the metaphase-anaphase period. Distal parts of different bundles fuse during anaphase and gradually become undetectable (Fig. 4). On the basis of preliminary observations in the Nomarski system, phase contrast, and polarized light, using plant endosperm, it appears likely that there are some differences in the arrangements of the fibrils at prometaphase and at metaphase. In prometaphase, fibrils connected with adjacent kinetochores are slightly intermingled at the polar region. Fibrils are intermingled more at the polar region during metaphase (Fig. 3), but the process of mixing takes place mainly during the progress of anaphase (Fig. 4). This permits more individual movement during the formation of the metaphase plate. The entire bundle of fibers connected with the kinetochore is longer during prometaphase and shortens during the formation of the metaphase plate and in this way contributes to the shortening of the entire metaphase spindle and reorganization of the polar region before the start of anaphase. It is an open question as to the cause of the shortening. It is possible that it may be denser packing or a change in length of microtubules during formation of the metaphase plate. As prometaphase progresses, the spindle shortens and the birefringence changes. Birefringence of zones that represent chromosomal fibers is stronger in prometaphase than in metaphase [20]. At the same time in the polar regions, which have been shown to have a very loose fibrillar structure [19], numerous akinetic bodies accumulate.

There are important differences between movements of chromosomes in prometaphase and anaphase. Individual kinetochores show independent movement during prometaphase, whereas during normal anaphase they

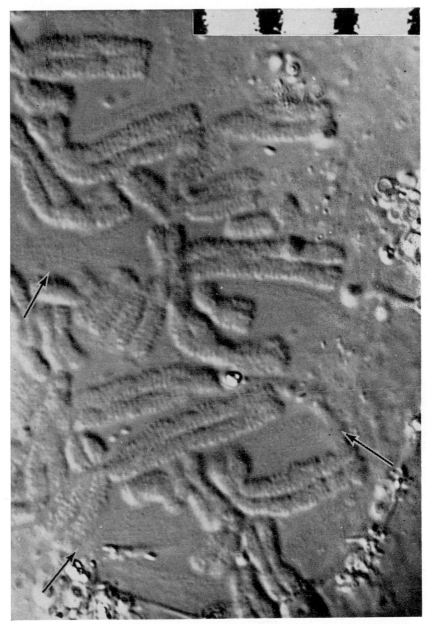

FIG. 3. Very flattened living cell of *Haemanthus katherinae* endosperm in Nomarski interference contrast system. Bundles from adjacent kinetochores intermingle and fuse at the polar region (arrows). 10-μ scale on the edge.

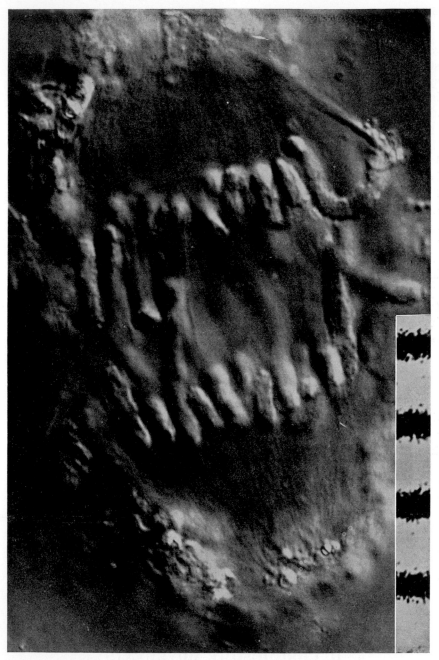

Fig. 4. Anaphase in living cell of endosperm of *Haemanthus katherinae* in Nomarski interference contrast system. Bundles of chromosomal fibers connected with several kinetochores are seen. A gradual intermingling and fusing of bundles of adjacent kinetochores toward the poles is very clearly seen. 10-μ scale on the edge.

move as a compact group.   However, data on the changes of fibrillar structure of the spindle during anaphase are very scarce.   In the Nomarski system, fibrils cease to be visible in late anaphase when they are 5 to 10 μ in length.   It is not known whether they disintegrate or change in another way.   One possibility is schematically represented in Fig. 9d.

Fibrils between chromosome groups also appear during anaphase. These fibrils, which are described from light microscope observations, are known as continuous fibers.   Their origin and formation are unclear.   It is possible that one type of fiber prevails in a particular material.   The fiber may be present in metaphase or may be formed mainly during anaphase.   In later stages of anaphase, there is no doubt that the fibrils are formed *de novo* and that they contribute to the formation of the phragmoplast in plant material and of the midbody in animal material. The relation of fibers seen in the mid and early anaphase to those seen in later stages is not clear.

These short remarks indicate that the data concerning the ultrastructure of the spindle are fragmentary.   However, it is possible to draw important inferences concerning the structure based indirectly on the behavior of chromosomes and other bodies.

On the light microscopic level, variations of the spindle structure and chromosomal movements are easily demonstrable in diverse organisms. Closer examination reveals that basic features of movement are similar. Any morphological differences do not indicate that the mechanism is different.   For instance, differences in the structure such as the spindle with and without asters are probably not essential [21].   The same applies to the behavior of chromosomes in the mitotic spindle.

Spindle types can be classified in a different way, e.g., into two types: spindles with asters, as found in most animal mitosis, and spindles without asters, as found in most plant mitosis.   Asters appear to influence chromosome arrangement but not chromosome movement, especially during anaphase.   It has been proved with an elegant method that, if the asters are removed, the division progresses in a normal way [21].

Although the basic principles of the mechanism of movement are the same, the size of the spindle, the size of the chromosomes, the dimensions of asters, and the presence or absence of asters will modify the morphological course of mitosis.

II. CHROMOSOME MOVEMENTS

More details concerning movements of chromosomes are available from experiments with plant mitosis.   During mitosis, there are two essential

types of movements which must always be considered: (1) movement of kinetochores, and (2) movement of akinetic bodies (bodies not attached to the spindle).

1. *Movement of Kinetochores.* At the beginning of prometaphase, two sister chromosomes are held together by means of the proximal ends of the arms adjacent to the kinetochores. Kinetochore activity is most evident during formation of the metaphase plate and anaphase separation. With the exception of neocentric activity, most chromosome movements involve the participation of both the kinetochores and the spindle fibers. At the beginning of cooperation, the kinetochore region often is stretched, and a "hole" between sister chromatids is seen (Fig. 5b). The "hole" often appears asymetric and is pulled in the direction of kinetochore movement [22]. The stretching of kinetochores during movement occurs in later stages (Fig. 5d). Chromosomes usually move without any visible effect on the kinetochores. After the stretching process, the kinetochores lead the chromosomes in their movements. There appears to be more independence or individuality of single kinetochores during prometaphase than during anaphase. There is no doubt that kinetochores are connected with fibrils. Kinetochore movement may be referred to as the movement of bodies attached to the spindle. The kinetochore-spindle fiber attachment exists from prometaphase to early telophase. However, it is not only at the kinetochores that the spindle fibers attach [9, 23]. Attachment to other parts of the chromosome is manifested as a pulling activity lasting for a few minutes up to 10 min or longer. It is of some interest that such pulling movements can be stimulated by chemicals, light, mechanical injury, and various other factors. The pulling, resembling that at kinetochores, was found first in meiosis [24, 25]. The term neocenter was given to this part of the chromosome by Rhoades [26]. This process in living cells has been analyzed in detail by Östergren and Bajer [23] and by Bajer and Östergren [9] and was termed "neocentric activity" [9, 23]. During typical neocentric movement in mitotic prometaphase or metaphase, the fibers attach to the chromosome and immediately begin pulling. This results in an abrupt bending of the chromosome arm. Also, the part of the chromosome where the chromosomal fibers attach sometimes is visibly stretched. In some cases, for a short time the chromosomes may be reversed in their movements. Neocentric activity may appear in any part of the chromosome during division and may be expressed once or several times in each of the influenced chromosome regions.

2. *Movement of Akinetic Bodies.* During prometaphase, there is a tendency toward elimination from the spindle of all bodies that are not connected to spindle fibers. All akinetic bodies, such as fragments found

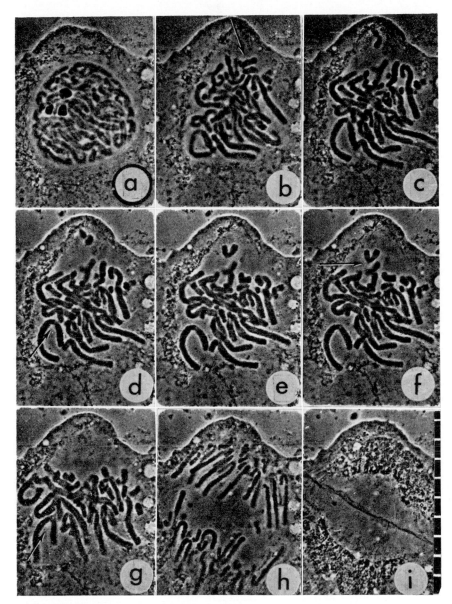

FIG. 5. Course of mitosis in *Haemanthus katherinae* endosperm. Prometaphase movements and stretching of kinetochores. (a) Well-formed, clear zone. (b) Early prometaphase; one chromosome (arrow) begins to move toward the pole. It turns (d) and returns to the plate (e)–(g). Stretched part of this chromosome is seen in (e) and (f) (arrow). In another chromosome, it is seen that stretching may occur more than once. No stretching in (d) (arrow); slight stretching in (e); no stretching again in (f); and strong stretching in (g). Times after (a): (b) 49 min, (c) 1 hr 3 min, (d) 1 hr 4 min, (e) 1 hr 9 min, (f) 1 hr 14 min, (g) 1 hr 37 min, (h) 3 hr 11 min, (i) 4 hr 23 min. 10-μ scale in (i). Cell no. 71/61. Prints from 16-mm film (from Bajer and Molè-Bajer [38]).

after irradiation and small granules, are removed from the spindle and usually accumulate outside or at the spindle poles. Long chromosome arms show the same tendency but are held by kinetochores in the equatorial position and arranged parallel to the long axis or the oriented structure of the spindle. In all cells, bodies that move toward the poles move with approximately the same speed. This speed is similar in all cases and is of the order of chromosome movement during anaphase.

Thus the most characteristic feature of prometaphase is the simultaneous movement of different bodies in opposite directions toward the equatorial region and the poles. These bodies often are located very close to each other in the spindle (Fig. 8a). The kinetochores show strong tendencies to arrange themselves in a regular plane approximately at the equator of the spindle. They do not always move to their future position on the plate by the shortest and simplest path. They move in parallel, obliquely, or transversely to the long axis of the spindle. Some chromosomes move rapidly toward the pole, turn, and then return to the plate (Fig. 5). Such movements toward the pole are executed by a few chromosomes or not at all. These movements appear to be most common in animal mitosis and especially meiosis, where often only a few chromosomes of the set are motionless and most oscillate several times toward one and then the other pole before the start of anaphase. All types of movements differ slightly in their details depending on the cell, the various mechanical conditions inside the cell, and other factors.

The process just described refers mainly to plant mitosis. In animal mitosis, some details are different, such as a hollow spindle in cold-blooded animals, where the spindle is too small to house the large chromosome arms that protrude into the cytoplasm. We can predict that in such examples the behavior of fragments will be different. Unfortunately, no data from living material are available.

Individuality of chromosome movements and independence of the movement of one chromosome in relation to its neighbor are evident during the formation of the metaphase plate. However, during anaphase, chromosomes appear to move as a compact group. For this reason, the question arises as to what extent the kinetochores retain the individuality of their movement during anaphase and whether any of them are influenced by the movement of their neighbors. The measurements of movements of kinetochores connected by bridges throws some light on this process. Some cases have been observed where kinetochores connected by a bridge are retarded up to the moment the bridge breaks. Kinetochores of normal chromosomes which are distant from the kinetochores connected by the bridge show no retardation. Kinetochores that are close often show retardation, even though they are not connected by bridges

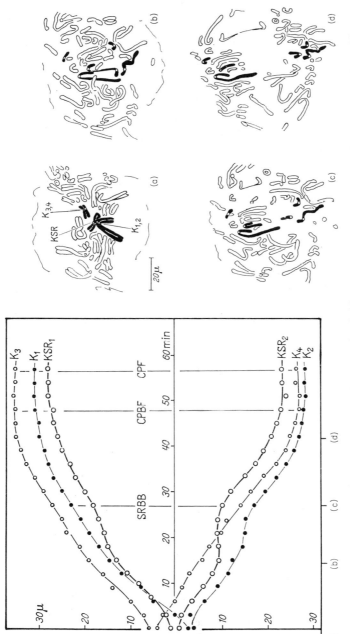

FIG. 6 (left). Retardation of kinetochores with sister reunion bridge (KSR₁, KSR₂, and kinetochores close to them, K₁, K₂; cf. Fig. 7). K₁ and K₂ are not connected by the bridge but are also retarded (black circles in lower graph). Kinetochores not connected by a bridge and further apart (K₃,K₄) are not retarded. The distance of two pairs of kinetochores K₁,₂, K₃,₄ and kinetochores connected by sister reunion bridge from the approximate metaphase plane plotted against time. SRBB: sister reunion bridge breaks; CPBF: cell plate begins to form; CPF: cell plate formed. Cell no. 122/63 A irradiated with 200 rad (x rays) 2 days before observations. Letters (a)–(d) indicate position of drawings in Fig. 7 (from Bajer [27] in endosperm of *Haemanthus katherinae*).

FIG. 7 (right). Drawing of the cell presented in Fig. 6.

themselves and speed up their movements as soon as the bridge breaks (Figs. 6 and 7). This shows clearly the influence of one chromosome on the other during anaphase [27].

Another important question concerns the possibility of anaphase separation in the spindle without interchromosomal influence on movement. Studies on the action of chloral hydrate throw light on this problem [28]. Chloral hydrate modifies the mitotic spindle, and, as a result, the chromosome arrangement is that of a typical c-metaphase[1] without any polarity of the spindle. During anaphase in chloral hydrate treated cells, kinetochores guide the chromosomes in their movement, but no directioned movement prevails. In some treated cells, one chromosome moves independently from the others, whereas in other cases a few chromosomes move in a group. As a result, several micronuclei are formed because of the multipolar division (Molè-Bajer, unpublished).

During anaphase, two factors must be considered: the shortening of the half spindle and chromosomal fibers; and the movement apart of whole half-spindles as separate units. These two processes contribute in varying degrees toward chromosomal separation in different material.

During telophase, at least three changes have to be considered: (1) disintegration of the spindle, (2) formation of sister nuclei, and (3) cytokinesis. We have very little information concerning spindle disintegration (cf. suggestions in Section III). Chromosomal fibers do not appear to shorten until the end, and chromosomes stop moving when the fibers are of a length of from 5 to 10 μ [19].

The formation of sister nuclei and cytokinesis are not directly connected with the problems just mentioned. Cytokinesis differs considerably in plant and animal cells. In animals, a cleavage occurs which pinches the cell body in two, whereas in plants the phragmoplast, followed by the cell plate and the dividing cell wall, is formed. The phragmoplast plays an important role in the distribution of chromosomes. It prevents the approaching of sister nuclei during telophase and also shows properties similar to a prometaphase spindle. There is a tendency to eliminate all bodies toward the poles. The properties of the phragmoplast have been analyzed in detail [28, 29]. Unfortunately few data are available on movements during telophase in animal mitosis. There are reasons to believe that the interzonal region, in its late stages of development, has many features similar to the early phragmoplast.

---

[1] Under the influence of colchicine or chemicals with similar effects, cells reach a stage of division just prior to splitting of chromosomes at the kinetochore region into daughter chromatids. The structure of the spindle is destroyed and the chromosomes are arranged irregularly in the area which was occupied previously by the mitotic spindle.

These few examples of deviant mitosis illustrate the diverse possibilities of chromosome movement in the same material, depending on the experimental treatment.

III. DISCUSSION

Interpretations of chromosome movements should consider the facts reported here and should be based as much as possible on changes in the ultrastructure of the spindle. The picture of the ultrastructural changes is not yet complete. Therefore, conclusions below are based to a great extent on observations of chromosome movement in different experimental conditions and studies of the structure in the light microscope.

The movements during mitosis are summarized schematically in Fig. 8. This figure shows only the most important factors that are responsible for chromosomal arrangement [30, 31]. Variations in these factors in different organisms to a great extent explain deviant types of divisions.

The basic facts concerning movement which must be explained are the following: (1) movement of kinetochores during formation of the metaphase plate toward the equatorial and at the same time the movement of akinetic bodies toward the poles, (2) the possible movement in the opposite direction of closely situated kinetochores, (3) movement after treatment with chloral hydrate of the chromosomes without defined poles (indicating that chromosomes can move even if the fibers are not fixed at the poles [28], and (4) the retardation of kinetochores not connected by bridges if the neighboring chromosome has a bridge [27].

Any acceptable hypothesis of chromosomal movement should consider and explain the foregoing facts. The hypothesis of Östergren et al. [32] fulfills these requirements. The general terms in which this hypothesis was suggested makes it difficult to test. If the interpretation is based on the ultrastructure of the spindle, all basic principles become testable. Figure 9 is a schematic representation of one possibility of ultrastructural changes during mitosis. Many details are not clear, and this representation is considered as a working hypothesis and not an actual representation of occurring events. Evidence from studies on chromosome movement leaves no doubt that kinetochores are pulled during most of the movements. Even very complicated movements during coorientation can be explained on this basis [33]. The important question arises as to whether and how the fibrillar material is involved in the process of pulling. There is abundant evidence, such as experiments with chloral hydrate [28], that chromosomes can move without fibers fixed at the poles. Thus, the required mechanism must maintain the chromosomal fibers in tension

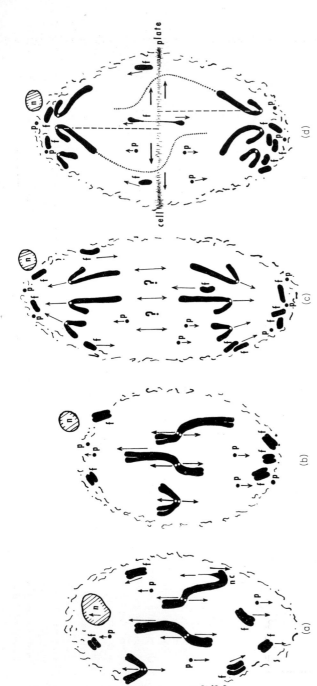

Fig. 8. Schematic representation of movements during plant mitosis. Arrows indicate the direction of acting forces (but not their magnitude). *n*: nucleolus; *f*: akinetic fragment; *p*: small particle; white circles: kinetochores. Outline of the spindle drawn. (a) Prometaphase; movement of kinetochores toward the equatorial plane and all akinetic bodies (fragments, persistent nucleoli, small particles) toward the pole. Arms straighten. One chromosome shows neocentric activity (*nc*; cf. the text). (b) Metaphase; kinetochores on equatorial plane, akinetic bodies in the polar regions or outside the spindle. (c) Anaphase; kinetochores move toward the poles. Some fragments move toward the equator. Question marks indicate that the action of the pushing body is doubtful. (d) Telophase and activity of the phragmoplast; paths of long trailing chromosome arms (dotted) do not follow paths of kinetochores (dashed) due to transverse activity of the phragmoplast (transverse arrows). All akinetic bodies move toward the poles. Fragments, if caught by cell plate, are stretched.

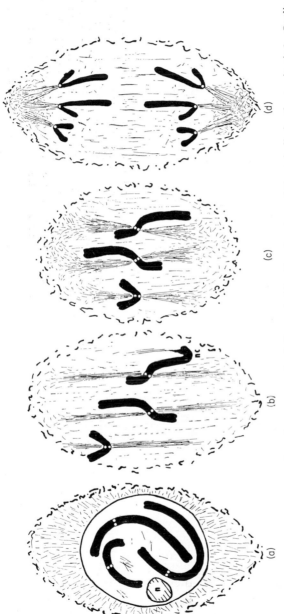

Fig. 9. Schematic representation of some aspects of the probable ultrastructure of the spindle in plant mitosis.[2] Outline of the spindle drawn. *n*: nucleolus; *nc*: neocentric activity; white circles: kinetochores. (a) Late prophase; microtubules arranged around the prophase nucleus (clear zone). Some might be present or penetrate inside the nucleus. (b) Prometaphase; microtubules arranged into long, thin chromosomal fibers only slightly intermingling at the poles. One chromosome end shows neocentric activity. (c) Metaphase; bundle that forms chromosomal fiber is thicker but shorter and more intermingled at the polar region. (d) Anaphase; intermingling of bundles from adjacent kinetochores and disorganization of the bundles at the polar region. Microtubules appear in the interzonal region.

[2] Note added in proof: New ultrastructural data, especially from endosperm, have now been obtained. This data fully supports the assumption that the microtubules are arranged irregularly in the clear zone. It appears likely that during prometaphase and metaphase only long microtubules are present in the spindle, and that they do not disintegrate by breaking into shorter pieces at the polar region, as might be suggested by the above schematic drawing. More detailed data will be published elsewhere.

during movement. It is suggested that the fibers are kept in tension by the activity of interfibrillar material. Each microtubule may be surrounded by a clear halo [34], which may suggest some interaction of tubules and intertubular material. Activity of the intertubular material would be responsible for the elimination of all akinetic bodies toward the poles. All bodies, regardless of size, would move to the poles with the same speed. This prediction is confirmed by measurements [28]. Also, data by Forer [35] indicate a general poleward transporting tendency in the spindle. In his experiments with the ultraviolet microbeam, he has found that the movement of a zone with reduced birefringence can be faster, equal to, or slower than anaphase movement.

In the author's interpretation, it is not assumed that the fibrillar material (microtubules) is not important in chromosomal movement. It is only suggested that both microtubular and intertubular material play an important role during the movement. The possibility exists that the activity of microtubules is responsible for the elimination of bodies from the spindle. It has been found that fibers on the light microscope level (bundles of microtubules [19]) sway slightly in a direction perpendicular to the long axis of the spindle. The swaying is slow, as observed with time lapse, and is not detected during direct observation in dividing cells. It is questionable whether such swaying is sufficient to keep the tubules in tension. The microtubules found in mitotic spindles are not very different from those in flagella and in other materials [34]. Therefore, it would not be unreasonable to expect some kind of cyclic deformation of the structures, although Ambrose [36] has pointed out that such vibration of microtubules is highly improbable. In general terms, it can be stated that microtubules are kept in tension due to the interaction with intertubular material, although we do not know what the mechanism is on the ultrastructural level.

Another important question arises concerning the shortening of the half-spindles during anaphase. There are a few possibilities, and the simplest is a contraction or a denser packing. No evidence for any of these possibilities has been reported during anaphase. Especially instructive are studies with the Nomarski system which permit an observation of changes of arrangement of fibrillar material during the movement. The appearance of bundles of fibrils close to kinetochores as seen in the Nomarski system appears not to change during chromosome movement throughout mitosis, even though the changes in fibrillar material in the distal part of the bundle are seen (Figs. 9b and 9c). Clearly, the distal parts of the chromosomal fibers are no longer detectable as anaphase progresses. Neither the light microscope (Nomarski system 3, 4) nor the electron microscope shows any evidence of changes in fiber thickness when

the chromosomes move. The foregoing suggests that the fibrillar material is disarranged or disintegrates at the polar region. Irregular arrangements of microtubules during metaphase at the polar region have been reported by Krishan and Buck [17]. Obviously, further studies are necessary to investigate their origin.

It has been found on the basis of measurements during anaphase that the chromosomes move faster than the spindle fibers shorten, considering the elongation of the spindle [20]. This leads to the conclusion that the chromosomal fibers are shifted in the mitotic spindle during anaphase and are disorganized mainly at the spindle poles. The movement of kinetochores arranged in a row parallel to the long axis of the spindle suggests the manner of fiber disorganization (Figs. 10 and 11). It is observed *in vitro* in several cases that chromosomes moving in a row are connected to one chromosomal bundle formed by a fusing of the separate bundles connected to individual kinetochores. The distance between kinetochores diminishes at the beginning of anaphase and remains constant during the movement, even though there is enough space for the chromosomes to approach each other. This suggests a gradient of disorganization of chromosomal fibers during movement at the distal parts of the bundle with little or no change close to the kinetochore. The fact that few kinetochores can be attached to one chromosomal fiber is clearly observed with chloral hydrate treatment [28]. Intermingling of chromosomal fibers from different kinetochores during anaphase explains the retardation of kinetochores if the neighboring kinetochores are slowed. This also explains the more or less simultaneous start of anaphase and the more independent movement of kinetochores during prometaphase than during anaphase. It is obvious, however, that the later movement depends also on the difference of the structure of the spindle during prometaphase and anaphase, the structure of chromosomes, and the attachment of fibers from one pole during anaphase and to two poles during prometaphase-metaphase. Extensive theoretical consideration of this and other problems is given by Östergren [33].

The data available at present do not permit a presentation of the complete picture of the ultrastructure and its changes in the mitotic spindle. Some changes, such as the formation of fibers found in the interzonal region and their relation to fibers seen in the metaphase spindle and to fibers found later in the phragmoplast, are not clear. Even this fragmentary model of the spindle suggested here permits an explanation of diverse movements and behavior of chromosomes from different material. Some variation in the structure, which will probably be found during disturbances, etc., should elucidate several problems whose explanation is based at present on speculation.

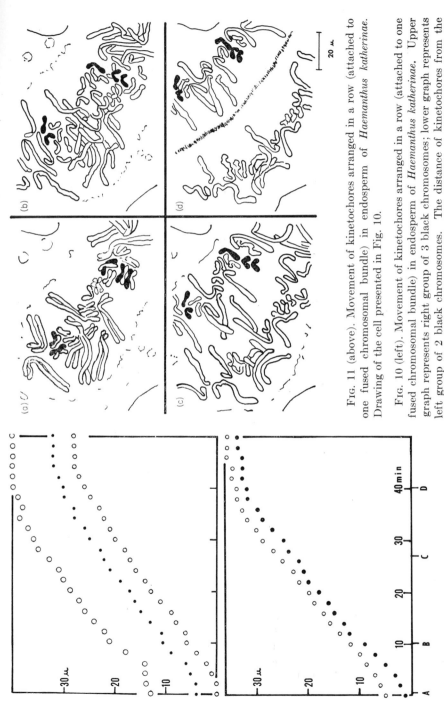

Fig. 11 (above). Movement of kinetochores arranged in a row (attached to one fused chromosomal bundle) in endosperm of *Haemanthus katherinae*. Drawing of the cell presented in Fig. 10.

Fig. 10 (left). Movement of kinetochores arranged in a row (attached to one fused chromosomal bundle) in endosperm of *Haemanthus katherinae*. Upper graph represents right group of 3 black chromosomes; lower graph represents left group of 2 black chromosomes. The distance of kinetochores from the approximate position of the equatorial plane is plotted against the time. It is clearly seen that the distance between kinetochores changes at the beginning of movement (decreases) and then is more or less constant to the end of anaphase. Chromosomes stop their movement at certain distances from each other, which indicates that chromosomal fibers do not shorten at the end.

IV. SUMMARY AND CONCLUSIONS

Most of the facts reported here are based on observations of mitosis in endosperm material of *Haemanthus katherinae in vitro* with the use of the time-lapse technique. It is suggested, however, that these general conclusions can be applied with slight modifications to any type of mitosis. A review of the various movements is presented, and also many unpublished data are included. Both movements of chromosomes and structure of the spindle are considered. Under different experimental conditions (influence of chemicals, radiation, etc.), the normal course of mitosis in endosperm can be modified to a great extent and resemble highly specialized division that is reported in some deviant courses of mitosis. This indicates that the basic mechanism of movement is the same in all cases.

1. *Movement of Chromosomes and of Akinetic Bodies.* During mitosis, chromosomes execute very complicated movements. Formation of the metaphase plate is characterized by a simultaneous movement in two opposite directions: (a) kinetochores move toward the equatorial plate and show a strong tendency to arrange themselves in one plane, and (b) all akinetic bodies, such as small granules, akinetic fragments, persistent nucleoli, etc., are transported toward the pole. Kinetochores do not always take the simplest and shortest path to their future position in the metaphase plate. Chromosomal fibers can cooperate for usually a short period with parts of the chromosome other than the kinetochore. Two factors contribute to the anaphase movement of chromosomes: the shortening of the half-spindle, and the elongation of the whole spindle. Formation of the phragmoplast and telophase movements is only briefly discussed.

2. *The Spindle.* The observations are based on studies using phase contrast, polarized light, Nomarski interference contrast system, and partly the electron microscope. The spindle begins to form in prophase and appears as a clear zone around the nucleus from which all cytoplasmic inclusions are removed. It shows uniform birefringence. After the disappearance of the nuclear membrane, the spindle differentiates into bundles of chromosomal fibers that represent zones of stronger birefringence. During prometaphase, the bundles are long and thin and shorten during the formation of the metaphase plate, contributing to the decrease in length of the whole metaphase spindle. The bundles diverge toward the poles, and fibrils connected with adjacent kinetochores intermingle at the poles to a small extent during prometaphase-metaphase and to a greater extent during anaphase. This explains why chromosomes,

during the formation of the metaphase plate, show more independent movement, and why the movement of one chromosome influences the behavior of its neighboring chromosome during anaphase. The part of the bundle adjacent to the kinetochore does not appear to change during movements. Anaphase movement stops when the bundle is still 5 to 10 μ in length, which suggests that the changes of structure of the bundle take place at the spindle pole.

It is suggested that the basis of chromosome movement is due to the shifting of chromosomal fibers or microtubules at the ultrastructural level within the spindle and to their disorganization or change of regular arrangement at the polar region. Different interactions and arrangements of microtubules at different stages of mitosis and the preceding conclusions are sufficient for the explanation of even very complicated behavior patterns of chromosomes during the normal and deviant courses of mitosis.

ACKNOWLEDGMENTS

Experiments applying the Nomarski interference contrast system have been supported by grants: NSF GB 3335 to A. Bajer; and NIH GM 08691 to R. D. Allen. I would like to express my sincere thanks to Dr. W. Jackson of the Department of Biological Sciences, Dartmouth College, Hanover, New Hampshire for supplying plant material in the proper stage for the foregoing studies. I would also like to thank Dr. K. R. Porter and Dr. M. C. Ledbetter of the Biological Laboratories, Harvard University, Cambridge, Massachusetts for permission to publish one of their excellent micrographs. Thanks also go to Dr. R. D. Allen of the Department of Biology, Princeton University, Princeton, New Jersey for critically reading the manuscript and to Mrs. Martha Ann Kaplan and Miss Jeanette Aagaard for their patient and valuable help during the preparation of the manuscript.

REFERENCES

1. Malheiros, N. and Castro, D., *Nature* **160,** 156 (1947).
2. Östergren, G., *Hereditas* **35,** 445 (1949).
3. Metz, C. W., *Biol. Bull.* **64,** 333 (1933).
4. Hughes Schrader, S., *Z. Zellforsch. Mikroskop. Anat. Abt. Histochem.* **13,** 742 (1931.)
5. Inoué, S., *in* "Primitive Motile Systems in Cell Biology" (G. Rose, ed.), pp. 549–598. Academic Press, New York.
6. Mazia, D., *in* "The Cell" (J. Brachet and A. E. Mirsky, eds.), pp. 77–412. Academic Press, New York, 1961.
7. Lettré, H. and Lettré, R., *Naturwissenschaften* **44,** 406 (1957).
8. Robbins, E. and Gonatas, N. K., *J. Cell Biol.* **21,** 429 (1964).
9. Bajer, A. and Östergren, G., *Hereditas* **47,** 563 (1961).
10. Schmidt, W. J., *Chromosoma* **1,** 253 (1939).
11. Inoué, S., *Chromosoma* **5,** 487 (1953).
12. Inoué, S. and Bajer, A., *Chromosoma* **12,** 48 (1961).
13. Bernhard, W. and de Harven, E., *Proc. Intern. Congr. Electron Microscopy Berlin* **2,** 217 (1960).
14. Harris, P., *J. Cell Biol.* **14,** 475 (1962).

15. Ledbetter, M. C. and Porter, K. R., *J. Cell Biol.* **19**, 239 (1963).
16. Roth, L. E. and Daniels, E. W., *J. Cell Biol.* **12**, 57 (1962).
17. Krishan, A. and Buck, R. C., *J. Cell Biol.* **24**, 433 (1965).
18. Manton, I., *J. Roy. Microscop. Soc.* **83**, 317 (1964).
19. Bajer, A. and Allen, R. D., *Science* (in press).
20. Bajer, A., *Chromosoma* **12**, 64 (1961).
21. Dietz, R., *Z. Naturforsch.* **14b**, 749 (1959).
22. Bajer, A., *Exptl. Cell Res.* **13**, 493 (1957).
23. Östergren, G. and Bajer, A., *Colloq. Intern. Centre Natl. Rech. Sci. Paris* **88**, 199 (1960).
24. Prakken, R. and Müntzing, A., *Hereditas* **28**, 177 (1942).
25. Rhoades, M. M. and Vilkomerson, H., *Proc. Natl. Acad. Sci. US* **28**, 433 (1942).
26. Rhoades, M. M., *in* "Heterosis" (J. W. Gowen, ed.), pp. 66–130. Iowa Univ. Press, Ames, Iowa, 1952.
27. Bajer, A., *Chromosoma* **15**, 630 (1964).
28. Molè-Bajer, J., *Univ. Jagellonica Cracoviensis, Acta Sci. Lit. Math. Phys. Chem.* **46**, 1 (1962).
29. Bajer, A. and Östergren, G., *Hereditas* **50**, 179 (1963).
30. Östergren, G., *Hereditas* **35**, 525 (1949).
31. Östergren, G., *Hereditas* **36**, 1 (1950).
32. Östergren, G., Molè-Bajer, J. and Bajer, A., *Ann. NY Acad. Sci.* **90**, 381 1960).
33. Östergren, G., *Hereditas* **37**, 85 (1951).
34. Ledbetter, M. C. and Porter, K. R., *Science* **144**, 872 (1964).
35. Forer, A., *J. Cell Biol.* **25**, 95 (1965).
36. Ambrose, E. J., *Endeavor* **44**, 27 (1965).
37. Harris, P. and Bajer, A., *Chromosoma* **16**, 624 (1965).
38. Bajer, A., and Molè-Bajer, J., *in* "Cinamctography in Cell Biology" (G. Rose, ed.), pp. 357–409. Academic Press, New York, 1963.
39. Bajer, A. and Molè-Bajer, *Chromosoma* **7**, 558 (1956).

SECTION II

Special Lectures on
Rheology and Stellar Dynamics

edited by

G. N. TRYTTEN

The Fundamental Equations of

Nonlinear Continuum Mechanics

R. S. RIVLIN

DIVISION OF APPLIED MATHEMATICS
BROWN UNIVERSITY
PROVIDENCE, RHODE ISLAND

An account is given of a procedure for deriving the fundamental field equations of continuum thermomechanics from the balance of energy equation and the entropy production inequality, by using certain considerations of invariance under rigid motions.

This is followed by an account of recent work on the use of invariance considerations in the formulation of constitutive equations in nonlinear continuum mechanics.

I. INTRODUCTION

In the past 20 years, considerable activity has taken place in the development of theories in continuum mechanics relating to materials whose behavior is more general than that to which classical elasticity theory and the classical hydrodynamics of viscous fluids are applicable. In most respects, these theories are patterned after the classical theories. The fundamental equations of each theory are the field equations and constitutive equations. The theories can be classified[1] as simple and nonsimple theories and the materials with which they are concerned as simple and nonsimple materials.

A simple material is one in which the constitutive assumption involves the dependence of an appropriately defined stress or thermodynamic function at a particle on the kinematic variables through the first spatial derivatives at the particle of the displacement and its rates of change of various orders. A nonsimple material is one in which the stress, for example, at a particle, may depend on higher-order spatial derivatives of the displacement or of its time derivatives, or on the values of the first spatial derivatives of the displacement in some region about the particle, or on kinematic variables other than the spatial derivatives of

---

[1] The terminology is due to Noll (1958).

the displacement and its time derivatives. The present paper is concerned entirely with the development of continuum-mechanical theories for simple materials.

During the past 20 years, there has been a continuous development of more powerful approaches to the problems arising in the formulation of these theories. It is the aim of the present paper to present some of the more fundamental results in the light of these methods. However, the discussion is by no means exhaustive, and inevitably many valuable results are not touched on and others too briefly mentioned.

Sections II–V are concerned with the development of the fundamental thermodynamical and mechanical relations that are valid for all simple materials. The results obtained are classical, but the method used is unconventional in that all the results are derived from two statements expressing the applicability of the first and second laws of thermodynamics (Green and Rivlin, 1964c). By this means, we develop the concept of stress, the equations of motion, expressions for the surface forces, and an inequality that is satisfied by the stress power. The method used for deriving these well-known results has the merit, which is not exploited in the present paper, that it can be extended easily to the discussion of nonsimple materials (Green and Rivlin, 1964a, 1964b, 1965).

In Section VI, the stress power inequality is used to derive an expression for the stress in terms of the Helmholtz free energy for isothermal deformations of an elastic material. In Section VII, a similar analysis is used in the case of a material with memory which possesses instantaneous elasticity.[2]

The remainder of the paper is concerned with the development of constitutive equations for simple materials. In Sections VIII and IX, it is shown how the fact that a rigid rotation of the body superposed on the assumed deformation leaves the Helmholtz free energy and Piola stress tensor unaltered may be used to restrict the manner in which the Helmholtz free energy for an elastic material and the Piola stress tensor (and through it the other stress tensors) for a material with memory can depend on the deformation gradients. Although the restrictions on the form of the Helmholtz free energy for a material with memory which possesses instantaneous elasticity, of the type discussed in Section VII, are not developed, it is evident that the methods employed may be readily applied to this problem.

In Section X, it is shown that in certain circumstances the constitutive

---

[2] This problem was originally discussed by Coleman (1964) and, using a simpler procedure, different from that given in the present paper, by Wang (private communication).

equation for a material with memory may be replaced by one that does not formally involve the deformation history, but in which the latter is replaced by the deformation gradients and time derivatives of these at the instant of measurement of stress.

In Section XI, a particular case of the constitutive equation for a material with memory is discussed which appears to be applicable to materials with mechanical properties that we may generally recognize as fluid-like. Although such a constitutive equation may apply to fluids that are initially anisotropic,[3] we do not claim that it represents the most general[4] constitutive equation possible for a fluid with memory, in which the stress depends on the deformation history only through the first spatial derivatives of the displacement. Indeed, we prefer to take the point of view that the distinction between a solid and a fluid is not a sharp one. One cannot, however, take exception to the arbitrary introduction, in the interests of mathematical order, of a sharp distinction between solids and fluids, even if this leaves outside the definition of a fluid certain materials, which, from a physical point of view, one would ordinarily recognize as fluid-like. Such a sharp distinction has, in fact, been made by Noll (1958) and has been taken up by other writers, including the present author (see, for example, Green and Rivlin, 1960; Rivlin, 1965a).

In Section XII, we discuss the restriction imposed on the constitutive equation for a material with memory by the assumption that it is rate-independent, i.e., that the stress in the material depends on the deformation path and not on the rate at which this is executed.

In Section XIII, we discuss the manner in which constraints on the deformation, such as incompressibility or inextensibility in a certain direction, may be reflected in the constitutive equation.

The remaining sections of the paper (Sections XIV–XIX) are devoted to a discussion of the restrictions that are imposed on the constitutive equations by symmetry of the material. It is shown that, whether we are dealing with elastic materials, materials with memory, or constitutive equations of the differential type, the determination of the effect of symmetry on the form of the constitutive equation can be reduced to an

---

[3] The constitutive equations in Section XI may, in fact, be regarded conceptually as a particular case of the constitutive equations for anisotropic fluids discussed by Ericksen (1960a, 1960b, 1960c, 1961) in which the directors introduced by Ericksen are here assumed to depend on the deformation gradients in the material. It should be recalled, however, that Ericksen's constitutive equations are of the differential type.

[4] A more general constitutive equation for anisotropic fluids with memory, in which the deformation history enters only through the first spatial derivatives of the displacement, has been discussed by Green (1964) and by Coleman (1965).

invariant-theoretical problem. This, in turn, can be reduced to the problem of determining the integrity basis for an appropriate set of tensors under the group describing the material symmetry. In the case of finite elasticity, this integrity basis is simply that for a single second-order symmetric tensor, the Cauchy-Green strain tensor. The appropriate integrity bases are given for the cases when the material is isotropic, when it possesses transverse isotropy, and when the symmetry group is that appropriate to each of the 32 crystal classes. In the latter case, it is seen that only 11 different integrity bases are involved.

In the case of constitutive equations of the differential type, it is shown that the canonical form for the stress can be obtained from a knowledge of the integrity basis for an arbitrary number of symmetric second-order tensors under the symmetry group of the material. Such an integrity basis is given for an isotropic material, for which the appropriate symmetry group is the full (or proper) orthogonal group. In the case of materials with memory, a canonical form may be obtained from the same integrity basis, but now only multilinear elements in it are required.

The discussion of the effect on constitutive equations of material symmetry given in the present paper rests heavily on the results of Wineman and Pipkin (1963, 1964). In the case of constitutive equations in which the dependent variables are functions of the independent variables, these results enable us to avoid making continuity assumptions that admit the approximation of the functions by polynomials, as was done in the earlier work (see, for example, Rivlin, 1955; Pipkin and Rivlin, 1959). In the case of constitutive equations in which the dependent variables are functionals of the independent variables, the results enable us to avoid making continuity assumptions justifying the use of integral representations (see, for example, Green and Rivlin, 1957; Green et al., 1959; Rivlin, 1960; Chacon and Rivlin, 1964; Rivlin, 1965b). It is, of course, understood that integral representations may still be introduced when they are appropriate in a given context.[5]

II. THE FUNDAMENTAL THERMODYNAMIC RELATIONS

The deformation of a body is completely described if we specify the dependence of the coordinates $x_i(\tau)$ of a generic particle, at time τ, in a

---

[5] After this paper was written, a monumental review of the area covered by it appeared (Truesdell, C. A. and Noll, W., "The Non-Linear Field Theories of Mechanics," vol. 3 of "Handbuch der Physik," Springer, Berlin). Although substantially all of the topics treated in the present paper are discussed by Truesdell and Noll, the methods used, and to some extent the point of view adopted, are different.

rectangular cartesian coordinate system x, on time τ and the coordinates X_A of the particle at some reference time t_0 (say); thus,

$$x_i(\tau) = x_i(X_A, \tau). \tag{2.1}$$

The velocity v_i of the particle at time τ is then given by

$$v_i(\tau) = \dot{x}_i(\tau), \tag{2.2}$$

where the dot denotes differentiation with respect to time keeping X_A fixed, i.e., it denotes the material time derivative.

We consider a body that undergoes an arbitrary time-dependent deformation described by (2.1) and in which the absolute temperature distribution $T(X_A, \tau)$ varies in an arbitrary manner. Subject to certain smoothness conditions on these fields, they result if appropriate body forces F_i and surface forces T_i are applied to the body and if an appropriate rate of heat generation[6] r exists throughout the volume of the body and an appropriate heat flux Q takes place out of the body through its surface. The body fields F_i and r are defined per unit mass, and the surface fields T_i and Q are defined per unit surface area measured at the reference time t_0.

We denote by ρ_0 the density of the material at time t_0 and by U and S the internal energy and entropy, respectively, per unit mass. We consider that at the time t_0 the body occupies the domain V bounded by the surface A.

We shall now express in mathematical terms the first and second laws of thermodynamics for the body considered.

A. The First Law of Thermodynamics

The first law of thermodynamics states that the sum of the rates at which work is done by the applied forces acting on the body and at which heat enters the body is equal to the sum of the rates at which the internal and kinetic energies increase. In mathematical terms, this is expressed by

$$\int_V \rho_0 F_i v_i \, dV + \int_A T_i v_i \, dA + \int_V \rho_0 r \, dV - \int_A Q \, dA$$
$$= \int \rho_0 \dot{U} \, dV + \int_V \rho_0 v_i \dot{v}_i \, dV. \tag{2.3}$$

This is the energy balance equation.

---

[6] The scalar rate of heat generation field appears to have been introduced by Truesdell and Toupin (1960) and employed by Coleman and Noll (1963). If this is omitted, then we cannot consider the deformation and temperature fields to be arbitrary throughout the body.

B. The Second Law of Thermodynamics

The second law of thermodynamics may be most conveniently expressed for our purpose by the Clausius-Duhem inequality. This states that the rate at which the entropy of the body increases is not less than the integral over the body of the quotient of the rate at which heat is added over the absolute temperature at the point at which it is added. In mathematical terms, this is expressed by

$$\int_V \rho_0 \dot{S} \, dV \geq \int_V \frac{\rho_0 r}{T} \, dV - \int_A \frac{Q}{T} \, dA . \tag{2.4}$$

This is the entropy inequality.

III. THE STRESS TENSOR AND HEAT FLUX VECTOR

The energy balance equation (2.3) and the entropy inequality (2.4) are applicable to the whole body, or to any portion of it, provided T_i, Q, V, and A are interpreted appropriately.

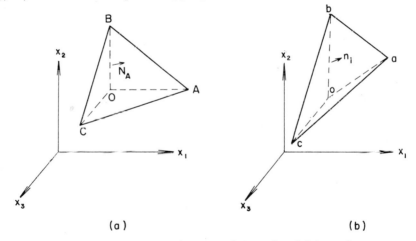

Fig. 1. Elementary tetrahedron in undeformed and deformed states.

We now apply the energy balance equation (2.3) to an elementary material tetrahedron $OABC$ in the body, at time t_0, three faces of which are parallel to the coordinate planes and the fourth face of which has unit normal N_A (see Fig. 1a). In the deformed body, at time t, the faces obc, oca, oab of the tetrahedron $oabc$ into which $OABC$ is deformed in the interval t_0 to t will, in general, no longer be parallel to the coordinate planes, nor even will they be mutually perpendicular (see Fig. 1b).

We assume that the elementary tetrahedron is sufficiently small so that the surface force T_i and heat flux Q on each face of the tetrahedron are substantially constant over it and that v_i and the remaining quantities occurring in the integrands of the volume integrals in (2.3) are substantially constant over the volume of the tetrahedron.

Let Π_{1i} be the force acting on obc per unit area of OBC, i.e.,

$$\Pi_{1i} = \text{(total force acting on } obc\text{)/(area of } OBC\text{)}.$$

We define in a similar manner Π_{2i} and Π_{3i} for the forces acting on the faces oca and oab. We denote Π_{1i}, Π_{2i}, and Π_{3i} collectively by Π_{Ai}. We retain the notation T_i for the force per unit area of ABC acting on abc.

In an analogous manner, let Q_1 be the heat flux through obc per unit area of OBC. We define Q_2 and Q_3 in a similar manner and denote Q_1, Q_2, and Q_3 collectively by Q_A.

Applying the energy balance equation (2.3) to the elementary tetrahedron, we obtain

$$(T_i v_i - Q)\alpha = (\Pi_{Ai} v_i - Q_A)\alpha_A \\ + \rho_0(\dot{U} + v_i \dot{v}_i - F_i v_i)\Delta, \tag{3.1}$$

where α_A is the area of the face OBC perpendicular to the x_A axis, α is the area of the face ABC, and Δ is the volume of $OABC$. We have

$$\alpha_A = \alpha N_A. \tag{3.2}$$

We now decrease the linear dimensions of the elementary tetrahedron to zero proportionately, so that $\Delta/\alpha \to 0$ and (3.2) is satisfied, the remaining quantities in (3.1) resting unchanged. We then obtain

$$T_i v_i - Q = \Pi_{Ai} N_A v_i - Q_A N_A. \tag{3.3}$$

We note that, if we superpose on the assumed deformation of the body a uniform translational velocity c_i, we do not alter T_i, Π_{Ai}, Q, and Q_A. Therefore,

$$T_i(v_i + c_i) - Q = \Pi_{Ai} N_A(v_i + c_i) - Q_A N_A. \tag{3.4}$$

From (3.3) and (3.4), we obtain

$$(T_i - \Pi_{Ai} N_A)c_i = 0. \tag{3.5}$$

Since c_i may be arbitrarily chosen, Eq. (3.5) yields

$$T_i = \Pi_{Ai} N_A. \tag{3.6}$$

Introducing (3.6) into (3.3), we have

$$Q = Q_A N_A. \tag{3.7}$$

We now consider a second rectangular cartesian coordinate system $\bar{x}$ related to x by the time-dependent orthogonal transformation $a_{ij}(\tau)$. Then,

$$\bar{x}_i(\tau) = a_{ij}(\tau)x_j(\tau). \tag{3.8}$$

We define $\bar{T}_i$, $\overline{\Pi}_{Ai}$, $\bar{Q}$, and $\bar{Q}_A$ with respect to the coordinate system $\bar{x}$ in precisely the same way as T_i, Π_{Ai}, Q, and Q_A are defined with respect to the system x, $\bar{T}_i$ being the force at time t per unit area (measured at time t_0) on an element of area that has unit normal $\bar{N}_A$ in the system $\bar{x}$ and N_A in the system x. Then,

$$\bar{N}_A = a_{AB}(t_0)N_B, \tag{3.9}$$

$$\bar{T}_i = a_{ij}(t)T_j, \tag{3.10}$$

and

$$\bar{Q} = Q. \tag{3.11}$$

Also by analogy with (3.6) and (3.7), we have

$$\bar{T}_i = \overline{\Pi}_{Ai}\bar{N}_A \tag{3.12}$$

and

$$\bar{Q} = \bar{Q}_A\bar{N}_A \tag{3.13}$$

respectively.

From (3.6), (3.9), (3.10), and (3.12), we obtain

$$\overline{\Pi}_{Ai}a_{AB}(t_0)N_B = a_{ij}(t)\Pi_{Bj}N_B. \tag{3.14}$$

Employing the orthogonality condition,[7] we obtain

$$\Pi_{Bj}N_B = a_{ij}(t)a_{AB}(t_0)\overline{\Pi}_{Ai}N_B. \tag{3.15}$$

Since this relation is valid for all N_B, we obtain, by taking N_B equal to δ_{1B}, δ_{2B}, and δ_{3B} in turn (i.e., unit vectors parallel to the x_1, x_2, and x_3 axes, respectively),

$$\Pi_{Bj} = a_{ij}(t)a_{AB}(t_0)\overline{\Pi}_{Ai}, \tag{3.16}$$

whence

$$\overline{\Pi}_{Ai} = a_{AB}(t_0)a_{ij}(t)\Pi_{Bj}. \tag{3.17}$$

Thus, Π_{Ai} transforms as a second-order cartesian tensor.[8] It is called the Kirchhoff-Piola stress tensor.

We note that, if the coordinate systems x and $\bar{x}$ coincide at time t_0, we have $a_{AB}(t_0) = \delta_{AB}$, and relation (3.17) becomes

$$\Pi_{Ai} = a_{ij}(t)\Pi_{Aj}. \tag{3.18}$$

[7] Since $a_{ij}(\tau)$ is a proper orthogonal transformation, we have $a_{ji}(\tau)a_{jk}(\tau) = a_{ij}(\tau)a_{kj}(\tau) = \delta_{ik}$, $|a_{ij}(\tau)| = 1$.
[8] It is, strictly, a two-point cartesian tensor.

In a similar manner, we obtain from (3.7), (3.9), (3.11), and (3.13) the relation

$$\bar{Q}_A = a_{AB}(t_0)Q_B,\qquad(3.19)$$

from which it is apparent that Q_B transforms as a cartesian vector. We shall call this the Kirchhoff-Piola heat flux vector.

We have so far taken the reference state at arbitrary time t_0. In the particular case when the reference state is that at the time t at which the forces applied to the body and the heat entering it are measured, it is evident from the definitions of Π_{Ai} and Q_A that they become the usual Cauchy stress tensor σ_{ji}, say, and Cauchy heat flux vector q_i, say, respectively. Then, ρ_0 becomes the density of the material at time t; we shall denote this by ρ. Also, N_A becomes the unit normal to the surface at time t, and we shall denote this by n_i. T_i becomes the surface force acting on a surface element in the body per unit area of surface measured at time t; we shall denote this by t_i. Q becomes the heat flux through a surface element in the body per unit area of surface measured at time t; we denote this by q. Equations (3.6) and (3.7) then yield

$$t_i = \sigma_{ji}n_j\qquad(3.20)$$

and

$$q = q_i n_i.\qquad(3.21)$$

The relation between the Cauchy and Kirchhoff-Piola stress tensors may be easily established by comparing Eqs. (3.6) and (3.20). We have

$$T_i = \Pi_{Ai}N_A \qquad \text{and} \qquad t_i = \sigma_{ji}n_j.\qquad(3.22)$$

We recall that T_i and t_i are both forces acting on an element of area at time t, but they are measured per unit area at times t_0 and t, respectively. Thus, if dA and da are corresponding elements of area measured at times t_0 and t, respectively,

$$T_i\, dA = t_i\, da.\qquad(3.23)$$

N_A and n_j are the unit normals to these elements of area. From (3.22) and (3.23), we have

$$\Pi_{Ai}N_A\, dA = \sigma_{ji}n_j\, da.\qquad(3.24)$$

It can easily be shown by rather simple considerations in differential geometry that[9]

$$N_A = n_p x_{p,A}/[n_j n_k x_{j,B}x_{k,B}]^{1/2}$$

and

$$dA/da = |\partial x/\partial X|^{-1}[n_j n_k x_{j,B}x_{k,B}]^{1/2}.\qquad(3.25)$$

[9] Throughout this paper the subscript $,_A$ denotes $\partial/\partial x_A$, and the subscript $,_i$ denotes $\partial/\partial x_i$.

Introducing (3.25) into (3.24), we obtain

$$n_j \sigma_{ji} = |\partial x / \partial X|^{-1} \Pi_{Ai} n_j x_{j,A}. \tag{3.26}$$

Taking $n_j = \delta_{1j}$, δ_{2j}, δ_{3j} in turn, we obtain

$$\sigma_{ji} = |\partial x / \partial X|^{-1} \Pi_{Ai} x_{j,A}. \tag{3.27}$$

We shall have occasion in later sections to employ yet a further stress tensor, the Piola stress tensor, which we denote by P_{AB} and define by

$$\Pi_{Ai} = x_{i,B} P_{AB} \qquad \text{or} \qquad \sigma_{ji} = |\partial x / \partial X|^{-1} x_{j,A} x_{i,B} P_{AB}. \tag{3.28}$$

From (3.18), it follows that, in a fixed rectangular cartesian coordinate system x, a rotation of the body in which a particle initially at x_i moves to $\bar{x}_i(\tau)$ at time τ, given by

$$\bar{x}_i(\tau) = a_{ij}(\tau) x_j, \tag{3.29}$$

alters the components of the Kirchoff-Piola stress tensor from Π_{Ai} to $\overline{\Pi}_{Ai}$, where

$$\overline{\Pi}_{Ai} = a_{ij}(t) \Pi_{Aj}. \tag{3.30}$$

It follows with (3.28) that the rotation of the body leaves the components of the Piola stress tensor in the system x unaltered.

IV. THE EQUATIONS OF MOTION

We now return to the energy balance equation (2.3). Using (3.3) and the divergence theorem, we have

$$\int_A (T_i v_i - Q) \, dA = \int_A (\Pi_{Ai} v_i - Q_A) N_A \, dA$$
$$= \int_V (\Pi_{Ai,A} v_i + \Pi_{Ai} v_{i,A} - Q_{A,A}) \, dV. \tag{4.1}$$

Introducing (4.1) into (2.3) and applying the relation so obtained to an infinitesimal volume element, we obtain

$$(\Pi_{Ai,A} + \rho_0 F_i - \rho_0 \dot{v}_i) v_i + \Pi_{Ai} v_{i,A} + \rho_0 r - Q_{A,A} = \rho_0 \dot{U}. \tag{4.2}$$

Again, as in Section III, we superpose on the assumed deformation of the body an arbitrary uniform translational velocity c_i. Since this does not alter the coefficient of v_i on the left-hand side of (4.2) or the remaining terms of the equation, we obtain

$$\Pi_{Ai,A} + \rho_0 F_i - \rho_0 \dot{v}_i = 0 \tag{4.3}$$

and

$$\Pi_{Ai}v_{i,A} = \rho_0 \dot{U} + Q_{A,A} - \rho_0 r. \tag{4.4}$$

Equation (4.3) is the Kirchoff-Piola equation of motion and (4.4) provides an expression for the stress power $\Pi_{Ai}v_{i,A}$.

Equation (4.4) may be written in the alternative form

$$\Pi_{Ai}v_{i,j}x_{j,A} = \rho_0\dot{U} + Q_{A,A} - \rho_0 r. \tag{4.5}$$

We now superpose on the assumed deformation of the body an additional arbitrary rigid rotation that leaves the deformation unchanged at time t. Let c_i be the velocity field associated with this rigid rotation. Then

$$c_{i,j} = -c_{j,i}. \tag{4.6}$$

For the new deformation, we have, introducing the fact that Π_{Ai} and the terms on the right-hand side of (4.5) are unaltered by the superposed rigid rotation,

$$\Pi_{Ai}(v_{i,j} + c_{i,j})x_{j,A} = \rho_0\dot{U} + Q_{A,A} - \rho_0 r, \tag{4.7}$$

whence, with (4.5), we obtain

$$\Pi_{Ai}x_{j,A}c_{i,j} = 0, \tag{4.8}$$

and this equation must be satisfied for all $c_{i,j}$ satisfying (4.6). It follows that

$$\Pi_{Ai}x_{j,A} = \Pi_{Aj}x_{i,A}. \tag{4.9}$$

If we take the reference state to be the state at time t, then, replacing X_A by x_A $(= \delta_{iA}x_i)$, Π_{Ai} by σ_{Ai} $(= \delta_{jA}\sigma_{ji})$, Q_A by q_A $(= \delta_{Ai}q_i)$, and ρ_0 by ρ in (4.3), (4.4), and (4.9), we obtain the Cauchy equations

$$\sigma_{ji,j} + \rho F_i - \rho\dot{v}_i = 0,$$
$$\sigma_{ji}v_{i,j} = \rho\dot{U} + q_{i,i} - \rho r, \tag{4.10}$$

and

$$\sigma_{ji} = \sigma_{ij}.$$

V. IMPLICATIONS OF THE ENTROPY INEQUALITY

Introducing (3.7) into the entropy inequality (2.4), using the divergence theorem, and applying the resulting inequality to an infinitesimal volume element, we obtain

$$\rho_0\dot{S} \geq \frac{\rho_0 r}{T} - \left(\frac{Q_A}{T}\right)_{,A}. \tag{5.1}$$

If we bear in mind that T is essentially positive, Eq. (5.1) may be rewritten as

$$\rho_0 T \dot{S} \geq \rho_0 r - Q_{A,A} + \frac{Q_A T_{,A}}{T}. \tag{5.2}$$

Using (4.4) to substitute for $\rho_0 r - Q_{A,A}$ in (5.2), we obtain

$$\rho_0(\dot{U} - T\dot{S}) \leq \Pi_{Ai} v_{i,A} - \frac{Q_A T_{,A}}{T}. \tag{5.3}$$

For isentropic deformations, $\dot{S} = 0$, and the inequality (5.3) becomes

$$\rho_0 \dot{U} \leq \Pi_{Ai} v_{i,A} - \frac{Q_A T_{,A}}{T}. \tag{5.4}$$

The Helmholtz free energy $\mathcal{C}$ per unit mass is defined by

$$\mathcal{C} = U - TS. \tag{5.5}$$

For isothermal deformations, $\dot{T} = 0$, and (5.3) becomes

$$\rho_0 \dot{\mathcal{C}} \leq \Pi_{Ai} v_{i,A} - \frac{Q_A T_{,A}}{T}. \tag{5.6}$$

If, furthermore, the temperature is uniform throughout the body, i.e., $T_{,A} = 0$, the inequality (5.6) becomes

$$\rho_0 \dot{\mathcal{C}} \leq \Pi_{Ai} v_{i,A}. \tag{5.7}$$

VI. ELASTIC MATERIALS

We now consider that the Helmholtz free energy at time t depends on the deformation only through the deformation gradients $x_{i,A} [= x_{i,A}(t)]$ and is also a function of the temperature T at time t. Then, for isothermal deformations,

$$\dot{\mathcal{C}} = \frac{\partial \mathcal{C}}{\partial x_{i,A}} v_{i,A}. \tag{6.1}$$

Introducing this result into (5.6), we obtain

$$\left(\rho_0 \frac{\partial \mathcal{C}}{\partial x_{i,A}} - \Pi_{Ai}\right) v_{i,A} \leq -\frac{Q_A T_{,A}}{T}. \tag{6.2}$$

We assume that Π_{Bi} and Q_B are independent of $v_{i,A}$; therefore, the coefficients of $v_{i,A}$ and $T_{,A}$ are independent of these quantities. The relation (6.2) is valid for all deformation-temperature fields. We consider two deformation-temperature fields for which $x_{i,A}$ and $T_{,A}$ are the

same at the point considered but for which the velocity gradients are $\lambda v^*_{i,A}$ and $-\lambda v^*_{i,A}$, where λ is positive and can be made arbitrarily large. The left-hand side of (6.2) can evidently be made as large as we please while the right-hand side is maintained constant. It follows that the relation (6.2) can be satisfied for both of these velocity fields only if

$$\left(\rho_0 \frac{\partial \mathcal{Q}}{\partial x_{i,A}} - \Pi_{Ai} \right) v_{i,A} = 0. \tag{6.3}$$

The relation (6.3) is valid for arbitrary choice of $v_{i,A}$, and we shall assume the material is such that $v_{i,A}$ can be chosen arbitrarily. Then (6.3) yields the well-known relation

$$\Pi_{Ai} = \rho_0 \frac{\partial \mathcal{Q}}{\partial x_{i,A}}. \tag{6.4}$$

From (6.3) and (6.2), we also obtain, using the fact that T is essentially positive,

$$Q_A T_{,A} \leq 0. \tag{6.5}$$

VII. INSTANTANEOUS ELASTICITY

Let us suppose now, following Coleman (1964), that U and S, and hence $\mathcal{Q}$, depend not only on the values of the deformation gradients and temperature at time t but also on their values at all times prior to t; i.e., they are functionals of $x_{i,A}(\tau)$ and of the temperature $T(\tau)$.

For simplicity, we shall here consider that the deformation is carried out isothermally, i.e., $T(\tau) = T$ (constant). (The extension to the case of nonisothermal deformation will be evident.) We then have

$$\mathcal{Q} = \mathcal{Q}\underset{\tau=-\infty}{\overset{t}{[}}x_{i,A}(\tau), T]. \tag{7.1}$$

We also assume that the deformation is such that we may vary the deformation gradients at a particle at time t in an arbitrary manner without changing them prior to t. This is equivalent to assuming that the material possesses *instantaneous elasticity*.

We introduce the Heaviside function defined by

$$H(\tau - t) = 0 \ (\tau < t), \qquad H(\tau - t) = 1 \ (\tau \geq t), \tag{7.2}$$

and we consider a deformation of the body described by

$$\bar{x}_i(\tau) = x_i(X_A, \tau) + \delta x_i H(\tau - t), \tag{7.3}$$

where δx_i is independent of τ; i.e., we superpose on the original deformation field an instantaneous jump δx_i taking place at time t. We now define $\delta \mathcal{C}$ as the change in the Helmholtz free energy resulting from this change in deformation. Thus, from (7.1), we have

$$\delta \mathcal{C} = \mathop{\mathcal{C}[\bar{x}_{i,A}(\tau)}\limits_{\tau=-\infty}^{t}, T] - \mathop{\mathcal{C}[x_{i,A}(\tau)}\limits_{\tau=-\infty}^{t}, T]. \tag{7.4}$$

We now define $\mathcal{C}_{x_{i,A}}$ by

$$\mathcal{C}_{x_{i,A}} = \lim_{\delta x_{i,A} \to 0} \delta \mathcal{C} / \delta x_{i,A} \tag{7.5}$$

and we assume that the material is such that this limit exists. Then we may write

$$\delta \mathcal{C} = \mathcal{C}_{x_{i,A}} \delta x_{i,A} + O(\delta x_{i,A} \delta x_{i,A}). \tag{7.6}$$

Since we are now concerned with the limiting case in which we consider that the deformation can change instantaneously at time t, it is convenient to use the variational form of the inequality (5.6); thus,

$$\rho_0 \delta \mathcal{C} \leq \Pi_{Ai} \delta x_{i,A} - \frac{\delta H_A T_{,A}}{T}, \tag{7.7}$$

where δH_A is the instantaneous heat flux at time t. Introducing (7.6) into (7.7), we obtain

$$\rho_0 \mathcal{C}_{x_{i,A}} \delta x_{i,A} + O(\delta x_{i,A} \delta x_{i,A}) \leq \Pi_{Ai} \delta x_{i,A} - \frac{\delta H_A T_{,A}}{T}. \tag{7.8}$$

Then, with the assumption that Π_{Ai} is independent of $\delta x_{i,A}$, and bearing in mind that the relation (7.8) is valid for arbitrary infinitesimal δH_A and $\delta x_{i,A}$, we obtain (cf. Coleman, 1964)

$$\Pi_{Ai} = \rho_0 \mathcal{C}_{x_{i,A}} \tag{7.9}$$

and

$$\delta H_A T_{,A} \leq 0. \tag{7.10}$$

VIII. THE FREE ENERGY IN FINITE ELASTICITY

We have pointed out in Section VI that, if we assume that the Helmholtz free energy and Kirchhoff-Piola stress tensor at time t depend only on the deformation gradients at that time, then for isothermal deformations we have

$$\Pi_{Ai} = \rho_0 \frac{\partial \mathcal{C}}{\partial x_{i,A}}. \tag{8.1}$$

Now $\mathcal{C}$ cannot depend on the deformation gradients in an arbitrary manner. In order to demonstrate this, we consider two deformations, which we shall designate α and β, described in the reference system x by

$$x_i(\tau) = x_i(X_A, \tau), \qquad \bar{x}_i(\tau) = \bar{x}_i(X_A, \tau), \qquad (8.2)$$

respectively. These are assumed to differ only by a rigid rotation, so that

$$\bar{x}_i(\tau) = a_{ij}(\tau) x_j(\tau), \qquad (8.3)$$

where $a_{ij}(\tau)$ is a proper orthogonal tensor and therefore satisfies the relations

$$a_{ij}(\tau) a_{ik}(\tau) = a_{ji}(\tau) a_{ki}(\tau) = \delta_{jk}, \qquad |a_{ij}(\tau)| = 1. \qquad (8.4)$$

For brevity, we shall use the notation

$$a_{ij} = a_{ij}(t). \qquad (8.5)$$

Plainly, the Helmholtz free energy is unaltered by the rigid rotation. Thus,

$$\mathcal{C}(\bar{x}_{i,A}) = \mathcal{C}(x_{i,A}). \qquad (8.6)$$

Introducing (8.3) into (8.6), we have

$$\mathcal{C}(a_{ij}x_{j,A}) = \mathcal{C}(x_{i,A}). \qquad (8.7)$$

This relation is valid for all rigid rotations, i.e., for all proper orthogonal a_{ij}. The restrictions on $\mathcal{C}$ implied by (8.7) may be made explicit.

Method 1. We recognize that Eq. (8.7) expresses the fact that $\mathcal{C}$ is a scalar invariant under the proper orthogonal group of the three vectors $x_{j,1}$, $x_{j,2}$, and $x_{j,3}$. It must therefore be expressible as a function of the elements of a function basis[10] for these three vectors under the proper orthogonal group. Such a function basis is well known.[11] It consists of the six inner products that can be formed from the three vectors together with the scalar triple product of the three vectors, i.e., of

$$G_{AB} = x_{i,A} x_{i,B} \qquad \text{and} \qquad |x_{i,A}|. \qquad (8.8)$$

We note that

$$|x_{i,A}|^2 = |G_{AB}|. \qquad (8.9)$$

For deformations that are possible in a real body, $|x_{i,A}| > 0$. (We note that $|x_{i,A}|$ is the ratio between the volume of an element in the deformed

---

[10] A function basis is a set of invariants in terms of which any other invariant can be expressed as a single-valued function.
[11] The necessary result is due to Cauchy.

and undeformed states.)   Consequently,

$$|x_{i,A}| = |G_{AB}|^{1/2}. \tag{8.10}$$

It follows that α is a single-valued function of G_{AB}.

It can easily be seen from the definition (8.8) that G_{AB} transforms from one fixed rectangular cartesian coordinate system to another as a second-order tensor, and it is evidently symmetric.   The tensor G_{AB} is called the Cauchy-Green strain tensor.

Method 2.   Since (8.7) is valid for all proper orthogonal a_{ij}, it is certainly valid for the particular choice[12]

$$a_{ij} = (\mathbf{G}^{-1/2})_{iB}x_{j,B}. \tag{8.11}$$

Introducing this into (8.7), we see, with (8.8), that α is expressible as a function of G_{AB}.   Now, any scalar function of G_{AB} automatically satisfies the relation (8.7) for all proper orthogonal a_{ij}.

Introducing

$$\alpha = \alpha(G_{PQ}) \tag{8.12}$$

into (8.1), we obtain

$$\begin{aligned}
\Pi_{Ai} &= \frac{1}{2}\,\rho_0 \left(\frac{\partial\alpha}{\partial G_{PQ}} \frac{\partial G_{PQ}}{\partial x_{i,A}} + \frac{\partial\alpha}{\partial G_{QP}} \frac{\partial G_{QP}}{\partial x_{i,A}} \right) \\
&= \rho_0 x_{i,Q} \left(\frac{\partial\alpha}{\partial G_{AQ}} + \frac{\partial\alpha}{\partial G_{QA}} \right).
\end{aligned} \tag{8.13}$$

From (8.13) and (3.27), we obtain the Cauchy stress tensor as

$$\sigma_{ij} = \rho x_{i,Q} x_{j,A} \left(\frac{\partial\alpha}{\partial G_{AQ}} + \frac{\partial\alpha}{\partial G_{QA}} \right), \tag{8.14}$$

where ρ is the density of the material at time t and is therefore related to ρ_0 by

$$\rho = \rho_0/|\partial x/\partial X|. \tag{8.15}$$

IX. MATERIALS WITH MEMORY

A. Constitutive Assumption

We now consider materials for which it is appropriate to make the constitutive assumption that the stress components at time t depend on the deformation gradients at time t and at all previous times, i.e., are

[12] It is easily verified that a_{ij} defined in this manner is proper orthogonal by substitution in the relations $a_{ji}a_{ki} = \delta_{jk}$, $|a_{ij}| = 1$, which are obtained from (8.4) by taking $\tau = t$.

functionals of $x_{i,A}(\tau)$ over the interval $-\infty < \tau \le t$. It is of no significance which of the stress tensors is taken, for if the constitutive assumption is made for one of the stress tensors, it follows from (3.27) and (3.28)
that it is valid for the others. It is convenient to make this assumption
for the Piola stress tensor P_{AB}. Then

$$P_{AB} = \underset{\tau = -\infty}{\overset{t}{\mathfrak{F}_{AB}}}[x_{i,Q}(\tau)]. \tag{9.1}$$

Materials obeying this constitutive assumption are called simple materials.[13] For convenience, we apply the following transformation to the
time variable:

$$s = (t - \tau + 1)^{-1}. \tag{9.2}$$

We note that this transforms the time interval $-\infty < \tau \le t$ monotoni-
cally into the interval $0 \le s \le 1$. Equation (9.1) then takes the form

$$P_{AB} = \underset{s=0}{\overset{1}{\mathfrak{F}_{AB}}}[x_{i,Q}(s), t]. \tag{9.3}$$

B. Hereditary Materials

We note that P_{AB} is a functional of $x_{i,Q}(s)$ and an ordinary function of t.
We consider a new deformation identical with the one considered but
shifted in time by an amount T, and we denote by $\bar{P}_{AB}$ the corresponding
Piola stress at time $t + T$. Then

$$\bar{P}_{AB} = \underset{s=0}{\overset{1}{\mathfrak{F}_{AB}}}[x_{i,Q}(s), t + T]. \tag{9.4}$$

If

$$\bar{P}_{AB} = P_{AB}, \tag{9.5}$$

it follows that P_{AB} in (9.3) must be independent of t, and Eq. (9.3)
becomes

$$P_{AB} = \underset{s=0}{\overset{1}{\mathfrak{F}_{AB}}}[x_{i,Q}(s)]. \tag{9.6}$$

Materials for which the assumptions leading to (9.6) are valid are
called hereditary materials.

C. Restriction on the Form of the Functional

We now discuss a restriction on the form of the functionals $\mathfrak{F}_{AB}$,
paralleling that which we discussed in the case of finite elasticity theory
in Section VIII. In this case, we must, however, discuss the effect on
the *stress* of a rigid rotation superposed on the assumed deformation.

---

[13] This terminology is due to Noll (1958).

Accordingly, we consider the two deformations α and β described in a fixed rectangular cartesian coordinate system x by (8.2) and (8.3), which differ only by a time-dependent rigid rotation.

Let P_{AB} and $\bar{P}_{AB}$ be the Piola stress components in the system x for the deformations α and β, respectively. We have seen in Section III that a rigid rotation of a body and its applied force system leaves the Piola stress components unaltered. We therefore have

$$P_{AB} = \bar{P}_{AB}. \tag{9.7}$$

Now, from (9.3), we see that

$$P_{AB} = \mathfrak{F}_{AB}\underset{s=0}{\overset{1}{[}}x_{i,Q}(s)\,,\,t] \qquad \text{and} \qquad \bar{P}_{AB} = \mathfrak{F}_{AB}\underset{s=0}{\overset{1}{[}}\bar{x}_{i,Q}(s)\,,\,t]. \tag{9.8}$$

From (9.7), (9.8), and (8.3) we have

$$\mathfrak{F}_{AB}\underset{s=0}{\overset{1}{[}}a_{ij}(s)x_{j,Q}(s)\,,\,t] = \mathfrak{F}_{AB}\underset{s=0}{\overset{1}{[}}x_{i,Q}(s)\,,\,t]. \tag{9.9}$$

This relation must be valid for all proper orthogonal $a_{ij}(s)$. The restrictions on $\mathfrak{F}_{AB}$ implied by (9.9) can be made explicit. We give two methods[14] by which this can be done.

Method 1.   Equation (9.9) expresses the fact that $\mathfrak{F}_{AB}$ is a scalar functional invariant under the proper orthogonal group of the three vector functions $x_{i,1}(s)$, $x_{i,2}(s)$, $x_{i,3}(s)$. We choose $a_{ij}(s) = \delta_{ij}$ for $0 \leq s \leq 1$ ($s \neq \bar{s}$, say). Then, so far as the dependence on $x_{i,A}(\bar{s})$ is concerned, the relation (9.9) becomes an ordinary function relation of the form

$$F_{AB}[a_{ij}(\bar{s})x_{j,P}(\bar{s})\,,\,t] = F_{AB}[x_{i,P}(\bar{s})\,,\,t]. \tag{9.10}$$

As in the discussion in Method 1 of Section VIII, we see that this implies that F_{AB} depends on $x_{i,A}(\bar{s})$ only through $G_{PQ}(\bar{s})$, where $G_{PQ}(s)$ is defined by

$$G_{PQ}(s) = x_{i,P}(s)x_{i,Q}(s). \tag{9.11}$$

We can carry out this procedure for each instant of time s in the interval $[0, 1]$ in turn to obtain the result that P_{AB} must be a functional of the

---

[14] Method 1 is the same in principle as that used by Green and Rivlin (1957). However, the detailed algebra was there carried out in a more clumsy fashion, which incidentally introduced certain continuity restrictions on $\mathfrak{F}_{AB}$. These are here removed. Method 2 is substantially that of Noll (1958). Yet another method, heuristic in character, was given earlier by Oldroyd (1950).

Cauchy-Green strain tensor $G_{PQ}(s)$; thus,

$$P_{AB} = \underset{s=0}{\overset{1}{\mathfrak{F}_{AB}}}[G_{PQ}(s), t]. \tag{9.12}$$

Method 2. Paralleling the procedure used in Method 2 for discussing the Helmholtz free energy in finite elasticity, we take

$$a_{ij}(s) = \{\mathbf{G}(s)\}_{iB}^{-1/2} x_{j,B}(s), \tag{9.13}$$

where $\mathbf{G}(s)$ ($= \|G_{AB}(s)\|$) is defined by (9.11). We introduce this into (9.9) to obtain immediately (9.12). We note then that a functional of this form satisfies the relation (9.9) for all proper orthogonal $a_{ij}(s)$.

In (9.12), we can if we wish change the time variable from s to τ by means of (9.2) obtaining

$$P_{AB} = \underset{\tau=-\infty}{\overset{t}{\mathfrak{F}_{AB}}}[G_{PQ}(\tau), t]. \tag{9.14}$$

If the material is a hereditary material, we may omit t as an argument in (9.12), and (9.14) may then be rewritten in the form

$$P_{AB} = \underset{\tau=0}{\overset{\infty}{\mathfrak{F}_{AB}}}[G_{PQ}(t-\tau)]. \tag{9.15}$$

Having obtained restrictions on the manner in which the Piola stress tensor can depend on the deformation gradients, we can easily write down, from Eqs. (3.28), the corresponding equations for the Kirchhoff-Piola and Cauchy stress tensors. Corresponding to the Piola stress given by (9.14), we obtain

$$\Pi_{Ai} = x_{i,B}\underset{\tau=-\infty}{\overset{t}{\mathfrak{F}_{AB}}}[G_{PQ}(\tau), t] \tag{9.16}$$

and

$$\sigma_{ij} = |\partial x/\partial X|^{-1}x_{i,A}x_{j,B}\underset{\tau=-\infty}{\overset{t}{\mathfrak{F}_{AB}}}[G_{PQ}(\tau), t]. \tag{9.17}$$

It is convenient, for many purposes, to replace the argument function $G_{PQ}(\tau)$ in (9.14) by $E_{PQ}(\tau)$, defined by

$$E_{PQ}(\tau) = G_{PQ}(\tau) - \delta_{PQ}. \tag{9.18}$$

We then have an expression for P_{AB} of the form

$$P_{AB} = \underset{\tau=-\infty}{\overset{t}{\mathfrak{F}_{AB}}}[E_{PQ}(\tau), t], \tag{9.19}$$

with corresponding changes in expressions (9.15)–(9.17).

X. CONSTITUTIVE EQUATIONS OF THE DIFFERENTIAL TYPE

For a wide class of deformations, the Cauchy-Green strain tensor at time τ may be expressed as a Taylor series about t. Thus,

$$G_{PQ}(\tau) = \sum_{n=0}^{N} \frac{1}{n!} (\tau - t)^n \overset{(n)}{G}_{PQ} + R_N, \qquad (10.1)$$

where $\overset{(n)}{G}_{PQ}$ denotes $[d^n G_{PQ}(\tau)/d\tau^n]_{\tau=t}$, $\overset{(0)}{G}_{PQ} = G_{PQ}$, and R_N is the usual remainder term. Depending on the magnitude of R_N and the nature of the tensor functional $\mathfrak{F}_{AB}$, it may be possible to replace $\mathfrak{F}_{AB}$ either precisely, or to an adequate degree of approximation, by an ordinary tensor function of $\overset{(n)}{G}_{PQ}$ ($n = 0, 1, 2, \ldots, N$).[15] We then have

$$P_{AB} = F_{AB}(\overset{(n)}{G}_{PQ}), \qquad n = 0, 1, 2, \ldots. \qquad (10.2)$$

Formulae for calculating $\overset{(n)}{G}_{PQ}$ in terms of the velocity gradients, acceleration gradients, second acceleration gradients, and so on may be easily obtained.

From (9.11), we have

$$G_{PQ} = x_{i,P}x_{i,Q}. \qquad (10.3)$$

We define tensors $A_{ij}^{(n)}$ ($n = 0, 1, 2, \ldots$) by

$$\overset{(n)}{G}_{PQ} = 2x_{i,P}x_{j,Q}A_{ij}^{(n)}. \qquad (10.4)$$

Thus,

$$A_{ij}^{(0)} = \tfrac{1}{2}\delta_{ij}, \qquad (10.5)$$

where δ_{ij} denotes the Kronecker delta.

Differentiating (10.4) with respect to t, we obtain

$$\overset{(n+1)}{G}_{PQ} = 2\left(x_{i,P}x_{j,Q} \frac{dA_{ij}^{(n)}}{dt} + v_{i,P}x_{j,Q}A_{ij}^{(n)} + x_{i,P}v_{j,Q}A_{ij}^{(n)} \right). \qquad (10.6)$$

Now, we have from (10.4)

$$A_{ij}^{(n+1)} = \tfrac{1}{2}X_{P,i}X_{Q,j}\overset{(n+1)}{G}_{PQ}. \qquad (10.7)$$

[15] This was first pointed out by Green and Rivlin (1957). Sufficient conditions for such a replacement to be valid have been given by Coleman and Noll (1961).

With (10.6), this yields

$$A_{ij}^{(n+1)} = \frac{dA_{ij}^{(n)}}{dt} + v_{k,i}A_{kj}^{(n)} + v_{k,j}A_{ik}^{(n)}. \tag{10.8}$$

Equation (10.8), together with (10.5), provides formulae for calculating the tensors $A_{ij}^{(n)}$. These tensors are called the Rivlin-Ericksen tensors (Rivlin and Ericksen, 1955). We note, by taking $n = 0$ in (10.8), that

$$A_{ij}^{(1)} = \tfrac{1}{2}(v_{i,j} + v_{j,i}). \tag{10.9}$$

Thus, $A_{ij}^{(1)}$ is the usual strain-velocity tensor. Through (10.4), $G_{PQ}^{(n)}$ ($n \geq 0$) can be calculated. Introducing (10.4) into (10.2), we see that the Piola stress tensor P_{AB} may be expressed in the form

$$P_{AB} = F_{AB}(x_{i,P}x_{j,Q}A_{ij}^{(n)}), \qquad n = 0, 1, 2, \ldots \tag{10.10}$$

With (3.28), we obtain the Cauchy stress tensor[16]

$$\sigma_{ij} = |\partial x/\partial X|^{-1}x_{i,A}x_{j,B}F_{AB}(x_{k,P}x_{l,Q}A_{kl}^{(n)}), \qquad n = 0, 1, 2, \ldots \tag{10.11}$$

XI. FLUIDS

Materials to which the constitutive equations developed in Sections IX and X apply may be either solids or fluids. We shall consider a particular case of the constitutive equation (9.17) which describes materials with properties that we recognize as being fluid-like.

We first define the relative Cauchy-Green strain tensor $\mathbf{G}^*(\tau)$ $[= \|G_{ij}^*(\tau)\|]$ at time τ by

$$G_{ij}^*(\tau) = x_{k,i}(\tau)x_{k,j}(\tau). \tag{11.1}$$

$\mathbf{G}^*(\tau)$ is then the Cauchy-Green strain tensor at time τ referred to the state at time t as the reference state, i.e., the Cauchy-Green strain tensor obtained by taking $t_0 = t$.

We now consider the particular case of (9.17) which has the form

$$\sigma_{ij} = a_{iM}a_{jN}\mathfrak{F}_{MN}[\overset{t}{\underset{\tau=-\infty}{G_{kl}^*(\tau)}}a_{kP}a_{lQ}, t], \tag{11.2}$$

where a_{iK} is a proper orthogonal tensor of the form

$$a_{iK} = h_{KP}(\mathbf{G})x_{i,P}. \tag{11.3}$$

---

[16] We note that the factor $|\partial x/\partial X|^{-1}$ occurring in (10.11) may be absorbed into the function F_{AB}.

In (11.3), h_{KP} is a function of $\mathbf{G}$ ($= \|G_{PQ}\|$), the Cauchy-Green strain tensor at time t. Since a_{im} is a proper orthogonal tensor, we must have

$$h_{KP}h_{LQ}G_{PQ} = \delta_{KL}, \qquad |h_{KP}x_{i,P}| = 1. \qquad (11.4)$$

We can see immediately that a functional of $G_{kl}^{*}(\tau)a_{kP}a_{lQ}$ is also a functional of $G_{PQ}(\tau)$ by making the substitution (11.3) for a_{iK} in the former and using the relation (11.1).

The constitutive equation (11.2) implies that σ_{ij} depends on the deformation gradients relative to the reference state at time t_0 only through a rotation, which is given in terms of the deformation gradients. Consequently, the mechanical properties of the material described by (11.2) will be fluid-like in the sense that infinite values of the deformation gradients with respect to the state at time t_0 enter into the constitutive equations in combinations that are finite. The constitutive equation (11.2) is not the most general constitutive equation of the form (9.17), which describes a fluid in which the stress is a functional of the history of the deformation gradients. More general discussions of the constitutive equations of fluids with memory have been given by Green (1964) and by Coleman (1965).

We can discuss the constitutive equation of the differential type (10.11) in a similar way. We note that the relation

$$\sigma_{ij} = a_{iM}a_{jN}F_{MN}(a_{kP}a_{lQ}A_{kl}^{(n)}), \qquad n = 0, 1, 2, \ldots, \qquad (11.5)$$

with a_{iK} defined by (11.3) and (11.4), is a particular case of (10.11), in which σ_{ij} depends on the configuration at time t_0 only through rotations.

XII. RATE-INDEPENDENT MATERIALS

We now consider materials for which the stress at time t depends on the deformation history up to and including t, but not on the rate at which this deformation path is traversed. Such materials are called rate-independent materials. Provided they are simple materials, i.e., the stress depends on the deformation history only through the deformation gradients, they must arise as a special case of the materials with memory discussed in Section IX. We must therefore discuss the restriction on the form of the constitutive equation (9.19) which arises as a result of rate-independence.

The behavior of $E_{PQ}(\tau)$ as a function of τ can be described by a curve in nine-dimensional strain space, τ being a parameter defining the various points on the curve. We now define $l(\tau)$, the length along the curve

in strain space from $E_{PQ}(-\infty)$ to $E_{PQ}(\tau)$, by

$$l(\tau) = \int_{-\infty}^{\tau} \{dE_{PQ}(\tau)\, dE_{PQ}(\tau)\}^{1/2}. \tag{12.1}$$

We also employ the notation

$$l = l(t). \tag{12.2}$$

Then the behavior of $E_{PQ}(\tau)$ as a function of τ can be described by specifying it as a function of $l(\tau)$ and by specifying $l(\tau)$ as a function of τ.
Thus, we may replace Eq. (9.19) by an equation of the form

$$P_{AB} = \mathcal{F}_{AB}[\underset{l(\tau)=0}{\overset{l(\tau)=l}{E_{PQ}\{\ l(\tau)\ \}}},\ \underset{\tau=-\infty}{\overset{t}{l(\tau)}}\ ,\ t]. \tag{12.3}$$

If the material is rate-independent, then P_{AB} is independent of $l(\tau)$,
which describes completely the rate at which the path in strain space is
described. So, for rate-independent materials, Eq. (12.3) becomes

$$P_{AB} = \mathcal{F}_{AB}[\underset{l(\tau)=0}{\overset{l(\tau)=l}{E_{PQ}\{\ l(\tau)\ \}}},\ t]. \tag{12.4}$$

This result is due to Pipkin and Rivlin (1965).

XIII. CONSTRAINTS

In discussing the theory of finite elasticity, we derived an expression
[Eq. (6.4)] for the Kirchhoff-Piola stress from relation (6.3).   In order to
do this, we assumed that the velocity gradients $v_{i,A}$ can be varied independently.   It may, in some circumstances, be undesirable to make this
assumption.   This is the case if the material considered is subject to
certain kinematic constraints.

For example, if the material is incompressible, the ratio between the
volume of an element in the deformed and undeformed states is unity, i.e.,
$|\partial x/\partial X| = 1$, and consequently the velocity gradients cannot be varied
independently.   In this case, since

$$|\partial x/\partial X| = e_{ijk}x_{i,1}x_{j,2}x_{k,3}, \tag{13.1}$$

we have

$$\frac{d}{dt}|\partial x/\partial X| = e_{ijk}(v_{i,1}x_{j,2}x_{k,3} + v_{i,2}x_{j,3}x_{k,1} + v_{i,3}x_{j,1}x_{k,2})$$

$$= 0. \tag{13.2}$$

As another example, we mention the possibility that the material may be inextensible in a direction that is initially parallel to the x_1-axis of a rectangular cartesian coordinate system x. Then,

$$G_{11} = x_{i,1}x_{i,1} = 1. \tag{13.3}$$

The velocity gradients $v_{i,A}$ are then constrained by the relation

$$x_{i,1}v_{i,1} = 0. \tag{13.4}$$

There may, of course, be more than one constraint on the deformation gradients. For example, both of the constraints (13.2) and (13.4) may apply simultaneously. Suppose now that there are α constraints

$$f_\beta(x_{i,A}) = 0 \qquad (\beta = 1, \ldots, \alpha). \tag{13.5}$$

We obtain

$$\frac{df_\beta}{dt} = \frac{\partial f_\beta}{\partial x_{i,A}} v_{i,A} = 0 \qquad (\beta = 1, \ldots, \alpha). \tag{13.6}$$

With (6.3), we then have, for isothermal deformation of an elastic material subject to constraints,

$$\left(\Pi_{Ai} - \rho_0 \frac{\partial \mathcal{Q}}{\partial x_{i,A}} + \sum_{\beta=1}^{\alpha} \lambda_\beta \frac{\partial f_\beta}{\partial x_{i,A}} \right) v_{i,A} = 0, \tag{13.7}$$

where λ_β ($\beta = 1, \ldots, \alpha$) are Lagrange undetermined multipliers, which may vary from point to point of the material. Equation (13.7) is valid for arbitrary $v_{i,A}$.

We thus have, for isothermal deformation of the elastic material,[17]

$$\Pi_{Ai} = \rho_0 \frac{\partial \mathcal{Q}}{\partial x_{i,A}} - \sum_{\beta=1}^{\alpha} \lambda_\beta \frac{\partial f_\beta}{\partial x_{i,A}}. \tag{13.8}$$

If the material is not elastic, we return to the inequality (5.6), again assuming that the deformation is carried out isothermally. With (13.6), we obtain from (5.6)

$$\rho_0 \dot{\mathcal{Q}} \leq \left(\Pi_{Ai} + \sum_{\beta=1}^{\alpha} \lambda_\beta \frac{\partial f_\beta}{\partial x_{i,A}} \right) v_{i,A} - \frac{Q_A T_{,A}}{T} \tag{13.9}$$

[17] The constraint of incompressibility was introduced into the equation for the Cauchy stress for an elastic material undergoing finite deformations by Rivlin (1948). The constraint of inextensibility in specified directions of an elastic material was discussed by Adkins and Rivlin (1955) and by Adkins (1956a, 1956b, 1958a). The general question of constraints in elastic materials was discussed by Ericksen and Rivlin (1954).

for arbitrary λ_β. This relation is now valid without constraint on $v_{i,A}$. It indicates that we have to make a constitutive assumption regarding $\Pi_{Ai} + \sum_{\beta=1}^{\alpha} \lambda_\beta \, \partial f_\beta / \partial x_{i,A}$. Depending on the material we wish to describe, this may be made in any of the ways discussed in Sections IX–XII.

There are certain restrictions that can be imposed on the constraints (13.5). We consider a new deformation consisting of the original deformation with a superposed rigid rotation. For this deformation we must have, from (13.5),

$$f_\beta(a_{ij}x_{j,A}) = 0, \tag{13.10}$$

where a_{ij} is the transformation describing the rotation. Equation (13.10) must be satisfied for all proper orthogonal a_{ij}. In particular, it must be satisfied if a_{ij} is given by (8.11). It follows that the constraint must be expressible in the form

$$f_\beta(G_{AB}) = 0 \qquad (\beta = 1, \ldots, \alpha). \tag{13.11}$$

We note that a constraint of this form satisfies the condition (13.10) for all proper orthogonal a_{ij}. Since there are only six independent components of G_{AB}, at most six independent constraints on the deformation gradients can be simultaneously valid (i.e., $\alpha \leq 6$).

XIV. MATERIAL SYMMETRY: GENERAL CONSIDERATIONS

Most materials with which we are concerned in practice possess some symmetry. They may, for example, be isotropic, possess rotational symmetry about an axis (i.e., fiber symmetry), or they may belong to one or other of the classes of crystal symmetry.

Material symmetry may be defined by means of equivalent coordinate systems. Let x and $\bar{x}$ be two fixed rectangular cartesian coordinate systems with a common origin. We consider two deformations α and β. The deformation α is described in the coordinate system x by the relation

$$x_i(\tau) = f_i(X_A, \tau). \tag{14.1}$$

The deformation β is described in the system $\bar{x}$ by the relation

$$\bar{x}_i(\tau) = f_i(\bar{X}_A, \tau). \tag{14.2}$$

X_A and $\bar{X}_A$ are the coordinates in the system x and $\bar{x}$, respectively, of two generic particles P and $\bar{P}$, respectively, at the reference time t_0. $x_i(\tau)$ and $\bar{x}_i(\tau)$ are the coordinates in the systems x and $\bar{x}$, respectively, of P

and $\bar{P}$, respectively, at time τ.   Let $\bar{X}_A{}^*$ and $\bar{x}_i{}^*(\tau)$ be the coordinates in the system x of the particle $\bar{P}$ at times t_0 and τ, respectively.   Then

$$\bar{X}_A{}^* = S_{AB}\bar{X}_B \qquad \text{and} \qquad \bar{x}_i{}^*(\tau) = S_{ij}\bar{x}_j(\tau), \qquad (14.3)$$

where S_{AB} is an orthogonal transformation.

The components $G_{AB}(X_P, \tau)$ in the system x of the Cauchy-Green strain tensor for the deformation α at the particle P are given by

$$G_{AB}(X_P, \tau) = \frac{\partial x_i(\tau)}{\partial X_A}\frac{\partial x_i(\tau)}{\partial X_B}. \qquad (14.4)$$

The components $\bar{G}_{AB}(\bar{X}_P, \tau)$ in the system $\bar{x}$ of the Cauchy-Green strain tensor for the deformation β at the particle $\bar{P}$ are given by

$$\bar{G}_{AB}(\bar{X}_P, \tau) = \frac{\partial \bar{x}_i(\tau)}{\partial \bar{X}_A}\frac{\partial \bar{x}_i(\tau)}{\partial \bar{X}_B}. \qquad (14.5)$$

We note from (14.1), (14.2), (14.4), and (14.5) that

$$\bar{G}_{AB}(\bar{X}_P, \tau) = G_{AB}(X_P, \tau) \qquad \text{if} \quad X_P = \bar{X}_P. \qquad (14.6)$$

Let $\bar{G}^*_{AB}(\bar{X}_P, \tau)$ be the components of the Cauchy-Green strain tensor for the deformation β in the system x.   We have, from (14.3),

$$\bar{G}^*_{AB}(\bar{X}_P, \tau) = S_{AK}S_{BL}\bar{G}_{KL}(\bar{X}_P, \tau). \qquad (14.7)$$

Then, from (14.6), it follows that

$$\bar{G}^*_{AB}(\bar{X}_P, \tau) = S_{AK}S_{BL}G_{KL}(X_P, \tau) \qquad \text{if} \quad \bar{X}_P = X_P. \qquad (14.8)$$

We shall denote by $\mathfrak{a}(X_K)$ the Helmholtz free energy per unit mass and by $P_{AB}(X_K)$ the Piola stress components in the system x, both applying at the particle X_K at time t, for the deformation α.   We shall denote by $\bar{\mathfrak{a}}(\bar{X}_K)$ and $\bar{P}_{AB}(\bar{X}_K)$ the corresponding quantities in the system $\bar{x}$ at the particle $\bar{P}$ at time t for the deformation β.   If the constitutive assumption is made in terms of the dependence of the Helmholtz free energy on kinematic variables, then we say that the coordinate systems x and $\bar{x}$ are equivalent if and only if

$$\mathfrak{a}(X_K) = \bar{\mathfrak{a}}(\bar{X}_K) \qquad \text{when} \quad X_K = \bar{X}_K. \qquad (14.9)$$

If, on the other hand, the constitutive assumption is made in terms of the dependence of the Piola stress on kinematic variables, then we say that the systems x and $\bar{x}$ are equivalent only if

$$P_{AB}(X_K) = \bar{P}_{AB}(\bar{X}_K) \qquad \text{when} \quad X_K = \bar{X}_K. \qquad (14.10)$$

Let $\bar{P}^*_{AB}(\bar{X}_K)$ be the components of the Piola stress at time t in the system x for the deformation β at the particle $\bar{P}$.   Then, by the usual law for the

transformation of Piola stress, we have

$$\bar{P}^*_{AB}(\bar{X}_K) = S_{AM}S_{BN}\bar{P}_{MN}(\bar{X}_K).\qquad(14.11)$$

If the coordinate systems x and $\bar{x}$ are equivalent, we have, with (14.10),

$$\bar{P}^*_{AB}(\bar{X}_K) = S_{AM}S_{BN}P_{MN}(X_K)\quad\text{when}\quad X_K = \bar{X}_K.\qquad(14.12)$$

Material symmetry is described by a group of transformations **s**, say, each element of which is an orthogonal transformation that transforms any rectangular cartesian coordinate system x, say, into an equivalent coordinate system.

XV. SYMMETRY RESTRICTIONS IN ELASTIC MATERIALS

In the case of finite elasticity theory, discussed in Section VIII, we assumed that the Helmholtz free energy α at time t is a function of the deformation gradients at time t, and we showed that it must be expressible in terms of these through the components of the Cauchy-Green strain tensor G_{PQ}. Thus, for the deformation α,

$$\alpha(X_K) = \alpha(G_{PQ}, X_K)\qquad(15.1)$$

and, for the deformation β,

$$\bar{\alpha}(\bar{X}_K) = \bar{\alpha}(\bar{G}_{PQ}, \bar{X}_K) = \alpha(\bar{G}^*_{PQ}, \bar{X}_K{}^*).\qquad(15.2)$$

We note, from (14.8), that $G_{PQ}(X_K)$ and $\bar{G}^*_{PQ}(\bar{X}_K)$ are related by

$$\bar{G}^*_{PQ}(\bar{X}_K) = S_{PM}S_{QN}G_{MN}(X_K)\quad\text{if}\quad X_K = \bar{X}_K.\qquad(15.3)$$

If the coordinate systems x and $\bar{x}$ are equivalent, we have from (14.9) and (15.1)–(15.3)

$$\alpha(S_{PM}S_{QN}G_{MN}) = \alpha(G_{PQ}),\qquad(15.4)$$

and this relation must be valid for all transformations S_{PQ} of the group **s** describing the symmetry of the material. The relation (15.4) then expresses the fact that α must be a scalar invariant, under the group **s**, of the symmetric second-order tensor G_{PQ}.

XVI. SYMMETRY RESTRICTIONS IN MATERIALS WITH MEMORY

We now turn to the restrictions imposed by material symmetry on materials with memory. We saw in Section IX that starting with the

constitutive assumption (9.1) we arrived at the conclusion that the Piola stress must depend on the deformation gradients through the components of the Cauchy-Green strain tensor. This fact is expressed by Eq. (9.14). The passage from Eq. (9.1) to Eq. (9.14) involved no assumption regarding the symmetry of the material.

We again consider the two deformations α and β described in the coordinate systems x and $\bar{x}$, respectively, by Eqs. (14.1) and (14.2), respectively. For the deformation α, the components of Piola stress in the system x are given, from (9.14), by

$$P_{AB} = \mathfrak{F}_{AB}[\underset{\tau=-\infty}{\overset{t}{G_{PQ}(\tau)}}, t]. \tag{16.1}$$

For the deformation β, the components of Piola stress in the system x are given, from (9.14), by

$$\bar{P}_{AB}{}^* = \mathfrak{F}_{AB}[\underset{\tau=-\infty}{\overset{t}{\bar{G}_{PQ}^*(\tau)}}, t]. \tag{16.2}$$

Equations (16.1) and (16.2) yield, together with (14.8) and (14.12),

$$\mathfrak{F}_{AB}[\underset{\tau=-\infty}{\overset{t}{S_{PK}S_{QL}G_{KL}(\tau)}}, t] = S_{AM}S_{BN}\mathfrak{F}_{MN}[\underset{\tau=-\infty}{\overset{t}{G_{PQ}(\tau)}}, t]. \tag{16.3}$$

This relation must, of course, be valid for all transformations of the group $\mathbf{S}$ describing the material symmetry.

XVII. SYMMETRY RESTRICTIONS FOR CONSTITUTIVE EQUATIONS OF THE DIFFERENTIAL TYPE

We now discuss the restrictions imposed on the constitutive equation (10.2) by material symmetry. We again consider the two deformations α and β described by (14.1) and (14.2). We see, from (14.8), that

$$\overset{(n)}{\bar{G}_{AB}^*}(\bar{X}_P, t) = S_{AK}S_{BL}\overset{(n)}{G_{KL}}(X_P, t) \quad \text{if} \quad \bar{X}_P = X_P. \tag{17.1}$$

From (10.2), we have for the deformation α

$$P_{AB} = F_{AB}(\overset{(n)}{G_{PQ}}) \quad (n = 0, 1, 2, \ldots) \tag{17.2}$$

and for the deformation β we have

$$\bar{P}_{AB}^* = F_{AB}(\overset{(n)}{\bar{G}_{PQ}^*}) \quad (n = 0, 1, 2, \ldots). \tag{17.3}$$

Introducing (17.2) and (17.3) into (14.12), we obtain

$$F_{AB}(\overset{(n)}{\tilde{G}^{*}_{PQ}}) = S_{AM}S_{BN}F_{MN}(\overset{(n)}{G_{PQ}}),\qquad (17.4)$$

where $\overset{(n)}{\tilde{G}^{*}_{PQ}}$ and $\overset{(n)}{G_{PQ}}$ are related by (17.1). This relation must, of course, be valid for all transformations of the group **s** describing the material symmetry.

XVIII. CANONICAL FORMS FOR THE CONSTITUTIVE EQUATIONS OF FINITE ELASTICITY

In Sections XV–XVII, we have obtained the restrictions imposed by material symmetry on the forms of the constitutive equations, for various types of material, in implicit form. These restrictions may be made explicit by means of invariant-theoretical considerations.

Any polynomial scalar invariant of any number of tensors under any of the groups with which we are concerned (the full orthogonal group or a subgroup of it) can be expressed as a polynomial in a *finite* number of polynomial scalar invariants, none of which is expressible as a polynomial in the remaining ones. Such a set of scalar invariants is called an irreducible integrity basis for the tensors under the group with which we are concerned. Any scalar invariant, whether polynomial or not, may be expressed as a single-valued function of the elements of this integrity basis.

In the case of finite elasticity theory, we have seen that the Helmholtz free energy $\mathcal{C}$ must satisfy the restriction (15.4) for all transformations of the group **s** describing the material symmetry. This expresses the fact that $\mathcal{C}$ must be a scalar invariant of the symmetric second-order tensor G_{AB} (the Cauchy-Green strain tensor) under the group **s**. If the material is isotropic, **s** is the orthogonal group,[18] and an irreducible integrity basis is well known to consist of three invariants I_1, I_2, I_3 defined by

$$I_1 = \operatorname{tr} \mathbf{G}, \qquad I_2 = \tfrac{1}{2}[(\operatorname{tr} \mathbf{G})^2 - \operatorname{tr} \mathbf{G}^2], \qquad I_3 = \det \mathbf{G}, \quad (18.1)$$

where $\mathbf{G} = \|G_{AB}\|$. We then have

$$\mathcal{C} = \mathcal{C}(I_1, I_2, I_3). \qquad (18.2)$$

[18] It is immaterial whether we take this as the full or proper orthogonal group, because the integrity basis is the same in both cases.

Introducing (18.2) into (8.13), we obtain the constitutive equation for the Kirchhoff-Piola stress, for isothermal finite elastic deformations of an isotropic material:

$$\Pi_{Ai} = 2\rho_0 \left[\left(\frac{\partial\alpha}{\partial I_1} + I_1 \frac{\partial\alpha}{\partial I_2} \right) x_{i,A} - \frac{\partial\alpha}{\partial I_2} G_{AC} x_{i,C} \right.$$
$$+ \frac{\partial\alpha}{\partial I_3} I_3^{1/2} e_{iqr} (\delta_{A1} x_{q,2} x_{r,3}$$
$$\left. + \delta_{A2} x_{q,3} x_{r,1} + \delta_{A3} x_{q,1} x_{r,2}) \right]. \tag{18.3}$$

The corresponding constitutive equation for the Cauchy stress is given, from (8.14), by

$$\sigma_{ji} = 2\rho \left[\left(\frac{\partial\alpha}{\partial I_1} + I_1 \frac{\partial\alpha}{\partial I_2} \right) g_{ij} - \frac{\partial\alpha}{\partial I_2} g_{ik} g_{kj} + \frac{\partial\alpha}{\partial I_3} I_3 \delta_{ij} \right] \tag{18.4}$$

where

$$g_{ij} = x_{i,A} x_{j,A}. \tag{18.5}$$

For elastic materials whose symmetry is expressed by groups other than the full or proper orthogonal group, the appropriate integrity basis replaces (18.1), and the expressions for the Kirchhoff-Piola and Cauchy stress tensors may then be derived from (8.13) and (8.14) in a manner similar to that employed in the case of the full or proper orthogonal group. Suppose that $J_1, J_2, \ldots, J_\alpha$ are the elements of an irreducible integrity basis for the group **s**. We then have

$$\alpha = \alpha(J_1, J_2, \ldots, J_\alpha). \tag{18.6}$$

Introducing this into (8.13), we obtain

$$\Pi_{Ai} = \rho_0 x_{i,Q} \sum_{\beta=1}^{\alpha} \frac{\partial\alpha}{\partial J_\beta} \left(\frac{\partial J_\beta}{\partial G_{AQ}} + \frac{\partial J_\beta}{\partial G_{QA}} \right). \tag{18.7}$$

An irreducible integrity basis for a symmetric second-order tensor under each of the 32 crystallographic point groups has been obtained by Smith and Rivlin (1958).[19] They are given in Table I.

In each case, the symmetry is conveniently described with respect to a particular rectangular cartesian coordinate system x, which relates to preferred directions in the material. If this system is appropriately chosen in each case, then the transformations that enter into the descrip-

[19] That these are, in fact, irreducible was shown by Smith (1962).

TABLE I

| Crystal class | | Generating | |
Schoen-flies	Hermann-Mauguin	transform-tions	Integrity basis
Triclinic system			
C_1	1	**I**	G_{AB} $(A, B = 1, 2, 3)$
S_2	$\bar{1}$	**C**	
Monoclinic system			
C_2	2	$\mathbf{D}_1$	$G_{11}, G_{22}, G_{33}, G_{23}, G_{31}{}^2, G_{12}{}^2,$
C_{1h}	m	$\mathbf{R}_1$	$G_{12}G_{31}$
C_{2h}	$2/m$	$\mathbf{C}, \mathbf{R}_1$	
Orthorhombic system			
V	222	$\mathbf{D}_1, \mathbf{D}_2$	$G_{11}, G_{22}, G_{33}, G_{23}{}^2, G_{31}{}^2, G_{12}{}^2,$
C_{2v}	$2mm$	$\mathbf{D}_1, \mathbf{R}_2$	$G_{23}G_{31}G_{12}$
V_h	mmm	$\mathbf{C}, \mathbf{R}_1, \mathbf{R}_2$	
Tetragonal system			
S_4	$\bar{4}$	$\mathbf{D}_1\mathbf{T}_3$	$G_{11} + G_{22}, G_{33}, G_{23}{}^2 + G_{31}{}^2, G_{12}{}^2,$
C_4	4	$\mathbf{R}_1\mathbf{T}_3$	$G_{11}G_{22}, G_{12}(G_{11} - G_{22}),$
C_{4h}	$4/m$	$\mathbf{C}, \mathbf{R}_1\mathbf{T}_3$	$G_{23}G_{31}(G_{11} - G_{22}), G_{23}G_{31}G_{12},$
			$G_{12}(G_{31}{}^2 - G_{23}{}^2), G_{11}G_{23}{}^2 + G_{22}G_{31}{}^2,$
			$G_{23}G_{31}(G_{31}{}^2 - G_{23}{}^2), G_{23}{}^2G_{31}{}^2$
D_4	422	$\mathbf{R}_1\mathbf{T}_3, \mathbf{D}_1$	$G_{11} + G_{22}, G_{33}, G_{23}{}^2 + G_{31}{}^2, G_{12}{}^2,$
V_d	$\bar{4}2m$	$\mathbf{D}_1\mathbf{T}_3, \mathbf{D}_1$	$G_{11}G_{22}, G_{23}G_{31}G_{12},$
C_{4v}	$4mm$	$\mathbf{R}_1\mathbf{T}_3, \mathbf{R}_1$	$G_{11}G_{23}{}^2 + G_{22}G_{31}{}^2, G_{23}{}^2G_{31}{}^2$
D_{4h}	$4/mmm$	$\mathbf{C}, \mathbf{R}_1, \mathbf{R}_1\mathbf{T}_3$	
Hexagonal system			
C_3	3	$\mathbf{S}_1$	$G_{33}, G_{11} + G_{22}, G_{11}G_{22} - G_{12}{}^2,$
C_{3i}	$\bar{3}$	$\mathbf{CS}_1$	$G_{11}[(G_{11} + 3G_{22})^2 - 12G_{12}{}^2], G_{31}{}^2 + G_{23}{}^2,$
			$G_{31}(G_{31}{}^2 - 3G_{23}{}^2), (G_{11} - G_{22})G_{31} -$
			$2G_{12}G_{23}, (G_{22} - G_{11})G_{23} - 2G_{12}G_{31},$
			$3G_{12}(G_{11} - G_{22})^2 - 4G_{12}{}^3, G_{23}(G_{23}{}^2 -$
			$3G_{31}{}^2), G_{22}G_{31}{}^2 + G_{11}G_{23}{}^2 - 2G_{23}G_{31}G_{12},$
			$G_{31}[(G_{11} + G_{22})^2 + 4(G_{12}{}^2 - G_{22}{}^2)] -$
			$8G_{11}G_{12}G_{23}, G_{23}[(G_{11} + G_{22})^2 +$
			$4(G_{12}{}^2 - G_{22}{}^2)] + 8G_{11}G_{12}G_{31},$
			$(G_{11} - G_{22})G_{23}G_{31} + G_{12}(G_{23}{}^2 - G_{31}{}^2)$

TABLE I (*Continued*)

Crystal class		Generating	
Schoen-flies	Hermann-Mauguin	transform-tions	Integrity basis
D_3	32	$\mathbf{S}_1$, $\mathbf{D}_1$	G_{33}, $G_{11} + G_{22}$, $G_{11}G_{22} - G_{12}{}^2$, $G_{31}{}^2 + G_{23}{}^2$,
C_{3v}	$3m$	$\mathbf{S}_1$, $\mathbf{R}_1$	$G_{11}[(G_{11} + 3G_{22})^2 - 12G_{12}{}^2]$, $G_{23}(G_{23}{}^2 -$
D_{3d}	$\overline{3}2/m$	$\mathbf{R}_1$, $\mathbf{CS}_1$	$3G_{31}{}^2)$, $(G_{11} - G_{22})G_{23} + 2G_{12}G_{31}$, $G_{11}G_{31}{}^2$
			$+ G_{22}G_{23}{}^2 + 2G_{23}G_{31}G_{12}$, $G_{23}[(G_{11} + G_{22})^2$
			$- 4(G_{22}{}^2 - G_{12}{}^2)] + 8G_{11}G_{12}G_{31}$
C_{3h}	$\overline{6}$	$\mathbf{R}_3\mathbf{S}_1$	G_{33}, $G_{11} + G_{22}$, $G_{11}G_{22} - G_{12}{}^2$, $G_{31}{}^2 + G_{23}{}^2$,
C_6	6	$\mathbf{D}_3\mathbf{S}_1$	$G_{11}[(G_{11} + 3G_{22})^2 - 12G_{12}{}^2]$,
C_{6h}	$6/m$	$\mathbf{CS}_1$, $\mathbf{R}_3$	$G_{31}{}^2(G_{31}{}^2 - 3G_{23}{}^2)^2$, $G_{11}G_{23}{}^2 +$
			$G_{22}G_{31}{}^2 - 2G_{23}G_{31}G_{12}$, $G_{12}(G_{31}{}^2 - G_{23}{}^2) +$
			$(G_{22} - G_{11})G_{31}G_{23}$, $3G_{12}(G_{11} - G_{22})^2 -$
			$4G_{12}{}^3$, $G_{31}G_{23}[3(G_{31}{}^2 - G_{23}{}^2)^2 -$
			$4G_{31}{}^2G_{23}{}^2]$, $G_{11}(G_{31}{}^4 + 3G_{23}{}^4) +$
			$2G_{22}G_{31}{}^2(G_{31}{}^2 + 3G_{23}{}^2) - 8G_{12}G_{23}G_{31}{}^3$,
			$G_{31}{}^2[(G_{11} + G_{22})^2 - 4(G_{22}{}^2 - G_{12}{}^2)]$
			$- 2G_{11}[(G_{11} + 3G_{22})(G_{31}{}^2 + G_{23}{}^2)$
			$- 4G_{23}G_{31}G_{12}]$, $G_{23}G_{31}[(G_{11} + G_{22})^2 -$
			$4(G_{22}{}^2 - G_{12}{}^2)] + 4G_{11}G_{12}(G_{23}{}^2 - G_{31}{}^2)$,
			$G_{12}[(G_{31}{}^2 + G_{23}{}^2)^2 + 4G_{23}{}^2(G_{31}{}^2 - G_{23}{}^2)]$
			$- 4G_{31}{}^3G_{23}(G_{11} - G_{22})$
D_{3h}	$\overline{6}m2$	$\mathbf{R}_3\mathbf{S}_1$, $\mathbf{R}_1$	G_{33}, $G_{11} + G_{22}$, $G_{11}G_{22} - G_{12}{}^2$, $G_{31}{}^2 + G_{23}{}^2$,
D_6	622	$\mathbf{D}_3\mathbf{S}_1$, $\mathbf{D}_1$	$G_{11}[(G_{11} + 3G_{22})^2 - 12G_{12}{}^2]$,
C_{6v}	$6mm$	$\mathbf{D}_3\mathbf{S}_1$, $\mathbf{R}_1$	$G_{31}{}^2(G_{31}{}^2 - 3G_{23}{}^2)^2$, $G_{11}G_{23}{}^2 + G_{22}G_{31}{}^2$
D_{6h}	$6/mmm$	$\mathbf{D}_3\mathbf{S}_1$, $\mathbf{R}_1$, $\mathbf{C}$	$- 2G_{23}G_{31}G_{12}$, $G_{11}(G_{31}{}^4 + 3G_{23}{}^4) +$
			$2G_{22}G_{31}{}^2(G_{31}{}^2 + 3G_{23}{}^2) - 8G_{12}G_{23}G_{31}{}^3$,
			$G_{31}{}^2[(G_{11} + G_{22})^2 - 4(G_{22}{}^2 - G_{12}{}^2)]$
			$- 2G_{11}[(G_{11} + 3G_{22})(G_{31}{}^2 + G_{23}{}^2)$
			$- 4G_{23}G_{31}G_{12}]$
Cubic system			
T	23	$\mathbf{D}_1$, $\mathbf{M}_1$	ΣG_{11}, $\Sigma G_{22}G_{33}$, $\Sigma G_{23}{}^2$, $G_{11}G_{22}G_{33}$,
T_h	$m3$	$\mathbf{C}$, $\mathbf{D}_1$, $\mathbf{M}_1$	$G_{23}G_{31}G_{12}$, $\Sigma G_{31}{}^2G_{12}{}^2$, $\Sigma G_{22}G_{12}{}^2$,
			$\Sigma G_{33}G_{31}{}^2$, $\Sigma G_{33}G_{22}{}^2$, $\Sigma G_{12}{}^2G_{31}{}^4$,
			$\Sigma G_{11}G_{31}{}^2G_{12}{}^2$, $\Sigma G_{23}{}^2G_{22}G_{33}$,
			$\Sigma G_{23}{}^2G_{33}G_{11}$, $\Sigma G_{23}{}^2G_{31}{}^2G_{22}$
T_d	$\overline{4}3m$	$\mathbf{D}_1$, $\mathbf{M}_1$, $\mathbf{T}_1$	ΣG_{11}, $\Sigma G_{22}G_{33}$, $\Sigma G_{23}{}^2$, $G_{11}G_{22}G_{33}$,
0	432	$\mathbf{R}_3\mathbf{T}_1$, $\mathbf{M}_2$	$G_{23}G_{31}G_{12}$, $\Sigma G_{31}{}^2G_{12}{}^2$, $\Sigma G_{33}G_{12}{}^2$,
0_h	$m3m$	$\mathbf{R}_3\mathbf{T}_1$, $\mathbf{M}_2$, $\mathbf{C}$	$\Sigma G_{11}G_{31}{}^2G_{12}{}^2$, $\Sigma G_{23}{}^2G_{22}G_{33}$

tion of the symmetry for all 32 classes are the following transformations and their products:

$$\mathbf{I} = (1, 1, 1), \quad \mathbf{C} = (-1, -1, -1),$$

$$\mathbf{R}_1 = (-1, 1, 1), \quad \mathbf{R}_2 = (1, -1, 1), \quad \mathbf{R}_3 = (1, 1, -1),$$

$$\mathbf{D}_1 = (1, -1, -1), \quad \mathbf{D}_2 = (-1, 1, -1), \quad \mathbf{D}_3 = (-1, -1, 1),$$

$$\mathbf{T}_1 = \begin{Vmatrix} 1 & 0 & 0 \\ 0 & 0 & 1 \\ 0 & 1 & 0 \end{Vmatrix}, \quad \mathbf{T}_2 = \begin{Vmatrix} 0 & 0 & 1 \\ 0 & 1 & 0 \\ 1 & 0 & 0 \end{Vmatrix}, \quad \mathbf{T}_3 = \begin{Vmatrix} 0 & 1 & 0 \\ 1 & 0 & 0 \\ 0 & 0 & 1 \end{Vmatrix},$$

$$\mathbf{M}_1 = \begin{Vmatrix} 0 & 1 & 0 \\ 0 & 0 & 1 \\ 1 & 0 & 0 \end{Vmatrix}, \quad \mathbf{M}_2 = \begin{Vmatrix} 0 & 0 & 1 \\ 1 & 0 & 0 \\ 0 & 1 & 0 \end{Vmatrix},$$

$$\mathbf{S}_1 = \begin{Vmatrix} -1/2 & \sqrt{3}/2 & 0 \\ -\sqrt{3}/2 & -1/2 & 0 \\ 0 & 0 & 1 \end{Vmatrix}, \quad \mathbf{S}_2 = \begin{Vmatrix} -1/2 & -\sqrt{3}/2 & 0 \\ \sqrt{3}/2 & -1/2 & 0 \\ 0 & 0 & 1 \end{Vmatrix},$$

where the notation

$$\begin{Vmatrix} a & 0 & 0 \\ 0 & b & 0 \\ 0 & 0 & c \end{Vmatrix} = (a, b, c)$$

is used. We note that $\mathbf{I}$ is the identity transformation; $\mathbf{C}$ is the central inversion transformation; $\mathbf{R}_1$, $\mathbf{R}_2$, $\mathbf{R}_3$ are reflections in the x_2x_3, x_3x_1, and x_1x_2 planes, respectively; $\mathbf{D}_1$, $\mathbf{D}_2$, $\mathbf{D}_3$ are rotations through 180° about the x_1, x_2, x_3 axes, respectively; $\mathbf{T}_1$ is a rotation through 90° about the x_1 axis followed by a reflection in the x_3x_1 plane, with $\mathbf{T}_2$ and $\mathbf{T}_3$ analogously defined; $\mathbf{M}_1$ and $\mathbf{M}_2$ are rotations through 120° and $-120°$, respectively, about an axis making equal acute angles with the axes x_1, x_2, x_3; $\mathbf{S}_1$ and $\mathbf{S}_2$ are rotations through 120° and $-120°$, respectively, about the x_3 axis.

In Table I, we give the generating transformations[20] for each of the 32 crystallographic point groups, together with the elements of an integrity basis for a symmetric tensor with components G_{AB} in the reference system x for each of these groups.

The case of transverse isotropy[21] has been discussed by Ericksen and Rivlin (1954). An irreducible integrity basis in this case consists of five

[20] The transformations of the group are the generating transformations and all products that can be formed from them.

[21] A material is said to possess transverse isotropy if it has a single axis of rotational symmetry and any plane containing this axis is a plane of reflection symmetry.

elements, which, referred to a rectangular cartesian coordinate system x, with the x_3 axis normal to the plane of isotropy, are

$$I_1, I_2, I_3, G_{33}, G_{31}{}^2 + G_{23}{}^2, \tag{18.8}$$

where I_1, I_2, I_3 are given by (18.1), and the G's are components of the Cauchy-Green strain tensor.

XIX. CANONICAL FORMS FOR CONSTITUTIVE EQUATIONS OF THE DIFFERENTIAL TYPE

For the remaining cases discussed in Sections XVI and XVII, the constitutive equation was derived in the form of the dependence of the Piola stress on the kinematic variables. The restrictions imposed by material symmetry on the form of this second-order symmetric tensor function, or functional, of the kinematic variables were obtained in implicit form. This relation, which in each case takes the form of a second-order tensor equation, may be converted into a scalar relation in a manner that we illustrate in the case of the constitutive equation of the differential type [Eq. (17.4)]. Let Ψ_{AB}^* and Ψ_{AB} be the components in the equivalent coordinate systems x and $\bar{x}$, respectively, of an arbitrary symmetric second-order tensor. We then have

$$\Psi_{AB} = S_{KA} S_{LB} \Psi_{KL}^*. \tag{19.1}$$

Multiplying (17.4) throughout by Ψ_{AB}^* and employing (19.1), we obtain

$$\Psi_{AB}^* F_{AB}(\overset{(n)}{\bar{G}_{PQ}^*}) = \Psi_{AB} F_{AB}(\overset{(n)}{G_{PQ}}) = F \text{ (say)}, \tag{19.2}$$

where $\overset{(n)}{\bar{G}_{PQ}^*}$ and $\overset{(n)}{G_{PQ}}$ are related by (17.1).

This equation expresses the fact that F is a scalar invariant, under the group $\mathbf{S}$ describing the material symmetry, of the symmetric second-order tensors Ψ_{PQ} and $\overset{(n)}{G_{PQ}}$ ($n = 0, 1, 2, \ldots$). Let $J_1, J_2, \ldots, J_\alpha$ be the elements[22] of an irreducible integrity basis, under the group $\mathbf{S}$, for the tensors Ψ_{PQ} and $\overset{(n)}{G_{PQ}}$ ($n = 0, 1, 2, \ldots$), which are independent of the tensor Ψ_{PQ}. Let $K_1, \ldots, K_\nu$ be the elements of this integrity basis which are linear in Ψ_{PQ}. Then, since F is linear in the tensor Ψ_{AB}, it

---

[22] $J_1, \ldots, J_\alpha$ are, of course, the elements of an irreducible integrity basis, under $\mathbf{S}$, for the tensors $\overset{(n)}{G_{PQ}}$ ($n = 0, 1, 2, \ldots$).

must be expressible in the form[23]

$$F = \sum_{\beta=1}^{\nu} \chi_\beta K_\beta, \tag{19.3}$$

where the χ's are functions of $J_1,\ldots,J_\alpha$. We note that

$$P_{AB} = F_{AB}(\overset{(n)}{G}_{PQ}) = \frac{1}{2} \sum_{\beta=1}^{\nu} \chi_\beta \left(\frac{\partial K_\beta}{\partial \Psi_{AB}} + \frac{\partial K_\beta}{\Psi_{BA}} \right). \tag{19.4}$$

In order to proceed further, we need to know the elements $J_1,\ldots,J_\alpha$ and $K_1,\ldots,K_\nu$ of an irreducible integrity basis for an arbitrary number of symmetric second-order tensors under the group $\mathbf{s}$. Such an integrity basis has been obtained by Rivlin and Ericksen (1955), Rivlin (1955), Spencer and Rivlin (1959a, 1959b, 1960), and Spencer (1961)[24] for the case when $\mathbf{s}$ is the full, or proper, orthogonal group and by Adkins (1958b, 1960a, 1960b) when it is the transverse isotropy group.

For the full orthogonal group or any subgroup of it, an irreducible integrity basis for an arbitrary number of symmetric second-order tensors is obtained from a table of typical invariants for symmetric second-order tensors and the group. The table of typical invariants is a table of invariants under the group of one, two, $\ldots$, N tensors, where N depends on the group, from which an irreducible integrity basis for an arbitrary number M of symmetric second-order tensors can be obtained in the following way. For the elements in the table involving one tensor, substitute each of the M tensors in turn; for the elements involving two tensors, substitute in turn each pair that can be selected from the M tensors; for the elements involving three tensors, substitute in turn each set of three tensors that can be selected from the M tensors, and so on. Finally, for the elements involving N tensors, substitute in turn each set of N tensors that can be selected from the M tensors.

In the case of the full orthogonal group, $N = 6$, and the table of typical invariants is given in Table II.

From Table II, a canonical form for the constitutive equation (17.2) of the differential type for the Piola stress can be obtained which expresses explicitly the restrictions implied by isotropy. The terms $\partial K_\beta/\partial \Psi_{AB}$

---

[23] This is evident in the case when F_{AB} is a polynomial in its arguments and then the χ's are polynomials in $J_1,\ldots,J_\alpha$. That the result is true when F_{AB} is a single-valued function of its argument has been proved by Wineman and Pipkin (1963).

[24] The original papers in which this was done were somewhat discursive and contain much extraneous matter unnecessary for the derivation of the final result. A recent paper by Rivlin and Smith (1966) obtained the final result without introducing this irrelevant material. That the integrity basis derived is in fact irreducible was shown by Smith (1960).

TABLE II

<small>Table   of   Typical   Invariants   for   Symmetric   Second-Order
Tensors   under   Orthogonal   Group</small>

1. tr a, tr a², tr a³;
2. tr ab, tr ab², tr a²b, tr a²b²;
3. tr abc, tr abc², tr bca², tr cab²;
4. tr ab²c², tr bc²a², tr ca²b²;
5. tr abcd, tr abdc;
6. tr abcd², tr acbd², tr dabc², tr dbac²;
7. tr cdab², tr cadb², tr bcda², tr bdca²;
8. tr abc²d², tr acb²d², tr adb²c²;
9. tr bca²d², tr bda²c², tr cda²b²;
10. tr bacda², tr cbdab², tr dcabc², tr adbcd²;
11. tr abcde, tr abdec, tr abecd;
12. tr acdbe, tr acbed, tr adbce;
13. tr abcde², tr abdce², tr adcbe², tr bacde², and invariants obtained
    from these by cyclically permuting abcde;
14. tr acfebd, tr adcbfe, tr adcfbe;
15. tr adfbce, tr adfcbe, tr aebdcf;
16. tr aecbdf, tr aecdbf, tr aedbcf;
17. tr aedcbf.

TABLE III

1. I, b, b²;
2. bc, bc², b²c, b²c²;
3. bcd, bdc;
4. bcd², b²cd, bc²d;
5. cbd², db²c, c²db;
6. bc²d², cb²d², db²c²;
7. dbcd², b²cbd, bc²dc;
8. bcde, bdec, becd, cdbe, cbed, dbce;
9. bcde², b²cde, bc²de, bcd²e;
10. bdce², eb²cd, c²deb, cbd²e;
11. dcbe², edb²c, ec²db, d²ecb;
12. cde²b, b²dce, bc²ed, ebcd²;
13. cfebd, dcbfe, dcfbe;
14. dfbce, dfcbe, ebdcf;
15. ecbdf, ecdbf, edbcf;
16. edcbf.

($\beta = 1, \ldots, \nu$) in Eq. (19.4) can, in this case, be obtained from Table III,
which is derived from Table II in the following manner.   In Table II, we
consider only those terms that are linear in **a** and substitute **Ψ** for **a** in
each of these.   We differentiate[25] each of these terms with respect to **Ψ**

[25] By $\partial(\text{tr } \psi \mathbf{II})/\partial \psi$, where **II** is a product of matrices other than ψ, we mean
$\|\partial(\psi_{MN}\Pi_{MN})/\partial\psi_{AB}\| = \|\Pi_{AB}\|$.

and thus obtain Table III. From Table III, the terms $\partial K_\beta / \partial \Psi_{AB}$ in (19.4) can be obtained in the following way. In line 1, we replace **b** by each of the matrices $\overset{(n)}{\mathbf{G}}$ in turn; in line 2, we replace the pair of matrices **b**, **c** in turn by each pair of different matrices that can be selected from $\overset{(n)}{\mathbf{G}}$ ($n = 0, 1, \ldots$), and so on; finally, in lines 13–16, we replace **b**, **c**, **d**, **e**, **f** by each set of five different matrices that can be selected from $\overset{(n)}{\mathbf{G}}$ ($n = 0, 1, \ldots$). Since $\partial K_\beta / \partial \Psi_{BA}$ is the transpose of $\partial K_\beta / \partial \Psi_{AB}$, we obtain $\partial K_\beta / \partial \Psi_{BA}$ from $\partial K_\beta / \partial \Psi_{AB}$ by writing the factors in the latter matrix product in reversed order.

We have already remarked that the χ's in (19.4) are functions of the elements of an irreducible integrity basis for the symmetric tensors $\overset{(n)}{\mathbf{G}}$ ($n = 0, 1, \ldots$) under the symmetry group of the material. For isotropic materials, such an irreducible integrity basis can be obtained from Table II in the following manner. We substitute for **a** in line 1 each of the matrices $\overset{(n)}{\mathbf{G}}$ in turn; we substitute for **a** and **b** in line 2, in turn, each pair of different matrices that can be selected from the matrices $\overset{(n)}{\mathbf{G}}$; we substitute for **a**, **b**, and **c** in lines 3 and 4, in turn, each selection of three different matrices that can be made from the matrices $\overset{(n)}{\mathbf{G}}$; and so on; finally, we substitute for **a**, **b**, ..., **f** in lines 14–17, in turn, each selection of six different matrices that can be made from the matrices $\overset{(n)}{\mathbf{G}}$. The set of traces of matrix products so obtained is an irreducible integrity basis for the tensors $\overset{(n)}{\mathbf{G}}$ ($n = 0, 1, \ldots$) under the orthogonal group.

Using the formula (3.28), we can obtain the corresponding expression for the Cauchy stress matrix $\boldsymbol{\sigma}(= \|\sigma_{ij}\|)$. We have, from (3.28) and (19.4),

$$\sigma_{ij} = \frac{1}{|\partial x / \partial X|} \, x_{i,A} x_{j,B} \left\{ \sum_{\beta=1}^{\nu} \frac{1}{2} \chi_\beta \left(\frac{\partial K_\beta}{\partial \psi_{AB}} + \frac{\partial K_\beta}{\partial \psi_{BA}} \right) \right\}. \qquad (19.5)$$

It is convenient for our purpose to rewrite the equations in matrix notation. We write

$$\mathbf{d} = \|d_{iA}\| = \|x_{i,A}\|, \qquad |\partial x / \partial X| = \det \mathbf{d}, \qquad \boldsymbol{\kappa}_\beta = \|\partial K_\beta / \partial \psi_{AB}\|. \qquad (19.6)$$

Equation (19.5) may then be rewritten as

$$\boldsymbol{\sigma} = \frac{1}{\det \mathbf{d}} \frac{1}{2} \sum_{\beta=1}^{\nu} \chi_\beta \mathbf{d} (\boldsymbol{\kappa}_\beta + \boldsymbol{\kappa}_\beta{}^t) \mathbf{d}^t, \qquad (19.7)$$

where $\mathbf{d}^t$ and $\boldsymbol{\kappa}_\beta{}^t$ denote the transposes of $\mathbf{d}$ and $\boldsymbol{\kappa}_\beta$, respectively.

We note that, for an isotropic material, each of the terms κ_β may be written in the form

$$\kappa_\beta = \overset{(n_1)}{\mathbf{G}}\ \overset{(n_2)}{\mathbf{G}}\ \ldots\ \overset{(n_\alpha)}{\mathbf{G}} \qquad (n = 0, 1, 2,\ldots \text{ including repetitions}).\qquad (19.8)$$

Using the notation (19.6), Eq. (10.4) can be rewritten as

$$\overset{(n)}{\mathbf{G}} = 2\mathbf{d}^t\mathbf{A}_n\mathbf{d}, \qquad (19.9)$$

where

$$\mathbf{A}_n = \|A_{ij}^{(n)}\|. \qquad (19.10)$$

Using (19.9) and the notation [cf. Eq. (18.5)]

$$\mathbf{g} = \|g_{ij}\| = \|x_{i,A}x_{j,A}\| = \mathbf{d}\mathbf{d}^t, \qquad (19.11)$$

we obtain from (19.8)

$$\begin{aligned}\mathbf{d}\kappa_\beta\mathbf{d}^t &= 2^\alpha\mathbf{d}(\mathbf{d}^t\mathbf{A}_{n_1}\mathbf{d})(\mathbf{d}^t\mathbf{A}_{n_2}\mathbf{d}) \ldots (\mathbf{d}^t\mathbf{A}_{n_\alpha}\mathbf{d})\mathbf{d}^t \\ &= 2^\alpha\mathbf{g}\mathbf{A}_{n_1}\mathbf{g}\mathbf{A}_{n_2} \ldots \mathbf{g}\mathbf{A}_{n_\alpha}\mathbf{g}. \end{aligned} \qquad (19.12)$$

Since the χ's in (19.5) are functions of traces of products of the matrices $\overset{(n)}{\mathbf{G}}$ $(n = 0, 1, \ldots)$, it follows from similar considerations that they are functions of traces of products of the matrices $\mathbf{g}$, $\mathbf{A}_n$ $(n = 1, 2,\ldots)$.[26]

The expression for $\mathbf{\delta}$ obtained from (19.7) by using these results is a symmetric tensor function of $\mathbf{g}$ and $\mathbf{A}^{(n)}$ $(n = 1, 2,\ldots)$, $\|F_{ij}(g_{pq}, A_{pq}^{(n)})\|$, say, which satisfies the relation

$$F_{ij}(S_{pk}S_{ql}g_{kl}, S_{pk}S_{ql}A_{kl}^{(n)}) = S_{im}S_{jn}F_{mn}(g_{pq}, A_{pq}^{(n)}) \qquad (19.13)$$

for all transformations $\|S_{ij}\|$ of the full orthogonal group. By analogy with the discussion of Section XIX for the Piola stress, it follows that it may be expressed in canonical form[27] using Tables II and III; thus,

$$\mathbf{\delta} = \sum_\beta \chi_\beta(\kappa_\beta + \kappa_\beta^t), \qquad (19.14)$$

where the matrices κ_β are obtained from Table III in the following manner. We substitute for b in line 1 each of the matrices $\mathbf{g}$, $\mathbf{A}^{(n)}$ $(n = 1, 2,\ldots)$ in turn; next we substitute for b and c in line 2 each pair of different matrices that can be selected from $\mathbf{g}$, $\mathbf{A}^{(n)}$ $(n = 1, 2,\ldots)$; and so on. Finally, we substitute for b, c, d, e, f in lines 13–16 each selection of five different matrices that can be made from $\mathbf{g}$, $\mathbf{A}^{(n)}$ $(n =$

[26] We bear in mind that $2\mathbf{A}_0 = \mathbf{I}$, the unit matrix [cf. Eq. (10.5)].

[27] That it is not already in this form is evident, since the expression for $\mathbf{d}\kappa_\beta\,\mathbf{d}^\tau$ given in (19.12) is of higher degree in the matrices $\mathbf{g}$, $\mathbf{A}^{(n)}$ $(n = 1, 2, \ldots)$ than is the expression (19.8) for κ_β, from which it was derived, in $\overset{(n)}{\mathbf{G}}$ $(n = 0, 1, \ldots)$.

$1, 2, \ldots$). The scalars χ_β are functions of the elements of an irreducible integrity basis, under the orthogonal group, for $\mathbf{g}$ and $\mathbf{A}^{(n)}$ $(n = 1, 2, \ldots)$. These are obtained from Table II in an analogous manner.

XX. CANONICAL FORMS FOR CONSTITUTIVE EQUATIONS IN MATERIALS WITH MEMORY

Starting with the constitutive equation (16.1) for a material with memory, we may proceed in a manner similar to that employed in discussing the constitutive equation of the differential type. We have seen that, if $\mathbf{s}$ is the symmetry group for the material, then the relation (16.3), viz.

$$\mathfrak{F}_{AB}[\overset{t}{\underset{\tau=-\infty}{S_{PK}S_{QL}G_{KL}(\tau)}}, t] = S_{AM}S_{BN}\mathfrak{F}_{MN}[\overset{t}{\underset{\tau=-\infty}{G_{PQ}(\tau)}}, t], \qquad (20.1)$$

is valid for all transformations S_{AB} of the group $\mathbf{s}$. We again convert the tensor relation into a scalar relation by introducing the arbitrary symmetric tensor ψ_{AB} and obtain, from (20.1) and (19.1), the relation

$$\psi_{AB}^* \mathfrak{F}_{AB}[\overset{t}{\underset{\tau=-\infty}{\bar{G}_{PQ}^*(\tau)}}] = \psi_{AB}\mathfrak{F}_{AB}[\overset{t}{\underset{\tau=-\infty}{G_{PQ}(\tau)}}] = \mathfrak{F} \text{ (say)}, \qquad (20.2)$$

where

$$\bar{G}_{PQ}^*(\tau) = S_{PM}S_{QN}G_{MN}(\tau). \qquad (20.3)$$

We then have

$$P_{AB} = \mathfrak{F}_{AB}[\overset{t}{\underset{\tau=-\infty}{G_{PQ}(\tau)}}] = \frac{1}{2}\left(\frac{\partial \mathfrak{F}}{\partial \psi_{AB}} + \frac{\partial \mathfrak{F}}{\partial \psi_{BA}}\right). \qquad (20.4)$$

We note that Eq. (20.2) expresses the fact that $\mathfrak{F}$ is an invariant scalar functional, linear in ψ_{PQ}, of the symmetric tensor ψ_{PQ} and the symmetric tensor function $G_{PQ}(\tau)$, under the group $\mathbf{s}$.

Now, it can be shown that any such functional may be expressed as a linear functional in the multilinear elements of an irreducible integrity basis for the $N + 1$ tensors ψ_{PQ}, $G_{PQ}(\tau_1), \ldots, G_{PQ}(\tau_N)$, under the group $\mathbf{s}$, where $N + 1$ is the maximum number of tensors which enters into the table of typical invariants for the irreducible integrity basis under $\mathbf{s}$ of an arbitrary number of symmetric second-order tensors and as a functional of the multilinear elements of an irreducible integrity basis for $G_{PQ}(\tau_1), \ldots, G_{PQ}(\tau_{N+1})$. This was shown by Green and Rivlin (1957) subject to certain continuity restrictions on the invariant functional and by Wineman and Pipkin (1964) without any such restriction.

In the case when the material is isotropic so that the appropriate symmetry group is the full (or proper) orthogonal group, it can be seen from Tables II and III that

$$\mathfrak{F} = \mathop{\mathfrak{F}}_{\tau's = -\infty}^{t}[\mathrm{tr}\ \mathbf{G}(\tau_1)\ \cdots\ \mathbf{G}(\tau_{M+1}),\qquad \mathrm{tr}\ \psi\mathbf{G}(\tau_1)\ \cdots\ \mathbf{G}(\tau_M)]$$
$$(M = 0,.\ .\ .\ ,5).\quad (20.5)$$

From (20.4) and (20.5), it follows that[28]

$$\mathbf{F} = \|\mathfrak{F}_{AB}\| = \mathop{\mathfrak{F}}_{\tau's = -\infty}^{t}[\mathrm{tr}\ \mathbf{G}(\tau_1)\ \cdots\ \mathbf{G}(\tau_{M+1}),\qquad \mathbf{G}(\tau_1)\ \cdots\ \mathbf{G}(\tau_M)]$$
$$(M = 0,.\ .\ .\ ,5).\quad (20.6)$$

In (20.6), $\mathbf{F}$ is a linear tensor functional of the six arguments $\mathbf{G}(\tau_1)\ \cdots\ \mathbf{G}(\tau_M)$ $(M = 0,.\ .\ .\ ,5)$[29] and a scalar functional of the six arguments $\mathrm{tr}\ \mathbf{G}(\tau_1)\ \cdots\ \mathbf{G}(\tau_{M+1})$.

XXI. CANONICAL FORMS FOR THE CONSTITUTIVE EQUATIONS OF FLUIDS

For the fluids with memory discussed in Section XI, we may start with the constitutive equation (11.2) for the Cauchy stress, viz.,

$$\sigma_{ij} = a_{iM}a_{jN}\mathop{\mathfrak{F}}_{\tau = -\infty}^{t}{}_{MN}[G_{kl}^{*}(\tau)a_{kP}a_{lQ},\ t],\qquad (21.1)$$

where a_{iK} is defined by

$$a_{iK} = h_{KP}(\mathbf{G})x_{i,P}\qquad (21.2)$$
$$h_{KP}h_{LQ}G_{PQ} = \delta_{KL},\qquad |h_{KP}x_{i,P}| = 1$$

and $G_{kl}{}^{*}(\tau)$ is defined by

$$G_{kl}^{*}(\tau) = x_{i,k}(\tau)x_{i,l}(\tau).\qquad (21.3)$$

We note that, so far, a_{iP} has been defined in a specific rectangular cartesian coordinate system x. We now assume that it transforms as a second-order tensor between fixed rectangular cartesian coordinate systems. It follows that $a_{kP}a_{lQ}G_{kl}^{*}(\tau)$ transforms as a second-order symmetric tensor between fixed rectangular cartesian coordinate systems.

[28] In deriving (20.6), we have used the fact that, if $\mathfrak{L}[\mathbf{G}(\tau_1)\ \cdots\ \mathbf{G}(\tau_M) + \mathbf{G}(\tau_M)\ \cdots\ \mathbf{G}(\tau_1)]$ is a linear tensor functional of the indicated tensor arguments, it is equal to $2\mathfrak{L}[\mathbf{G}(\tau_1)\ \cdots\ \mathbf{G}(\tau_M)]$.

[29] This argument for $M = 0$ is simply the unit matrix.

We now define a second-order symmetric tensor with components P'_{MN} in the rectangular cartesian coordinate system x by

$$P'_{MN} = a_{iM}a_{jN}\sigma_{ij}. \qquad (21.4)$$

We note that P'_{MN} transforms as a second-order symmetric tensor. From (21.1), (21.2), and (21.4), we have

$$P'_{MN} = \mathfrak{F}_{MN}[\underset{\tau=-\infty}{\overset{t}{G^*_{kl}(\tau)}}a_{kP}a_{lQ}, t]. \qquad (21.5)$$

By an argument similar to that leading to Eq. (20.1) in the general case of materials with memory, we see that, if in the reference state at time t_0 the material has symmetry described by the group $\mathbf{s}$, the functionals $\mathfrak{F}_{MN}$ in (21.5) must satisfy the relation

$$\mathfrak{F}_{MN}[\underset{\tau=-\infty}{\overset{t}{S_{PK}S_{QL}G^*_{kl}(\tau)}}a_{kK}a_{lL}, t] = S_{MA}S_{NB}\mathfrak{F}_{AB}[\underset{\tau=-\infty}{\overset{t}{G^*_{kl}(\tau)}}a_{kP}a_{lQ}, t]. \qquad (21.6)$$

Comparing (21.6) with (20.1), it is evident that a constitutive equation for P'_{MN}, which embodies the symmetry with respect to the group $\mathbf{s}$, may be obtained from that for P_{AB} simply by substituting $a_{kP}a_{lQ}G^*_{kl}(\tau)$ for $G_{PQ}(\tau)$, i.e., by substituting $\mathbf{a}^t\mathbf{G}^*(\tau)\mathbf{a}$ for $\mathbf{G}(\tau)$, where $\mathbf{a} = \|a_{lQ}\|$ and $\mathbf{a}^t$ denotes the transpose of $\mathbf{a}$. In the case when the fluid is isotropic at time t_0, we make this substitution in (20.6) and obtain[30]

$$\|P_{MN}'\| = \mathfrak{F} = \underset{\tau's=-\infty}{\overset{t}{\mathfrak{F}}}[\operatorname{tr}\mathbf{G}^*(\tau_1) \cdots \mathbf{G}^*(\tau_{M+1}), \mathbf{a}^t\mathbf{G}^*(\tau_1) \cdots \mathbf{G}^*(\tau_M)\mathbf{a}],$$
$$(M = 0, \ldots, 5). \qquad (21.7)$$

From (21.7) and (21.4), we obtain, bearing in mind that $\mathfrak{F}$ is a linear functional in the arguments $\mathbf{a}^t\mathbf{G}^*(\tau_1) \cdots \mathbf{G}^*(\tau_M)\mathbf{a}$,

$$\boldsymbol{\sigma} = \|\sigma_{ij}\| = \mathbf{a}\mathfrak{F}\mathbf{a}^t$$
$$= \underset{\tau's=-\infty}{\overset{t}{\mathfrak{F}}}[\operatorname{tr}\mathbf{G}^*(\tau_1) \cdots \mathbf{G}^*(\tau_{M+1}), \mathbf{G}^*(\tau_1) \cdots \mathbf{G}^*(\tau_M)]$$
$$(M = 0, \ldots, 5). \qquad (21.8)$$

In the case of the constitutive equation of the differential type for a fluid, discussed in Section XI, we have [cf. Eq. (11.5)]

$$\sigma_{ij} = a_{iM}a_{jN}F_{MN}(a_{kP}a_{lQ}A_{Kl}^{(n)}), \qquad n = 1, 2, \ldots, \qquad (21.9)$$

where a_{iK} is defined by Eqs. (21.2). We assume, as in the case of fluids with memory, that a_{iP} transforms as a second-order symmetric tensor between fixed rectangular cartesian coordinate systems. It follows that

[30] We note from (21.2) that $\mathbf{aa}^t = \mathbf{I}$.

$a_{kP}a_{lQ}A_{Kl}^{(n)}$ transforms as a second-order symmetric tensor between fixed rectangular cartesian coordinate systems. We again define P_{MN}' by (21.4) and obtain in place of (21.6) the equation

$$F_{MN}(S_{PK}S_{QL}a_{kK}a_{lL}A_{Kl}^{(n)}, t)$$
$$= S_{MA}S_{NB}F_{AB}(a_{kP}a_{lQ}A_{Kl}^{(n)}, t) \qquad (n = 1, 2, \ldots) \quad (21.10)$$

Comparing Eq. (21.10) with Eq. (17.4), it is evident that a constitutive equation for P_{AB}', which embodies the restrictions imposed by symmetry with respect to the group **s**, may be obtained from that for the general constitutive equation of the differential type simply by substituting $a_{kP}a_{lQ}A_{Kl}^{(n)}$ for $\overset{(n-1)}{G}_{PQ}$.

In the case when the material is isotropic, we saw in Section XIX that the general constitutive equation of the differential type may be written in the form (19.4), which, with the notation (19.6), may be rewritten as

$$\mathbf{P} = \|P_{AB}\| = \tfrac{1}{2} \sum_{\beta=1}^{\nu} \chi_\beta(\varkappa_\beta + \varkappa_\beta^t), \qquad (21.11)$$

where the matrices $\varkappa_\beta$ are of the form (19.8). We introduce the notation

$$\mathbf{a} = \|a_{kP}\|, \qquad \mathbf{A}^{(n)} = \|A_{kl}^{(n)}\|, \qquad (21.12)$$

so that

$$\mathbf{a}^t\mathbf{A}^{(n)}\mathbf{a} = \|a_{kP}a_{lQ}A_{kl}^{(n)}\|, \qquad (21.13)$$

and we substitute $\mathbf{a}^t\mathbf{A}^{(n)}\mathbf{a}$ for $\overset{(n)}{G}$ in (19.8). We obtain, using the orthogonality condition $\mathbf{aa}^t = \mathbf{I}$,

$$\varkappa_\beta = (\mathbf{a}^t\mathbf{A}^{(n_1)}\mathbf{a})(\mathbf{a}^t\mathbf{A}^{(n_2)}\mathbf{a}) \cdots (\mathbf{a}^t\mathbf{A}^{(n_\alpha)}\mathbf{a})$$
$$= \mathbf{a}^t\mathbf{A}^{(n_1)}\mathbf{A}^{(n_2)} \cdots \mathbf{A}^{(n_\alpha)}\mathbf{a}. \qquad (21.14)$$

We therefore have

$$\mathbf{P}' = \|P_{AB}\| = \tfrac{1}{2}\mathbf{a}^t \left\{ \sum_\beta \chi_\beta(\varkappa_\beta + \varkappa_\beta^t) \right\} \mathbf{a}, \qquad (21.15)$$

where $\varkappa_\beta$ are now expressions obtained from (19.8) by substituting $\mathbf{A}^{(n+1)}$ for $\overset{(n)}{G}$ $(n = 0, 1, \ldots)$. It follows from (21.15) and (21.4) together with the orthogonality condition that

$$\eth = \tfrac{1}{2} \sum_\beta \chi_\beta(\varkappa_\beta + \varkappa_\beta^t). \qquad (21.16)$$

We note that the matrices $\varkappa_\beta$ can be obtained from Table III by making the following substitutions. In line 1, we substitute for **b** each of

the matrices $\mathbf{A}^{(n)}$ ($n = 1, 2, \ldots$) in turn; in line 2, we substitute for **b** and **c** each pair of different matrices that can be selected for $\mathbf{A}^{(n)}$ ($n = 1, 2, \ldots$); and so on. Finally, in lines 13–16, we substitute for **b**, **c**, **d**, **e**, **f** each set of five different matrices that can be selected from $\mathbf{A}^{(n)}$ ($n = 1, 2, \ldots$). It is evident in a similar manner that the χ's in (21.15) are functions of the elements of an irreducible integrity basis for the second-order symmetric tensors $\mathbf{A}^{(n)}$ ($n = 1, 2, \ldots$) under the orthogonal group. They can therefore be obtained from the table of typical invariants (Table II) by making substitutions for **a**, **b**, . . . , **f** from $\mathbf{A}^{(n)}$ ($n = 1, 2, \ldots$).

In this section, we have seen that, if we introduce into either the constitutive equation (11.2) or (11.5) for a fluid the restrictions imposed by isotropy, the resulting constitutive equation does not involve the deformation relative to the initial state in any way. This is not the case if the assumptions of isotropy are introduced into the more general constitutive equations discussed by Green (1964).

Acknowledgments

This paper was written with the support of Contract Nonr 562(40) between the Office of Naval Research, U.S. Navy, and Brown University. I am indebted to Professors A. E. Green and G. F. Smith for valuable discussions.

References

Adkins, J. E. (1956a), *J. Ratl. Mech. Anal.* **5**, 189.
Adkins, J. E. (1956b), *Phil. Trans. Roy. Soc. (London) Ser. A* **249**, 125.
Adkins, J. E. (1958a), *Quart. J. Mech. Appl. Math.* **11**, 88.
Adkins, J. E. (1958b), *Phil. Trans. Roy. Soc. (London) Ser. A* **250**, 519.
Adkins, J. E. (1960a), *Arch. Ratl. Mech. Anal.* **4**, 193.
Adkins, J. E. (1960b), *Arch. Ratl. Mech. Anal.* **5**, 263.
Adkins, J. E. and Rivlin, R. S. (1955), *Phil. Trans. Roy. Soc. (London) Ser. A* **248**, 201.
Chacon, R. V. S. and Rivlin, R. S. (1964), *Z. Angew. Math. Phys.* **15**, 444.
Coleman, B. D. (1964), *Arch. Ratl. Mech. Anal.* **17**, 1.
Coleman, B. D. (1965), *Arch. Ratl. Mach. Anal.* **20**, 41.
Coleman, B. D. and Noll, W. (1961), *Rev. Mod. Phys.* **33**, 239.
Coleman, B. D. and Noll, W. (1963), *Arch. Ratl. Mech. Anal.* **13**, 167.
Ericksen, J. L. (1960a), *Arch. Ratl. Mech. Anal.* **4**, 231.
Ericksen, J. L. (1960b), *Kolloid-Z.* **173**, 117.
Ericksen, J. L. (1960c), *Trans. Soc. Rheol.* **4**, 29.
Ericksen, J. L. (1961), *Trans. Soc. Rheol.* **5**, 23.
Ericksen, J. L. and Rivlin, R. S. (1954), *J. Ratl. Mech. Anal.* **3**, 281.
Green, A. E. (1964), *Proc. Roy. Soc. (London) Ser. A* **279**, 437.
Green, A. E. and Rivlin, R. S. (1957), *Arch. Ratl. Mech. Anal.* **1**, 1.
Green, A. E. and Rivlin, R. S. (1960), *Arch. Ratl. Mech. Anal.* **4**, 387.
Green, A. E. and Rivlin, R. S. (1964a), *Arch. Ratl. Mech. Anal.* **16**, 325.
Green, A. E. and Rivlin, R. S. (1964b), *Arch. Ratl. Mech. Anal.* **17**, 113.

GREEN, A. E. and RIVLIN, R. S. (1964c), *Z. Angew. Math. Phys.* **15,** 290.

GREEN, A. E. and RIVLIN, R. S. (1965), *Proc. Roy. Soc. (London) Ser. A* **284,** 303.

GREEN, A. E., RIVLIN, R. S., and SPENCER, A. J. M. (1959), *Arch. Ratl. Mech. Anal.* **3,** 82.

NOLL, W. (1958), *Arch. Ratl. Mech. Anal.* **2,** 197.

OLDROYD, J. G. (1950), *Proc. Roy. Soc. (London) Ser. A* **200,** 523.

PIPKIN, A. C. and RIVLIN, R. S. (1959), *Arch. Ratl. Mech. Anal.* **4,** 129.

PIPKIN, A. C. and RIVLIN, R. S. (1965), *Z. Angew. Math. Phys.* **16,** 313.

RIVLIN, R. S. (1948), *Phil. Trans. Roy. Soc. (London) Ser. A* **241,** 379.

RIVLIN, R. S. (1955), *J. Ratl. Mech. Anal.* **4,** 681.

RIVLIN, R. S. (1960), *Arch. Ratl. Mech. Anal.* **4,** 262.

RIVLIN, R. S. (1965a), Viscoelastic Fluids, in "Frontiers of Research in Fluid Dynamics," (G. Temple and R. Seeger, eds.).

RIVLIN, R. S. (1965b), *Soc. Ind. Appl. Math. Rev.* **7,** 323.

RIVLIN, R. S. and ERICKSEN, J. L. (1955), *J. Ratl. Mech. Anal.* **4,** 323.

RIVLIN, R. S. and SMITH, G. F. (1966), "Reiner Anniversary Volume." In press.

SMITH, G. F. (1960), *Arch. Ratl. Mech. Anal.* **5,** 382.

SMITH, G. F. (1962), *Arch. Ratl. Mech. Anal.* **10,** 108.

SMITH, G. F. and RIVLIN, R. S. (1958), *Trans. Am. Math. Soc.* **88,** 175.

SPENCER, A. J. M. (1961), *Arch. Ratl. Mech. Anal.* **7,** 64.

SPENCER, A. J. M. and RIVLIN, R. S. (1959a), *Arch. Ratl. Mech. Anal.* **2,** 309.

SPENCER, A. J. M. and RIVLIN, R. S. (1959b), *Arch. Ratl. Mech. Anal.* **2,** 405.

SPENCER, A. J. M. and RIVLIN, R. S. (1960), *Arch. Ratl. Mech. Anal.* **4,** 214.

TRUESDELL, C. A. and TOUPIN, R. (1960), "The Classical Field Theories," vol. III of "Handbuch der Physik." Springer, Berlin.

WINEMAN, A. S. and PIPKIN, A. C. (1963), *Arch. Ratl. Mech. Anal.* **12,** 420.

WINEMAN, A. S. and PIPKIN, A. C. (1964), *Arch. Ratl. Mech. Anal.* **17,** 184.

Stellar Dynamics and Galactic Spirals

C. C. LIN

MASSACHUSETTS INSTITUTE OF TECHNOLOGY
CAMBRIDGE, MASSACHUSETTS

Professor J. M. Burgers initiated the first of a series of symposia on Cosmic Aerodynamics. It therefore befits this occasion to honor him with a discussion of stellar dynamics and galactic structure, since this is a problem combining the dynamics of gas and plasma, the plasma being the stellar system held together by gravitational forces. The frequency of close encounters involving stars, or bound systems of binary stars, is extremely small and can be neglected for the time scale under consideration, which does not exceed 10 billion years.

Since the detailed exposition of the theory has been published elsewhere, the following extended abstract is prepared especially for the proceedings of this symposium.

I. GENERAL BACKGROUND

Galaxies of stars are usually classified in terms of their appearance into elliptical galaxies, normal spirals, barred spirals, and irregular galaxies (Fig. 1). Most galaxies (about 70%) are normal spirals whose side view is a disk with a central bulge (Fig. 2).

The main contents of a galaxy are the stars, the gas, and the associated magnetic field. Components that are less important from a dynamical point of view are cosmic ray particles (including high-energy photons), other electromagnetic radiation of various wavelengths, dust, etc. The basic equations governing these main components are (a) the equations of stellar dynamics, which consist of the collisionless Boltzmann equation and Poisson's equation, with mass density contributed by both the stars and the gas, and (b) the equations of hydromagnetics, including both the gas-dynamical equations and the Maxwell equations. The gas is "infinitely conducting" because of the large scales involved. Thus, the equations governing the magnetic field essentially state that the magnetic flux is frozen into the gas.

The dimensions of a normal spiral galaxy are of the order of 10^4 parsec

Fig. 1. Examples of galaxies.

Fig. 2. Side view of a galaxy.

in radius and 600 parsec in thickness outside of the central bulge and excluding the halo region. Thus, to a first approximation, it may be regarded as an infinitesimally thick disk. [One parsec (1 pc) is approximately 3.24 light years or the distance covered in one million years at the speed of 1 km/sec.]

The stars are in differential rotation about the center of the galaxy. Indeed, for a major part of our own galaxy, the linear speed is nearly constant at 250 km/sec. The period of revolution about the galactic center is about 250 million years for our vicinity.

Besides the circular motion just mentioned, the individual stars have peculiar velocities, like the molecules of a gas. These velocities are, however, only of the order of 10% of the circular velocity.

It is known that the contrast of stellar density between the spiral arms and the interarm regions is small. The contrast in gas density may, however, be as large as 3 or 4. The brilliant young stars are mostly associated with the gas.

It can be shown, by an estimation of the orders of magnitude of the various forces, that the magnetic field might be important for the scale of a spiral arm but is definitely not important for the scale of a whole disk.

II. DENSITY WAVES

The spiral structure in a galaxy appears to be at least quasi-permanent in spite of the differential rotation. This suggests that it is a *pattern* associated with a density wave maintained by gravitational forces. The individual young stars do move out of the gaseous arm in which they were born; but the young stellar arm cannot deviate very much from the gaseous arm, since the angle of inclination is small. If the wave pattern is traveling at 20 km/sec-kpc around the center of our galaxy, the distance between these arms does not exceed 200 pc. The stellar arm is ahead of the gaseous arm.

Although the young stars give the billiant manifestations, the older stars maintain the spiral structure, since the total mass in them is predominant. It should, however, be realized that the oldest stars with the highest dispersion are not effectively participating in the formation of a spiral pattern at (say) 2 kpc spacing. Since their epicyclic motion can cover about this distance, their distribution is consequently smoothed out on such a scale. Only the low-speed stars and the gas are effective.

The linear theory of small disturbances over a symmetric disk can be developed to show the existence of density waves propagating around the galactic center in a spiral form, i.e., to an observer moving in a framework

rotating at the pattern speed, the lines of constant density are given by

$$m(\theta - \theta_0) = \Phi(\varpi) - \Phi(\varpi_0) \tag{1}$$

where (ϖ, θ) are the cylindrical coordinates in the plane of the disk, and m is the number of arms. To give the appearance of a tightly wound spiral, the function $\Phi(\varpi)$ must be of the form of a slowly varying monotone function multiplied by a large parameter. The radial wave number of the spiral pattern is given by $|k(\varpi)|$, where

$$k(\varpi) = \Phi'(\varpi) \tag{2}$$

Trailing waves are given by $k(\varpi) < 0$, if the motion of the stars is counterclockwise. The angle of inclination i is given by

$$(1/m) \tan i = (k\varpi)^{-1} \tag{3}$$

In the mathematical theory, a small parameter ϵ of this order is used for asymptotic integration. It is an asymptotic process based on a rapidly varying phase.

To the order of ϵ^0, the theory yields neutral waves with a wave number $|k|$ given by

$$|k| = \frac{\kappa^2(1 - \nu^2)}{2\pi G[\sigma_0 + \sigma_* \mathfrak{F}_\nu(x)]}, \qquad (1 - \nu^2 > 0). \tag{4}$$

In the foregoing formula, σ_0 is the surface density of the gas, σ_* is that for the stars, and κ is the epicyclic frequency related to the circular velocity $\Omega(\varpi)$ of the stars by

$$\kappa^2 = (2\Omega)^2 \left\{ 1 + \frac{\varpi}{2\Omega} \frac{d\Omega}{d\varpi} \right\}. \tag{5}$$

The parameter ν is defined by

$$\nu = \frac{m(\Omega_p - \Omega)}{\kappa} \tag{6}$$

for a spiral wave of m arms propagating around the center at an angular velocity Ω_p. The numerical values of the "reduction factor," i.e., the function $\mathfrak{F}_\nu(x)$, are shown in Fig. 3, where the variable x is defined by

$$x = \frac{k^2 \langle c_{\tilde\omega}^2 \rangle}{\kappa^2}, \tag{7}$$

which is a measure of the mean square dispersion of the ϖ-component of the stellar peculiar velocity in the basic state. The relative importance of the gas and the stars can be easily seen by taking x to be of the order of 3–5. It is clear that the stars are still more important than the gas if the reduction factor is 10% while the gas density is 2% of the total stellar density.

As pointed out by Lindblad, the values of $\Omega(\varpi)$ and $\kappa(\varpi)$ are usually such that $\Omega - \kappa/2$ is nearly constant for the interior part of our galaxy. This accounts for the fact that two-armed waves extend over a major part of our galaxy [cf. Eq. (4)]. Similar arguments hold for other galaxies. The "3-kpc arm" is possibly a consequence of sharp resonance at that location.

To the order of ϵ, the theory yields a slight amplification of the trailing waves of the order of ϵ, and consequently we may expect a final equilibrium amplitude of the order of $\epsilon^{1/2}$. This amplification depends on quanti-

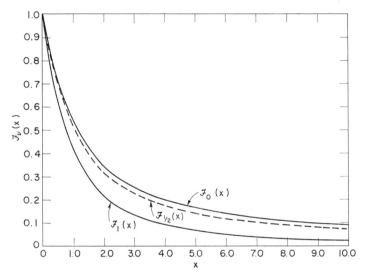

Fig. 3. The reduction factor.

ties of a gradient character, such as

$$\frac{d \log \sigma_0}{d \log \varpi}, \qquad \frac{d \log \langle c_{\tilde{\omega}}^2 \rangle}{d \log \varpi}, \qquad \frac{d \log \Omega}{d \log \varpi}. \qquad (8)$$

The first two items give amplification of trailing waves, whereas the last terms tend to shear down the trailing waves. Clearly, more loosely wound spirals would be more effectively discouraged by differential rotation.

REFERENCES

LIN, C. C. and SHU, F. H. (1964), On the spiral structure of disk galaxies. *Astrophys. J.* **140**, 646–655.

LIN, C. C. and SHU, F. H. (1966), On the spiral structure of disk galaxies II. *Proc. Natl. Acad. Sci. U.S.* **55**, 229–234.

LIN, C. C. (1965), On the mathematical theory of a galaxy of stars. Lecture at SIAM Symposium in New York; also *J. Soc. Ind. Appl. Math.* (in press).

SECTION III

Kinetic Theory and
Flow with Chemical Reaction

edited by

S. I. PAI

Chemical Studies Using Gasdynamic Wave Interactions

E. L. RESLER, JR.

GRADUATE SCHOOL OF
AEROSPACE ENGINEERING
CORNELL UNIVERSITY
ITHACA, NEW YORK

Many chemical rate constants, particularly at high temperatures, have been determined with gasdynamic wave techniques. The shock tube, instrumented to follow the course of a reaction behind the shock wave, has been used extensively. Wave interactions within a shock tube are now well understood and under control, so that more sophisticated wave processes can be used to develop our knowledge of chemical kinetics. Different wave processes that have been successfully used in studies of this type and typical results obtained are discussed. In particular, the development of the single-pulse shock tube is emphasized, and the role of vibration in four-center transition states is discussed as typical of the chemical studies possible with such wave interactions.

I. INTRODUCTION

Chemistry, especially chemical kinetic processes, and aerospace engineering have become intimately linked because of mutual interests. Aerospace engineers have required the chemists' guidance in a whole variety of re-entry problems, whereas the chemist has found many of the simulation techniques used by the engineer capable of extension to the study of purely chemical processes. A summary of the processes useful to both the engineer and the chemist and then those techniques peculiarly of present use to the chemical kineticist along with typical current results are presented below. Such an interplay between various branches of science and engineering is typical of the wide interests of Professor J. M. Burgers, in whose honor this paper is presented.

II. SHOCK TUBE TECHNIQUES USED TO STUDY SIMPLE REACTIONS

The main advantage of a shock tube [1] in chemical kinetic studies is that the wave heating occurs in the bulk of the gas and not via the walls

of the container. Thus, the wall influence is minimized. For most diatomic gases, the processes of vibrational excitation, dissociation, and ionization are separated in energy and time sequence sufficiently that they are easily studied separately. As the internal degrees of freedom of the molecules are excited, energy is acquired at the expense of the translational and rotational degrees of freedom. This energy exchange is conveniently viewed if one arranges to measure the density variations behind a shock wave in a shock tube that is strong enough to initiate the reaction in a gas. Only one parameter need be followed behind the shock wave when there is only a single process occurring, e.g., dissociation.

Figure 1 shows typical shock tube instrumentation to measure density changes. In this case, it is a Mach-Zehnder interferometer. A slit perpendicular to the shock motion and parallel to the shock front is imaged on the drum of a drum camera. The slit contains several interference fringes whose motion is followed on the film as the shock front and chemical relaxation zone moves down the tube. In this arrangement, the compensating beam is also located in the shock tube. If the chemical shock structure extends over a distance less than the distance between the two beams, one views on the film the chemical structure twice. Since density variations due to chemical structure are independent of the position along the tube, whereas unwanted gasdynamic wave interactions are not, a check that a chemical structure is indeed being measured is obtained. In Fig. 2, a typical drum camera record is shown [2]. In this case, the shock wave had a Mach number of about 7 and was proceeding into a quiescent gas mixture of argon and hydrogen. White light fringes were used in this photograph, and the chemical structure is recorded twice. Using the shock conservation laws and the recorded density changes, all the pertinent quantities of interest may be calculated as a function of time from the instant they were "shocked." The results of such a calculation for the data in Fig. 2 are shown in Fig. 3. Note that the degree of dissociation α ranges from 0 to 30%, whereas the temperature changes by about 600°K in a time interval of 5 μsec. Initially, the dissociation must be due to hydrogen molecule or argon atom collisions with hydrogen molecules, and so the initial slopes are used to determine these collision efficiencies. Later in time, the hydrogen atommolecule collisions become important and can therefore be determined. To determine these collision efficiencies, various runs at different concentrations are made, and these efficiencies are finally plotted as rate constants as a function of temperature, as in Fig. 4. Of course, other quantities may be measured behind the shock, such as a species concentration spectroscopically, or the density measured by recording the attenuation of an x-ray or electron beam, etc. Current use of a ruby laser light

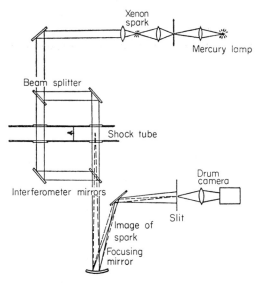

Fig. 1. Experimental apparatus to study chemical structure behind shock waves [2].

Fig. 2. Drum camera interferogram taken of a shock wave in hydrogen.

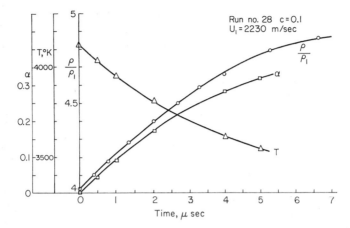

FIG. 3. Analysis of interferogram shown in Fig. 2.

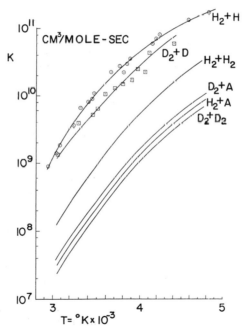

FIG. 4. Rate constants for H_2 and D_2 dissociation reactions.

source in combination with a Kerr cell shutter allows one to photograph the shock front and minimize the blurring due to shock motion. Thus the initial rates can be determined with a high confidence level. This technique, used with the drum camera technique just described, allows simultaneous recording of the same reaction process on two very different time scales.

Although usually dissociation rate data are actually measured, many physical situations of interest require a knowledge of the recombination rates or the inverse process for interpretation, for example, chemical processes in a rocket nozzle or in the wake of a re-entry body. At equilib-

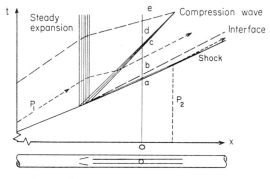

x - t Diagram of flow through airfoils

FIG. 5. Schematic of apparatus to measure association rate constants. Dashed lines labeled P_1, P_2 are particle paths. Airfoils create the steady expansion. The gas in region d–e has been cooled by the expansion wave, and an absorption measurement yielding the molecular concentration can be used to determine the rate constant [3].

rium, the dissociation and association rates are obviously equal, the ratio of the rate constants being the equilibrium constant. It is common practice to find the association rate constant by assuming that the ratio of dissociation to association rate constant is the equilibrium constant, although the Boltzmann distribution may be disturbed. This assumption is not necessarily correct and should be used with caution during very rapid processes involving large energy exchanges.

It is possible to measure the association rate constants directly. One way to accomplish this is to arrange airfoils in the shock tube so that they generate expansion waves that cool the gas rapidly, so that after the cooling the atoms must recombine to adjust to the new state. Such an arrangement is shown schematically in Fig. 5. The cooled gas is directed

into a constant area duct, where measurements can be made to ascertain the chemical composition. This arrangement reminds one of a slotted wind tunnel, and a wave-starting process is to be expected. This wave-starting process is indicated on the $x - t$ wave diagram of Fig. 5. Light absorption measurements [3] to determine oxygen molecule concentrations were used to measure the recombination or association rate directly. Within the range and accuracy of the experiments, the ratio of the individually determined rate constants was found to be the equilibrium constant.

These two experiments are typical of those performed to determine the rates of rather simple reactions. Since in the preceding cases the process was known to be the splitting of molecules into atoms, a few simple measurements were sufficient to determine the rates.

For more complex reactions, one usually requires the various species concentrations as a function of time during the reaction process. If the reaction process is occurring behind a shock wave in a shock tube, it is difficult to make all the simultaneous measurements required. An alternative procedure is to attempt to preserve the species concentrations until analyzed. Thus one must quench the reaction processes or prevent collisions while the gas sample of interest is transported from the reaction zone to the "analyzer." One instrument that has been successfully used for such a purpose is the "time-of-flight" mass spectrometer [4]. This instrument can record a complete mass spectra in 10 μsec. To use this instrument in conjunction with the shock tube, the sample must be transported from behind the shock wave, where a density is typically 10^{19} particles/cm^3, to the mass spectrometer, where the density is necessarily about 10^{11} particles/cm^3 for proper operation. This involves a transition from continuum to free molecular flow and hopefully in so short a time that all reaction processes are quenched.

Consider a shock wave moving out of a tube into an expansion nozzle, as shown in Fig. 6. For temperatures of interest, the shock wave is strong enough that the flow behind the shock wave is supersonic. The expansion wave originating at the edge of the tube sets up a steady flow that expands the flow and alleviates the nozzle starting problem. The nozzle intercepts a bit of the flow, and cooling continues. Note that the cooling rate along the centerline is determined by the tube diameter and then the nozzle diameter. A succession of nozzles gives more rapid cooling than one large nozzle, as the expansion process always has its origin at the boundaries of the flow. The starting problem in the nozzle can be altered so that the chemical integrity of the sample is not compromised by initially having a diaphragm at the nozzle so that a pressure difference can be maintained before the shock arrives.

In Fig. 7 is shown a complete design under test at Cornell University [5]. As far as practicable, the experience gained at Cornell Aeronautical Laboratory [6] in the design of a molecular beam was exploited. Note the cryopumping panels and the sleeve inserted in the shock tube to increase the initial cooling rate and to minimize the amount of gas which need be processed. In contrast with other sampling procedures in current use, this design does not compromise the integrity of the sample by possible

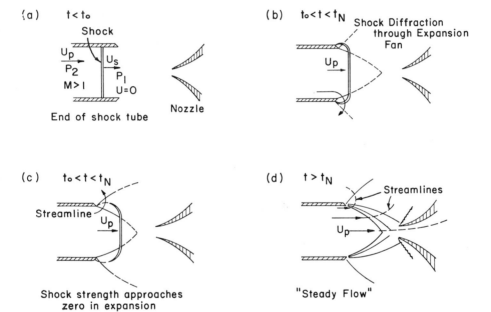

FIG. 6. Nozzle pickup at end of open shock tube. Shock arrives at open end of shock tube at t_0. Flow arrives at inlet of nozzle at t_N.

boundary-layer contamination. With this design, the sample can be removed from the shock tube and injected at the electron beam location of the spectrometer in a time during which the molecules making up the sample will have collided with one another about 1000 times. Since it takes 10 to 10^5 collisions to change the vibrational states of the molecule and more for a reaction involving an atomic rearrangement, it is hoped this cooling is fast enough for most purposes. This technique, although admittedly complex, does permit the detection of short-lived products that may be present in the reaction zone.

E. L. Resler, Jr.

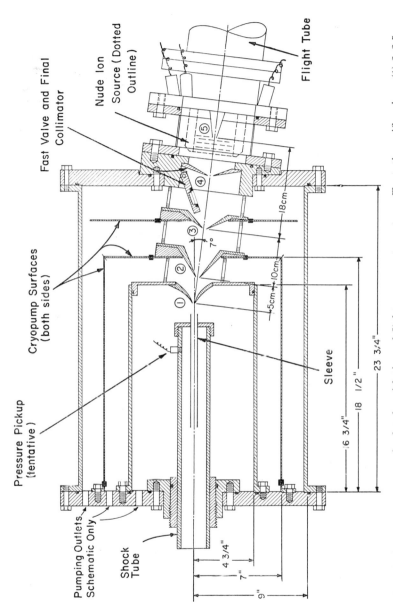

FIG. 7. Apparatus to mate shock tube with time-of-flight mass spectrometer. Tentative orifice sizes: (1) 2–2.5 mm diam, (2) 8 mm diam, (3) 5 mm diam, (4) 10 mm diam, (5) 7 × 5 mm.

III. SINGLE-PULSE SHOCK TUBE

There are a large variety of reactions that can be studied if the sample is subjected to step temperature pulses. If the time spent at an elevated temperature is varied and if the reactions are arrested or quenched after various times of development, then "long-lived" products can be analyzed by very sensitive techniques on a leisurely time scale. Since shock waves heat a gas in approximately five collision times, shock waves are a good approximation to a step temperature pulse. Expansion shocks are not observed in nature; hence, consider the expansion requirement, with reference to Fig. 8. The dwell time at the high temperature T_0 is Δt, and the slope of the cooling curve is K. Reaction rates are exponentially proportional to an activation energy A divided by kT, where k is Boltz-

FIG. 8. Assumed temperature pulse for analysis in text.

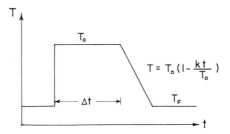

mann's constant. The cooling rate should be great enough that during the cooling the products do not change their concentration appreciably compared with their concentration after the dwell time Δt, or

$$\frac{\int_0^{t(T_F)} \rho e^{-A/kT}\, dt}{\rho_0\, \Delta t\, e^{-A/kT_0}} \ll 1 .$$

For the assumed linear dependence of T on t as assumed in Fig. 8, this implies using a rough approximation to the integral and assuming an isentropic expansion

$$\frac{\int_{T_F}^{T_0} \left(\frac{T}{T_0}\right)^{1/(\gamma-1)} e^{-A/kT}\, \frac{dT}{K}}{\Delta t\, e^{-A/kT_0}} = \frac{kT_0{}^2}{AK} \frac{\int_{T_F}^{T_0} \left(\frac{T}{T_0}\right)^{(2\gamma-1)/(\gamma-1)} d[e^{-A/kT}]}{\Delta t\, e^{-A/kT_0}}$$

$$\approx \left(\frac{\bar{T}}{T_0}\right)^{(2\gamma-1)/(\gamma-1)} \frac{kT_0{}^2}{AK\, \Delta t} \ll 1 ,$$

or, if $\bar{T} = \alpha T_0$, where $\alpha < 1$, then $K \gg (kT_0/A)(T_0/\Delta t)\, \alpha^{(2\gamma-1)/(\gamma-1)}$.

Thus, the apparatus design depends on the anticipated activation energy A. To study a variety of reactions, various cooling rates are required. A typical temperature of interest is in the range 2000°–3000°K, and, for activation energies near 1 V, the required K is 10^5 to 10^6°K/sec.

Among the early workers with a scheme of this sort were a group at the Cornell Aeronautical Laboratory measuring rates of formation of nitric oxide [7]. These workers used a "tailored interface" to increase the dwell time Δt and a large tank to generate an expansion wave at the end of the

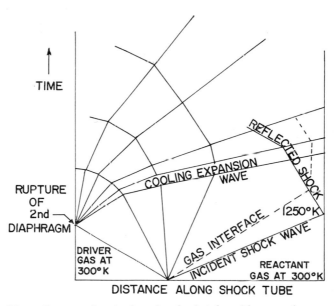

Fig. 9. Wave diagrams for single-pulse shock tube with expansion generated with a large tank at end of tube and "tailored" interface.

shock tube opposite the reflected wave (see Fig. 9). The large tank quenches all wave processes other than those desired and also sucks the driver gas out of the shock tube so that the chemical sample is not contaminated; the tailored interface means that the conditions were such in the tube that the reflected shock wave passes into the driver gas without generating any reflected wave.

Tailoring the interface requires a shock wave in the driver gas which gives the same velocity and pressure increment as in the driven gas. If the ratio of the specific heats γ is the same in both the driven and driver gas, the pressure ratio would be the same if the Mach number of the shocks were the same. The velocity increment across a shock wave is propor-

tional to the product of the sound velocity and a function of shock Mach number only so that the sound speeds must be the same in both gases for "tailoring." This is consistent with ordinary acoustic considerations, i.e., ρa should be the same, but at the interface the pressure p or ρa^2 is the same, and so a in this case is the same.

Note in this apparatus that the cooling rate is determined by the length of the shock tube. If the diaphragm were closer, the cooling rate would be higher. One can use a cylindrical diaphragm [8] to get a higher cooling rate; however, the diaphragm and the apparatus required to break it at the correct time are always additional complications.

IV. CORNELL SINGLE-PULSE SHOCK TUBE

In the apparatus discussed in Section III, the interface was intentionally tailored. Without precautions, the interface is usually not tailored, and a reflection results. It is easy to arrange the properties of the gases across the interface so that the reflected wave will be an expansion wave that can be used to quench the reaction [9–11]. The reflected wave will be an expansion wave if the sound speed in the driver gas is higher than in the driven gas that the reflected shock initially moves through. This requires a light gas driver as is usually used in shock tubes. This arrangement (Fig. 10) results in a more rapid cooling rate as the expansion is created nearer the shocked gas. The driver section should then be "tuned" to provide more cooling from the reflected expansion wave in the driver section. To test experimentally these ideas, pressure traces were taken at the end of a shock tube. Figure 11 shows a number of pressure traces. Consider first the pressure traces in the lower left-hand corner. The lower trace is the pressure trace with a relatively long time scale. Note that the initial cooling curve has a plateau on it, indicating that the driver section is too long or the tube is not tuned. The lower trace in the pressure oscillogram in the lower right-hand corner shows the tube "tuned." Now in both these cases the shock wave returns and reheats the gas before the gas finally attains its final low pressure level. Clearly, something must be done to avoid this, as these subsequent waves are of sufficient strength to cause further chemical reaction after the supposed quench. These undesirable waves can be removed by inserting a tank connected to the shock tube just downstream of the diaphragm. There is no diaphragm separating the tank and shock tube, but the orifice size is carefully chosen. The orifice must remain choked while the incident shock makes its traverse of the tube so that the initial shock wave has

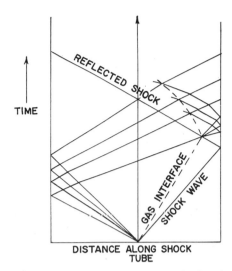

FIG. 10. Wave diagram for Cornell single-pulse shock tube utilizing the expansion wave reflected from the shock wave gas interface intersection.

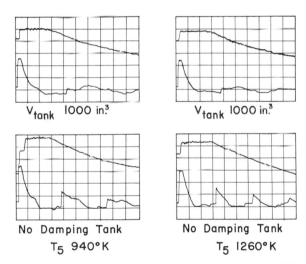

FIG. 11. Pressure traces in Cornell single-pulse shock tube with different time scales and with and without orifice and tank described in text.

uniform conditions behind it. After the initial shock reflection, it is hoped that enough gas will flow into the tank that there will not be enough gas left in the tube to drive the shock down a second time. Figure 12 shows a schematic diagram of the complete apparatus [12]. Note the adjustable end wall in the driver section for tuning. The tank size is

chosen by considerations of where one desires the gas interface along the tube axis at the conclusion of the run. The upper two oscillograms in Fig. 11 show pressure traces in the tube after the tank is inserted in the system. The upper traces in each figure are at a much faster sweep speed than the lower and enable one to calculate the cooling rate initially. These traces showed a cooling rate greater than 10^6 °K/sec.

Although the pressure traces indicate the tube is indeed providing a reasonably square temperature pulse, chemists have a number of reactions

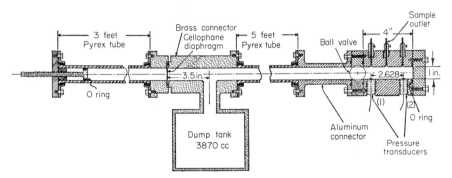

FIG. 12. Schematic of Cornell single-pulse shock tube [12].

that are well understood which can be used to test the system kinetically. One of these is the rate of transformation from cis to trans (and vice versa) of Butene-2 (C_4H_8) [12]:

The apparatus depicted in Fig. 12 was used, and the products were analyzed by vapor phase chromatography, and concentrations as small as 10^{-9} mole could be detected. It was found that the reaction was unimolecular over the complete temperature range covered. Since there had been other measurements at lower temperatures (using conventional techniques), the use of the low-temperature and high-temperature single-pulse shock tube results together, since they spanned a large range of $1/T$, enabled one to fix the activation energy for the reaction at 65 rather than 62.4 or 62.8 kcal/mole as determined from the low-temperature

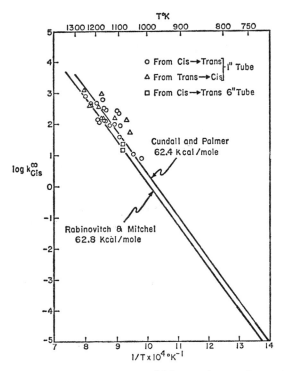

Fig. 13. Plot of k_{cis}^{∞} versus $1/T$ for 1% butene-2 tests [12].

measurements only (Fig. 13). It is interesting that the mechanism of the reaction does not change, although the rate changes by a factor of 10^8. Note also the amount of scatter which is typical of shock tube data.

V. VIBRATIONAL EXCITATION IN SOME FOUR-CENTER TRANSITION STATES

Soon after deuterium, the isotope of hydrogen, was discovered, the reaction rate of hydrogen with deuterium to form HD was attacked both theoretically and experimentally. The classical process for the homogeneous reaction was expected to be a bimolecular four-center process as depicted below:

$$
\begin{array}{ccccc}
\text{H} & \text{D} & \text{H}\cdots\text{D} & & \text{H—D} \\
| & | & \cdot & & \cdot \\
| & | \rightleftarrows \cdot & & \cdot \rightarrow & + \\
| & | & \cdot & & \cdot \\
\text{H} & \text{D} & \text{H}\cdots\text{D} & & \text{H—D}
\end{array}
$$

The rate of formation would then be governed by the rate of formation of the four-center complex, which then quickly decayed to the two HD molecules.   Thus, the reaction rate would be proportional to the product of the H_2 and D_2 concentrations.   In experiments designed to test the theory, hot tubes were used, and the formation of HD was shown to be

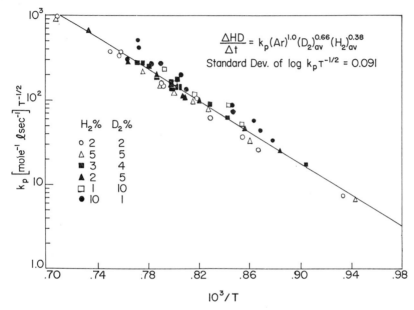

FIG. 14. Rate of formation of HD from experiments with H_2, D_2, and Ar mixtures (T in °K).

governed by the dissociation reaction catalyzed by the hot wall followed by atomic displacement in the gas phase, e.g.,

$$H_2, D_2 \xrightarrow{\text{walls}} H, D$$
$$H + D_2 \longrightarrow H \cdots D \cdots D \longrightarrow HD + D$$
$$D + H_2 \longrightarrow D \cdots H \cdots H \longrightarrow HD + H,$$

The homogeneous mechanism could not be checked.   This seemed a simple and useful experiment to perform with the single-pulse shock tube.

This experiment was performed [13] using various H_2 and D_2 concentrations in argon, with the result shown in Fig. 14.   Again note the scatter shown in the experiment.   The rate measured was found to be 10 to 100 times larger than the maximum computed utilizing bimolecular collisions.

Note that the power of the concentrations differs from the expected one, and also note that the exponent of the D_2 concentration is about twice that of the H_2 concentration. These results seem reliable, as subsequent tests have borne them out.

A possible clue to the key of this puzzle was provided by subsequent studies of HD exchange reactions with ammonia NH_3 and hydrogen sulfide H_2S. The results of these experiments were that the rate of formation of HD was zero order with respect to NH_3 and H_2S, and thus did not depend at all on the concentration of either NH_3 or H_2S, e.g., for

$$D_2 + NH_3 \rightleftharpoons HD + NH_2D$$

and

$$D_2 + H_2S \rightleftharpoons HD + HDS.$$

it was found experimentally that $d(HD)/dt = K(Ar)(D_2)$. Thus, the step controlling the rate of formation of HD cannot be the bimolecular encounter of the principal reactants. The rate-controlling step can only be the activation of D_2 by collisions with argon. An explanation that seems to be consistent with all the data to date is that the reaction rate is controlled by the rate of excitation of the vibrational levels of D_2 above a critical level, and these molecules so excited then react quickly to form HD. The data indicate that the critical level in D_2 is the fourth vibrational level. The more active nature of D_2 as compared with H_2 in these exchange reactions has also been borne out in our experiments to date. Thus, the aerodynamically designed single-pulse shock tube has given the chemists a research tool that not only has changed some of the fundamental concepts in the kinetics of diatomic reactions but also promises to be useful in sorting out the various possible alternate mechanisms.

It has long been thought that the energy of reaction resided in that of translation along the line of centers of colliding molecules. Indeed, most experiments are interpreted using a theoretical structure that assumes this. To show that this is not the case in reactions as just described which require a certain vibrational level to be excited, Professor S. H. Bauer and his collaborators at Cornell University formed vibrationally excited molecules at room temperature as products of a reaction which then reacted with another species. In this case, there was not enough energy in translation along the line of centers to cause the reaction; thus, the rate had to be governed by those molecules possessing enough energy in the vibrational levels to permit the reaction to proceed. The expected products were indeed observed, and again the important role of vibrational excitation in the control of reaction rates was demonstrated.

Another type of chemical investigation possible with the single-pulse

shock tube is the pyrolyis of perfluorethylene, C_2F_4. Because of interest in possible re-entry materials, this was studied previously, and the direct product of the thermal decomposition was CF_2. Our present studies seem to indicate that at lower temperatures more complex species are subsequently generated during the dwell period and cooling, e.g., C_3F_6, C_4F_8, C_2F_6, etc.

The scatter in the data of experiments of this type is about the same as that in the typical data already presented. This scatter is caused mostly by inaccuracies in the determination of the temperature, which is not measured directly but calculated from the measured shock speed. The determination of temperature is especially important, since it usually affects the rate constant exponentially. The temperature is inferred from shock speed because no better method has been devised. Dr. Wing Tsang at the National Bureau of Standards made the very useful suggestion of using a known rate constant as a "thermometer." His method involved measuring unknown rate constants relative to a well-known one. His measurements [14] involved the decomposition of tert-butyl chloride and tert-butyl bromide compared with the rate of decomposition of isopropyl bromide as a standard ($C_3H_7Br \rightarrow C_3H_6 + HBr$). The experiments were carried out in a single-pulse shock tube similar to the Cornell one described. His experimental results are reproduced in Fig. 15. Note in particular the great reduction of scatter achieved as compared with the previously discussed experimental results. This technique is very sensitive if the temperature dependence of the rates is the same.

To make possible the study of another set of reactions, we have another technique currently under study at Cornell which shows promise. This technique involves using an inner tube in the driven end of the shock tube proper. The physical circumstance is depicted in Fig. 16. The incident shock wave is reflected in the inner tube, whereas the conditions outside the inner tube are appropriate to the conditions behind the incident shock wave. The reflected shock wave leaves the inner tube, and an expansion wave is generated in the inner tube while the reflected shock wave stands ahead of the tube. The expansion wave cools the gas in the inner tube and accelerates it out of the tube as shown. The subsequent cooling is then controlled by techniques already described. The advantage of this scheme is twofold: the cooling rate is now very conveniently under control, being proportional to the length l_0 of the inner tube; the other advantage is that the inner tube may be easily heated to contain chemical samples that need to be heated to exist in a vapor phase; thus, condensation studies may be made. The cooling rate can be calculated [15], and the results are plotted in Fig. 17. Thus, it should be possible to extend the shock tube studies of rates to a greater class of reactions.

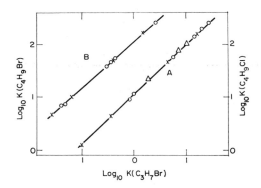

FIG. 15. Comparative rate measurements for the unimolecular dehydrohalogenation of $t - C_4H_9Cl$ and $i - C_3H_7Br$ [14].

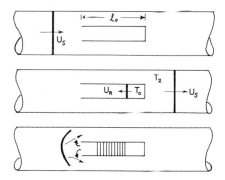

FIG. 16. Schematic of another technique for heating with a shock wave and cooling by expansion.

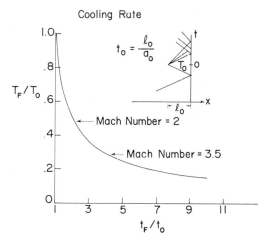

FIG. 17. Cooling rate and ultimate temperature ratio across expansion fan reflected at the wall for physical circumstances depicted in Fig. 16.

VI. CONCLUSIONS

With this brief summary of typical chemical kinetic studies made possible by the cooperation of the chemist with the gasdynamicist, it is evident that gasdynamic studies using continuum theory have led to a detailed understanding of nonlinear wave interactions and thus enabled experiments to be designed to investigate atomic interactions in molecular chemistry.

ACKNOWLEDGMENT

This study was supported by the Air Force Office of Scientific Research, Contract No. AF 49(638)-1448.

REFERENCES

1. Resler, E. L., Jr., The Shock Tube and Chemical Kinetics, *in* "Fluid Dynamics and Applied Mathematics" (Diaz and Pai, eds.), pp. 125–145. Gordon and Breach, New York, 1962.
2. Sutton, E. A., *J. Chem. Phys.* **36,** 2923 (1962).
3. Wilson, J., An Experiment to Measure the Recombination Rate of Oxygen. *J. Fluid Mech.* **15,** Part 4, 497–512 (1963).
4. Bradley, J. N. and Kistiakowsky, G. B., *J. Chem. Phys.* **35,** 256 (1961).
5. Marsters, G. F., Bauer, S. H., and Resler, E. L., Jr., Optimized Geometry for Coupling a Mass Spectrometer to a Shock Tube. *Proc. 5th Internat. Shock Tube Sym.*, pp. 155–170. Naval Ordnance Lab. White Oak, Silver Spring, Maryland (1965).
6. Skinner, G. T. and Moyzio, J., *Phys. Fluids* **8,** 452 (1965).
7. Glick, H. S., Klein, J. J., and Squire, W., *J. Chem. Phys.* **27,** 850 (1957).
8. Jacobs, T. A., Hartunian, R. A., Geidt, R. R., and Wilkins, R., *Phys. Fluids* **6,** 972 (1963).
9. Greene, E. F., Taylor, R. L., and Patterson, W. L., *J. Phys. Chem.* **62,** 238 (1958).
10. Klepeis, J. E., M. Aero. E. Thesis, Grad. School of Aeronautical Engineering, Cornell University, Ithaca, New York (1961).
11. Swanson, B. C., M. Aero. E. Thesis, Grad. School of Aeronautical Engineering, Cornell University, Ithaca, New York (1962).
12. Lifshitz, A., Bauer, S. H., and Resler, E. L., Jr., *J. Chem. Phys.* **38,** 2056 (1963).
13. Bauer, S. H. and Resler, E. L., Jr., *Science* **146,** 1045 (1964).
14. Tsang, W., *J. Chem. Phys.* **40,** 1171 (1964).
15. Courant, R. and Friedrichs, K. O., "Supersonic Flow and Shock Waves." Wiley (Interscience), New York, 1948.

Gas Kinetic Equations and Their Applications to

Nonequilibrium Flows with Diffusion and Chemical Reaction

TING YI LI

DEPARTMENT OF AERONAUTICAL
AND ASTRONAUTICAL ENGINEERING
OHIO STATE UNIVERSITY
COLUMBUS, OHIO

In the study of nonequilibrium flows of reacting gases, attention must be given to the important processes of diffusion and chemical reactions. Following Burgers, we shall examine, in the present paper, some aspects of the gas kinetic equations and their applications to nonequilibrium flows with diffusion and chemical reaction. First, we shall deal with the diffusion problem. We write down the Boltzmann equation for the distribution function of each component gas. In this equation, the left-hand side is linear in the distribution function, whereas the right-hand side is nonlinear. We shall assume that the distribution function contains certain deviations from the equilibrium Maxwellian distribution. By calculations similar to Grad's thirteen-moment method, we shall be able to demonstrate the important effects of (1) diffusion velocities and (2) nonuniform temperatures of the component gases. These calculations are concluded with an examination of the problems of the flows of rarefied gaseous mixture under conditions of large departures from equilibrium. Next, we shall deal with the flows of reacting gases. Bhatnagar-Gross-Krook's approximation for the right-hand side of the Boltzmann equation is adopted. Proceeding along the lines of attack established by Burgers, we give special considerations of the transfer of momentum and of energy associated with reactive and nonreactive collisions and study their effects on the flow equations. The method of moment can again be applied to the construction of the flow equations. These flow equations are of rather complicated forms. We shall consider some schemes of simplification. Finally, we shall attempt to simplify an extended form of the Boltzmann equation which was proposed by Burgers in 1959. This Burgers-Boltzmann equation deals with a realistic kinetic model of the reacting gaseous mixture and forms a logical basis of further developments in nonequilibrium reacting flows. Using some approximate arguments, we shall reduce this equation into a simplified form. This simplified model gas kinetic equation preserves the basic features that characterize the nonequilibrium reacting flows.

I. INTRODUCTION

The fundamental equations of aerothermochemistry can be deduced by either of two methods: (1) the method of irreversible thermodynamics,

155

or (2) the method of kinetic theory of nonuniform gases. The former method, in its present stage of development, is suitable for applications to systems with small deviations from local equilibrium. In order to extend our knowledge concerning nonequilibrium flows, the method of kinetic theory appears to hold good promise. Burgers, during the past decade, has made many significant studies of the various aspects of the kinetic theory approach and its applications to nonequilibrium flows. The present writer, greatly indebted to Burgers for the privilege of having been exposed to these interesting developments, would attempt to bring forth some of his results that deal with several important aspects of the gas kinetic equations and their applications to nonequilibrium flows. The present paper is dedicated to Professor Burgers on the happy occasion of his seventieth birthday.

II. NONEQUILIBRIUM FLOW OF GASEOUS MIXTURE

We consider a gas consisting of molecules of various types and use the subscript s (or t) to distinguish between different types. The molecules are assumed to be spherically symmetric, and they are surrounded by spherically symmetric fields of force. They are assumed to possess kinetic energy of translation, but no rotational, vibrational, and other internal energies. Chemical reactions will not be considered in the present section. We also leave aside exterior forces acting on the molecules in the interval between collisions. This represents a rather simple system that corresponds to a mixture of monatomic gases. The state of the s-gas in this gaseous mixture can be specified by the following variables of state:

N_s = number density of s-molecules.

u_{sk} = mass velocity of the s-gas (subscript k signifies the k-component of the velocity vector, $k = 1, 2, 3$)

$(p_s)_{hk}$ = the hk-component of the stress tensor of the s-gas ($k, h = 1, 2, 3$)

$(q_s)_k$ = the k-component of the heat flux vector of the s-gas ($k = 1, 2, 3$)

The objective of the present study is to construct the equations of motion which can be used to determine these variables of state as functions of (x_h, t), where (x_h) signifies a point in the field and t signifies an instant of time.

We write down the Boltzmann equation for the distribution function of the s-molecules, denoted as $F_s(t, x_h, \xi_{sh})$. F_s is here defined as the

number of s-molecules per unit volume at the time, t, having coordinates lying between $(x_h, x_h + dx_h)$ and translational velocities between $(\xi_{sh}, \xi_{sh} + d\xi_{sh})$. More elaborate distribution functions will be used in a later section when internal motions (rotation, vibration) or electronic states are to be considered. In the present case, the Boltzmann equation for F_s can be written as follows:

$$\frac{\partial F_s}{\partial t} + \xi_{sh}\frac{\partial F_s}{\partial x_h} = \frac{\delta F_s}{\delta t}. \tag{1}$$

$\delta F_s/\delta t$ here denotes the change in F_s caused by molecular encounters. In the present section, we adopt the familiar binary collision model; thus, we obtain

$$\frac{\delta F_s}{\delta t} = \sum_t \iint d\xi_t \, (F_s'F_t' - F_sF_t)|g_{st}|b \, db \, d\epsilon \tag{2}$$

where

$$F_t = F_t(t, x_h, \xi_{th})$$
$$F_t' = F_t(t, x_h, \xi_{th}') \qquad \text{etc.}$$

The primed quantities pertain to the quantities after the collision between the pair of s and t molecules. $|g_{st}| = g$ denotes the magnitude of the relative velocity between the colliding partners. b and ϵ are variables that specify the geometry of the encounter [1]. The double integral signs in Eq. (2) signify integrations over all possible binary encounters with all ranges of molecular velocities $\xi_t = (\xi_{th})$ for a complete range of b and ϵ. In the summation with respect to t, we must include $t = s$, i.e., encounters between the s-molecules. It may be noted that, in Eq. (1), we have used the summation convention for the subscript h, i.e.,

$$\xi_{sh}\frac{\partial F_s}{\partial x_h} = \xi_{s1}\frac{\partial F_s}{\partial x_1} + \xi_{s2}\frac{\partial F_s}{\partial x_2} + \xi_{s3}\frac{\partial F_s}{\partial x_3}$$

This convention will be adopted throughout the present paper. However, if a summation with respect to t (or s, which labels the various types of molecules) is required, the summation sign will be written explicitly as in Eq. (2).

The mass velocity for the s-gas can be suitably combined to yield the mass velocity of the mixture as a whole. Therefore, we define

$$u_k = \frac{\displaystyle\sum_s N_s m_s u_{sk}}{\displaystyle\sum_s N_s m_s} \tag{3}$$

where m_s is the s-molecule mass and $u_k(t, x_k)$ is the mass velocity of the mixture.   We introduce

$$c_{sk} = \xi_{sk} - u_k \tag{4}$$

where c_{sk} is the peculiar velocity of the s-molecules.   Equation (1) has been written in the variables (t, x_h, ξ_{sh}).   We now rewrite it in terms of the variables (t, x_h, c_{sh}) and obtain

$$DF_s = \frac{DF_s}{Dt} + c_{sh}\frac{\partial F_s}{\partial x_h} - \left(\frac{Du_i}{Dt} + c_{sh}\frac{\partial u_i}{\partial x_h}\right)\frac{\partial F_s}{\partial c_{si}} = \frac{\delta F_s}{\delta t} \tag{1a}$$

where

$$\frac{D}{Dt} = \frac{\partial}{\partial t} + u_h\frac{\partial}{\partial x_h} \tag{5}$$

$$\frac{\delta F_s}{\delta t} = \sum_t \iint d\mathbf{c}_t\,(F_s'F_t' - F_sF_t)gb\,db\,d\epsilon. \tag{2a}$$

At this point, it must be recognized that F_s gives a description of the state of the s-molecules at the microscopic level, whereas N_s, u_{sk}, $(p_s)_{hk}$, and $(q_s)_k$ give a description of the state of the s-molecules at the macroscopic level.   The connection between these descriptions at different levels is obtained through the following definitions:

$$N_s = \int F_s\,d\mathbf{c}_s \tag{6}$$
$$\bar{Q} = (1/N_s)\int F_sQ\,d\mathbf{c}_s. \tag{7}$$

Equation (7) gives the definition of the statistical average $\bar{Q}$ of a quantity Q (we use the barred quantities to represent statistical averages), for instance,

$$\bar{\xi}_{sk} = u_{sk} = (1/N_s)\int F_s\xi_{sk}\,d\mathbf{c}_s \tag{8}$$
$$m_s\overline{c_{sh}c_{sk}} = (1/N_s)(p_s)_{hk} = (1/N_s)\int F_sm_sc_{sh}c_{sk}\,d\mathbf{c}_s \tag{9}$$
$$\tfrac{1}{2}m_s\overline{c_s^2c_{sk}} = (1/N_s)(q_s)_k = (1/N_s)\int F_s\tfrac{1}{2}m_sc_s^2c_{sk}\,d\mathbf{c}_s. \tag{10}$$

Equation (8) can also be written as

$$u_{sk} = u_k + w_{sk} \tag{11}$$

where

$$\bar{c}_{sk} = w_{sk} = (1/N_s)\int F_sc_{sk}\,d\mathbf{c}_s \tag{12}$$

and w_{sk} is the diffusion velocity of the s-gas.   From Eqs. (3) and (11), we deduce

$$\sum_s N_sm_sw_{sk} = \sum_s \rho_sw_{sk} = 0 \tag{13}$$

where ρ_s denotes the mass density of the s-gas.   Having established these useful relations, we now proceed to translate the gas kinetic (Boltzmann)

equation into an approximately equivalent macroscopic system of equations. Therefore, from Eq. (1a), we obtain the Maxwell transfer equation:

$$\int Q D F_s \, d\mathbf{c}_s = \int Q(\delta F_s / \delta t) \, d\mathbf{c}_s \tag{14}$$

where Q represents one of the following transferable quantities (in each case, $\bar{Q}$ is also given below):

$$Q^0 = m_s \qquad\qquad N_s \overline{Q^0} = \rho_s \tag{15}$$

$$Q_k{}^{\mathrm{I}} = m_s c_{sk} \qquad\qquad N_s \overline{Q_k{}^{\mathrm{I}}} = \rho_s w_{sk} \tag{16}$$

$$Q_{kh}{}^{\mathrm{II}} = m_s c_{sk} c_{sh} \qquad N_s \overline{Q_{kh}{}^{\mathrm{II}}} = (p_s)_{kh} \tag{17}$$

$$Q_k{}^{\mathrm{III}} = \tfrac{1}{2} m_s c_s{}^2 c_{sk} \qquad N_s \overline{Q_h{}^{\mathrm{III}}} = (q_s)_k . \tag{18}$$

In this manner, we are able to obtain, from Eq. (14), the equations of motion for the s-gas. In the literature, this procedure has been applied to the study of a simple gas system by Grad [2], Krook [3], and Lees [4] among other authors. Burgers [5] has applied it to the problem of the present section. $N_s \overline{Q^0}$, $N_s \overline{Q_k{}^{\mathrm{I}}}$, $N_s \overline{Q_{kh}{}^{\mathrm{II}}}$, and $N_s \overline{Q_k{}^{\mathrm{III}}}$ are sometimes known as the zeroth, first, second, and third (contracted) moments of the distribution function F_s. Results of calculations from Eq. (14) give a set of 13 equations of motion (13 moment equations). This set, however, is not a determinate set. This difficulty arises from the fact that the equation deduced from Eq. (14) for the nth moment always contains terms involving the $(n+1)$th moment. Thus we do not obtain a determinate set of equations. To demonstrate this difficulty, we formally carry out the calculations of the left-hand side of Eq. (14) to obtain

$$\int Q D F_s \, d\mathbf{c}_s = \frac{D}{Dt} (N_s \bar{Q}) + \frac{\partial}{\partial x_h} (N_s \overline{c_{sh} Q}) + N_s \bar{Q} \frac{\partial u_i}{\partial x_i}$$

$$+ \frac{D u_i}{Dt} N_s \overline{\frac{\partial Q}{\partial c_{si}}} + \frac{\partial u_i}{\partial x_h} N_s \overline{c_{sh} \frac{\partial Q}{\partial c_{si}}} . \tag{19}$$

In Eq. (19), if $N_s \bar{Q}$ is the nth moment, then $N_s \overline{c_{sh} Q}$ is the $(n+1)$th moment. The appearance of the $(n+1)$th moment term in the equation for the nth moment is therefore plainly seen. To obtain a closed system, Burgers [5] adopted Grad's [2] approximate expressions for the higher moments in terms of the 13 basic ones.[1] In this manner, a determinate set of equations of motion can be obtained provided the integration of the right-hand side of Eq. (14) can be accomplished. As Eq. (2a) shows that $\delta F_s / \delta t$ is nonlinear in the distribution function, this necessitates the adoption of an explicit expression for the distribution function in order to accomplish the calculations of the right-hand side of Eq. (14).

---

[1] An alternative scheme is the Maxwellian iteration scheme used by Truesdell and Ikenberry [6] and Burgers [7].

Following Burgers [5], we assume that the distribution function F_s can be expressed as follows.

FORMULATION I:

$$F_s = F_{s0}(1 + \phi_s) \tag{20}$$

where

$$F_{s0} = N_s \left(\frac{m_s}{2\pi kT} \right)^{3/2} \exp \left(- \frac{m_s c_s^2}{2kT} \right)$$

$$\phi_s = A_{si} c_{si} + B_s(c_s^2 - \tfrac{3}{2} a_s^2) \tag{21}$$
$$+ B_{shk}(c_{sh} c_{sk} - \tfrac{1}{3} \delta_{hk} c_s^2)$$
$$+ C_{sh}(c_s^2 c_{sh} - \tfrac{5}{2} a_s^2 c_{sh}) \tag{22}$$

$$a_s^2 = 2kT/m_s \tag{23}$$
$$c_{sh} = \xi_{sh} - u_h \tag{4}$$

where k is the Boltzmann constant.

We repeat Eq. (4) here in order to emphasize the point that F_{s0}, as just defined, represents an equilibrium Maxwellian distribution that is characterized by the mean velocity u_h and the mean temperature T for the mixture as a whole.

The quantity T is expressible as

$$T = (1/N) \sum_s N_s T_s \tag{24}$$

where T_s is the temperature of the s-gas defined as follows:

$$kT_s = \tfrac{1}{3} m_s \overline{c_s^2} - (1/N_s)[\tfrac{1}{3}(p_s)_{hh}] . \tag{25}$$

We define the hydrostatic pressure of the s-gas:

$$p_s = \tfrac{1}{3}(p_s)_{hh} . \tag{26}$$

Then, Eq. (25) becomes the thermal equation of state of the s-gas. For the mixture, the equation of state is

$$p = NkT . \tag{27}$$

Then, Eq. (24) yields the Dalton's law

$$p = \sum_s p_s . \tag{28}$$

Returning now to Eq. (20), we remark that ϕ_s represents the deviation from the equilibrium distribution. In Eq. (22), ϕ_s has been expressed

as a series in ascending powers of the peculiar velocity c_{sk}. There are 13 unknown coefficients A_{si}, B_s, etc., which are assumed to be functions of (x_h, t). Substitution of Eqs. (20) and (22) into the right-hand side of Eq. (14) would yield expressions containing these undetermined coefficients. Burgers [5] showed that these coefficients are expressible in terms of the 13 variables of state of the s-gas:

$$A_{si} = \frac{m_s}{kT} w_{si} \tag{29}$$

$$B_s = \frac{m_s}{2kT} \left(\frac{T_s}{T} - 1 \right) \tag{30}$$

$$B_{shk} - \frac{1}{3} \delta_{hk} B_{sii} = \frac{m_s}{2kT} \frac{(P_s)_{hk}}{N_s kT} \tag{31}$$

$$C_{sh} = \frac{(q_s{}^*)_h}{5 N_s kT} \left(\frac{m_s}{kT} \right)^2 \tag{32}$$

where

$$(P_s)_{hk} = (p_s)_{hk} - \delta_{hk} p_s \tag{33}$$

$$(q_s{}^*)_h = (q_s)_h - \tfrac{5}{2} N_s kT w_{sh} . \tag{34}$$

By Eqs. (13) and (24), we must have

$$\sum_s N_s A_{si} = 0 \tag{35}$$

$$\sum_s N_s (B_s/m_s) = 0 . \tag{36}$$

In the final forms of the equations of motion obtained from Eq. (14), the use of the relations in Eqs. (29)–(32) would permit the elimination of the unknown coefficients in terms of the basic set of the variables of state. Thus, a determinate set of equations of motion of the s-gas can be obtained. These calculations were carried through by Burgers [5].

The procedure just described is useful in that its application provides the equations of motion for the 13 moments that have been here adopted as the basic variables of state. This procedure can be extended if the equations of higher moments are desired [5]. In general, such calculations, although long and tedious, would promise further refinements within formulation I. The interesting question now is, to what class of nonequilibrium flow problems is the formulation I particularly useful? The answer to this question is important and perhaps would determine the future course of developments. Formulation I has been based on the important assumption that F_s is expressible as in Eqs. (20)–(22).

Taking into account the relationships of Eqs. (29)–(32), we rewrite Eq. (20) as follows:

$$F_s = F_{s0} \left\{ 1 + \frac{(P_s)_{hk}}{2N_s kT} \frac{c_{sh}c_{sk}}{kT/m_s} + \frac{m_s}{kT} \frac{(q_s)_h}{N_s kT} \left(\frac{1}{5} \frac{c_s{}^2}{kT/m_s} - 1 \right) c_{sh} \right.$$

$$+ \left(\frac{T_s}{T} - 1 \right) \left[1 + \frac{5}{2} \left(\frac{1}{5} \frac{c_s{}^2}{kT/m_s} - 1 \right) \right]$$

$$\left. + \left[1 - \frac{5}{2} \left(\frac{1}{5} \frac{c_s{}^2}{kT/m_s} - 1 \right) \right] c_{sh} w_{sh} \frac{1}{kT/m_s} \right\}. \tag{37}$$

The following observations on Eq. (37) can be made:

(1)   As already pointed out, an equilibrium distribution F_{s0} for the mixture as a whole has been adopted in formulation I.   This equilibrium state can be completely specified by N_s, T, u_k as functions of (t, x_h). This equilibrium mixture is distinguished by the following conditions: (a) $(P_s)_{hk} = 0$, (b) $(q_s)_k = 0$, (c) $T_s/T = 1$, and (d) $w_{sh} = 0$.

(2) The state of the s-gas is deviated from this equilibrium state by ϕ_s, which consists of small departures as represented by $(P_s)_{hk} \neq 0$, $(q_s)_k \neq 0$, $(T_s/T) - 1 \neq 0$, $w_{sh} \neq 0$. In the detail calculations [5], quadratic terms of ϕ_s are regarded as higher-order terms and are neglected.   Therefore, formulation I is not applicable if the state of the s-gas is deviated by large departures from the mixture's equilibrium state.

(3) Among the nonequilibrium effects, $(P_s)_{hk}$ and $(q_s)_h$ would exist in a simple gas; thus T_s/T (i.e., nonuniform temperatures of the component gases) and w_{sh} (i.e., diffusion velocities) must be regarded as the important nonequilibrium flow features of a mixture.   Indeed, if we simplify Eq. (37) under the simple gas assumption, then formulation I becomes identical to Grad's thirteen-moment method [2] for a simple gas.

Now, we can provide a definite answer to the question posed earlier. The present formulation I is particularly useful if the diffusion velocities and the temperature differences among all species are small so that the mixture behaves as a whole.   Most of the nonequilibrium mixture flow calculations available today belong to this class of problems.

In a dilute mixture when collisions are infrequent and each species behaves almost independently of the other species, Burgers [8,5] advanced an approach that is particularly useful in problems involving large departures from equilibrium $[(T_s/T) - 1 = 0(1), w_{sh}/(kT/m_s)^{1/2} = 0(1)]$. In this approach, we replace Eqs. (20)–(22) by the following.

FORMULATION II:

$$F_s = F_{s0}{}^*(1 + \phi_s{}^*) \tag{38}$$

where

$$F_{s0}{}^* = N_s \left(\frac{m_s}{2\pi k T_s}\right)^{3/2} \exp\left(-\frac{m_s c_s{}^{*2}}{2kT_s}\right), \tag{39}$$

$$\phi_s{}^* = B_{shk}{}^*(c_{sh}{}^* c_{sk}{}^* - \tfrac{1}{3}\delta_{hk}c_s{}^{*2})$$
$$\qquad + C_{sh}{}^*(c_s{}^{*2}c_{sh}{}^* - \tfrac{5}{2}a_s{}^{*2}c_{sh}{}^*), \tag{40}$$

$$a_s{}^{*2} = 2kT_s/m_s, \tag{41}$$

$$c_{sh}{}^* = \xi_{sh} - u_{sh} = c_{sh} - w_{sh}. \tag{42}$$

In formulation II, $F_{s0}{}^*$ represents an equilibrium Maxwellian distribution for the s-molecules. Each type of molecule possesses its own equilibrium state characterized by N_s, T_s, and u_{sh}. The state of the s-gas in the mixture is deviated from such an equilibrium by $\phi_s{}^*$ given in Eq. (40). Again, we shall neglect quadratic terms of $\phi_s{}^*$. This neglect implies that the viscous stresses and the heat conduction within the s-gas must be restricted to small values. However, the severe restrictions of $(T_s/T) - 1 \to \epsilon$, $w_{sk}/(kT/m_s)^{1/2} \to \epsilon$, $\epsilon \ll 1$ are removed; thus, we are able to deal with a nonequilibrium mixture with the proper attention to the multifluid nature of the problem. The unknown coefficients introduced in Eq. (40) can again be expressed in terms of the basic variables of state:

$$B_{shk}^* - \tfrac{1}{3}\delta_{hk}B_{sii}^* = \frac{m_s}{2kT_s}\frac{(P_s{}^*)_{hk}}{(N_s kT_s)}, \tag{43}$$

$$C_{sh}{}^* = \frac{(q_s{}^{**})_h}{5N_s kT_s}\left(\frac{m_s}{kT_s}\right)^2. \tag{44}$$

We note that

$$(P_s{}^*)_{hk} = \int F_s m_s c_{sh}{}^* c_{sk}{}^* \, d\mathbf{c}_s{}^*, \tag{45}$$

$$(q_s{}^{**})_h = \int F_s \tfrac{1}{2}m_s c_s{}^{*2} c_{sh}{}^* \, d\mathbf{c}_s{}^*, \tag{46}$$

$$(P_s{}^*)_{hk} = (p_s{}^*)_{hk} - \delta_{hk}p_s{}^*, \tag{47}$$

$$p_s{}^* = \tfrac{1}{3}(p_s{}^*)_{hh}. \tag{48}$$

With this set of relations replacing Eqs. (9), (10), (33), and (26), the pressure tensor components and the heat flow vector components are defined for each separate species. They cannot be added to yield the corresponding components of the mixture.[2] This again emphasizes the significant multifluid nature of formulation II. In this new formulation

[2] With definitions such as Eqs. (9) and (10), we have

$$(p)_{hk} = \sum_s (p_s)_{hk}, \qquad (q)_h = \sum_s (q_s)_h$$

for the mixture.

Eq. (14) should be rewritten in terms of the variables c_s^* as follows:

$$\int Q D^* F_s \, d\mathbf{c}_s^* = \int Q \frac{\delta^* F_s}{\delta t} \, d\mathbf{c}_s^* \tag{49}$$

where

$$D^* F_s = \frac{D^* F_s}{Dt} + c_{sh}^* \frac{\partial F_s}{\partial x_h} - \left[\frac{D^* u_{si}}{Dt} + c_{sh}^* \frac{\partial u_{si}}{\partial x_h} \right] \frac{\partial F_s}{\partial c_{si}^*}, \tag{50}$$

$$\frac{D^*}{Dt} = \frac{\partial}{\partial t} + u_{sh} \frac{\partial}{\partial x_h}, \tag{51}$$

$$\frac{\delta^* F_s}{\delta t} = \sum_t \iint d\mathbf{c}_t^* \, (F_s' F_t' - F_s F_t) g b \, db \, d\epsilon. \tag{52}$$

A determinate set of equations of motion for the s-gas can be obtained, as before, from Eq. (49). These results due to Burgers should be of great value in the future developments of the highly nonequilibrium flow of a mixture. To close the present section, we would like to show that formulation II actually includes formulation I as a special case. Thus, we have, from Eqs. (42) and (30),

$$\frac{c_s^{*2}}{c_s^2} = 1 - 2 \frac{c_{sk} w_{sk}}{c_s^2} + O\left(\frac{w_{sk} w_{sk}}{c_s^2} \right), \tag{53}$$

$$\frac{T_s}{T} = 1 + 2B_s \frac{kT}{m_s}. \tag{54}$$

We substitute these relations into Eq. (39) to obtain

$$F_{s0}^* = F_{s0}[1 + A_{sk} c_{sk} + B_s(c_s^2 - \tfrac{3}{2} a_s^2)] \tag{55}$$

where only terms to the linear order of A_{si}, B_s are retained. Equations (38) and (55) may be combined to obtain F_s, which now becomes identical to Eqs. (20) and (22). Therefore, we are led to believe that formulation II is more generally applicable to the nonequilibrium flow of a mixture. A_{si} and B_s in these calculations are directly proportional to w_{si} and $[(T_s/T) - 1]$, respectively. The neglect of the quadratic-order terms involving A_{si} and B_s would reduce Eqs. (38) and (40) to the formulation in Eqs. (20) and (22) for a mixture in which only small diffusion velocities and small nonuniformities in temperatures exist.

III. NONEQUILIBRIUM FLOW OF REACTING GASEOUS MIXTURE

A basic restriction of the developments reviewed in the preceding section is imposed by the assumption of spherical molecules. This

assumption must be discarded in the study of a reacting mixture. In the present section, we consider a mixture of four chemical species, $S = A, B, C, D$, which may undergo the one-step bimolecular chemical reaction as follows:

$$A + B \rightleftarrows C + D \tag{56}$$

These molecules, in fact, have internal structure and may exist in a spectrum of internal states due to the possibility of electronic, vibrational, rotational, etc., degrees of freedom. We shall defer, however, a detailed account of these complexities to the next section. We assign only a single quantum state for each species, i.e., A, B, C, D each has a single quantum state with a single definite internal energy denoted by E_A, E_B, E_C, E_D referred to a common zero level. The translational energies are not included in these values. The microscopic description of the state of each gas may again be determined from Eq. (1). The right-hand side of this equation, however, should be re-examined. The expression in Eq. (2) applies only for binary collisions of spherical molecules. For a simple reaction as in Eq. (56), we tentatively keep the binary collision model. For nonspherical molecules, the collisional geometry becomes more difficult, and, in a reacting mixture, we must consider both elastic (nonreactive) and inelastic (reactive) collisions. We therefore must introduce a new expression for the right-hand side of Eq. (1). In some investigations on the kinetic theory of reacting gases, such as Refs. [9–11], this expression is written in two groups: (1) elastic collisions, and (2) inelastic collisions. Following this approach, we have, for $S = A$,

$$\frac{\delta F_A}{\delta t} = \sum_t \iint d\xi_t \, (F_A' F_t' - F_A F_t) |g_{tA}| \sigma_{tA}(g, \Omega) \, d\Omega$$

$$+ \iint d\xi_B \, (F_C' F_D' - F_A F_B) |g_{AB}| \sigma_{AB}^*(g, \Omega) \, d\Omega \tag{57}$$

where, besides the symbols we have already used, we introduce some new symbols: $\sigma_{tA}(g, \Omega)$ is the differential elastic scattering cross section that is a function of the absolute value of the relative velocity $|g_{tA}| = g$ and the solid scattering angle Ω, and $\sigma_{AB}^*(g, \Omega)$ is the differential chemical reaction cross section that is a function of $|g_{AB}| = g$ and the solid scattering angle Ω. The Boltzmann equation for the A-species in the reacting mixture can therefore be written as

$$\frac{\partial F_A}{\partial t} + \xi_{Ah} \frac{\partial F_A}{\partial x_h} = \frac{\partial F_A}{\delta t}. \tag{58}$$

In Refs. [9–11], Eq. (58) has been treated by an extension of Chapman-Enskog's method. In a more recent article by Burgers [12], he intro-

duced Bhatnagar-Gross-Krook's [13] approximation[3] in Eq. (58). This approximation is based upon the idea of a far-reaching randomization of particle velocities in a collision. Specifically, we assume that the translational velocities of particles of the A-species coming out of a non-reactive collision between A and S $(=A, B, C, D,)$ are represented by a Maxwellian distribution (normalized to unity) $\psi_{A(AS)}$:

$$\psi_{A(AS)} = \left(\frac{m_A}{2\pi k T_{A(AS)}}\right)^{3/2} \exp\left(-\frac{m_A(\xi_A - u_{A(AS)})^2}{2k T_{A(AS)}}\right), \tag{59}$$

$$F_A' = N_A \psi_{A(AS)}. \tag{60}$$

The (AS) is to indicate that we consider molecules just produced by a collision of A and S. This notation is useful particularly in the case of a reactive collision. For the reactive collisions of C and D, the resulting A-particles are represented by a Maxwellian distribution as follows:

$$\psi_{A(CD)} = \left(\frac{m_A}{2\pi k T_{A(CD)}}\right)^{3/2} \exp\left(-\frac{m_A(\xi_A - u_{A(CD)})^2}{2k T_{A(CD)}}\right), \tag{61}$$

and we shall write

$$F_C' F_D' = N_C N_D \psi_{A(CD)} \psi_{B(CD)}. \tag{62}$$

Equations (59) and (61) contain the mean flow velocities $u_{A(AS)}$, $u_{A(CD)}$ and the translational temperatures $T_{A(AS)}$, $T_{A(CD)}$. Applying the condition of conservation of momentum and energy of the colliding molecules in reactive collisions, Burgers [12] showed that

$$u_{A(CD)} = u_{B(CD)} = \frac{m_C u_C + m_D u_D}{m_C + m_D}, \tag{63}$$

$$\frac{3}{2} k T_{A(CD)} = \frac{3}{2} k T_C \frac{m_A m_C + m_B m_D}{(m_C + m_D)^2} + \frac{3}{2} k T_D \frac{m_A m_D + m_B m_C}{(m_C + m_D)^2}$$

$$+ \frac{m_B}{m_C + m_D}\left\{\frac{m_C m_D}{m_A + m_B} \frac{(u_C - u_D)^2}{2} + E_0\right\}, \tag{64}$$

where

$$E_0 = E_C + E_D - E_A - E_B; \tag{65}$$

If $E_0 > 0$, the reaction[4] is exothermic; if $E_0 < 0$, the reaction is endothermic. $T_{A(CD)}$ is always positive; thus, an endothermic reaction is possible only for the combination of T_C, T_D, u_C, u_D which yields positive values for the right-hand-side expression of Eq. (64). For nonreactive collisions, Eq. (63) may be rewritten as

$$u_{A(As)} = \frac{m_A u_A + m_s u_s}{m_A + m_s}. \tag{66}$$

---

[3] Burgers used this approximation in Refs. [7] and [8], too.
[4] $C + D \rightarrow A + B$.

In Eq. (64), we let $A = C$, $B = D$, $E_0 = 0$, etc. to obtain the translational temperature $T_{A(AB)}$:

$$\frac{3}{2} k T_{A(AB)} = \frac{3}{2} k T_A \frac{m_A{}^2 + m_B{}^2}{(m_A + m_B)^2} + \frac{3}{2} k T_B \frac{2 m_A m_B}{(m_A + m_B)^2}$$
$$+ \left\{ \frac{m_A m_B{}^2}{(m_A + m_B)^2} \frac{(\mathbf{u}_A - \mathbf{u}_B)^2}{2} \right\}. \qquad (67)$$

Interchanging the subscripts A and B, we have

$$\frac{3}{2} k T_{B(AB)} = \frac{3}{2} k T_B \frac{m_A{}^2 + m_B{}^2}{(m_A + m_B)^2} + \frac{3}{2} k T_A \frac{2 m_A m_B}{(m_A + m_B)^2}$$
$$+ \frac{m_A{}^2 m_B}{(m_A + m_B)^2} \frac{(\mathbf{u}_A - \mathbf{u}_B)^2}{2}. \qquad (68)$$

These formulas can also be written as follows:

$$T_{A(AB)} = T_A + (T_B - T_A) \frac{2 m_A m_B}{(m_A + m_B)^2}$$
$$+ \frac{m_A m_B{}^2}{(m_A + m_B)^2} \frac{(\mathbf{u}_A - \mathbf{u}_B)^2}{3k}, \qquad (67a)$$

$$T_{B(AB)} = T_B - (T_B - T_A) \frac{2 m_A m_B}{(m_A + m_B)^2}$$
$$+ \frac{m_A{}^2 m_B}{(m_A + m_B)^2} \frac{(\mathbf{u}_A - \mathbf{u}_B)^2}{3k}. \qquad (68a)$$

It is clear, from Eqs. (67a) and (68a), that $T_B - T_A$ (different temperatures of species) and $\mathbf{u}_B - \mathbf{u}_A$ (different velocities of species, i.e., diffusion) are important factors in the calculation of $T_{A(AB)}$ and $T_{B(AB)}$. In reactive collisions, in addition to these important effects, the energy exchange E_0 must be taken into account, as in Eq. (64). These special considerations of the transfer of momentum and of energy associated with reactive and nonreactive collisions are the outstanding features of Ref. [12]. With Bhatnagar-Gross-Krook's approximation, we may adopt the following expression:

$$\frac{\delta F_A}{\delta t} = \sum_s \int d\xi_S \, N_A \psi_{A(AS)} N_S \psi_{S(AS)} g_{AS} \int \sigma_{AS} \, d\Omega$$
$$+ \int d\xi_B \, N_C \psi_{A(CD)} N_D \psi_{B(CD)} g_{CD} \int \sigma_{CD}{}^* \, d\Omega$$
$$- \sum_s F_A \int d\xi_S \, F_S g_{AS} \int \sigma_{AS} \, d\Omega$$
$$- F_A \int d\xi_B \, F_B g_{AB} \int \sigma_{AB}{}^* \, d\Omega. \qquad (69)$$

In Eq. (69), replace $g_{CD} \int \sigma_{CD}^* \, d\Omega$ by $g_{AB} \int \sigma_{AB}^* \, d\Omega$, and then we have essentially Eq. (57). Now, we define the collision cross sections:

$$S_{AS} = \int \sigma_{AS} \, d\Omega, \tag{70}$$

$$S_{AB}^* = \int \sigma_{AB}^* \, d\Omega, \tag{71}$$

$$S_{CD}^* = \int \sigma_{CD}^* \, d\Omega. \tag{72}$$

Equation (69) becomes

$$\begin{aligned}
\delta F_A / \delta t &= \sum_s N_A N_s \psi_{A(AS)} \int d\xi_S \, \psi_{S(AS)} g_{AS} S_{AS} \\
&+ N_C N_D \psi_{A(CD)} \int d\xi_B \, \psi_{B(CD)} g_{CD} S_{CD}^* \\
&- \sum_s F_A \int d\xi_S \, F_S g_{AS} S_{AS} \\
&- F_A \int d\xi_B \, F_B g_{AB} S_{AB}^*.
\end{aligned} \tag{73}$$

The integrals in Eq. (73) can be interpreted as the statistical averages according to Eq. (7); therefore,

$$(1/N_B) \int F_B g_{AB} S_{AB}^* \, d\xi_B = \overline{g_{AB} S_{AB}^*} = \kappa_{AB}^*, \tag{74}$$

$$\int \psi_{B(CD)} g_{CD} S_{CD}^* \, d\xi_B = \overline{g_{CD} S_{CD}^*} = \kappa_{CD}^*, \tag{75}$$

$$(1/N_S) \int F_S g_{AS} S_{AS} \, d\xi_S = \overline{g_{AS} S_{AS}} = \kappa_{AS}, \tag{76}$$

$$\int \psi_{S(AS)} g_{AS} S_{AS} \, d\xi_S = \overline{g_{AS} S_{AS}} = \kappa_{AS}. \tag{77}$$

Therefore, we obtain from Eq. (73)

$$\begin{aligned}
\delta F_A / \delta t &= \sum_s N_A N_s \psi_{A(AS)} \kappa_{AS} + N_C N_D \psi_{A(CD)} \kappa_{CD}^* \\
&- \sum_s N_S F_A \kappa_{AS} - N_B F_A \kappa_{AB}^*.
\end{aligned} \tag{78}$$

Combination of Eqs. (58) and (78) yields the gas kinetic equation used by Burgers [12]. The coefficients κ_{AS}, etc., here are collision frequencies. They are not at all or only very inexactly known. The main difficulty in the kinetic theory of reacting gases lies in this aspect of the problem. In the present approximation, we assume these coefficients κ_{AS}, etc., are given quantities. Then, we may regard Eq. (78) as being linear in F_A. We shall apply again the thirteen-moment method to obtain the flow equation for reacting gases.[5]

The Boltzmann-type gas kinetic equation for the A-species is written

[5] In Ref. [12], eight-moment method has been used.

as follows:

$$D^*F_A = \delta^*F_A/\delta t \qquad (79)$$

where

$$D^*F_A = \frac{D^*F_A}{Dt} + c_{Ah}{}^* \frac{\partial F_A}{\partial x_h} - \left[\frac{D^*u_{Ai}}{Dt} + c_{Ah}{}^* \frac{\partial u_{Ai}}{\partial x_h} \right] \frac{\partial F_A}{\partial c_{Ai}{}^*}, \qquad (80)$$

$$\frac{\delta^*F_A}{\delta t} = \sum_s N_A N_s \psi_{A(AS)} \kappa_{AS} - \sum_s N_s F_{A} \kappa_{AS}$$

$$+ N_C N_D \psi_{A(CD)} \kappa_{CD}{}^* - N_B F_A \kappa_{AB}{}^*. \qquad (81)$$

D^*/Dt is already defined in Eq. (51) $(S = A)$. In the present problem, we adopt formulation II with $c_A{}^* = \xi_A - u_A$, as in Eq. (42). To obtain the thirteen-moment equations from Eq. (79), we obtain

$$\int Q^* D^* F_A \, dc_A{}^* = \int Q^* \frac{\delta^*F_A}{\delta t} \, dc_A{}^* \qquad (82)$$

where Q^* denotes one of the following transferable quantities:

$$Q^{0*} = m_A, \qquad (83)$$

$$Q_k{}^{I*} = m_A c_{Ak}{}^*, \qquad (84)$$

$$Q_{hk}{}^{II*} = m_A c_{Ah}{}^* c_{Ak}{}^*, \qquad (85)$$

$$Q_k{}^{III*} = \tfrac{1}{2} m_A c_A{}^{*2} c_{Ak}{}^*. \qquad {}^6(86)$$

To carry out the calculations indicated in Eq. (82), it is not necessary to assume an explicit expression for F_A. This must be regarded as a simplification due to the adoption of the Bhatnagar-Gross-Krook's approximation. The integration of the left-hand side of Eq. (82) will again have the following difficulty. The nth moment equation contains the $(n + 1)$ moment. To alleviate this difficulty, we adopt [2]

$$(p_A{}^*)_{hki} = \tfrac{2}{5}(\delta_{ki} q_{Ah}{}^{**} + \delta_{hi} q_{Ak}{}^{**} + \delta_{hk} q_{Ai}{}^{**}), \qquad (87)$$

$$(p_A{}^*)_{iikr} = 7 \left(\frac{p_A{}^*}{m_A N_A} \right) (P_A{}^*)_{kr} + 5 \frac{(p_A{}^*)^2}{N_A m_A} \delta_{kr}, \qquad (88)$$

where, besides the symbols already defined in Eqs. (45)–(48), we have

$$(p_A{}^*)_{hki} = \int F_A m_A c_{Ah}{}^* c_{Ak}{}^* c_{Ai}{}^* \, dc_A{}^*, \qquad (89)$$

$$(p_A{}^*)_{iikr} = \int F_A m_A c_A{}^{*2} c_{Ak}{}^* c_{Ar}{}^* \, dc_A{}^*. \qquad (90)$$

Equations (87) and (88) have been used in the following calculations.

---

^{6} Alternatively, we may take $Q_k^{III**} = \tfrac{1}{2} m_A c_A{}^{*2} c_{Ak}{}^* + E_A$, but, since E_A is assumed constant, we have $Q_k^{III**} = Q_k^{III*} + (E_A/m_A) Q^{0*}$.

We obtain the flow equations as follows:

$$Q^{0*}: \quad \frac{D^*}{Dt} N_A + N_A \frac{\partial u_{Ah}}{\partial x_h}$$

$$= -\kappa_{AB}^* N_A N_B + \kappa_{CD}^* N_C N_D \qquad \text{(continuity)}, \qquad (91)$$

$$Q_k^{I*}: \quad N_{\cdot} m_A \frac{D^*}{Dt} u_{Ak} + \frac{\partial}{\partial x_h} (p_A^*)_{hk}$$

$$= -\sum_s K_{AS}(u_{Ak} - u_{Sk})$$

$$+ N_C N_D m_A [u_{A(CD)k} - u_{Ak}] \kappa_{CD}^* \qquad \text{(momentum)}, \qquad (92)$$

$$Q_{hk}^{II*}: \quad \frac{D^*}{Dt} (P_A^*)_{hk} + \delta_{hk} \frac{D^*}{Dt} (p_A^*)$$

$$+ \frac{2}{5} \frac{\partial}{\partial x_h} [\delta_{ki} q_{Ah}^{**} + \delta_{hi} q_{Ak}^{**} + \delta_{hk} q_{Ai}^{**}]$$

$$+ (P_A^*)_{hk} \frac{\partial u_{Ah}}{\partial x_h} + (P_A^*)_{hj} \frac{\partial u_{Ak}}{\partial x_j} + (P_A^*)_{kj} \frac{\partial u_{Ak}}{\partial x_j}$$

$$+ p_A^* \left(\delta_{hk} \frac{\partial u_{Ah}}{\partial x_h} + \delta_{hj} \frac{\partial u_{Ak}}{\partial x_j} + \delta_{kj} \frac{\partial u_{Ah}}{\partial x_j} \right)$$

$$= \sum_s K_{AS} \delta_{hk} \left\{ \frac{2k}{m_A + m_S} (T_S - T_A) + \frac{m_S}{m_A + m_S} \frac{1}{3} (\mathbf{u}_A - \mathbf{u}_S)^2 \right\}$$

$$+ \sum_s K_{AS} \frac{m_S}{m_A + m_S} (u_{Ah} - u_{Sh})(u_{Ak} - u_{Sk})$$

$$- \sum_s N_S \kappa_{AS} (P_A^*)_{hk} - N_B \kappa_{AB}^* [(P_A^*)_{hk} + \delta_{hk} p_A^*]$$

$$+ N_C N_D \kappa_{CD}^* \{ \delta_{hk} k T_{A(CD)} + m_A [u_{A(CD)h} - u_{Ah}] [u_{A(CD)k} - u_{Ak}] \} \qquad \text{(stress-component)}, \qquad (93)$$

$$Q_k^{III*}: \quad \frac{D^*}{Dt} (q_A^{**})_k + \frac{7}{5} (q_A^{**})_h \frac{\partial u_{Ak}}{\partial x_h} + \frac{7}{5} (q_A^{**})_k \frac{\partial u_{Ah}}{\partial x_h}$$

$$+ \frac{2}{5} (q_A^{**})_i \frac{\partial u_{Ai}}{\partial x_k} + \frac{7}{2} \frac{\partial}{\partial x_h} \left[\frac{p_A^* (P_A^*)_{hk}}{N_A m_A} \right] + \frac{2}{5} \frac{\partial}{\partial x_k} \left(\frac{(p_A^*)^2}{N_A m_A} \right)$$

$$+ \left[(P_A^*)_{ki} + \frac{5}{2} \delta_{ki} p_A^* \right] \left[\Delta Q_i^I - \frac{\partial}{\partial x_h} \{ (P_A^*)_{hi} + \delta_{hi} p_A^* \} \right] \frac{1}{N_A m_A}$$

$$= -\sum_s K_{AS} \frac{15 k T_A}{2 m_A} (u_{Ak} - u_{Sk})$$

$$- \sum_s K_{AS} \frac{15 k m_S}{(m_A + m_S)^2} (T_S - T_A)(u_{Ak} - u_{Sk})$$

$$- \sum_s 3K_{AS} \left(\frac{m_S}{m_A + m_S} \right)^2 (\mathbf{u}_A - \mathbf{u}_S)^2 (u_{Ak} - u_{Sk})$$

$$- \sum_s N_{S\kappa AS}(q_A^{**})_k$$

$$- N_{B\kappa AB}^* (q_A^{**})_k$$

$$+ N_C N_{D\kappa CD}^* \left\{ \frac{15}{2} kT_{A(CD)}(u_{A(CD)k} - u_{Ak}) \right.$$

$$+ \frac{m_A}{2} [u_{A(CD)k} - u_{Ak}][\mathbf{u}_{A(CD)} - \mathbf{u}_A]^2 \right\} \qquad \text{(heat flux component)}.$$

$$(94)$$

In these equations, the following notation is used:

$$K_{AS} = \frac{N_A N_{S\kappa AS} m_A m_S}{m_A + m_S} \qquad (95)$$

K_{AS} is the resistance coefficient [12]. In Eq. (94), the symbol

$$\Delta Q_i^{I} = \frac{\partial}{\partial x_h} (p_A^*)_{hi} + N_A m_A \frac{D^* u_{Ai}}{Dt}. \qquad (96)$$

By contraction of Eq. (93), we have the energy equations as follows:

$$Q_0^{II*} = \frac{1}{2} Q_{hh}^{II*}: \quad \frac{D^*}{Dt} \left(\frac{3}{2} p_A^* \right) + \frac{\partial}{\partial x_i} (q_{Ai}^{**})$$

$$+ (P_A^*)_{hj} \frac{\partial u_{Ah}}{\partial x_j} + \frac{5}{2} p_A^* \frac{\partial u_{Ah}}{\partial x_h}$$

$$= \sum_s K_{As} \frac{3k(T_s - T_A)}{m_A + m_s} + \sum_s K_{As} \frac{m_s}{m_A + m_s} (\mathbf{u}_s - \mathbf{u}_A)^2$$

$$- N_{B\kappa AB}^* N_A \frac{3}{2} kT_A$$

$$+ N_C N_{D\kappa CD}^* \left\{ \frac{3}{2} kT_{A(CD)} + \frac{m_A}{2} (\mathbf{u}_{A(CD)} - \mathbf{u}_A)^2 \right\}$$

$$\text{(energy)} \quad (97)$$

These flow equations are easily reduced to Burgers' eight-moment equations [12] by letting $(P_A^*)_{hk} = 0$. By letting $\kappa_{AB}^* = \kappa_{CD}^* = 0$, we obtain the thirteen-moment equations for the A-gas of a nonreacting mixture, within the Bhatnagar-Gross-Krook's approximation. These flow equations, Eqs. (91)–(94), when written out for all species of the reacting mixture of gases, form a closed set if the coefficient κ_{AS}, κ_{AB}^*, etc., is considered as given. This set of equations is not linear, and, in general, the boundary conditions to be adopted for a specific problem

are also nonlinear. Therefore, the solution of the reacting nonequilibrium flow problem is indeed difficult. To simplify, several schemes of
simplification can be considered:

(1) In the flow equations, certain terms can be neglected, and an
iteration scheme such as suggested in Refs. [6] and [7] can be devised.

(2) When we consider the forward reaction $A + B \rightarrow C + D$, we
suppose that the reaction just begins, so that we may neglect all encounters between A and C or A and D.

Finally, we observe from Eqs. (91)–(94) that the nonequilibrium flows
of reacting gases are characterized by the following:

(1) Different velocities of different species. Thus, interdiffusion
phenomena are important.

(2) Different temperatures of different species. Thus, phenomena of
heat exchange are important for temperature equilibration. These effects
are important in the problems treated in the preceding section, too.
Besides these effects, the chemical reactions have the important effects
of introducing the new values of $\mathbf{u}_{A(CD)}$ and $T_{A(CD)}$ as defined in Eqs. (63)
and (64). These new values pertain to the A particles just coming out
of the reactive collisions of C and D particles. $T_{A(CD)}$ and $\mathbf{u}_{A(CD)}$ are
different from T_A and $\mathbf{u}_A$, respectively. These differences are responsible
for additional diffusion and additional heat exchange. These characteristics of nonequilibrium flows seem to suggest that formulation II as
adopted here is the logical choice for future developments. The significance of the multifluid nature for reacting flows with large departures
from equilibrium is therefore once again brought out clearly.

IV. BURGERS–BOLTZMANN EQUATION OF GAS KINETICS

In the preceding section, we assigned a single quantum state for each
species of the reacting gases, and we considered only binary collisions.
The molecules actually may exist in a spectrum of internal states. A
set of quantum numbers specifying completely the internal state of a
molecule is then necessary in a semi-quantum-mechanical description [14].
This set of quantum numbers is denoted by a quantum number n. Let
us define the α-class of particles as the particles of the s-species in the
quantum state n with internal energy E_n and moving with translational
velocity ξ_s between the limits $(\xi_s, \xi_s + d\xi_s)$. The number of particles
of the α-class in a unit volume at $\mathbf{x}$ at an instant t can be defined as
$F_{s,n}(\mathbf{x}, t, \xi_s, E_n) \, d\xi_s$, where $F_{s,n}$ is the distribution function of the

particles of the α-class. We again adopt an equation of the Boltzmann type:

$$\frac{\partial F_{s,n}}{\partial t} + \xi_{sh} \frac{\partial F_{s,n}}{\partial x_h} = \frac{\delta F_{s,n}}{\delta t}. \tag{98}$$

The molecules are again assumed to be moving in a force-free field. The right-hand-side term of Eq. (98) will be obtained as in Ref. [15] in which Burgers considered a gas kinetic model that includes many realistic features:

(1) We define the β-class of particles as the particles of the t-species in the quantum state n_1 with internal energy E_{n_1} and moving with translational velocity ξ_t in the range $(\xi_t, \xi_t + d\xi_t)$. Encounters of α and β particles may cause a chemical reaction of the l-type, which produces a γ-class of particles, which are particles of the k-species in quantum state $n_2(E_{n_2})$ with ξ_k in the range $(\xi_k, \xi_k + d\xi_k)$. In the particular case of collisions without chemical reaction, both s and t-particles will reappear generally with changed translational velocities and new quantum states. In reactive collisions, let $\nu_{k(l)}$ denote the number of k-particles coming out of a reaction l. For nonreactive collisions, we write $l = 0; \nu_{s(0)} = \nu_{t(0)} = 1$.

(2) Besides changes due to collisions, the particles of the α-class may undergo spontaneous changes. These spontaneous changes are characterized by a relaxation time τ_m. Many spontaneous processes are possible. For instance, a particle in a high quantum state can spontaneously pass into a lower state with the emission of radiation. Another important class of spontaneous processes is spontaneous dissociation. Consideration of this latter process permits an approximate treatment of multiparticle collisions which may be the required mechanism for certain reactions. For instance, as Burgers showed, in triple collisions involving particles of species s, t, k, we may postulate the formation of an "activated complex," denoted by $(st)^*$, from binary encounters of s and t. Then, $(st)^*$ possesses a relaxation time: it may dissociate spontaneously back into s and t before encounter with k, or else it may have an encounter with k with a finite probability of losing its excess energy and assuming the ground state of the new particles (st). In this manner, we need only to consider binary collisions in our formalism.

For this realistic gas kinetic model, we may write

$$\frac{\delta F_{s,n}}{\delta t} = \left(\frac{\delta F_{s,n}}{\delta t}\right)_{coll} + \left(\frac{\delta F_{s,n}}{\delta t}\right)_{spon\ proc}. \tag{99}$$

The right-hand-side terms signify, respectively, the changes brought

about by collisions and spontaneous processes.   From Eq. (73), we may
write (for $S = A$)

$$
\left(\frac{\delta F_{A,n}}{\delta t}\right)_{coll} = \sum_{s,n_1} \nu_{s(0)}\nu_{A(0)}N_{A,n}N_{s,n_1}\psi_{A,n(0)} \int d\xi_s\, \psi_{s,n_1(0)}g_{A,n;s,n_1}S_{A,n;s,n_1(0)}
$$

$$
+ \sum_{C,D,n_2,n_3,n_4,l} \nu_{A(l)}\nu_{B(l)}N_{c,n_2}N_{D,n_3}\psi_{A,n(l)}
$$

$$
\times \int d\xi_B\, \psi_{B,n_4(l)}g_{C,n_2;\,D,n_3}S_{C,n_2;\,D,n_3(l)}
$$

$$
- \sum_{s,n_1} F_{A,n} \int d\xi_s\, F_{s,n_1}g_{A,n;\,s,n_1}S_{A,n;\,s,n_1(0)}
$$

$$
- \sum_{B,n',l} F_{A,n} \int d\xi_B\, F_{B,n_1}g_{A,n;\,B,n_1}S_{A,n,B,n_1(l)}\,. \tag{100}
$$

In Eq. (100), the lth reaction is assumed as follows:

$$
\nu_{A(l)}A(n) + \nu_{B(l)}B(n_4) \rightleftarrows C(n_2) + D(n_3) \tag{101}
$$

Also, the nonreactive collision is denoted by $l = 0$; thus,

$$
A(n) + S(n_1) \to \nu_{A(0)}A(n) + \nu_{s(0)}S(n_1), \tag{102}
$$
$$
A(n) + S(n_1) \to \nu_{A(0)}A(n^*) + \nu_{s(0)}S(n_1^*). \tag{103}
$$

In Eq. (102), the collision causes translational velocities to change; in
Eq. (103), the collision causes both translational velocities and quantum
states to change.   In these equations, $\nu_{A(0)} = \nu_{s(0)} = 1$.   Other notations used in Eq. (100) are analogous to those used in Eq. (73), except
we used the subscript l to designate the lth reaction and the subscripts
n, n_1, etc., for the respective quantum states.   We have adopted the
Bhatnagar-Gross-Krook's approximation for the velocity distribution
of particles coming out of collisions.   To identify the quantum state of
the A-particles coming out of collisions, we assume that the distribution
over the quantum states is independent of the distribution of translational
velocities.   Thus, we write

$$
\psi_{A,n(l)} = \left(\frac{m_A}{2\pi k T_{A(l)}}\right)^{3/2} \exp\left(-\frac{m_A(\xi_A - u_{A(l)})^2}{2k T_{A(l)}}\right)\phi_{A,n(l)} \tag{104}
$$

where

$$
\phi_{A,n(l)} = \frac{g_{A,n}}{Z}\exp\left(-\frac{E_{A,n}}{k T_{A(l)}}\right), \tag{105}
$$

$$
Z = \sum_n g_{A,n}\exp\left(-\frac{E_{A,n}}{k T_{A(l)}}\right). \tag{106}
$$

Burgers [15] gives the following expression for the spontaneous changes $(S = A)$:

$$\left(\frac{\delta F_{A,n}}{\delta t}\right)_{\text{spon proc}} = -F_{A,n}\sum_m \frac{1}{\tau_m} + \sum_{\substack{t \neq A, n_1 \\ m \neq 0}} \frac{N_{t,n_1}}{\tau_m} \nu_{A(m)} \psi_{A,n(m)}$$

$$+ \sum_{n^* \neq n} \frac{F_{A,n^*}}{\tau_0} \phi_{n^*}{}^n \tag{107}$$

where τ_m is the relaxation time, the subscript m referring to the type of spontaneous processes, $m \neq 0$ being the spontaneous chemical changes, $m = 0$ being spontaneous changes of quantum states. $\phi_{n^*}{}^n$ denotes the probability for a spontaneous transition from a quantum state n^* to the quantum state n of lower energy. We have

$$\sum_{n^* \neq n} \phi_{n^*}{}^n = 1. \tag{108}$$

Combining Eqs. (98), (99), (100), and (107) yields an extended form of the Boltzmann-type equation. This equation is designated here as the Burgers-Boltzmann equation. It may be used, as in previous sections, as the basis of construction of flow equations.

The Burgers-Boltzmann equation as just described contains many parameters that are not known at the present time. These parameters include the collisional cross sections, the relaxation times, etc. Much of the difficulty arises from the fact that quantum mechanical calculations are required in the determination of these parameters. Seeking to simplify the Burgers-Boltzmann equation, we may decide to obtain a simple model equation of the velocity distribution for A-species irrespective of the quantum states. In this simplification, we shall also discard the effects of spontaneous processes. We now introduce some mean values:

$$\psi_{s(0)} g_{A,n;\,s} S_{A,n;\,s(0)} = \frac{\sum\limits_{n_1} \psi_{s,n_1(0)} g_{A,n,s,n;\,} S_{A,n,s,n_1(0)} N_{s,n_1}}{\sum\limits_{n_1} N_{s,n_1}},$$

$$g_{CD} S_{CD(l)} = \frac{\sum\limits_{n_2,n_3} (N_{C,n_2} N_{D,n_3} g_{C,n_2;\,D,n_3} S_{C,n_2;\,D,n_3(l)})}{\sum\limits_{n_2,n_3} N_{C,n_2} N_{D,n_3}}.$$

etc., where $\displaystyle\sum_{n_1} N_{s,n_1} = N_s$, etc. Then, Eq. (100) becomes

$$\left(\frac{\delta F_{A,n}}{\delta t}\right)_{\text{coll}} = \sum_s N_s N_{A,n}\psi_{A,n(0)} \int d\xi_s\, \psi_{s(0)} g_{A,n;s} S_{A,n;s(0)}$$

$$+ \sum_l \nu_{A(l)}\nu_{B(l)} N_C N_D \psi_{A,n(l)} \int d\xi_B\, \psi_{B(l)} g_{CD} S_{CD(l)}$$

$$- \sum_s F_{A,n} \int d\xi_s\, F_s g_{A,n;s} S_{A,n;s(0)}$$

$$- \sum_l F_{A,n} \int d\xi_B\, F_B g_{A,n;B} S_{A,n;B(l)}\,. \qquad (109)$$

Taking summation over all quantum states n of the A-species and introducing some further mean values, we arrive at

$$\left(\frac{\delta F_A}{\delta t}\right)_{\text{coll}} = \sum_s N_s N_A \psi_{A(0)} \int d\xi_s\, \psi_{s(0)} g_{As} S_{As(0)}$$

$$+ \sum_{C,D,l} \nu_{A(l)}\nu_{B(l)} N_C N_D \psi_{A(l)} \int d\xi_B\, \psi_{B(l)} g_{CD} S_{CD(l)}$$

$$- \sum_s F_A \int d\xi_s\, F_s g_{As} S_{As(0)}$$

$$- \sum_{B,l} F_A \int d\xi_B\, F_B g_{AB} S_{AB(l)}\,. \qquad (110)$$

In Eq. (110), we obtain an expression for the collision effects which can be reduced to Eq. (73) when we let $\nu_{A(l)} = \nu_{B(l)} = 1$ and restrict ourselves to the single reaction described by Eq. (56). In Ref. [16], some further approximate arguments have been used to reduce the Burgers-Boltzmann equation into a still simpler model gas kinetic equation used in Ref. [8]. We shall not enter into these discussions here. To close the present section, we state that the right-hand-side terms of the Burgers-Boltzmann equation are reducible to Eq. (78), and that the flow equations obtained in the preceding section are useful for nonequilibrium flows of reacting gases.

V. CONCLUSION

In the present paper, we have studied some aspects of the gas kinetic equations of the Boltzmann type. In Section II, we apply the original

Boltzmann equation for a monatomic gas and obtain flow equations from it. In Section III, we modify the Boltzmann equation to account for chemical reaction in gases. We apply the resulting gas kinetic equation to obtain flow equations for reacting gases. In Section IV, the Burgers-Boltzmann equation has been connected to the gas kinetic equation used in Section III. All these discussions are intended to bring out some connections among many of the significant results obtained by Burgers during the past decade.

From the present calculations, we deduce that the characteristics of nonequilibrium flows of reacting gases are (1) unequal flow velocities of the different species and the interdiffusion effects, (2) unequal temperatures of the different species and the heat exchange effects, and (3) chemical effects with the appearance of characteristic velocity $\mathbf{u}_{A(CD)}$ and characteristic temperature $T_{A(CD)}$ (see Section III) for A-particles just created in $C - D$ reactive collisions. In order to account for these effects properly, formulation II (as discussed in Section II) must be considered the proper approach. This formulation tends to emphasize the multifluid aspect of the mixture which is necessary for highly nonequilibrium flows. Burgers' results shed much light on this important understanding.

In the actual construction of macroscopic flow equations, we select a proper set of variables of state. We then obtain the equations that determine these variables of state. The method of 13 moments is demonstrated in the present paper. This method was pioneered by Grad [2]. Much of the results in the present problems are due to Burgers. In Section III, we extend Burgers' results [12] to include effects due to the nonvanishing deviator stress components.

In the present report, we have excluded external forces. These external force fields are important in investigations of plasmadynamics. In most of the cited references due to Burgers, he has included these effects. Inclusion of these effects is entirely possible. However, in the flow of a mixture of charged particles, the right-hand-side terms of the gas kinetic equation again take possibly new forms. These interesting topics have been investigated by Burgers [17]. Some recent studies of the shock structure in an ionized gas [18] have been carried out on the basis of the plasma flow equations due to Burgers.

Acknowledgment

This work has been sponsored by the Advanced Research Projects Agency (Ballistic Missile Defense Office) and technically administered by the Fluid Dynamic Branch of the Office of Naval Research under Contract Nonr 2168(03), Subcontract No. 1, with the University of Cincinnati.

REFERENCES

1. Chapman, S. and Cowling, T. D., "The Mathematical Theory of Non-uniform Gases," p. 61. Cambridge Univ. Press, London and New York, 1952 ed.
2. Grad, H., On the Kinetic Theory of Rarefied Gases, *Commun. Pure Appl. Math.* **2**, 331–407 (December 1949).
3. Krook, M., Continuum Equations in the Dynamics of Rarefied Gases, *J. Fluid Mech.* **6**, 523–541 (1959).
4. Lees, L., Kinetic Theory Description of Rarefied Gas Flow, *J. Soc. Ind. Appl. Math.* **13**, 278–311 (March 1965).
5. Burgers, J. M., Selected Topics from the Theory of Gas Flow at High Temperature (V): The Application of Transfer Equations to the Calculation of Diffusion, Heat Conduction, Viscosity and Electric Conductivity. AFOSR TN-58-427, 427a, AD 158-230, 230a, Univ. of Maryland (May 1958).
6. Ikenberry, E. and Truesdell, C., On the Pressures and the Flux of Energy in a Gas According to Maxwell's Kinetic Theory, I, *J. Ratl. Mech. Anal.* **5**, 1–54, 1956; Truesdell, C., same title, II, *J. Ratl. Mech. Anal.* **5**, 55–128 (1956).
7. Burgers, J. M., Selected Topics from the Theory of Gas Flow at High Temperatures (IV). AFOSR TN-57-459, AD 136 450, Univ. of Maryland (July 1957).
8. Burgers, J. M., Selected Topics from the Theory of Gas Flow at High Temperatures (III). AFOSR TN-57-284, AD 132 355, Univ. of Maryland (March 1957).
9. Prigogine, I. and Xhrouet, E., On the Perturbation of Maxwell Distribution Function by Chemical Reactions in Gases, *Physica* **15**, 913–931 (1949).
10. Ross, J. and Mazur, P., Some Deductions from a Formal Statistical Theory of Chemical Kinetics, *J. Chem. Phys.* **35**, 19–28 (1961).
11. Ludwig, G. and Heil, M., Boundary-Layer Theory with Dissociation and Ionization, *in* "Advances in Applied Mechanics," Vol. VI, pp. 39–118. Academic Press, New York, 1960.
12. Burgers, J. M., The Construction of Equations of Motion for Reacting Gases. Presented at the Meeting of the Soc. Eng. Sci., East Lansing, Michigan (November 1964).
13. Bhatnagar, P. L., Gross, E. P., and Krook, M., A Model for Collision Processes in Gases I, *Phys. Rev.* **84**, 511–525 (1945); also Krook, M., Dynamics of Rarefied Gases, *Phys. Rev.* **99**, 1896–1897 (1955); also Gross, E. P. and Krook, M., Model for Collision Processes in Gases, *Phys. Rev.* **102**, 593–604 (1956).
14. Wang-Chang, C. S. and Uhlenbeck, G. E., Transport Phenomena in Polyatomic Gases. Rept. No. CM-681, Univ. of Michigan Eng. Res. Inst. (July 1951).
15. Burgers, J. M., The Boltzmann Equation for Flows with Chemical Reactions, *in* "Physical Chemistry in Aerodynamics and Space Flight" (A. L. Myerson and A. G. Harrison, eds.), pp. 4–11. Macmillan (Pergamon), New York, 1961.
16. Li, T. Y., Study of Burgers' Equation of the Kinetic Theory for a Reacting Gaseous Mixture. Univ. of Cincinnati, TR-AE-6402 (July 1964).
17. Burgers, J. M., The Bridge between Particle Mechanics and Continuum Mechanics, *in* "Plasma Dynamics" (F. H. Clauser, ed.), pp. 119–186. Addison-Wesley, Reading, Massachusetts, 1960.
18. Jaffrin, M. Y. and Probstein, R. F., Structure of a Plasma Shock Wave. *Phys. Fluids* **7**, 1658–1674 (1964); also Jaffrin, M. Y., Shock Structure in a Partially Ionized Gas. *Phys. Fluids* **8**, 606–625 (1965).

Nonequilibrium Effects on

Energy Transfer in an Ionized Fluid Flow

JOHN O. POWERS[1] AND S. I. PAI[2]

INSTITUTE FOR FLUID DYNAMICS AND APPLIED MATHEMATICS
UNIVERSITY OF MARYLAND
COLLEGE PARK, MARYLAND

A multifluid theory is formulated, and the resulting equation system is developed and then applied to an ionized fluid flow situation in order to evaluate the mechanisms of energy transfer. The effects of temperature and compositional nonequilibrium were explored for several temperature levels and for a range of fluid flow velocities. Comparisons of the multifluid theory results are made with results from conventional single-fluid theory for approximately equivalent fluid flow conditions. The multifluid theory investigations produced results that were generally consistent with the single-fluid theory procedures. The multifluid results were useful in evaluating the relative importance of the several different energy transfer mechanisms. In particular, it was demonstrated that conditions that yield electron temperatures greater than the heavy-particle temperature led to a reduction in total heat transfer with increased electron temperatures. Conditions of compositional nonequilibrium appeared to have only small effects on the energy transfer unless they were coupled with appreciable degrees of thermal nonequilibrium. The coupling of the viscous flow variables was manifested as an alternation in the heavy-particle conductive mode of energy transfer but did not affect the electron conductive mode. Of the several modes of energy transfer, however, the electron conductive mode is shown to be most susceptible to intentional alteration.

I. INTRODUCTION

The continued interest in high-energy gas flow phenomena has led to an increasing number of investigations directed at improving our knowledge and understanding of the influence of ionization on fluid flows. These investigations have, in general, been concentrated in two areas; namely, investigations of the electrical characteristic of flows, and investigations of surface heat transfer in ionized flows. The studies of plasma electrical characteristics are, in general, directed toward the improvement of diagnostic techniques such as the Langmuir-type probe, which is used to

---

[1] *Present address:* Aerophysics Division, Naval Ordnance Laboratory, White Oak, Maryland.

[2] *Present address:* Institute of Space and Aeronautical Science, University of Tokyo, Tokyo, Japan.

measure ion and electron number densities. The heat-transfer investigations are generally directed toward the solution of the problems of planetary entry or toward problems of design of very high temperature experimental facilities. The present investigation is concerned primarily with the study of heat-transfer mechanisms. Although these areas of investigation can in some cases be explored separately, it is probable that the electrical effects, whether induced or applied, will be present and hence, will contribute to the heat-transfer process.

Most of the investigations of heat transfer from an ionized gas were based on single-fluid theory with only a mean temperature for all species [1–4]. They do find that ionization has a significant effect on the heat transfer of the flow. However, when the degree of ionization increases new influences due to ionization occur. One is that the electron temperature may differ appreciably from those of the heavy particles. The other is that electromagnetic field, applied or induced, may change the degree of ionization and affect the heat-transfer rate of the flow field. Preliminary studies of these influences have been made [5–7]. Chung and Mullen [5] studied the weakly ionized boundary layer such that the neutral gas flow was unaffected by the charged particles. They found that the degree of equilibrium of the electron temperature with the neutral gas temperature was strongly dependent on the potential difference across the boundary layer.

Dix [6] considered the case of a partially ionized atomic hydrogen between two stationary parallel and electrically conducting plates at considerably different temperatures. He studied mainly the interaction of thermal conduction and diffusion in an ionized gas and particularly the energy transfer mechanism of energy transfer in ionized gases.

Camac and Kemp [7] investigated the end wall heat transfer behind a reflected shock of highly ionized argon by considering the difference of the electron temperature and the temperature of heavy particles. They did not discuss fully the significance of the aero-electrical coupling.

The present investigation [8] seeks to assess the effects of (1) the difference of temperature of electron and that of heavy particles, (2) the nonequilibrium in degree of ionization due to electrical field, and (3) the contribution of heat transfer by thermal conduction, diffusion, and viscous dissipation in the flow field of an ionized gas.

II. FLOW MODEL AND BASIC EQUATIONS

Since the objective of the present investigation was to study an ionized fluid flow system in which thermal nonequilibrium effects were existing, it was apparent that conventional single-fluid equation system could not

be used to meet these objectives. We have derived a system of equations of multifluid theory from the Boltzmann equation using a distribution function that is independent of the diffusional velocities and does not require an equality of species temperatures. The detailed derivation of this system of equation is given by Powers [8]. The procedures used are analogous to those outlined by Burgers [9].

The applicability of the multifluid equations in describing a given flow situation was considered to be most readily evaluated if the flow model was not too complicated. Hence, we consider a steady Couette flow of partially ionized monatomic argon gas consisting of three species, namely, atoms, ions, and electrons. The flow is contained between two parallel plates, a distance L apart, with the lower plate stationary and the upper plate moving at an appreciable velocity in the positive x direction (Fig. 1).

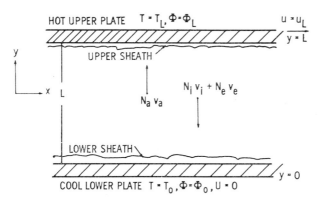

FIG. 1. Flow model.

The lower plate is considered to be the cooler surface and is completely catalytic in recombination of the ion-electron flux reaching it by diffusion. The upper moving plate is at quite a high temperature and is assumed to be capable of ionizing the incident atom flux with a specified efficiency. Although the surface ionization mechanism was not specified, its hypothesis was necessary, since only heterogeneous chemical reactions were assumed. Otherwise expressed, the diffusional flow normal to the plates consists of a flux of atoms, originating at the cool plate by the deionization, which flows to the hot plate and is ionized, thereby initiating a flux of ions and electrons from the hot to cooled plates. For the multifluid theory investigations, we make the further assumption that the cool plate has a small negative potential, whereas the hot plate has a slightly positive potential, but their magnitude is such that there is zero net current flow.

Two further assumptions were made which are generally considered

consistent with the assumed physical model. First, it was considered that the ions and atoms are mutually in thermal equilibrium. This assumption is based on the fact that particles of approximately equal mass exchange a large percentage of the initial difference in the kinetic energy in a collision, and, hence, very few collisions would be necessary for thermal equilibrium. The converse of this reasoning, when applied to electron-heavy particle collisions, is the basis of the concept of electron thermal nonequilibrium. The second assumption was that the x-component of all species velocities is considered equal.

Under the foregoing assumptions, all unknowns are functions of y-coordinate only. The basic equations are as follows:

    (i)   Equation of continuity of s-species:

$$\frac{dN_s V_s}{dy} = 0 \tag{1}$$

where N_s is the number density of s-species and V_s is the y-component of velocity of s-species. The subscript s may refer to the value of s-species, i.e., atoms (with $s = a$), ions (with $s = i$), or electrons (with $s = e$).

    (ii)   The x-wise momentum equation:

$$(\rho_a V_a + \rho_i V_i + \rho_e V_e)\frac{du}{dy} = \frac{d}{dy}\left[(\mu_a + \mu_i + \mu_e)\frac{du}{dy}\right] \tag{2}$$

where $\rho_s = m_s N_s = $ mass density of s-species, m_s is the mass of a particle of s-species, and μ_s is the coefficient of viscosity of s-species. Under the second assumption, $u_s = u$.

    (iii)   The y-wise momentum equations:

$$\rho_s V_s \frac{dV_s}{dy} - \frac{4}{3}\frac{d}{dy}\left(\mu_s \frac{dV_s}{dy}\right) + k\frac{dN_s T_s}{dy} = \sum_t K_{st}(V_s - V_t) \tag{3}$$

where k is Boltzmann constant, K_{st} is the resistance coefficient between species s and t, and the summation is over all species.

    (iv)   The energy equation for heavy particles:

$$\frac{3}{2}k(N_a V_a + N_i V_i)\frac{dT_a}{dy} - \frac{d}{dy}\left[(k_a + k_i)\frac{dT_a}{dy}\right] - (\mu_a + \mu_i)\left(\frac{du}{dy}\right)^2$$

$$- \frac{4}{3}\left[\mu_a\left(\frac{dV_a}{dy}\right)^2 + \mu_i\left(\frac{dV_i}{dy}\right)^2\right] + kT_a\left(N_a\frac{dV_a}{dy} + N_i\frac{dV_i}{dy}\right)$$

$$= K_{ai}(V_i - V_a)^2 + \frac{m_e}{m_a}\frac{T_a}{T_e}[K_{ea}(V_e - V_a)^2 + K_{ie}(V_e - V_i)^2]$$

$$+ \frac{m_e}{m_a}\left(\frac{T_e - T_a}{T_e}\right)(K_{ea}{}^T + K_{ei}{}^T) \tag{4}$$

Here we assume $T_a = T_i$, k_s is the coefficient of thermal conductivity of s-species, and $K_{st}{}^T$ is the thermal resistance coefficient between species s and t. The mass of an atom is assumed equal to that of an ion. The ratio m_e/m_a is negligibly small except when it is multiplied by quantities whose magnitudes are unknown a *priori*.

   (v) Energy equation of electrons:

$$\frac{3}{2} k N_e V_e \frac{dT_e}{dy} - \frac{d}{dy}\left(k_e \frac{dT_e}{dy}\right) - \mu_e \left[\left(\frac{du}{dy}\right)^2 + \frac{4}{3}\left(\frac{dV_e}{dy}\right)^2\right] + N_e k T_e \frac{dV_e}{dy}$$

$$= K_{ei}(V_i - V_e)^2 + K_{ea}(V_a - V_e)^2 + \frac{m_e}{m_a}\left(\frac{T_a - T_e}{T_e}\right)[K_{ei}{}^T + K_{ea}{}^T] \quad (5)$$

   (vi) Equation of electric field:

$$dE_y/dy = 4\pi e(N_i - N_e) \quad (6)$$

where E_y is the y-component of the electric field.

   We are going to solve Eqs. (1)–(6) for N_s, u, V_s, T_e, T_a, and E_y from given boundary conditions.

III. TRANSPORT COEFFICIENTS

   The solution of our problem depends on the accuracy of the determination of the transport coefficients μ_s, k_s, K_{st}, and $K_{st}{}^T$. Considerable effort has been made in determination of these coefficients. The details are given by Powers [8]. The variations of these transport coefficients with the state variables are as follows:

(1) COEFFICIENTS OF VISCOSITY:

$10^6 \mu_a = 0.816 T_a - 3.903 \times 10^{-4} T_a{}^2 + 1.073 \times 10^{-9} T_a{}^3$ g/cm-sec

$$\text{for} \quad T_a < 1500°\text{K} \quad (7a)$$

$10^4 \mu_a = 0.0249 T_a^{0.774}$ g/cm-sec   for $T_a > 1500°\text{K}$ $\quad (7b)$

$\mu_e = 0.434 \times 10^{-16} T_e^{5/2}/\ln(1.24 \times 10^4 T_e^{3/2}/N_e^{1/2})$ g/cm-sec $\quad (7c)$

$\mu_i = 1.171 \times 10^{-14} T_i^{5/2}/\ln(1.24 \times 10^4 T_i^{3/2}/N_i^{1/2})$ g/cm-sec $\quad (7d)$

(2) COEFFICIENTS OF THERMAL CONDUCTIVITY:

$$k_a = 0.1867\mu_a \qquad \text{cal/cm-sec-°K} \qquad (8a)$$
$$k_e = 1.334 \times 10^4 \mu_e \qquad \text{cal/cm-sec-°K} \qquad (8b)$$
$$k_i = 0.1861\mu_i \qquad \text{cal/cm-sec-°K} \qquad (8c)$$

Even though Eqs. (7) and (8) may be used without reservation for high-temperature, low-density plasma, it is apparent that Eqs. (7c) and

(7d) are singular when $T_s = 1.87 \times 10^{-3} N_s^{1/3}$. Physically, this corresponds to the condition that exists when the kinetic energy of the collision is equal to the coulombic potential energy at a distance of a Debye radius, and implies that such low-energy collisions should not be properly included. To circumvent this difficulty, the low-temperature values of ion or electron transport coefficients were assumed to be linear in temperature with the constant or proportionality chosen as a function of number density in such a manner as to insure continuity in the first derivatives with respect to temperature at the point of transition from low- to high-temperature expressions, i.e.,

$$\mu_e \sim k_e \sim \mu_i \sim k_i \sim K \{\exp \tfrac{3}{2}[1 - \ln (1.24 \times 10^4/N_s^{1/2}]\}^{3/2} T_s \quad (9)$$

When the transport properties of either the atoms, ions, or electrons in the presences of other species were required, these properties were derived in a manner analogous to the procedure suggested by Fay [10] which set forth mixture laws based on mean free path considerations. Otherwise expressed, the viscosity and thermal conductivity in the presence of other species was the pure species value multiplied by the ratio of the pure species mean free path to the mean free path taking into account collisions with other species.

(3) RESISTANCE COEFFICIENTS:

$$\log_{10} \left[\frac{K_{ia} \times 10^{32}}{N_a N_i} \right] = 0.168 \log_{10} T - 0.0356$$
$$+ [(0.168 \log_{10} T - 0.0356)^2 - 0.154 \log_{10} T + 2.54]^{1/2} \quad (10a)$$

where T is in degrees Kelvin.

$$K_{ie} = \frac{8\pi^{1/2}e^4 N_i N_e \ln (3kT_e r_D/e^2)}{\mu_{ie} q^3} \left[\frac{\pi^{1/2}}{2} \operatorname{erf} \frac{q}{\alpha^*} - \frac{q}{\alpha^*} e^{-q^2/\alpha^{*2}} \right] \quad (10b)$$

where

$$\mu_{ie} = m_i m_e/(m_i + m_e), \qquad r_D = (kT_e/4\pi N_e e)^{1/2}$$
$$\alpha^* = [2k(m_i T_e + m_e T_i)/m_i m_e]^{1/2}, \qquad q = |V_i - V_e| \qquad (10c)$$
$$K_{ie}^T = \frac{4\pi e^4 N_i N_e \ln (3kT_e r_D/e^2)}{\mu_{ie} q} \operatorname{erf} \left(\frac{q}{\alpha^*} \right)$$

We neglect K_{ea} and K_{ea}^T, which are found to be very small.

IV. PHYSICAL CONDITIONS AND BOUNDARY CONDITIONS

If we nondimensionalize the basic equations (1)–(6), we find the following nondimensional parameters that characterize our problem:

(i)   REYNOLDS NUMBER OF s-SPECIES:

$$R_{V_s} = m_s N_s V_s L / \mu_{s_L} \tag{11a}$$

where L is a reference length, $m_s N_s V_s$ is the mass flux of gas between the plates, and subscript L refers to the value at $y = L$.

(ii)   MACH NUMBER OF s-SPECIES:

$$M_{V_s} = \frac{V_{s_L}}{(2kT_{s_L}/m_s)^{1/2}}, \qquad M_{u_s} = \frac{U_L}{(2kT_{s_L}/m_s)^{1/2}} \tag{11b}$$

(iii)   PRANDTL NUMBER OF s-SPECIES:

$$P_{r_s} = \frac{C_{V_s} \mu_{s_L}}{k_{s_L}} = \frac{3}{2} \frac{k \mu_{s_L}}{m_s k_{s_L}} \tag{11c}$$

(iv)   ELECTRICAL POTENTIAL PARAMETERS:

$$P_i = \frac{4\pi e^2 N_{e_L} L^2}{m_i V_i^2}, \qquad P_e = \frac{4\pi e^2 N_{e_L} L^2}{m_e V_{e_L}^2} \tag{11d}$$

(v)   INTERACTION FORCE PARAMETERS:

$$R_{\mathrm{I}_{st}} = \frac{K_{st} L^2}{\mu_{s_L}}, \qquad R_{\mathrm{II}_{st}} = \frac{K_{st}^T L^2}{k_{s_L} T_{s_L}} \tag{11e}$$

In order to define our problem, we have to know the range of these nondimensional parameters.   What we have considered are the following physical conditions:

(1)   Temperature range is from 5000° to 10,000°K.
(2) U_L is from 1.2×10^3 to 7×10^3 m/sec.
(3)   Pressure is of the order of 10^{-3} atm.
(4) $L = 1$ cm.

Under these conditions, we found that $M_{V_s}^2 \ll 1$, $M_{V_s}/R_{V_s} \ll 1$, and $M_{vs}^2 P_s \gg 1$, and the inertial and viscous terms are negligible in the y-wise momentum equation, and ambipolar diffusion exists over a major portion of the core region.   There is a very thin sheath layer near the upper and lower walls, which are of a thickness of a few Debye lengths.   For the core region, our basic equations in nondimensional form are

$$\frac{d}{dy}\left(\mu_a \frac{du}{dy}\right) = 0 \tag{12a}$$

$$\frac{dV_a}{dy} = \frac{V_a}{T_a}\frac{dT_a}{dy} - \frac{2M_{V_a}^2}{R_{V_a}}\frac{V_a^2}{T_a}\left(\frac{K_{ia}L^2}{\mu_{a_L}}\right.$$

$$\left. + \frac{K_{ea}L^2}{\mu_{a_L}}\right)\left(\frac{V_{i_L}}{V_{a_L}}V_i - V_a\right) \tag{12b}$$

$$\frac{dV_i}{dy} = \left(\frac{V_i}{T_a + T_e}\right)\left(\frac{dT_a}{dy} + \frac{dT_e}{dy}\right) - \left(\frac{2V_i^2}{T_a + T_e}\right)\left(\frac{M_{V_i}^2}{R_{V_i}}\frac{K_{ia}L^2}{\mu_{i_L}}\right)$$

$$+ \frac{M_{V_e}^2}{R_{V_e}}\frac{K_{ea}L^2}{\mu_{e_L}}\right)\left(\frac{V_{a_L}}{V_{i_L}}V_a - V_i\right) \tag{12c}$$

$$\frac{d}{dy}\left(k_a\frac{dT_a}{dy}\right) = \frac{2}{3}P_{r_a}\left[T_a R_{V_a}\left(\frac{1}{V_a}\frac{dV_a}{dy} - \frac{1}{V_i}\frac{dV_i}{dy}\right)\right.$$

$$- 2M_{u_a}^2\mu_a\left(\frac{du}{dy}\right)^2 - 2M_{V_a}^2\frac{K_{ai}L^2}{\mu_{a_L}}\left(\frac{V_{i_L}}{V_{a_L}}V_i - V_a\right)^2$$

$$\left. - \frac{3}{2}\frac{m_e}{m_a P_{r_a}}\frac{K_{ei}^T L^2}{k_{a_L}T_{a_L}}\left(1 - \frac{T_{a_L}T_a}{T_{e_L}T_e}\right)\right] \tag{12d}$$

$$\frac{d}{dy}\left(k_e\frac{dT_e}{dy}\right) = \frac{2}{3}P_{r_e}\left[R_{V_e}\left(\frac{3}{2}\frac{dT_e}{dy} + \frac{T_e}{V_e}\frac{dV_e}{dy}\right)\right.$$

$$- 2M_{u_e}^2\mu_e\left(\frac{du}{dy}\right)^2 - 2M_{V_e}^2\frac{K_{ea}L^2}{\mu_{e_L}}\left(\frac{V_{a_L}}{V_{e_L}}V_a - V_e\right)^2$$

$$\left. + \frac{3}{2}\frac{m_e}{m_a P_{r_a}}\frac{K_{ei}^T L^2}{k_{e_L}T_{e_L}}\left(1 - \frac{T_{a_L}T_a}{T_{e_L}T_e}\right)\right] \tag{12e}$$

All physical quantities are expressed in terms of their values at $y = L$.

We consider only the cases where the species mean free path was always much smaller than the characteristic length L but greater than the Debye radius r_D. Hence, the zero slip conditions are applicable to all the velocity components. Because of the presence of the small sheath layer, the zero temperature jump condition was only applied directly to the argon atoms, and hence it was assumed that the atom temperatures at the upper and lower walls correspond to the actual wall temperatures.

The boundary condition on the electron temperature was evaluated by applying a very elementary sheath layer concept. The sheath layer near the upper and lower walls was considered to be only a few Debye lengths in extent. Within this distance, charge neutrality breaks down, and the sheath potential varies to its wall value in such a manner that there is zero net current flow to the walls. Under the physical model here considered, the lower wall was assumed to be at a small negative potential, and, hence, only electrons possessing kinetic energy, which is greater than the electrostatic potential energy of the wall, will be able to reach the wall. Similarly, the upper wall is assumed to be at a small positive potential. In this case, only electrons of sufficient kinetic energy can overcome the attractive potential and enter the core where they come under the influence of diffusive forces. Using these concepts and paralleling the procedures outlined by Jukes [1] or Camac and Kemp [7], one can compute the energy of the electrons at the edge of a sheath layer, and then, accounting for the

energy change across the sheath because of the wall potential ϕ, it is possible to obtain an electron energy balance between the core and sheath layers. From the energy balance, the boundary condition on the electron temperature is given in terms of the wall potentials. The remaining boundary condition is related to the value of the number flux, $N_s V_s$.

It was hypothesized that the upper wall was highly efficient in ionizing the incident atom flux and that this heterogeneous chemical reaction could be described by the phenomenological rate equations for the production of chemical species at a solid surface as developed by Rosner [11]. These rate equations are dependent on rate coefficients that are analogous to accommodation coefficients. In the present investigation, these rate coefficients were assumed to take on specific values, which in turn led to the final boundary conditions on the wall values of the normal component of the species velocities.

V. NUMERICAL PROCEDURES

The solution of the core system of equations consists mathematically of solving five ordinary differential equations for the five functions $u(y)$, $V_a(y)$, $V_i(y)$, $T_a(y)$, and $T_e(y)$. The equations are coupled, and the boundary conditions are split; hence, they must be integrated simultaneously, and one must deduce the correct values of a given number of initial conditions at one wall to satisfy the boundary conditions at the other wall.

Under the present investigation, the given boundary conditions and a set of trial values were used at one wall to start the integration of the equation system. If the trial values did not satisfy the boundary conditions at the other wall, the difference between the desired and obtained values was retained. Then small perturbations in each of the trial values were made successively, and the completed system of differential equations was integrated for each perturbation to obtain increments. Thus, it was possible to define approximate partial derivatives of the correction in the dependent variable with respect to a change in the trial values. These approximate partial derivatives formed a matrix whose inverse, when multiplied by the vector of desired corrections, yields the incremental corrections to the trial values. After a few iterations, a satisfactory solution was generally obtained. The actual procedure that was used consists of a fourth-order Adam Moulton predictor-corrector method with the Runge Kutta method for starting and stopping [12].

VI. SHEAR STRESS AND HEAT TRANSFER

After the functional dependence of the flow variables had been determined by the preceding numerical procedures, the description of the flow was essentially complete, and the quantities of interest, namely, the heat transfer and skin friction, could be expressed in terms of these variables. The skin friction and heat transfer at the lower wall are determined directly from the solution of the core flow equations, since the sheath layer is much smaller than the mean free paths. The sheath layer, in effect, serves primarily to control the electron temperature. Since any energy loss by the electrons in crossing the sheath is gained by the ions, and since dissipative mechanisms in the sheath layer are considered negligible, the energy flux into the sheath layer is the same as the energy flux into the wall. Accordingly, the shear stress was determined by first using the previously mentioned mixture rules to find the viscosity at the edge of the sheath layer and then multiplying by the gradient of the x-component of the velocity profile. This shear stress was then expressed in terms of the conventional skin friction coefficient, $C_f = 2\tau_0/\rho_L U_L{}^2$.

The expressions for the heat transfer are a bit more complex in that a careful accounting must be made of the several modes of energy transfer. The important modes for the scope of the present investigation were conduction by atoms and electrons, and the diffusion of deionization energy. The conduction by ions was negligible because of the very small value of the ions thermal conductivity, and diffusion of ion or electron thermal energy was negligible in comparison with the diffusion of deionization energy because of the low temperatures of these species at the lower wall. In terms of the core solution variables, the atom and electron conductive contributions are the species conductivities times their respective temperature gradients. The contribution resulting from the diffusion of deionization energy is effectively a constant of the flow situation, since the energy is supplied at the upper wall and removed at the lower wall. The magnitude of this contribution is directly proportional to the ion number flux. The two conductive and the diffusive energy fluxes are summed to obtain the total net heat flux. The heat transfer results may be presented in a nondimensional form by using the Stanton number [8]; however, only absolute magnitudes are presented to facilitate comparisons.

VII. SINGLE-FLUID THEORY

We compare our results of multifluid theory with the following two well-known single-fluid theories.

A. Equilibrium Single-Fluid Theory

In this theory, we assume that all the properties of the flowing, partially ionized gas can be determined by relations describing a stationary gas in thermochemical equilibrium.   Otherwise expressed, for the Couette flow model under consideration, it would be possible to determine the composition and thermodynamic properties from the local temperature and pressure.   The method of computing diffusion velocities, V_i, was based on the assumption that the ions and electrons travel in pairs, which is equivalent to assuming a binary diffusion model.   The diffusion coefficient used was taken as that of the ion-atom interaction, and the number densities that were dependent on the ion-electron partial pressures were given by a direct differentiation with respect to temperature of the Saha equation [13].

B. Frozen Flow Single-Fluid Equation System

The frozen flow single-fluid theory is based on the assumption that all chemical reactions are frozen in the flow.   This is the same assumption used in the multifluid theory, and, hence, the frozen single-fluid theory might be expected to serve as a better criterion for comparison with the multifluid theory results.   Since the single-fluid theory does not consider thermal nonequilibrium as does the multifluid theory, comparisons should be made on a qualitative rather than quantitative basis.

The equations used with the Couette flow model, again assuming ambipolar diffusion of the ion-electron pairs, are similar to the equilibrium equations, but in this case a diffusion equation is used to define the ion number density instead of the Saha equation.

VIII. DISCUSSION OF RESULTS

Numerical computations have been carried out for the physical conditions described in Section IV under the numerical procedure described in Section V by the IBM 7094 computer at the Naval Ordance Laboratory.   The detailed numerical results are given by Powers [8].   We summarize the main feature of the influence of thermal nonequilibrium of an ionized fluid flow as follows.

A. Dependence on Upper Wall Temperature

The effect of variation in upper wall temperature at the lower wall is presented in Fig. 2.   The temperature degree of ionization for these temperatures would vary from approximately zero at 5000°K to 64% at 10,000°K.   Accordingly, to be consistent with the concept of an upper

wall compositional nonequilibrium, the upper wall reaction was assumed
such that the degree of ionization varied from approximately 10 to 70%
over the same temperature range when applied to the multifluid and
frozen single-fluid theory calculations. It is observed in Fig. 2 that, at
the lower temperatures with moderate thermal nonequilibrium, the multifluid theory results are similar to the single-fluid theory results and that,

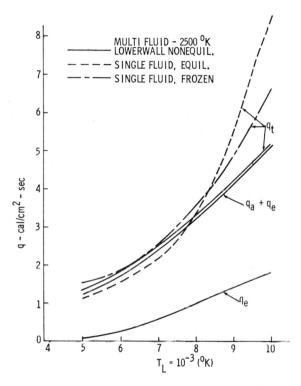

Fɪɢ. 2. Heat transfer versus upper wall temperature: comparison of theories.

at temperatures above 8000°K, there is a divergence of the theories. The
reasons for this appear to be twofold. First, the diffusion of deionization
energy is greater at the higher temperatures for the frozen single-fluid
theory because the diffusive mass flux is concentration controlled rather
than chemically rate controlled. Secondly, an examination of the corresponding temperature profiles emphasizes the role of the electron conduction contribution. With $T_L = 5000°K$ and a moderate thermal nonequilibrium, it was found that the heavy particle conduction controlled
heat transfer. With $T_L = 10,000°K$ and a moderate thermal nonequilib-

rium, we find that the electron contribution has become a very large percentage of the total heat transfer.

Now in Fig. 3 we compare calculations by the multifluid method with large lower wall thermal nonequilibrium with the previous results with a moderate thermal nonequilibrium. Here we see that the large thermal nonequilibrium has a large effect on the total heat transfer even at low upper wall temperatures. This again may be attributed to the electron contribution, which is negative over much of the temperature range.

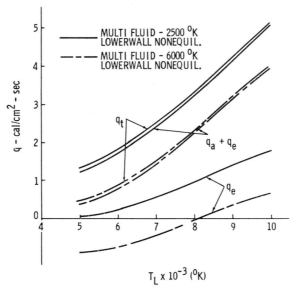

Fig. 3. Heat transfer versus upper wall temperature: varied lower wall temperature nonequilibrium.

B. Thermal Nonequilibrium Effects

As it became apparent that increased degrees of thermal nonequilibrium had a large effect on the electron conductive heat-transfer contributions, it appeared desirable to investigate the phenomenon in more detail. Accordingly, a series of computations was performed in which only the degree of thermal nonequilibrium was varied. Under the present flow model, this corresponds to a systematic variation in upper and lower wall electrical potential. In general, the magnitudes of the upper and lower wall potentials were approximately equal, and hence the computed results are presented in terms of voltage difference, $\Delta\phi = \phi_0 - \phi_L$, with the more positive $\Delta\phi$ corresponding to the greater differences between electron and heavy particle temperatures. Physically, this implies that, as the

potential difference becomes more positive, there is an increased attraction
for the electrons at the lower wall, and, hence, less of the electron's upper
wall thermal energy is lost in transit between the two walls.   When the
potential difference becomes positive, the lower wall electron temperature
could actually become greater than the upper wall electron temperature

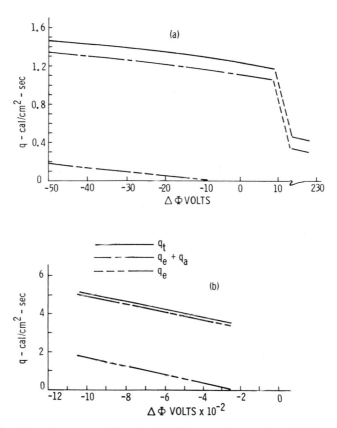

Fig. 4. Heat transfer versus wall potential difference ($\phi_0 - \phi_L$).   (a) $T_L = 5000°K$;
(b) $T_L = 10,000°K$.

and then the electron conductive energy flux would reverse in direction.
Under these conditions, the potential relations would not be expected to
apply.   As a result, values with a positive potential difference should be
considered only as tentative.

The dimensional presentation of the wall heat transfer as a function of
potential difference (Fig. 4) clearly shows that the heat transfer is
decreased with more positive potential differences.   This result is con-

sistent with the postulated physical situation, and, by examination of the figure, it is seen to result directly from the decrease in electron conduction contribution.

This fact is further confirmed by examining the velocity and temperature profiles as the wall potential changes. The only significant changes were in the electron temperature profile. The coupling with the atom temperature or velocity profile appeared to be negligible. Also, it was observed that even a greater potential difference than was used in the present calculations would be needed to realize a condition of thermal equilibrium at the lower wall. Conversely, this may be interpreted to indicate that, at very small potential difference, the electron temperature would persist from the upper to the lower walls.

C. Mach Number Effects and Skin Friction

One of the objectives of the present investigation was to evaluate the effect of the viscous coupling on the flow variables and then on the heat transfer. To accomplish this objective, a series of computations was performed with the upper wall temperature constant at either 5000° or 10,000°K, for upper wall velocities ranging from 1200 to 7000 m/sec, and for a constant degree of temperature nonequilibrium. The Mach number ranges corresponding to these velocities and temperatures were from 0.8 to 4.9 and 0.6 to 3.4, respectively, for the 5000° and 10,000°K upper wall temperatures.

The contribution of viscous coupling is expected to be manifested through the dissipation term in the atom and electron energy equations. In both energy equations, this term contains a Mach number squared factor; however, since the thermal velocity used is that of the species considered, the factor is smaller by the ratio of the electron to atom mass when it appears in the electron energy equation. This fact suggests that the electron conduction contribution to the total heat transfer should be relatively insensitive to velocity variation. In Fig. 5, it is seen that this expected result is realized, and, hence, for the range of velocities investigated, it may be concluded that the viscous coupling with the electron conductive heat-transfer contribution is negligible.

The viscous coupling does, however, make a large contribution to the total heat transfer. In general, the qualitative trends in either the dimensional heat transfer or the dimensionless Stanton number are similar for the multifluid theories.

An exception is noted for the high-velocity, low upper wall temperature computations performed using the multifluid theory. For these calculations, it was observed that excessive truncation errors were indicated in the numerical integration procedure at upper wall velocities greater than

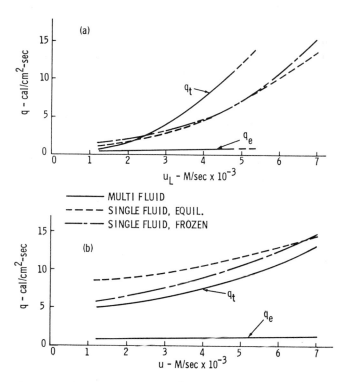

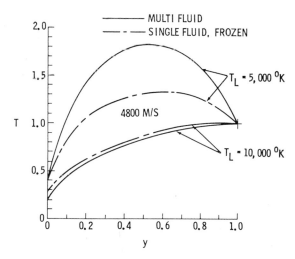

FIG. 5. Heat transfer versus upper wall velocity.   (a) $T_L = 5000°$K; (b) $T_L = 10,000°$K.

FIG. 6. Velocity and temperature profiles.

4000 m/sec.   An examination of the atom temperature profiles (Fig. 6) yields some insight into the nature of these difficulties.   At the higher velocities, represented by the profiles for an upper wall velocity of 4800 m/sec, it is seen that the larger dissipative contribution results in an increase in the temperature over the center of the core.   This, in turn,

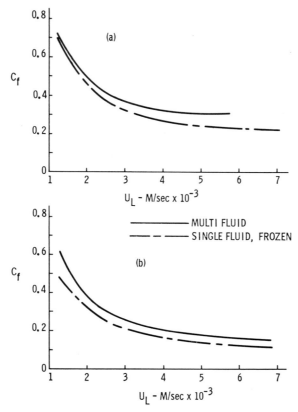

Fig. 7. Skin friction coefficient versus upper wall velocity.   (a) $T_L = 5000°K$; (b) $T_L = 10,000°K$.

results in a conductive heat flux into both walls as distinguished from just the lower wall.   The multifluid theory atom temperature profile for this condition is obviously approaching the limit of accuracy for the numerical procedure.   On the other hand, when the upper wall temperature is 10,000°K, the dissipative contributions are reduced, and the temperature maximum in the center of the core is not present.   Although the trend to higher temperatures in the center of the core is apparently correct, it is believed that magnitude of the temperature is overestimated.

The skin friction results are presented in Fig. 7 for both the 5000° and the 10,000°K upper wall temperatures. There appears to be reasonable similarity between the single- and multifluid frozen flow calculations. There also was enough similarity in form of the Stanton number and skin friction coefficient curves to suggest that these results might be presented in the form of a "Reynolds analogy" ($2 \operatorname{St} \operatorname{Pr}/C_f = $ const).

D. Dependence of Solution on Ionization Mechanism

In connection with the boundary conditions, the concept of an ionizing upper wall was introduced. This concept was based on the assumption that the upper wall chemical reactions could be described by a series of equations that define the species mass flux in terms of a nonequilibrium number density and a phenomenological efficiency coefficient, ϵ_{ai}, which is related to the probability of incident atoms being converted to ions at the wall. Using these equations, the mass or number flux of ions and electrons then becomes dependent on the reaction at the upper wall. Accordingly, it was deemed advisable to determine the dependence of the multifluid theory solutions on the ionization mechanism by alteration of the efficiency coefficient, ϵ_{ai}, which might conceptually be analogous to change in upper wall material. The number fluxes were varied by approximately a factor of 10 for two pressure levels at upper wall temperatures of 5000° and 10,000°K with a fixed degree of thermal nonequilibrium.

The results of these computations are presented in Fig. 8. At the lower pressure level, both of the conductive contributions, q_a and q_e, were fairly independent of the number flux. The diffusive contribution resulting from the release of the ionization energy by electron-ion recombination necessarily increases linearly with the number flux, causing the total heat transfer to increase similarly. At the higher pressure level, a somewhat unexpected result occurs. For both upper wall temperatures, the computations indicate a negative conductive contribution from the electrons and, hence a reduction in the total energy transfer.

Examination of the corresponding temperature profiles indicates that the heavy-particle temperature profiles and the velocity profiles are relatively insensitive to the range of pressure and flux variation considered here. The electron temperature profiles, however, are strongly dependent on the pressure level of the investigation. This dependence appears to indicate a tendancy of the electrons towards temperature equilibrium with the negative slope at the lower wall becoming necessary to satisfy the thermal nonequilibrium lower wall boundary condition. Otherwise expressed as the pressure level of the investigation is increased due to an increase in number density, the thermal resistance coefficient terms tend

to dominate the electron energy equation because of the increased number of particle collisions, which, in turn, promotes thermal equilibration.

Summarizing the present investigation in which we have sought to evaluate some of the effects of nonequilibrium ionization on surface heat

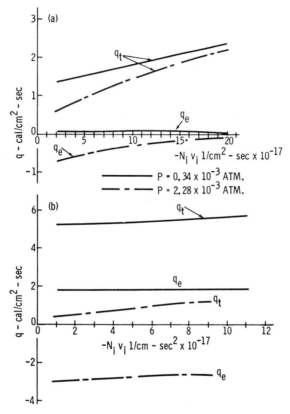

FIG. 8. Heat transfer versus ion number flux. (a) $T_L = 5000°K$; (b) $T_L = 10,000°K$.

transfer in a fluid flow situation, we have come to the following general conclusions:

(1) The multifluid theory equation system, when judiciously used, is consistent with single-fluid procedures and is particularly effective in evaluating the relative importance of different energy transfer mechanisms.

(2) Thermal nonequilibrium, which is characterized by electron temperature greater than heavy-particle temperatures, results in a reduced total heat transfer, and the possibility of controlling the wall heat transfer

by inducing thermal nonequilibrium through variations in the wall electrical potential is suggested.

(3) The coupling of the viscous flow variables is shown by the multi-fluid theory to have a significant effect on the heavy-particle temperature profiles and has a negligible effect on the electron temperature profiles.

(4) Finally, the pressure level of the investigation strongly influences the degree of thermal nonequilibrium which may be realized.

ACKNOWLEDGMENT

This research was supported in part by the U.S. Air Force through AFOSR under Grants No. AFOSR 141-65 and AFOSR 1015-66 and by the Fluid Mechanics and Flight Dynamics Branch of the Bureau of Naval Weapons.

REFERENCES

1. Jukes, J., Heat Transfer from Highly Ionized Argon Produced by Shock Waves. Thesis, Cornell Univ. (1956).
2. Adams, M. C., Avco Everett Res. Report AMP 53 (1960).
3. Scala, S. M. and Warren, W. R., G.E. Space Sciences Lab. Report R61SD185 (1961).
4. Fay, J. A. and Kemp, N. H., IAS Paper 63-60 (1963).
5. Chung, P. M. and Mullen, J. F., Aerospace Corp. Report TDR-169 (3230-12) TN-7 (1963).
6. Dix, D. M., *AIAA J.* **2**, 2081 (1964).
7. Camac, M. and Kemp, N. H., Avco Everett Report 184 (1964).
8. Powers, J. O., Nonequilibrium Effects on Energy Transfer in an Ionized Fluid Flow. Thesis, Univ. of Maryland (1965).
9. Burgers, J. M., "Plasma Dynamics," Chapter 5. Addison-Wesley, Reading, Massachusetts, 1960.
10. Fay, J. A., M.I.T. Magnetogasdynamics Lab. Report 61-8 (1961).
11. Rosner, D. E., *Jet Propulsion* **28**, 555 (1958).
12. Butler, J. F., U.S. Naval Ordnance Lab. NAVORD Report 6701 (1959).
13. Pai, S. I., "Magnetogasdynamics and Plasma Dynamics," Chapter 13. Springer, Vienna, and Prentice-Hall, Englewood Cliffs, New Jersey, 1962.

Transport Coefficients for Dense Gases

J. R. DORFMAN

UNIVERSITY OF MARYLAND

COLLEGE PARK, MARYLAND

A divergence has been discovered by several authors in the Bogoliubov-Cohen-Green density expansion for the pair distribution function of a dense gas not in equilibrium. This expansion, like its equilibrium counterpart, is given by a power series in the density, the coefficients of which depend upon the dynamics of two, three, . . . , particles. In the two-dimensional theory, the divergence first appears in the three particle term. The divergence is caused by the failure of the phase space volume for three successive binary collisions to remain bounded as the time between the first and last collision becomes large. In the three-dimensional theory, the divergence first appears in the four-particle term and is caused by a similar mechanism, involving four successive binary collisions. As a consequence of this divergence, transport coefficients for even a moderately dense gas cannot be given by a virial expansion. Instead, terms not analytic in the density, such as $\log n$, must be expected. Techniques have been developed recently which appear to predict such nonanalytic terms. A common ingredient in these theories is that, because of the presence of many particles in the gas, successive binary collision involving a few particles must be separated by intervals not larger than a few mean free times. The work of Frieman and Goldman, Kawasaki and Oppenheim, and the author and coworkers in this connection will be discussed. Finally, some comments on transport coefficients in the critical region of the gas liquid transition will be given.

I. INTRODUCTION

A major problem of the kinetic theory of gases is to describe the approach to equilibrium of a gas initially not in equilibrium. The Boltzmann equation does this completely for dilute gases, where only binary collisions play an important role [1]. Moreover, from the Boltzmann equation, Chapman and Enskog [1] were able to obtain expressions for transport coefficients, such as viscosity and heat conductivity, which characterize the final stages of the approach to equilibrium.

In order to describe more dense gases, one must generalize the Boltzmann equation to higher orders in the density, so as to include the effects

of triple, quadruple, . . . collisions in a systematic way. A step in this
direction was made in 1921 by Enskog [1], who extended the Boltzmann
equation for hard spheres to allow for the finite size of the molecules (the
"collisional transfer term") and for spatial inhomogeneities. Enskog was
also able to make a rough estimate of the effect of triple collisions. It
was not until 1947, though, that the work of Bogoliubov [2] made possible
a systematic generalization of the Boltzmann equation to arbitrary order
in the density. As Uhlenbeck has pointed out [3], the basic idea of
Bogoliubov is that the approach of a not too dense gas to equilibrium
proceeds in three stages. The stages are separated by three widely spaced
relaxation times:

$$t_{\text{coll}} \sim 10^{-12} \sec \ll t_{\text{m.f.p.}} \sim 10^{-9} \sec \ll t_{\text{macr}} \sim 10^{-5} \sec$$

In particular, for dilute and moderately dense gases, Bogoliubov
assumed that, starting from some initial state of the gas, the time dependence of the two-particle distribution function, $F_2(x_1, x_2; t)$, becomes
determined entirely by the time dependence of the single-particle distribution function, $F_1(x; t)$ after $t \gg t_{\text{coll}}$. Clearly, Bogoliubov had in mind
an analogy with the so-called "normal solutions" of the Boltzmann equation, in which, after a sufficiently long time, the single-particle distribution
function changes in time only through the time behavior of the local
particle density, mean velocity, and energy density. Bogoliubov showed
that, by making a functional assumption of the same type much earlier
in the history of the system, one can not only derive the Boltzmann equation but also find the correction to the Boltzmann equation for dense gases
in which the restriction to binary collisions is no longer valid. He first
found an explicit representation for the two-particle nonequilibrium distribution function in terms of the one-particle function, by making the
additional assumption that the two-particle function possesses a convergent series expansion in powers of the density, and by imposing a
boundary condition for the function when the particles are far apart.
The generalized Boltzmann equation is obtained by inserting Bogoliubov's
expression for F_2 into the first hierarchy equation:

$$(\partial F_1/\partial t) + v_i \cdot \nabla_r F_1 = n \int d\mathbf{r}_2 \int d\mathbf{p}_2 \theta_{12} F_2(x_1, x_2; t) \tag{1}$$

where

$$\theta_{12} = \frac{\partial \phi(|r_{12}|)}{\partial \mathbf{r}_1} \cdot \frac{\partial}{\partial \mathbf{p}_1} - \frac{\partial}{\partial \mathbf{p}_2} \tag{2}$$

and $\phi(|r_{12}|)$ is the intermolecular potential.

Similarly, Bogoliubov assumed that, after a time much greater than
the mean free time, the system is in a local equilibrium state, so that the

local number, velocity, and energy densities suffice to describe the system. At this point, it is necessary to make a generalization of the Chapman-Enskog procedure in order to obtain transport coefficients for a moderately dense gas. This procedure has been carried out in detail by Choh and Uhlenbeck [4]. They showed that, to lowest order in the density, the Bogoliubov method yields the Boltzmann equation from the first hierarchy equation. Choh and Uhlenbeck also considered the first-order density corrections to the Boltzmann equation, and obtained expressions for the viscosity and heat conductivity. For hard spheres, they obtained the results previously given by Enskog, as well as an exact prescription for the effect of triple collisions. The bulk viscosity in this order of the density is zero.

II. FORMAL JUSTIFICATION OF THE BOGOLIUBOV THEORY

There have been many attempts to justify Bogoliubov's assumption by means of more fundamental arguments. Two of these attempts are particularly noteworthy. Green [5] and, later, Green and Piccirelli [6] of the National Bureau of Standards used combinatorial and dynamical arguments to show that, under less restrictive conditions, the two-particle nonequilibrium distribution function can be obtained in the form of Bogoliubov's function, plus certain correction terms. These authors assumed that the initial state of the gas is characterized by distribution functions obeying an equilibrium-like product condition. The assumed product condition is the following. Suppose one knows the n particle distribution function at the initial time, $t = 0$. Then it is necessary that this n particle distribution function can be written as a product of lower-order distribution functions whenever separated configurations of the n particles occur. The correction terms take into account initial correlations present in the gas, and dynamical events which the Bogoliubov method does not treat correctly.

Another attempt to justify the Bogoliubov theory is due to Cohen [7], whose work was later extended by Cohen, Ernst, and the author [8,9] at the Rockefeller Institute. Their method involves a more thorough exploration of the equilibrium-like product assumption. In fact, Cohen has shown, on the basis of this assumption, that it is possible to apply practically all the methods of equilibrium distribution function theory to the nonequilibrium case. Thus, one can avoid most of the intricate combinatorial arguments of Green and Piccirelli, and obtain Bogoliubov's functional form by means of a very simple mathematical device borrowed

from equilibrium theory. This work led to exactly the same results as those obtained by Green and Piccirelli.

At this point, it might be worthwhile summarizing the formal results obtained by the forementioned authors [8] for the two-particle nonequilibrium distribution function, $F_2(x_1, x_2 ; t)$:

$$F_2(x_1, x_2 ; t) = F_2[x_1, x_2|F_1(\quad ; t)] + C_1(x_1, x_2 ; t) - C_2(x_1, x_2 ; t) \quad (3)$$

Where $F_2[x_1, x_2|F_1(\quad ; t)]$ is the Bogoliubov functional and is given by the series

$$
\begin{aligned}
F_2[x_1, x_2|F_1(\quad ; t)] &= F_2^{(0)} + nF_2^{(1)} + \cdots \\
&= S_\infty^{(2)}(1, 2)F_1(x_1, t)F_1(x_2, t) \\
&\quad + n \int dx_3 \, \mathfrak{Z}_\infty(12|3) \prod_{i=1}^{3} F_1(x_i ; t) + \cdots \quad (4)
\end{aligned}
$$

where

$$\mathfrak{Z}_\infty(12|3) = S_\infty^{(3)}(123) - S_\infty^{(2)}(12)S_\infty^{(2)}(13) - S_\infty^{(2)}(12)S_\infty^{(2)}(23) + S_\infty^{(2)}(12) \quad (5)$$

and

$$S_\infty^{(j)}(1, 2, \ldots, j) = \lim_{\tau \to \infty} S_{-\tau}^{(j)}(1, 2, \ldots, j) \prod_{i=1}^{j} S_{+\tau}^{(1)}(i) \quad (6)$$

$S_{-\tau}^{(j)}(1, 2, \ldots, j)$ is the streaming operator that replaces $(\mathbf{r}_1, \mathbf{p}_1, \mathbf{r}_2, \mathbf{p}_2 ; \ldots ; \mathbf{r}_j, \mathbf{p}_j)$ by the values at a time, τ, earlier. These earlier values are to be computed using only the dynamics of the j particles.

The "initial condition correction term," $C_1(x_1, x_2, t)$, is given by the series

$$
\begin{aligned}
C_1(x_1, x_2 ; t) &= C_1^{(0)} + nC_1^{(1)} = \cdots \\
&= S_{-t}^{(2)}(1, 2)[a_2(x_1, x_2 ; 0) - 1]S_{+t}^{(1)}(1)S_{+t}^{(2)}(2) \\
&\quad \times F_1(x_1 ; t)F_1(x_2 ; t) \\
&\quad + n \int dx_3 \, \{S_{-t}^{(3)}(1, 2, 3)[a_3(x_1, x_2, x_3 ; 0) - 1] \\
&\quad - S_{-t}^{(2)}(1, 2)[a_2(x_1, x_2 ; 0) - 1]S_{+t}^{(1)}(1)S_{-t}^{(2)}(13)a_2(x_1, x_3 ; 0) \\
&\quad - S_{-t}^{(2)}(1, 2)[a_2(x_1, x_2 ; 0) - 1]S_{+t}^{(1)}(2)S_{-t}^{(2)}(2, 3)a_2(x_2, x_3 ; 0) \\
&\quad - S_{-t}^{(2)}(12)a_2(x_1, x_2 ; 0)S_{+t}^{(1)}(1)S_{-t}^{(2)}(13)[a_2(x_1, x_3 ; 0) - 1] \\
&\quad - S_{-t}^{(2)}(12)a_2(x_1, x_2 ; 0)S_{+t}^{(1)}(2)S_{-t}^{(2)}(23)[a_2(x_2, x_3 ; 0) - 1] \\
&\quad + S_{-t}^{(2)}(1, 2)[a_2(x_1, x_2 ; 0) - 1]\} \prod_{i=1}^{3} S_{+t}^{(1)}(i)F_1(x_i ; t) + \cdots
\end{aligned}
$$

$$(7)$$

The $a_j(x_1, x_2, \ldots, x_j ; 0)$ characterize j-particle correlations that may initially be present in the gas.

The asymptotic correction term, $C_2(x_1, x_2, t)$, is given by the series

$$C_2(x_1, x_i ; t) = C_2^{(0)} + nC_2^{(1)} + \cdots$$

$$= [\mathcal{S}_\infty^{(2)}(12) - \mathcal{S}_t^{(2)}(12)]F_1(x_1 ; t)F_1(x_2 ; t)$$

$$+ n \int dx_3 \, [\mathfrak{Z}_\infty(12|3) - \mathfrak{Z}_t(12|3)] \prod_{i=1}^{3} F_1(x_i ; t) + \cdots \qquad (8)$$

A necessary condition that the functional $F_2[x_1, x_2|F_1(\quad ; t)]$ exists is that $C_2 \to 0$ as $t \to \infty$.

The sum of C_1 and C_2 is equivalent to the final "error" term $E(1, 2; t)$ obtained by Green and Piccirelli.

Cohen, Ernst, and the author [9] used the same method to evaluate the viscosity and thermal conductivity of a moderately dense gas. This evaluation was based upon the time correlation function formulae, which were originally derived by Green [10], H. Mori [11], and others, and which are extremely general in their range of applicability. It was discovered by Cohen, Ernst, and the author that the time correlation function formulae can be written in terms of a new set of nonequilibrium distribution functions for which the equilibrium-like product assumption can be *rigorously* justified. In fact, the transport coefficients are completely determined by two new distribution functions, $\psi_1(x_1 ; t)$ and $\psi_2(x_1, x_2 ; t)$. The two-particle function, ψ_2, can be expressed as a functional of the one-particle function, ψ_1, as

$$\psi_2(x_1, x_2 ; t) = \psi_2[x_1, x_2|\psi_1(\quad ; t)] + \tilde{C}_1(x_1, x_2 ; t) + \tilde{C}_2(x_1, x_2 ; t) \qquad (9)$$

where $\psi_2[x_1, x_2|\psi_1(\quad ; t)]$ is a time independent functional closely related to $F_2[x_1, x_2|F_1(\quad ; t)]$, given by Eq. (4), and $\tilde{C}_1(x_1, x_2 ; t)$, $\tilde{C}_2(x_1, x_2 ; t)$ are correction terms similar to Eqs. (7) and (8). The transport coefficients determined by this method exist and agree with those obtained by the Bogoliubov method, provided $\tilde{C}_1$ and $\tilde{C}_2$ vanish for long times.

The results presented so far have been purely formal, and very little has been calculated beyond the Boltzmann equation results, for any potential. In order to proceed beyond the formal development and to justify the Bogoliubov functional, one must consider two problems: (1) the *dynamical* problem, to specify and work out the mechanics for the dynamical events that contribute to the Bogoliubov functional and to the correction terms; and (2) the *integral* problem, to compute the Bogoliubov functional for some realistic potential and to show that, for sufficiently long times, the correction terms make no contribution to the pair function or to the transport coefficients.

III. THE CORRECTION TERMS AND THE DIVERGENCE

Cohen, Ernst, and the author [8] have considered the functional and the correction terms for both F_2 and ψ_2, assuming that (a) the intermolecular potential is repulsive and of finite range, r_0; (b) $t \gg t_{coll}$; (c) particles 1 and 2 are separated by a distance no greater than r_0; and (d) the $a_j(x_1, x_2, \ldots, x_j, 0)$ satisfy the product condition.

The dynamical events that determine $F_1[x_1, x_2|F_1(\quad ; t)]$ and C_1 and C_2 can be found immediately from the structure of the various terms in Eqs. (4), (7), and (8). Under the foregoing conditions, the following results obtain for the functional $F_1[x_1, x_2|F_1(\quad ; t)]$.

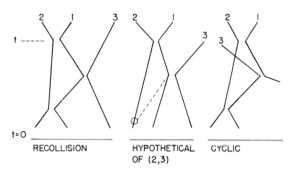

RECOLLISION   HYPOTHETICAL   CYCLIC
                     OF (2,3)

FIG. 1. Three successive collisions among three particles.

$F_2^{(0)}[x_1, x_2|F_1(\quad ; t)]$ includes only the effects of a binary collision between particles 1 and 2. $F_2^{(1)}[x_1, x_2|F_1(\quad ; t)]$ depends on the dynamics of three particles. The dynamical events that contribute to this term are genuine triple collisions and sequences of three or more successive binary collisions. Sequences of three binary collisions can be grouped into three types: the recollisions, the hypothetical collisions, and the cyclic collisions. Examples are given in Fig. 1. Sequences of four binary collisions among three particles have been found by Cohen and Foch [12] and by Thurston and Sandri [13].

One easily sees that, under the preceding conditions, both $C_1^{(0)}$ and $C_2^{(0)}$ are identically zero. Thus, the Bogoliubov functional form, $F_2^{(0)}[x_1, x_2|F_1(\quad ; t)]$, is exact if one neglects the higher-order terms.

A discussion of $C_1^{(1)}$ and $C_2^{(1)}$ can now be given. Upon inspection of Eqs. (7) and (8), one sees that sequences of three or more binary collisions among three particles are the only dynamical events that contribute to these correction terms. From Eq. (7) for $C_1^{(1)}$, one sees that the interval

between the first and last binary collision in the sequence must be exactly t. In other words, the pair function remembers its initial values by means of those dynamical events that directly connect $F_2(x_1, x_2; t)$ with the correlations $(a_2 - 1)$ at time $t = 0$. Also, from a consideration of Eq. (8) for $C_2^{(1)}$, one sees that the interval, T, between the first and last binary collision must lie in the interval $t \leq T \leq \infty$, for the sequence to contribute to $C_2^{(1)}$. That is, the Bogoliubov functional, $F_2^{(1)}[x_1, x_2|F_1(\quad; t)]$, includes dynamical events that take place in the interval $0 \leq T \leq \infty$, whereas an exact computation of $F_2(x_1, x_2; t)$ can only include events in the interval $0 \leq T \leq t$. If $C_2^{(1)}$ approaches zero as $t \to \infty$, the mistake is small for large t.

In order to determine the time dependence of $C_1^{(1)}$ and $C_2^{(1)}$, one estimates the volumes of the regions of the $(\mathbf{R}_3, \mathbf{P}_3)$ phase space for particle 3 such that the sequences of binary collisions occur in the correct order and in the appropriate time interval. Such estimates have been made, with the following results [8]:

For *three* dimensions,

$$C_1^{(1)} \sim (t_{\text{coll}}/t)^2 \tag{10a}$$
$$C_2^{(1)} \sim (t_{\text{coll}}/t) \tag{10b}$$

For *two* dimensions,

$$C_1^{(1)} \sim (t_{\text{coll}}/t) \tag{11a}$$

$$C_2^{(1)} \sim \int_t^\infty (t_{\text{coll}}/t)\, dt = \text{logarithmic divergence} \tag{11b}$$

Similar results obtain for $\tilde{C}_1^{(1)}$ and $\tilde{C}_2^{(1)}$, which appear in the evaluation of transport coefficients from time correlation formulae. In *three* dimensions, one can also show that

$$C_1^{(2)} \sim (t_{\text{coll}}/t) \tag{12a}$$

and

$$C_2^{(2)} \sim \int_t^\infty (t_{\text{coll}}/t)\, dt = \text{logarithmic divergence} \tag{12b}$$

The estimates just given are found by geometric arguments and by the requirement that the momentum function in the various correction terms be integrable. For example, consider the contribution of the hypothetical event to $C_1^{(1)}$. Particle 3 must pass through particle 1, say, without interaction, and collide with particle 2 at time t (see Fig. 2). If one fixes the magnitude of the velocity of particle 3, $|P_3/m|$, then the possible directions available to this velocity lie in a solid angle of size $\sim (r_0/v_{12}t)^2$. Furthermore, the requirement that the collision takes place at time t implies that the possible position, $\mathbf{R}_3$, for particle 3 lies in a region of size $\sim r_0^3$, for

given $\mathbf{P}_3$. Such arguments lead directly to the preceding estimates for $C_1^{(1)}$. Estimates for the asymptotic correction terms, $C_2^{(1)}$, can be put into the form of a time integral of $C_1^{(1)}$, the limits extending from t to infinity. This leads directly to Eqs. (10b), (11b), and (12b). The three-dimensional results for $C_2^{(1)}$ have also been obtained by Ono and Shizume [14], Weinstock [15], and Green and Piccirelli [6]. The result for $C_2^{(2)}$ has been obtained also by Weinstock [16] and by Frieman and Goldman [17].

One can conclude, therefore, that the phase space estimates provide us with a proof of the existence of $F_2^{(1)}[x_1, x_2|F_1(\quad ; t)]$ and $\psi_2^{(1)}[x_1, x_2|\psi_1(\quad ; t)]$ in three dimensions. This implies that the expressions obtained by Choh and Uhlenbeck for transport coefficients exist and are equivalent with those obtained from the time correlation functions to first order in the

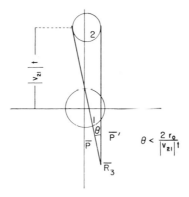

F IG. 2. Coordinate representation of (2, 3) hypothetical collision. For fixed $\mathbf{R}_3$, the largest angle between the possible directions of $\mathbf{P}_3$ is illustrated.

density [9, 18, 19]. However, the phase space estimates *do not* provide a proof of the existence of the Bogoliubov functional or the corresponding transport coefficients beyond the *zeroth* order in the density in two dimensions, and the *first* order in three dimensions.

In order to clarify the situation, Sengers [20], of the National Bureau of Standards, computed the shear viscosity for a two-dimensional hard sphere gas. In the calculation, he used the Bogoliubov functional form for the first-order density corrections to the Boltzmann equation. The calculations can be performed *exactly*. In the first Enskog approximation, Sengers found that the viscosity computed in this way *does* indeed diverge. As Sengers' result is not an estimate, but an exact calculation, and as the origin of the divergence is the same as that found by the phase space estimates, one can only conclude that the transport coefficients as determined by the Bogoliubov method do not exist beyond a low order in

the density. Sengers' results also strongly support the arguments that the functional itself does not exist.

The problem of determining the density development of the transport coefficients has also been studied by Oppenheim and Kawasaki [19, 21], using a method due to Zwanzig [22]. This method involves a binary collision expansion of the N particle streaming operator and yields a density expansion of the transport coefficients directly from the time correlation function formulae. Zwanzig's method is most conveniently formulated in terms of a Laplace transform in the time, the variable being ϵ, say, and a Fourier transform in the space coordinates, the variable being $\mathbf{k}$, say. In the limit $\epsilon \rightarrow 0$, the ordinary transport coefficients should be recovered. Oppenheim and Kawasaki [21] studied the transport coefficients in two dimensions and found for the $0(n)$ term that, if $\epsilon = 0$, the k integral diverges *like* $\log |k|$ for small k. Their discussion is not convincing, however, since one should take the limit, $\epsilon \rightarrow 0$, only after the $\mathbf{k}$ integrations have been performed [23]. Moreover, the connection between the divergence found by Kawasaki and Oppenheim [21] and that found by Cohen and the author [8] and by Sengers [20] is not clear. Haines, Ernst, and the author [24] have considered the work of Kawasaki and Oppenheim and have found the following result for hard disks. If one keeps $\epsilon > 0$, then the $\mathbf{k}$ integral can be performed and is quite well behaved. The transport coefficients diverge as $\log \epsilon$ when $\epsilon \rightarrow 0$. After suitable transformations, one sees that the origin of the divergence in $\log \epsilon$ is precisely the same as that found by Cohen and the author and by Sengers. In fact, a calculation of the coefficient of $\log \epsilon$ for the viscosity yields *precisely* the result of Sengers.

IV. TOWARD A CONVERGENT THEORY

The divergence is now considered to be fairly well established. The major problem now is to formulate a convergent theory of the non-equilibrium pair function or, equivalently, of the transport coefficients.

It is clear that the effect of all the particles in the gas must somehow be taken into account. The probability of any sequence of binary collisions taking place among a few particles must be determined not only by the phase space geometry but also by the probability that another particle will interrupt the sequence by colliding with one of the particles in the sequence. One can expect, therefore, that the correct pair function and transport coefficients will include not only the geometric effects discussed before but also a collisional damping. This damping should effectively

prevent the time interval between successive binary collisions from exceeding a few mean free times. The existence of such a damping was discussed by Jeans [25] as early as 1904 and, more recently, by Green [5].

Although a complete discussion of a convergent theory has not yet been given, some important results in this direction have been established by Frieman and Goldman [19], Oppenheim and Kawasaki [21], Weinstock [16], and the author and co-workers. The methods used by these authors appear to fall into two classes. One method, used by Oppenheim and Kawasaki and by Weinstock, consists of a resummation of the original Bogoliubov functional expansion to give a "renormalized" functional. The other method, used by Frieman and Goldman, essentially imitates the original Bogoliubov procedure but with an important addition. The pair function is found not as a functional series in $F_1(t)$, but instead as

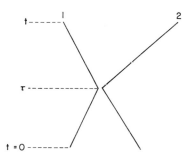

FIG. 3. Dynamical situation for Frieman-Goldman equation.

the solution of the *second* hierarchy equation, where F_3 is expressed as a functional of F_2 and F_1.

For an illustration of the methods, one may consider a simple example first discussed by Frieman and Goldman. Find the pair function for two particles whose momenta and coordinates are so arranged that, if the particles had been undisturbed, they would have suffered a collision at a time τ in the past (see Fig. 3). Frieman and Goldman derive an equation from the hierarchy method, for $G(12, t) = F_2(12, t) - F_1(1, t) F_1(2, t)$, i.e.,

$$\frac{\partial G_2(1, 2, t)}{\partial t} + \left(\frac{\mathbf{p}_1}{m} \cdot \nabla r_1 + \frac{\mathbf{p}_2}{m} \cdot \nabla r_2\right) G_2(12 ; t)$$
$$= n \int dx_3 \left[\theta_{13} \mathcal{S}_\infty(13) + \theta_{23} \mathcal{S}_\infty(23)\right]$$
$$\times G_2(12 ; t) F_1(3 ; t), \qquad t - \tau > t_{\text{coll}} \quad (13)$$

Under the conditions (a) the system is spatially homogeneous, (b) the potential is short range, e.g., that of a hard sphere of diameter r_0, and (c) F_1 is independent of the time (consider a steady-state situation), a solution to this equation is given by

$$G(12 \, ; t) \sim \exp \{ -(t - \tau) \nu \} G(12 \, ; \tau) \tag{14}$$

where

$$\nu = \pi r_0^2 n \!\int dv_3 \, (|v_3 - v_1| + |v_2 - v_3|) F_1(\mathbf{v}_3) \tag{15}$$

and

$$G(12 \, , \tau) = [S_\infty^{(2)}(12) - 1] F_1(v_1) F_1(v_2) \tag{16}$$

The quantity ν is a collision frequency and represents the collisional damping factor discussed before.

To understand the physical origin of the damping found by Frieman and Goldman, one may approach the same problem with the idea of

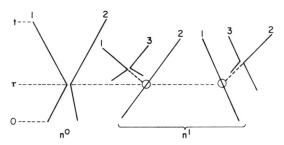

FIG. 4. Events included in resummation of Bogoliubov expansion, to order n, which lead to Frieman-Goldman result.

resumming the Bogoliubov functional expansion. One simply looks to the coefficient of any power of the density and picks out those dynamical events whose associated phase space volumes are most divergent in powers of $(t - \tau)$. Such events are listed in Fig. 4 for the first few terms in the expansion. In this way, one obtains the following expansion for $G_2(12, t)$, under the conditions just listed:

$$\begin{aligned}
G_2(12 \, , t) = {}& [S_\infty^{(2)}(12) - 1] F_1(v_1) F_1(v_2) \\
& - n \pi r_0^2 (t - \tau) \!\int dv_3 \, (|v_3 - v_1| + |v_3 - v_2|) F_1(v_3) [S_\infty^{(2)}(12) \\
& - 1] F_1(v_1) F_1(v_2) + \cdots
\end{aligned} \tag{17}$$

Part of the series is easily summed to the Frieman-Goldman result. The remaining parts sum to what appears to be convergent corrections to the Frieman-Goldman result. One can see from Fig. 4 that the collisional

mechanism mentioned before is indeed responsible for the Frieman-Goldman damping.

Oppenheim and Kawasaki, and also Weinstock, have in fact summed the originally divergent series for the transport coefficients and pair functions, respectively, using the binary collision expansion. Although it is not yet possible to give a complete discussion of their results, the following seems to be the case. In spite of the difficulties concerning the divergence, the resummation carried out by Oppenheim and Kawasaki seems to be free from serious objections. Haines, Ernst, and the author have made only a partial evaluation of their final expression. It has been found that the part of the resummed transport coefficients which could easily be evaluated for two-dimensional hard disks led to a contribution to the viscosity proportional to $n \log n$. The coefficient is exactly the same as that found for the coefficient of $n \log \epsilon$ and, hence, is exactly the same as that found by Sengers. These results, however, must be regarded as preliminary.

It does seem that in the near future a convergent theory for the nonequilibrium pair distribution function and for the transport coefficients will be available. What is really lacking, of course, is a new expansion parameter to take the place of the now discarded density.

V. TRANSPORT COEFFICIENTS IN THE CRITICAL REGION

In one sense, the entire discussion given previously is purely academic, for experimental verification of the presence of nonanalytic density dependences in the transport coefficients of moderately dense gases seems to be remote. For densities near the critical density of a gas-liquid phase transition, however, this is not the case. In fact, by means of some beautiful experiments, Sengers [26] has shown that the heat conductivity for CO_2 exhibits an anomalous behavior near the critical point. Sengers found that, as a function of the density, the heat conductivity shows a pronounced increase near the critical point. At 1°C away from the critical temperature, the heat conductivity shows a 250% anomaly at the critical density, but there does not seem to be such an anomaly in the viscosity. For binary mixtures, the viscosity shows an anomaly, but the heat conductivity does not. Nothing yet is known about the behavior of the bulk viscosity in this region.

A theoretical discussion of this situation presents a most challenging problem. Some closely related work has been done by Zwanzig [27], for the infinite frequency transport coefficients of a Lennard-Jones gas, and by Mori [28], Mermin [29], and others for transport coefficients near a

magnetic phase transition.   The problem is considerably complicated by the fact that for gases the equilibrium situation is not yet well understood.

It appears that there are two directions likely to be fruitful for theoretical discussions: (1) A study of magnetic systems, involving spin lattice models that can be treated exactly both for equilibrium and nonequilibrium situations.   An example of such a model has been given by Mermin.   For these models, one may be able to compute the time correlation functions near the critical points in more detail than is possible for gases.   This would give valuable information concerning transport coefficients near phase transitions.   (2) A study of the relations between various transport coefficients that hold near the critical point.   At low densities, one has the Euken relation between the shear viscosity, heat conductivity, and specific heat at constant volume [1].   It would be interesting to see if these quantities can be related near the critical point, especially since Sengers' data indicate that the ratio of the heat conductivity to the specific heat at constant volume shows no anomaly for CO_2 [30].

VI. SUMMARY

A discussion of the Bogoliubov theory of the two-particle nonequilibrium distribution function and the resulting transport coefficients has been given.   The formal expressions for the virial development of the transport coefficients, as determined by the Bogoliubov theory, and of the time correlation function formulae are equivalent.   However, in a low order of the density, such formal expressions for the pair function and the transport coefficients diverge.   This divergence has been substantiated by phase space estimates in the case of the pair function and by exact calculations of the viscosity for a simple model.   In both cases, the origin of the divergence is the same, the failure of the phase space volumes for sequences of binary collisions to remain bounded as the time interval between first and last collisions becomes large.   Two methods that promise to give a convergent theory have been discussed, and some preliminary results have been given.   In each method, one obtains a damping due to collisions which keeps the interval between successive binary collisions to within a few mean free times.   Finally, for high densities, anomalies in some of the transport coefficients have been found experimentally.   Some theoretical treatments of this problem are now available.

ACKNOWLEDGMENT

This work was supported in part by the Air Force Office of Scientific Research under Grant AFOSR-1015-66.

REFERENCES

1. Chapman, S. and Cowling, T. G., "Mathematical Theory of Non-Uniform Gases." Cambridge Univ. Press, London and New York, 1961.
2. Bogoliubov, N. N., "Studies in Statistical Mechanics," Vol. I. North-Holland Publ., Amsterdam, 1961.
3. Uhlenbeck, G. E., in "Probability and Related Topics in Physical Sciences" (M. Kac, ed.), p. 183. Wiley (Interscience), New York, 1959.
4. Choh, S. T. and Uhlenbeck, G. E., "The Kinetic Theory of Phenomena in Dense Gases." Univ. of Michigan (1958).
5. Green, M. S., J. Chem. Phys. 25, 836 (1956); also Physica 24, 393 (1958).
6. Green, M. S. and Piccirelli, R., Phys. Rev. 132, 1388 (1963).
7. Cohen, E. G. D., Physica 28, 1025, 1045, 1060 (1962); also J. Math. Phys. 4, 183 (1963).
8. Dorfman, J. R. and Cohen, E. G. D., J. Math. Phys. (to appear); also Dorfman, J. R. and Cohen, E. G. D., Phys. Lett. 16, 124 (1965); also Cohen, E. G. D., in "Statistical Mechanics of Equilibrium and Non-Equilibrium" (J. Meixner, ed.), pp. 140–157. North-Holland Publ., Amsterdam, 1965.
9. Ernst, M. H. J. J., Dorfman, J. R., and Cohen, E. G. D., Physica 31, 493 (1965); also Phys. Lett. 12, 319 (1964).
10. Green, M. S., J. Chem. Phys. 20, 1281 (1952); also Ibid. 22, 398 (1954).
11. Mori, H., "Studies in Statistical Mechanics," Vol. I. North-Holland Publ., Amsterdam, 1961.
12. Cohen, E. G. D. and Foch, J., to be published.
13. Thurston, W. and Sandri, G., Bull. Am. Phys. Soc. 9, 38 (1964).
14. Ono, S. and Shizume, T. J., Phys. Soc. Japan 18, 29 (1963).
15. Weinstock, J., Phys. Rev. 132, 454 (1963).
16. Weinstock, J., Phys. Rev. 140, A460 (1965).
17. Frieman, E. A. and Goldman, R., Bull. Am. Phys. Soc. 10, 531 (1965).
18. McLennan, J. A., Phys. Lett. 7, 332 (1963).
19. Kawasaki, K. and Oppenheim, I., Phys. Rev. 136, A1519 (1964).
20. Sengers, J. V., Phys. Rev. Lett. 15, 515 (1965).
21. Kawasaki, K. and Oppenheim, I., Phys. Rev. 139, A1763 (1965).
22. Zwanzig, R. W., Phys. Rev. 129, 486 (1963).
23. Swenson, R. (private communication) first pointed this out. More recent work of Kawasaki and Oppenheim has resulted in the elimination of some of these difficulties.
24. Haines, L., Dorfman, J. R., and Ernst, M. H. J. J., Univ. of Maryland Tech. Note BN-419, October 1965. Phys. Rev. 144, 207 (1966).
25. Jeans, J., "The Dynamical Theory of Gases," p. 235. Cambridge Univ. Press, London and New York, 1904.
26. Sengers, J. V., Thesis, Univ. of Amsterdam (1962).
27. Zwanzig, R. W., and Mountain, R. D., J. Chem. Phys. 43, 4464 (1965); also Ibid. 44, 2777 (1966).
28. Mori, H., Prog. Theoret. Phys. 34, 399 (1965).
29. Mermin, N. D., Phys. Rev. 134, 112 (1964).
30. Treatments of this problem for van der Waals models have been given by Kawasaki, K., Phys. Rev. (in press) and by Mountain, R. D., and Zwanzig, R. (to be published), and by Deutch, J. M., and Zwanzig, R., (to be published).

SECTION IV

Turbulence and Stability

edited by

ALAN J. FALLER

Introduction to the Kraichnan Theory of Turbulence

R. BETCHOV

AEROSPACE CORPORATION
EL SEGUNDO, CALIFORNIA

The nature of the assumptions used by R. H. Kraichnan in the formulation of his theory of turbulence is examined. A particular problem is treated as an example. Numerical solutions are obtained with a computer which are analogous to turbulent fluctuations. The correlation function and the regression function are determined experimentally. The Kraichnan theory can be applied without difficulties, and the final comparison of experiment with theory is favorable. It is also shown that the other theoretical approaches (discard of cumulants) are inadequate. An attempt is made to evaluate the importance of the indirect interactions.

I. INTRODUCTION

The object of this paper is to examine the approach to turbulence problems proposed by R. H. Kraichnan. This analysis is not a rigorous and complete treatment but a study of the basic assumptions, and it is closely tied to a particular problem of simple but general nature.

The original formulation of Kraichnan's theory can be found in Ref. [1], which is concerned with magnetohydrodynamical turbulence. Subsequent papers [2–5] narrow down to ordinary turbulence and culminate to a good agreement between the calculated and the experimentally measured values of the so-called skewness factor. This coefficient expresses an important physical quantity: the rate of production of mean square vorticity. These results are without precedents in the field of turbulence. Further work by Kraichnan and others [6] is in progress concerning magnetohydrodynamical turbulence, plasma oscillations, turbulent heat transfer, as well as inhomogeneous flows.

We shall review the salient points of Kraichnan's theory and put it to a test by investigating the behavior of a particular system. This system is much simpler than any actual case of turbulence, and yet it is sufficiently complicated to motivate the use of Kraichnan's theory. In particular,

215

we shall see that the approach relying primarily on the discard of fourth-order cumulants leads to unacceptable results.

The particular problem that we shall examine has the advantage that it can be solved numerically with the help of a digital computer. It is possible to obtain a variety of solutions that look turbulent and to measure correlation functions, thus processing the information and extracting the essential results. The Kraichnan theory can be applied without much trouble, and the patient reader will be rewarded by a comparison between theory and experiment (see Fig. 11).

II. STATEMENT OF THE MODEL PROBLEM

The study of turbulent flows starts from the nonlinear partial differential equations of Navier and Stokes. By introducing the spatial Fourier transform, one arrives at a very large system of nonlinear ordinary differential equations governing the behavior in time of every Fourier transform of the velocity. When necessary, the system can include the Fourier transform of the magnetic field, the pressure, or the electric charge density. The core of the difficulty is formed by the nonlinear terms. These terms are generally of a bilinear type, because the original partial differential equations contain double products, at worst. Let us specify that the use of complex functions promotes simplicity in the formal exposition of the problem, but, as far as computations are concerned, it is simpler to think in terms of real amplitudes. There are simply two amplitudes for each wave number: one in phase with the cosine, and one in phase with the sine. This corresponds to separation in real and imaginary terms.

In the equation giving the time derivative of a Fourier transform of wave vector k, one finds only linear terms corresponding to the same wave vector, or bilinear terms between components corresponding to two wave vectors k' and k'' such that the sum $k' + k''$ or the difference $k' - k''$ is precisely equal to k. This stems from well-known trigonometric relations giving the product of two sines in terms of the sums or difference of the angles. Thus the nonlinear interactions between Fourier components are limited to certain triads corresponding to simple relations between k' and k''.

In this paper, we shall consider a relatively simple problem where N real functions vary with the time. There is no equivalent to the wave vectors. We shall even formulate the problem in such a way that the N functions have the same statistical properties. Therefore, it will be

possible to use all available functions to form one large statistical sample, out of which we can extract averaged properties. This procedure will limit the computing expenses. For the basic system of equations, we choose

$$d/dt\, F_i(t) \; = \; c_{ijk}F_j(t)F_k(t) \tag{2.1}$$

where the coefficients c_{ijk} are real and constant. The summation over repeated indices is always implicit. No symmetry of the indices is assumed.

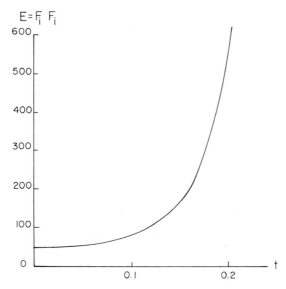

FIG. 1. An example showing the rapid divergence of the solution if the coefficients of Eq. (2.1) are chosen completely at random ($N = 48$).

We shall select initial conditions by pulling the $F_i(0)$ from a set of random numbers, with a Gaussian distribution and unit mean square. In fact, we shall even normalize any particular set of initial conditions in such a way that we have exactly

$$F_i(0)F_i(0) \; = \; N \tag{2.2}$$

If the coefficients c_{ijk} are chosen at random from a similar Gaussian set, the experiment shows that the solution diverges rapidly, as shown in Fig. 1, where $E(t) = F_iF_i$. This is not surprising if we can think of the F_i as the coordinates of a point in N dimensions: the initial conditions indicate a point somewhere on a sphere of given radius [see Eq. 2.2)], and,

in time, the point wanders towards infinity. Essentially, there is more space outside of the sphere than around the origin. In order to avoid this inconvenience and to have a statistically stationary system, we shall demand that the coefficients obey the following cyclic relations:

$$c_{ijk} + c_{kij} + c_{jki} = 0 \tag{2.3}$$

This has the effect that the quantity E remains invariant during the motion, as can be seen easily. We can say that the representative point will now stay on the surface of a given sphere.

Since we want the functions F_i to be statistically interchangeable, the motion on the surface of the sphere must be isotropic. This requires certain precautions in the manner in which we choose the coefficients c_{ijk} and the initial conditions. We shall now examine these two topics.

We shall generate $3M$ coefficients obeying Eq. (2.3) and decide that all others will vanish. In general, there could be N^3 coefficients, but we shall take $3M$ of the order of N^2. This creates an analogy with the situation existing in turbulent problems, where each F_i is associated with a particular wave number, and where most coefficients do vanish. Another important reason for taking $3M < N^3$ will be discussed later, and finally the cost of computations must also be kept in mind.

To generate the coefficients, we start by selecting M triplets of indices, by a random process. All indices from 1 to N have equal probability to appear at any stage. A triplet containing the same index more than once is rejected. Let us suppose that the first triplet of the list is 3, 2, 5. We now choose three numbers a, b, c out of the normalized Gaussian set and construct three coefficients as follows:

$$
\begin{aligned}
c_{3,2,5} &= (1/6^{1/2})(2a - b - c) \\
c_{5,3,2} &= (1/6^{1/2})(2b - c - a) \\
c_{2,5,3} &= (1/6^{1/2})(2c - a - b)
\end{aligned}
\tag{2.4}
$$

These coefficients satisfy the condition (2.3); they have a Gaussian distribution of unit mean square. They are, however, correlated two by two. In particular, we have

$$\langle c_{3,2,5}\, c_{5,3,2} \rangle = -\tfrac{1}{2} \tag{2.5}$$

where $\langle\ \rangle$ indicates the ensemble average. For the second triplet of indices, another set a, b, c is selected, and so forth. The complete set of coefficients has the following properties:

$$\langle c_{ijk}\, c_{ijk} \rangle = 3M \tag{2.6}$$

$$\langle c_{ijk}\, c_{kij} \rangle = -\tfrac{3}{2}M \tag{2.7}$$

Since each triplet is processed independently, all sums where the indices do not appear in the cyclic order will vanish statistically. Thus, we have

$$\langle c_{ijk} \, c_{ikj} \rangle = 0 \tag{2.8}$$

$$\langle c_{ijk} \, c_{jik} \rangle = 0 \tag{2.9}$$

$$\langle c_{ijk} \, c_{kji} \rangle = 0 \tag{2.10}$$

The initial conditions must also be such that any region of the N-dimensional spherical surface has an equal chance to be visited at $t = 0$. If N is large, it can be shown that the number of points having the specified radius with coordinates between F_i and $F_i + \Delta F_i$ varies as the Gaussian function. Thus the normalized set used previously is satisfactory. The magnitude of the initial radius is unimportant, since a solution $F_i(t)$ of the system of Eq. (2.1) can be used to obtain other solutions, such as $gF_i(gt)$, where g is an arbitrary constant.

These algorithms for selection of the coefficients and the initial conditions guarantee the statistical isotropy of the solution in the N-dimensional space. Of course, in a real turbulent problem, the coefficients are not random. Their magnitude is roughly related to that of the indices, and the signs depend upon complicated relations. One could perhaps use a normalization procedure and assume that the very complication of turbulent problems leads to randomization of the signs, but we shall not be concerned with such possible analogies. Our purpose is to test Kraichnan's theory. Similar systems with a small number of functions have already been examined [3], providing encouraging but less extensive evidence.

Finally, it was stated by Kraichnan [7] that his theory is exact for a large random system, so that it should function in the present case.

The problem is now defined, and several sets of $3M$ coefficients can be kept at hand in order to test the reproducibility of the results.

III. EXPERIMENTAL CORRELATION

A simple forward integration with constant step size was used. A typical sample of solution is shown in Fig. 2, where we used $N = 48$ and $3M = 3072$. With the IBM 7090, the computations take 1 min per unit of t. Preliminary attempts with $N = 6$ and $N = 12$ showed poor statistical reproducibility. The value of $3M$ was chosen slightly larger than N^2 to increase the number of interactions between the functions F_i.

The computer simply proceeds down the list of nonzero coefficients, increasing each F_i according to

$$F_i(t + \Delta t) = F_i(t) + c_{ijk} F_j F_k \, \Delta t - \lambda F_i \, \Delta t \tag{3.1}$$

The term $-\lambda F_i$ is introduced to compensate for a special kind of error. Indeed, if we compute the new radius, after a step, we find from Eq. (3.1)

$$(F_iF_i)_{t+\Delta t} = (F_iF_i)_t + (1 + \lambda^2)\frac{dF_i}{dt}\frac{dF_i}{dt}\Delta t^2$$

$$+ 2(1 - \lambda)F_i\frac{dF_i}{dt}\Delta t$$

$$- 2\lambda F_iF_i\Delta t \tag{3.2}$$

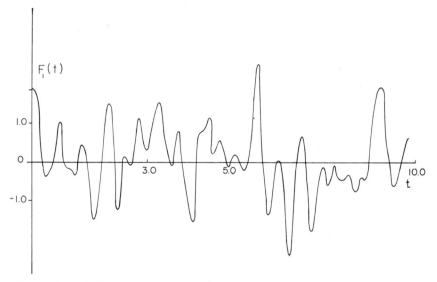

F$_{\rm ig}$. 2. A typical sample of a solution showing the turbulent behavior ($N = 48$, $3M = 3072$, $dt = 0.0025$, $\lambda = 0.07$).

In the average, the energy does not stay constant unless we have

$$\lambda = \frac{\langle dF_i/dt\ dF_i/dt\rangle\ \Delta t}{2N} \tag{3.3}$$

If t increases by a unit, the energy generally wanders by about 2% around the desired value, and we have occasionally renormalized the F_i at times $t = 1, 2, 3$, etc.

We measured the values of $\langle dF_i/dt\ dF_i/dt\rangle$ by averaging in time over several solutions, starting from different points or using alternate sets of coefficients. The results agree with the following approximation. From Eq. (2.1), we have

$$\langle dF_i/dt\ dF_i/dt\rangle = c_{ijk}\,c_{ipq}\langle F_jF_kF_pF_q\rangle \tag{3.4}$$

If the F_i functions are almost uncorrelated, the quadruple product can be approximated by a sum of three double products. This amounts to discarding the fourth-order cumulants. The result is

$$\langle dF_i/dt \; dF_i/dt \rangle = c_{ijk} \; c_{ipq}(\delta_{jk}\delta_{pq} + \delta_{jp}\delta_{kq} + \delta_{jq}\delta_{kp})$$
$$= 3M \tag{3.5}$$

The turbulent nature of the solution immediately suggests that we should limit our interest to averaged functions such as the power spectrum or the autocorrelation function. Let us define the correlation matrix

$$H_{ij}(\tau) = (1/N)\langle F_i(t + \tau)F_j(t)\rangle \tag{3.6}$$

The numerical results indicated that H_{ij} is proportional to δ_{ij}, as expected from isotropy. Thus, the main object of the problem is to determine a single function $H(\tau)$, defined as

$$H(\tau) = H_{jj} = (1/N)\langle F_i(t + \tau)F_i(t)\rangle \tag{3.7}$$

It follows from Eq. (2.2) that $H(0)$ is unity. The Fourier transform of $H(\tau)$ is the power spectrum of the function $F_i(t)$.

The correlation was measured, starting at times such as $t = 1, 2, 3$ and for various values of τ. The results are shown in Fig. 3. The dotted lines refer to one initial point on the sphere, with an average over three values of t. No systematic variation with t was noticed. The solid line extending up to $t = 0.5$ represents an average over three values of t and four sets of initial conditions. Each solid line extending to $t = 0.75$ is averaged over eight sets of initial conditions, and the measurements of H are performed at three values of t. We used a different set of coefficients for each line.

Formally, the basic equations admit singular solutions such that one function F has the value $N^{1/2}$ and all others are zero. They represent unstable stagnation points on the sphere and are statistically very improbable. A particular solution is perhaps limited to a certain portion of the sphere by the very nature of the coefficients and initial conditions. This explains perhaps the fact that $H(\tau)$ tends to stay slightly positive as τ varies between 0.5 and 0.75. We strongly doubt that H rises again at some large value of τ. Even if the basic equations would guarantee some long-time periodicity, the numerical errors would scramble the results.

In order to test the accuracy of the integrating procedure, we first determine $\overrightarrow{F}(t)$ by integrating from $t = 0$ up to $t = 2$. The values of Δt and λ were then reversed, and the computer was in effect ordered to back track and compute $\overleftarrow{F}(t)$, starting from $t = 2$. The correlation between

$\vec{F}$ and $\overleftarrow{F}$ was found high as long as t was greater than 1. Thus, the numerical errors produce irreversible effects in one unit of time, and this should cut off the correlation function.

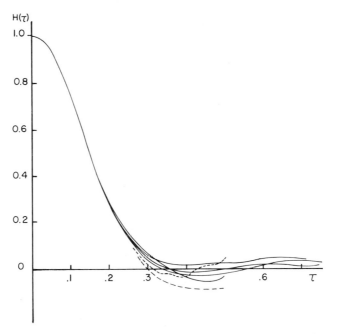

Fɪɢ. 3. The experimental autocorrelation function. Each dotted line is an average over three values of t from one initial condition. The solid line extending to $t = 0.5$ is an average over 12 correlations: three values of t from four initial conditions. The solid lines up to $\tau = 0.75$ are averaged over 24 functions each: three values of t and eight initial conditions. These last three curves have been obtained with three different sets of coefficients.

IV. THE CUMULANT-DISCARD APPROXIMATION

Let us try to determine $H(\tau)$ by assuming that quadruple correlations can be approximated as if the F_i functions were independent of each other. We shall first define the delayed functions

$$F_i' = F_i(t + \tau) \tag{4.1}$$

Multiplication of Eq. (2.1) by F_i' and averaging lead to

$$\frac{dH}{d\tau} = -\frac{1}{N}\left\langle F_i' \frac{dF_i}{dt} \right\rangle = -\frac{c_{ijk}}{N}\langle F_i'F_jF_k \rangle \tag{4.2}$$

This relation bears a certain analogy with the Karman-Horwath equation, although we now have a shift in time.   The time derivative of the right-hand side of Eq. (4.2) can be formed, and it leads to

$$\frac{d^2H}{d\tau^2} = - \frac{c_{ijk}\,c_{ipq}}{N}\, \langle F_p'F_q'F_jF_k \rangle \tag{4.3}$$

We can now separate the quadruple product in three terms, and, with proper consideration of Eq. (2.6), we find

$$\frac{d^2H}{d\tau^2} = - \frac{3M}{N}\, H^2 \tag{4.4}$$

The solution of this equation is sketched in Fig. 4; it has the proper curvature at the origin, but it plunges to $-\infty$.

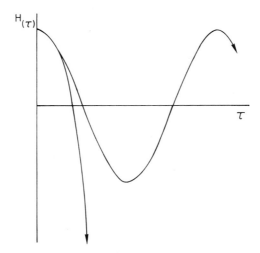

FIG. 4. The autocorrelation function according to unsatisfactory theories based on the discard of fourth-order cumulants.

Let us now return to the basic equation and try a slightly different procedure.   We differentiate Eq. (2.1) with respect to t, multiply by F_i', and average.   We obtain

$$\left\langle F_i'\frac{d^2F_i}{dt^2} \right\rangle = \frac{d^2H}{d\tau^2} = c_{ijk} \left\langle F_i'\frac{dF_j}{dt}F_k + F_i'F_j\frac{dF_k}{dt} \right\rangle$$

$$\frac{d^2H}{d\tau^2} = c_{ijk}\,c_{jpq}\langle F_i'F_pF_qF_k \rangle + c_{ijk}\,c_{kpq}\langle F_i'F_jF_pF_q \rangle$$

$$= - \frac{3M}{N}\, H(\tau) \tag{4.5}$$

The solution of this equation is a cosine.   As shown in Fig. 4, it has the correct initial curvature, but its long-time behavior is unsatisfactory.

Clearly, the discard of the fourth-order cumulants leads not only to unacceptable results but also to some deep contradictions between alternative approaches.

V. THE REGRESSION FUNCTION

The failure of the simple theory based on the discard of the cumulants shows that the functions F_i retain a sufficient amount of correlation to influence the results. Since it would be very difficult to express the exact

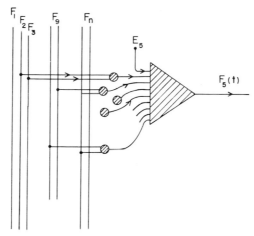

Fig. 5. The basic integrating unit of an imaginary analog computer. The circles are multipliers. Their outputs are summed and integrated to form the output $F_5(t)$.

effect of one function on another, we shall now direct our attention to the averaged effect of one function on another. This requires the definition of a special function that plays an essential role in Kraichnan's theory. It extends to random nonlinear systems the concept of the response to a small pulse, which plays an essential role in the theory of linear circuits. This function is also encountered in other statistical mechanical problems, where it is called the regression function. The history of this concept can be traced back to Onsager [8, 9] who assumed that the regression of microscopic thermodynamical fluctuations followed the same course as the regression of macroscopic fluctuations (see also De Groot [10]).

In order to have a clear view of the operations, we shall ask the reader to imagine an analog computer capable of integrating the basic Eq. (2.1). It consists of N circuits similar to the one shown in Fig. 5. The triangle represents an integrator: it receives many inputs from the left side and

forms the integral of their sum.   This is the output $F_5(t)$ in the form of a
fluctuating electric signal.   The round boxes are multipliers that generate
the bilinear terms.   They receive inputs such as F_2 and F_3 from the left
and deliver a signal $c_{5,2,3}F_2F_3$ to the integrator.   Thus the coefficients are
built into the multipliers.   The special input E_5 has no equivalent in the
basic equations and is provided for future usage.

The N integrators and their $3M$ multipliers are interconnected in the
manner sketched in Fig. 6, which gives only the outlines of the complete

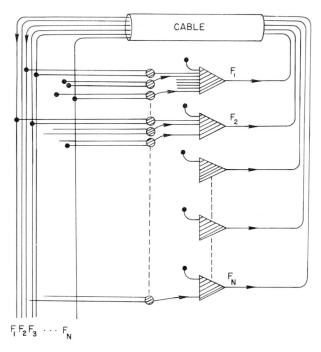

FIG. 6. The general outlines of an imaginary analog computer that could solve the
system of Eq. (2.1).   Each integrator has a special additional input.

circuit.   Through a cable, each integrator feeds a vertical line from which
the signal is directed to the appropriate multipliers.

The initial conditions would be applied by charging the N capacitors
contained in the integrators to the desired voltages.   Thus the N functions could be obtained, and we shall imagine that they are recorded on a
magnetic tape for future reference.   These functions would correspond
to a particular path on the surface of the N-dimensional sphere.

In principle, the computer can be reset, and the operation can be
repeated without any difference.   This can actually be done with a digital

computer, but it would be impossible with an analog machine. The reason is that the digital computer has on-or-off basic circuits, whereas the analog computer has thermal noise, aggravated by drift and poor memory.

We shall now perform a fundamental experiment. After recording the solution starting from a certain set of conditions $F_i(0)$, we shall repeat the operation by resetting the computer. At a certain time t_e, we apply a short pulse to input E_5. Thus, the second solution is identical with the first up to t_e, and we can now compare the disturbed solution with the undisturbed one.

If the time integral of the short pulse is ϵ, it will immediately cause a jump of magnitude ϵ in the function F_5. This modification will propagate through the cable and affect many other functions. Some of these variations, after a second passage through the cable, will be returned to the input side of the integrator delivering F_5.

If we imagine that the cable introduces a very small delay σ, we can define a hierarchy of effects of the pulse. The first effect is immediate and appears as a discontinuity of F_5. The second effect appears as a discontinuity in the first derivatives of some functions, with delay σ. The nth effect involves discontinuities of the $n - 1$ derivatives, with delay $(n - 1)\sigma$.

On the surface of the sphere, the two solutions coincide along some tortuous path from $t = 0$ up to $t = t_e$. Then the pulse sends the point on a new trajectory that will eventually differ completely from the unperturbed solution. After a long time, the points corresponding to the perturbed and the unperturbed solutions will be, on the average, something like one radius apart.

We can now compare the two solutions by using the stored information, and we define the normalized difference

$$G_5(\tau) = \frac{F_{5,\text{perturbed}} - F_{5,\text{unperturbed}}}{\epsilon} \tag{5.1}$$

with

$$\tau = t - t_e \tag{5.2}$$

Clearly, G_5 is zero for $\tau < 0$ and jumps to unity at $\tau = 0$. It will eventually become as large as $1/\epsilon$ as the two solutions become statistically independent. Indeed, the root mean square of F_5 is unity by Eq. (2.2).

The sign of G_5 when τ is small is positive, but, after a long time, it becomes uncertain. Indeed, the perturbed point may be on any side of the unperturbed one.

We shall now define the average of G_5, and, since the problem is isotropic, this function is the same for any one component. Thus we

write

$$G(\tau) = (1/N) \sum_{i=1}^{N} G_i(\tau) \qquad (5.3)$$

where it is understood that, in order to measure G, one must store the unperturbed solution and then carry N integrations, applying the pulse successively to F_1, F_2, F_3, . . . , etc. The experimental values of G

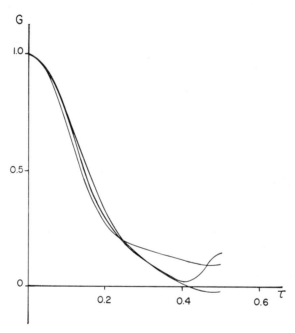

FIG. 7. The experimental regression function. Results with three different initial conditions and one set of coefficients. The perturbation $\epsilon = 0.01$ is applied successively to the 48 functions at $t_e = 0.5$.

are shown in Fig. 7 with $\epsilon = 0.01$. In Fig. 8, the results obtained with a variety of values of ϵ indicate that, as long as $\epsilon < 1$, the results are not affected.

In the average, the pulse increases the energy of the system so that it is not too surprising to find that, with a pulse comparable with the energy of the system (say, $\epsilon = 1$), the decay of G is simply accelerated.

These results show that, on the average, the effect of a pulse becomes unpredictable after a time of the order of $\tau = 0.3$. In order to evaluate how rapidly the two solutions drift away, we have defined the rms differ-

ence as

$$K(\tau) = \left[(1/N) \sum_{1}^{N} G_i^2 \right]^{1/2} \tag{5.4}$$

Typical values of K are shown in Figs. 8 and 9.   A special experiment was performed over a relatively long time to examine the asymptotic behavior of K.   As seen in Fig. 9, K grows exponentially while G fluctuates. There is little doubt that the fluctuations of G when τ is larger than 0.5 would disappear if we used a sufficiently large statistical sample.

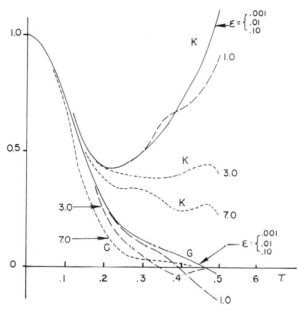

FIG. 8. The influence of ϵ on the functions G and K.   The values of ϵ are indicated, all other parameters being kept constant.   No effects are detected for $\epsilon = 0.001$, 0.01, and 0.1 (solid lines).

We conclude this section with some general remarks.   As can be noted from Fig. 8, G and K vary together for $\tau < 0.15$.   We surmise that, with a larger number of degrees of freedom (thus a larger value of N), these two curves would stay together for a longer time.   Eventually, with a system of 10^{23} modes, the deviations from the average effect of a pulse would be negligible.   Thus, if we compare the behavior of two very large systems, initially in the same microstates, we should be able to predict accurately the effect of a pulse, although, after a sufficiently long time, the two systems will be found in two completely different microstates.

One can also say that, as long as G and K coincide, the system has a hydrodynamical behavior.

The behavior of K also indicates that, if we used different roundoff procedures, two successive solutions would eventually diverge, even if no pulse is applied. In the case of our computations, each roundoff error is of the order of 10^{-8}. Since Δt is about 1% of the time during which the F_i functions are approximately constant, and since there are roughly 3000 operations per step, the total level of the equivalent perturbation is of the order of $(3 \times 10^5)^{1/2} \times 10^{-8}$, or 5×10^{-6}. With the rate of exponential

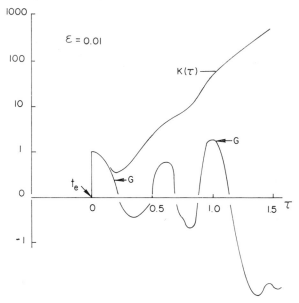

Fig. 9. The long-time behavior of G and K. Note the logarithmic vertical scale. The fluctuations of G would vanish with a larger statistical sample.

growth apparent in Fig. 9, one finds that the roundoff errors seriously disturb the solution in something like two units of time.

VI. A SUPERPOSITION PRINCIPLE

Let us now imagine that we apply to E_5 a sequence of small pulses forming a continuous function $f(t)$ produced by some external device such as a harmonic oscillator, square wave generator, etc. Although we are unable and unwilling to specify the exact effect of a single pulse, we may limit our ambition to the averaged effect of a pulse. This leads to the

idea that the averaged effect of f will be some small contribution to F_5 given by

$$\Delta F_5(t) = \int_{-\infty}^{t} G(t-s)f(s)\,ds \qquad (6.1)$$

Note that this includes not only the direct effect of f but also the indirect effects, reaching F_5 after one or more passages through the cable. Although ΔF_5 is not directly observable, it permits us to express the correlation between f and F_5. Indeed, we can assume that ΔF_5 is the only part of F_5 which correlates with f. Thus, we write

$$\langle f'F_5 \rangle = \int_{-\infty}^{t} G(t-s)h(t+\tau-s)\,ds \qquad (6.2)$$

where we have defined

$$\langle f(t+\tau)f(t)\rangle = h(\tau) \qquad (6.3)$$

Note that the derivation of Eq. (6.2) from Eq. (6.1) depends upon the fact that G does not fluctuate. It has already been averaged in Eq. (5.3).

VII. THE APPROXIMATION OF DIRECT INTERACTION

We are now coming to the focal point of Kraichnan's theory: the evaluation of the triple correlations by means of the regression function. As shown in Eq. (4.2), $dH/d\tau$ is given by a large sum of triple correlations. Since $dH/d\tau$ is of the order of unity and since each triple product could be as large as unity, the average of every triple product must be rather small.

Let us suppose that the triplet 6, 2, 9 appears somewhere in the list, and let us direct our attention to the quantity $\langle F_6'F_2F_9 \rangle$. In the general circuit of the analog computer, the presence of this triplet corresponds to the particular links shown in Fig. 10. In this drawing, we have added three switches α, β, γ which are normally closed. If these three switches are opened, the system would be as if the particular triplet of indices had not been selected.

We shall say that, if the three switches are opened, the triplet interaction 6, 2, 9 is disabled. We shall now assume that the correlation $\langle F_6'F_2F_9 \rangle$ is zero if the triplet is disabled. A priori there is no reason why this quantity should be positive or negative when the triplet is disabled. This crucial assumption will be re-examined in the next section, in a broader context.

Thus, when the three switches are opened, we are assuming that the complicated linkages between the three outputs cannot form a mean triple

product.   Let us now close one switch only, say α.   This adds one more input to the integrator, forming F_2.

According to the results of Section VI, we describe the effect of the switch closure as a new input

$$f(t) = c_{2,9,6}F_9F_6 \qquad (7.1)$$

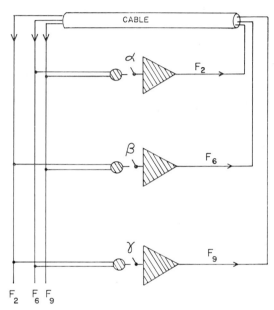

FIG. 10. The direct interactions produced by a particular triplet of coefficients, in the basic Eq. (2.1).   The opening of the switches disables the triplet.   All other connections are intact but not indicated.

which modifies F_2 by the amount

$$\Delta F_2(t) = c_{2,9,6} \int_{-\infty}^{t} G(t - s)F_9(s)F_6(s) \, ds \qquad (7.2)$$

The correlation between the three particular functions will now increase from zero up to the value

$$\langle F_6{}'F_2F_9 \rangle = c_{2,9,6} \int_{-\infty}^{t} G(t - s)\langle F_9(t)F_9(s)F_6(t + \tau)F_6(s) \rangle \, ds \qquad (7.3)$$

At this point, we shall assume that the quadruple correlations can be approximated by the product of double correlations.   It is apparent from Section IV that this approximation is dangerous for large values of the time separation.   However, in the present case, G drops to zero when $t - s$ is large, so that we really do not need more than an approximation for

small separations. In the limit of an infinitely large system with random coefficients, Kraichnan finds that the appropriate cumulants become exactly zero. In the case of turbulent flows, certain considerations of homogeneity justify this same step.

Furthermore, the fluctuations in the effect of a simple pulse, such as E_5, which are no longer described by the regression function $G(\tau)$ could be retained up to Eq. (7.3). These are the fluctuations that cause the buildup of $K(\tau)$.

This improved treatment leads to a modified form of Eq. (7.3), where G_i [see Eq. (5.1)] replaces G and where the average includes G_i and the four functions F. Kraichnan [7] shows that one can still separate it into a product of three averaged quantities.

Thus, after closing only switch α, we have

$$\langle F_6' F_2 F_9 \rangle = c_{2,9,6} \int_{-\infty}^{t} G(t - s)H(t - s)H(t + \tau - s)\,ds \qquad (7.4)$$

If we close switch β while leaving α and γ opened, the same argument can be applied to examine the effect on F_6. The results are

$$\Delta F_6' = c_{6,2,9} \int_{-\infty}^{t+\tau} G(t + \tau - s)F_2(s)F_9(s)\,ds \qquad (7.5)$$

$$\langle F_6' F_2 F_9 \rangle = c_{6,2,9} \int_{-\infty}^{t+\tau} G(t + \tau - s)H^2(t - s)\,ds \qquad (7.6)$$

The integration is carried up to $t + \tau$, since we are interested in F_6'. The closure of γ, and only γ, gives

$$\langle F_6' F_2 F_9 \rangle = c_{9,6,2} \int_{-\infty}^{t} G(t - s)H(t - s)H(t + \tau - s)\,ds \qquad (7.7)$$

Let us now examine the triple correlation when all three switches are closed. In view of our previous assumptions that the particular triple correlation disappears when the triplet is disabled, we shall now assume that the net value of $\langle F_6' F_2 F_9 \rangle$ is the sum of the three quantities contributed by the separate switching operations. This is simple, and any refinements would involve great complications. The left-hand sides of Eqs. (7.4), (7.6), and (7.7) are independent of t. Thus, we can choose any convenient value of t in the right-hand sides, and we shall take $t = 0$. Thus, the triple correlation, with all three switches closed, can be written as

$$\begin{aligned}
\langle F_6' F_2 F_9 \rangle &= c_{6,2,9} \int_{0}^{\tau} G(\tau - s)H^2(s)\,ds \\
&+ c_{6,2,9} \int_{-\infty}^{0} G(\tau - s)H^2(s)\,ds \\
&+ (c_{2,9,6} + c_{9,6,2}) \int_{-\infty}^{0} G(-s)H(s)H(\tau - s)\,ds \qquad (7.8)
\end{aligned}$$

where we use the symmetry of $H(\tau)$.   The relation between the coefficients [see Eq. (2.3)] can now be invoked and we find

$$\langle F_6' F_2 F_9 \rangle = c_{6,2,9} \int_0^\tau G(\tau - s) H^2(s)\ ds$$
$$+ c_{6,2,9} \int_{-\infty}^0 H(s)[G(\tau - s)H(s) - G(-s)H(\tau - s)]\ ds \quad (7.9)$$

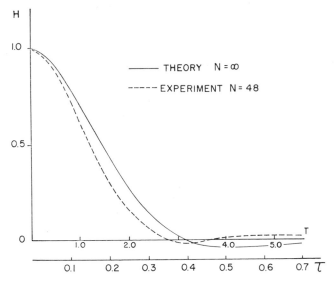

Fig. 11. Experimental and theoretical values of the autocorrelation function $H(\tau)$. $T = (3M/N)^{1/2}\tau = 8\tau$.

The same argument applies to every triplet, so that insertion of Eq. (7.9) into Eq. (4.2) gives

$$\frac{dH}{d\tau} = -\frac{3M}{N} \int_0^\tau G(\tau - s) H^2(s)\ ds$$
$$- \frac{3M}{N} \int_{-\infty}^0 H(s)[G(\tau - s)H(s) - G(-s)H(\tau - s)]\ ds \quad (7.10)$$

Since the solution is statistically stationary, $H(\tau)$ must be symmetric. Inspection of Eq. (7.10) shows that this is achieved if $G(\tau) = H(\tau)$ when $\tau > 0$.   The experimental results confirm this choice, and more will be said about it in Section IX.   This new step leads to the final relation giving the function $H(\tau)$:

$$\frac{dH}{d\tau} = -\frac{3M}{N} \int_0^\tau H(\tau - s) H^2(s)\ ds \quad (7.11)$$

We have integrated this equation numerically by using a special program. The arbitrary constant is fixed by the condition $H(0) = 1$. It is convenient to define the new variable $T = (3M/N)^{1/2}\tau$, which, in effect, removes the factor $3M/N$ from Eq. (7.11). The results are shown in Fig. 11, together with the experimental average over all available data. The step size in the calculation of $H(T)$ was $\Delta T = 0.0025$, and smaller steps might result in a better agreement between the two curves. We do not believe that a larger sample of numerical solutions would affect the results. The difference between the two curves is probably because the theory is valid in the limit of infinite N.

In view of the failure of the method relying primarily on the discard of the fourth-order cumulants, the present theory represents significant progress.

VIII. THE INDIRECT INTERACTIONS

If we review the chain of arguments leading to the results shown in Fig. 11, we find that the weakest link is the assumption that $Q = \langle F_6'F_2F_9 \rangle$ is zero when the three switches α, β, and γ are open. We shall now examine this question in some detail, although it becomes difficult to progress. We define as a direct interaction the effect of the closure of three switches corresponding to a triplet of coefficients. All other interactions will be referred to as being indirect.

The many effects that could contribute to the quantity under consideration, when the three switches are opened, must involve a number of passages of the information through the cable greater than 2. The larger the number of passages through the cable, the greater is the loss of information due to multiplications by uncorrelated functions, but the number of such combinations also grows. For correlations over long times, it may very well be that the indirect interactions play a major role.

We shall now consider one particular kind of indirect interaction as an example. The inspection of the list of triplets may reveal the existence of entries such as

$$(6, \lambda, \mu), \qquad (2, \mu, \nu), \qquad (9, \nu, \lambda) \qquad (8.1)$$

where λ, μ, and ν stand for any particular indices other than 2, 6, and 9. With the α, β, γ switches open, this means that F_6 contains a contribution proportional to the integral of $F_\lambda F_\mu$; F_2 contains a contribution from $F_\mu F_\nu$; and F_9 from $F_\nu F_\lambda$. As a result, we can expect a weak triple correlation, which, if we momentarily suspend the rule of summation over

repeated indices, reads as follows:

$$\Delta Q = c_{6\lambda\mu}c_{2\mu\nu}c_{9\nu\lambda}$$
$$\times \left\langle \int_{-\infty}^{0} GF_\lambda F_\mu \, ds \times \int_{-\infty}^{0} GF_\mu F_\nu \, ds' \times \int_{-\infty}^{0} GF_\nu F_\lambda \, ds'' \right\rangle \quad (8.2)$$

The probability that any particular coefficient is different from zero is roughly $3M/N^3$. Thus, the probability that the three coefficients appearing in Eq. (8.2) will not be zero is $27M^3/N^9$. Note that it becomes unity if all coefficients have been called up. If N is large, the indices λ, μ, and ν can be selected in $N^3/6$ different ways. Thus there are $\frac{27}{6}M^3N^{-6}$ nonzero forms of Eq. (8.2) for the particular choice of a triplet 6, 2, 9. If we added all such contributions to Q, we would have to include something like $5M^3N^{-6}$ terms.

Let us now evaluate the magnitude of any particular term. There are $3M/N$ inputs to each integrator, in the average, producing an output of unit rms. These signals are almost completely uncorrelated. The integration reduces their amplitude down to the level of $(N/3M)^{1/2}$, giving a sum of the order of unity.

Let us now consider an extreme case where all the contributions to Q, according to Eq. (8.2), have the same sign. This gives the estimated value

$$Q_{\text{indirect}} \approx 5(M^3/N^6)(M/N)^{3/2} \quad (8.3)$$

The correlation caused by closure of the three switches can be evaluated along similar lines of thought, and one finds

$$Q_{\text{direct}} \approx (N/M)^{1/2} \quad (8.4)$$

The ratio of these quantities gives

$$Q_{\text{indirect}}/Q_{\text{direct}} \approx M^2/N^5 \quad (8.5)$$

It we used all possible coefficients, M would be proportional to N^3, and the indirect triple correlations, in the extreme case, could be N times larger than the direct ones. If we take M of the order of N^2, the ratio of Eq. (8.5) becomes $1/N$, and the particular type of indirect interactions which we considered here become negligible.

If there are cancellations between the various contributions to Q_{indirect}, such as the one indicated in Eq. (8.2), the level of indirect interactions drops down. In the case of our particular problem, each triplet of coefficients is independent of the other, so that ΔQ has a random polarity. This guarantees the validity of the approach, even if $M \approx N^3$.

The problem treated in this paper is essentially free from indirect interactions, because the coefficients are generated three by three and disabled three by three in the construction of the theory. In the case of turbulent

problems, M is still limited to N^2 by the fact that coupled wave vectors must form triangles. However, the rules generating the coefficients are precise, although very intricate. In particular, the exchange between "real" and "imaginary" terms generates many complicated terms. The value of Kraichnan's theory probably depends upon this intricacy, so that the direct correlations represent the leading contribution to triple correlations.

IX. THEORY OF THE REGRESSION FUNCTION

In a nonstationary situation, the symmetry of H cannot be invoked to determine G. According to Kraichnan, a special general equation can be derived which gives G as a function of H. Thus one can obtain a closed system of equations. We shall now examine this topic, and, in order to shorten the equations, we shall momentarily assume the symmetry $c_{ijk} = c_{ikj}$.

If a pulse is applied to input E_5 of Fig. 5 at time t_o, the function F_5 will undergo a change ΔF_5, and every other function F_j will exhibit some smaller modification δF_j. In the long range, the differences ΔF_5 and δF_j between the perturbed and the unperturbed solutions will become of the order of the radius of the N-dimensional sphere, but we shall confine our attention to the times following t_e during which K is still comparable with G.

The linearization of the basic equations for $t > t_e$ gives

$$d/dt \ \Delta F_5 = 2c_{5jk} \ \delta F_j F_k \tag{9.1}$$

$$d/dt \ \delta F_j = 2c_{j5q} \ \Delta F_5 F_q + 2c_{jpq} \ \delta F_p F_q \tag{9.2}$$

In Eq. (9.2) we shall neglect the terms in δF_p on the grounds that $|\Delta F_5| \gg |\delta F_j|$ and on the grounds that these terms tend to cancel each other unless the coefficients are highly organized. We can also approximate δF_j by means of the regression function and replace Eq. (9.2) by the integral

$$\delta F_j = 2c_{j5q} \int_{t_e}^{t} G(t - s) \ \Delta F_5(s)F_q(s) \ ds \tag{9.3}$$

Substitution of Eq. (9.3) into Eq. (9.1) leads to

$$d/dt \ \Delta F_5 = 4c_{5jk} \ c_{j5q} \int_{t_e}^{t} G(t - s) \ \Delta F_5(s)F_q(s)F_k(t) \ ds \tag{9.4}$$

In this expression, G is a well-defined function, not subject to statistical fluctuations. Furthermore, ΔF_5 is the direct effect of a pulse, and its average is ϵG_5, by definition [see Eq. (5.1)].

The functions F_q and F_k, on the other hand, are fluctuating quantities. Each has an average of zero. The mean product, however, is $H(t - s)$ δ_{qk}, according to Eq. (3.6) and isotropy. Thus, we divide Eq. (9.4) by ϵ (the magnitude of the pulse), and after averaging and using the notation $\tau = t - t_e$, we find

$$dG/d\tau = 4c_{5jk}\, c_{j5k} \int_0^\tau G(\tau - s)G(s)H(\tau - s)\, ds \tag{9.5}$$

If we do not assume the symmetry of the coefficients, the factor 4 must be replaced by the factor 2. The summation over all values of the index i which has here the particular value 5, with notice of Eq. (2.7) and no symmetry in the coefficients, leads to the final result

$$dG/d\tau = -(3M/N) \int_0^\tau G(\tau - s)G(s)H(\tau - s)\, ds \tag{9.6}$$

We can consider Eq. (9.6) and Eq. (9.10) as forming a closed system. The initial conditions must be $G(0) = H(0) = 1$. If $G = H$, both equations become identical after a minor change of variable. Thus, $G = H$ (if $\tau > 0$) is a solution, and there is little doubt that it is the unique solution.

ACKNOWLEDGMENTS

The author wishes to thank Dr. R. H. Kraichnan for his help and valuable criticism. Professor S. Corrsin and L. S. G. Kovasznay have also provided stimulating remarks and questions. The author is also very grateful to Mrs. Barbara Gold, who prepared the computations program and its many ramifications with great diligence. This work was supported by the U.S. Air Force under Contract No. AF 04 (695)-469.

REFERENCES

1. Kraichnan, R. H., Irreversible Statistical Mechanics of Incompressible Hydromagnetic Turbulence. *Phys. Rev.* **109**, 1407 (1958).
2. Kraichnan, R. H., The Structure of Isotropic Turbulence at Very High Reynolds Numbers. *J. Fluid Mech.* **5**, 497–543 (1959).
3. Kraichnan, R. H., Direct-Interaction Approximation for a System of Several Interacting Simple Shear Waves. *Phys. Fluids* **6**, 1603–1609 (1963).
4. Kraichnan, R. H., Decay of Isotropic Turbulence in the Direct Interaction Approximation. *Phys. Fluids* **7**, 1030–1047 (1964).
5. Kraichnan, R. H., Lagrangian-History Closure Approximation for Turbulence. *Phys. Fluids* **7**, 1723 (1964).
6. Kraichnan, R. H., Direct Interaction Approximation for Shear and Thermally Driven Turbulence. *Phys. Fluids* **7**, 1048 (1964); also Erratum, *ibid.* **8**, 550 (1965).
7. Kraichnan, R. H., Dynamics of Nonlinear Stochastic Systems. *J. Math. Phys.* **2**, 124–148 (1961).
8. Onsager, L., *Phys. Rev.* **37**, 405 (1931).
9. Onsager, L., *Phys. Rev.* **38**, 2265 (1931).
10. DeGroot, S. R., "Thermodynamics of Irreversible Processes." Wiley (Interscience), New York, 1951.

Invariance Principles and

Approximation in Turbulence Dynamics

ROBERT H. KRAICHNAN

PETERBOROUGH, NEW HAMPSHIRE

Known expansion schemes for turbulence statistical functions appear to diverge at high Reynolds numbers. The expansions are an illusory guide for choosing a closure approximation for the statistical equations. They do not provide a means either of constructing successively more accurate approximations or of estimating the error in any given approximation. In this situation, an important principle for constructing appropriate approximations is to retain as much as possible of the basic conservation, invariance, and boundedness properties of the exact flow dynamics. Approximations that preserve such properties give a hope of qualitative agreement with reality. Unless some kind of convergent and practicable approximation scheme is developed, any accurate quantitative prediction from turbulence theory must be regarded as an accident or miracle.

I. EXPANSION IN POWERS OF REYNOLDS NUMBER

The past few years have seen a growing interest in formal expansions as tools for predicting some of the statistical properties of turbulent flows. The present paper discusses pitfalls shared by the known expansion schemes and suggests criteria that may help in finding valid statistical approximations.

Formal expansions have been invoked for a variety of problems in hydrodynamical and plasma turbulence [1–13]. The discussion here will be confined to homogeneous turbulence in an infinite incompressible fluid obeying the Navier-Stokes equation. Hopefully, this will illuminate the issues with minimum complication. In order to permit a consistent discussion of homogeneous turbulence which may also be statistically steady, the Navier-Stokes equation will be augmented with a solenoidal forcing term $\mathbf{f}(\mathbf{x}, t)$ so that it becomes

$$(\partial/\partial t - \nu\nabla^2)\mathbf{u}(\mathbf{x}, t) = -\mathbf{u}(\mathbf{x}, t) \cdot \nabla\mathbf{u}(\mathbf{x}, t) - \nabla p(\mathbf{x}, t) + \mathbf{f}(\mathbf{x}, t), \quad (1)$$

$$\nabla \cdot \mathbf{u}(\mathbf{x}, t) = 0, \qquad \nabla \cdot \mathbf{f}(\mathbf{x}, t) = 0. \quad (2)$$

The forcing term can be set to zero to describe freely decaying turbulence. The kinematic pressure $p(\mathbf{x}, t)$ can be eliminated from (1) by solving the Poisson equation

$$\nabla^2 p = -\partial^2(u_i u_j)/\partial x_i \, \partial x_j \tag{3}$$

with an appropriate boundary condition. The latter will be taken as constant pressure at spatial infinity. Then (3) shows that p is a purely bilinear functional of the velocity.

Suppose that a statistical ensemble of realizations of the velocity field is prescribed at an initial time t_0 and that the forcing field in each realization is prescribed for all $t \geq t_0$. Assume that the fields $\mathbf{u}(\mathbf{x}, t_0)$ and $\mathbf{f}(\mathbf{x}, t)$ have zero ensemble means and that their joint statistical distribution exhibits spatial homogeneity and invariance to spatial reflection. Then it can be seen from (1) and (3) that $\mathbf{u}(\mathbf{x}, t)$ has zero ensemble mean for all $\mathbf{x}$ and t.

Let it be required to evaluate the covariance tensor

$$U_{ij}(\mathbf{x}, t; \mathbf{x}', t') = \langle u_i(\mathbf{x}, t) u_j(\mathbf{x}', t') \rangle \tag{4}$$

for all $t \geq t_0$ and $t' \geq t_0$, Here $\langle \ \rangle$ denotes average over the ensemble of realizations. If (1) is linearized by neglecting the terms $-\mathbf{u} \cdot \nabla \mathbf{u} - \nabla p$, the task can be accomplished immediately. The solution $\mathbf{u}^{(0)}(\mathbf{x}, t)$ of the linearized equation is

$$\mathbf{u}^{(0)}(\mathbf{x}, t) = \int G^{(0)}(\mathbf{x}, t; \mathbf{y}, t_0)\mathbf{u}(\mathbf{y}, t_0) \, d^3y$$
$$+ \int_{t_0}^{t} ds \int G^{(0)}(\mathbf{x}, t; \mathbf{y}, s)\mathbf{f}(\mathbf{y}, s) \, d^3y, \tag{5}$$

where

$$G^{(0)}(\mathbf{x}, t; \mathbf{y}, s) = [4\pi\nu(t - s)]^{-3/2} \exp\{-|\mathbf{x} - \mathbf{y}|^2/[4\nu(t - s)]\}, \tag{6}$$

The covariance

$$U_{ij}^{(0)}(\mathbf{x}, t; \mathbf{x}', t') = \langle u_i^{(0)}(\mathbf{x}, t) u_j^{(0)}(\mathbf{x}', t') \rangle \tag{7}$$

can be expressed directly in terms of the prescribed covariances of the forcing field and initial velocity field.

An obvious formal procedure is to expand the actual covariance U_{ij} about the linearized solution $U_{ij}^{(0)}$ by reintroducing the neglected terms as a perturbation. The resulting expansion is in ascending powers of some characteristic Reynolds number of the turbulence. To see this, let v_0 and l_0 be characteristic velocity and length scales. In the case of steady-state turbulence (statistically steady forcing field and $t_0 = -\infty$), v_0 could be the rms velocity and l_0 the integral scale associated with $\mathbf{u}^{(0)}$. For freely decaying turbulence, v_0 and l_0 could be the rms velocity and

integral scale of the initial velocity field.[1] Introduce dimensionless variables by

$$\tilde{\mathbf{x}} = \mathbf{x}/l_0, \qquad \tilde{t} = t/(l_0^2/\nu), \qquad \tilde{\mathbf{u}}(\tilde{\mathbf{x}}, \tilde{t}) = \mathbf{u}(\mathbf{x}, t)/v_0,$$
$$\tilde{p}(\tilde{\mathbf{x}}, \tilde{t}) = p(\mathbf{x}, t)/(v_0\nu/l_0), \qquad \tilde{\mathbf{f}}(\tilde{\mathbf{x}}, \tilde{t}) = \mathbf{f}(\mathbf{x}, t)/(v_0\nu/l_0^2). \tag{8}$$

In terms of these variables (used exclusively hereafter and written with tildes suppressed), (1), (3), and (6) become

$$(\partial/\partial t - \nabla^2)\mathbf{u}(\mathbf{x}, t) - \mathbf{f}(\mathbf{x}, t) = -R_0[\mathbf{u}(\mathbf{x}, t) \cdot \nabla\mathbf{u}(\mathbf{x}, t) + \nabla p(\mathbf{x}, t)], \tag{9}$$
$$\nabla^2 p = -\partial^2(u_i u_j)/\partial x_i \partial x_j, \tag{10}$$
$$G^{(0)}(\mathbf{x}, t; \mathbf{y}, s) = [4\pi(t - s)]^{-3/2}$$
$$\times \exp[-\tfrac{1}{4}|\mathbf{x} - \mathbf{y}|^2/(t - s)], \tag{11}$$

where

$$R_0 = l_0 v_0/\nu \tag{12}$$

is the Reynolds number associated with v_0 and l_0, The parameter l_0^2/ν in (8) is the characteristic time for viscous decay of a velocity field whose scale of spatial variation is l_0.

Equation (9) can be formally integrated to yield

$$\mathbf{u}(\mathbf{x}, t) = \mathbf{u}^{(0)}(\mathbf{x}, t) - R_0 \int_{t_0}^{t} ds \int G^{(0)}(\mathbf{x}, t; \mathbf{y}, s)[\mathbf{u}(\mathbf{y}, s) \cdot \nabla\mathbf{u}(\mathbf{y}, s) + \nabla p(\mathbf{y}, s)] \, d^3y, \tag{13}$$

which lends itself easily to an iteration expansion of $\mathbf{u}(\mathbf{x}, t)$ in powers of R_0. Since turbulence typically involves large Reynolds numbers, an expansion in powers of Reynolds number would appear to offer dim hope of yielding useful information. However, a study of the inadequacies of this expansion is essential for appraisal of the more elaborate expansion schemes that have been proposed for the high Reynolds number range.

If $\mathbf{u}(\mathbf{x}, t)$ is expanded in the form

$$\mathbf{u}(\mathbf{x}, t) = \mathbf{u}^{(0)}(\mathbf{x}, t) + \sum_{n=1}^{\infty} R_0^n \mathbf{u}^{(n)}(\mathbf{x}, t), \tag{14}$$

the $\mathbf{u}^{(n)}(\mathbf{x}, t)$ can be determined by substituting into (13) and requiring that the equation be satisfied for each power of R_0. If this is carried out recursively starting with $n = 1$, it is easily seen [note (10)] that $\mathbf{u}^{(n)}(\mathbf{x}, t)$ is a homogeneous $(n + 1)$th degree functional of $\mathbf{u}^{(0)}(\mathbf{x}, t)$.

Now substitute (14) into (4). Since $\mathbf{u}^{(n)}$ is of degree $n + 1$ in $\mathbf{u}^{(0)}$,

[1] See Ref. [1], Chapter III, for a definition of integral scale.

the result has the form

$$U_{ij}(\mathbf{x}, t\,; \mathbf{x}', t') = U_{ij}^{(0)}(\mathbf{x}, t\,; \mathbf{x}', t') + \sum_{n=1}^{\infty} R_0{}^n U_{ij}^{(n)}(\mathbf{x}, t\,; \mathbf{x}', t'), \quad (15)$$

where $U_{ij}^{(n)}(\mathbf{x}, t\,; \mathbf{x}', t')$ is a linear functional of $(n+2)$th-order moments of the field $\mathbf{u}^{(0)}$. By (5), $U_{ij}(\mathbf{x}, t\,; \mathbf{x}', t')$ thus depends on moments of all orders of the forcing field and the initial velocity field. The joint statistical distribution of these fields must be prescribed completely in order to determine $U_{ij}(\mathbf{x}, t\,; \mathbf{x}', t')$ for t or $t' > t_0$.

The simplest choice, adopted hereinafter, is to take the forcing field and initial velocity field statistically independent of each other and multivariate-normal with zero means. Then $\mathbf{u}^{(0)}(\mathbf{x}, t)$ is multivariate-normal, because it is a linear functional of these two fields. Every odd-order moment of $\mathbf{u}^{(0)}$ vanishes, and the even-order moments can be reduced to sums of products of the covariance $U_{ij}^{(0)}$ according to the standard rules for normal distributions. The evaluation of the general fourth-order moment is

$$\langle u_i^{(0)}(\mathbf{x}, t) u_j^{(0)}(\mathbf{x}', t') u_m^{(0)}(\mathbf{x}'', t'') u_n^{(0)}(\mathbf{x}''', t''') \rangle$$
$$= U_{ij}^{(0)}(\mathbf{x}, t\,; \mathbf{x}', t') U_{mn}^{(0)}(\mathbf{x}'', t''\,; \mathbf{x}''', t''')$$
$$+ U_{im}^{(0)}(\mathbf{x}, t\,; \mathbf{x}'', t'') U_{jn}^{(0)}(\mathbf{x}', t'\,; \mathbf{x}''', t''')$$
$$+ U_{in}^{(0)}(\mathbf{x}, t\,; \mathbf{x}''', t''') U_{jm}^{(0)}(\mathbf{x}', t'\,; \mathbf{x}'', t'')\,. \quad (16)$$

The reduction of a moment of order $2n$ yields a sum of $(2n)!/(2^n n!)$ terms, each term being a product of n covariance factors.

The normal-distribution reduction rule for moments of $\mathbf{u}^{(0)}$ implies that $U_{ij}^{(n)}(\mathbf{x}, t\,; \mathbf{x}', t')$ vanishes for odd n and for even n consists of a sum of terms, each term being a functional of $U_{ij}^{(0)}$ of degree $(n+2)/2$. Equation (13) shows that the functionals have the general form of spacetime integrals over the history of the fluid. Each term in $U_{ij}^{(n)}$ involves n spacetime integrations. The space integrations associated with the inversion of (10) have been ignored in this accounting.

The number of terms that make up $U_{ij}^{(n)}$ increases very rapidly with n. As a consequence of the normal-distribution reduction algorithm, each nth-order moment of $u^{(0)}$ which is involved leads to $n!/[2^{n/2}(n/2)!]$ terms, each of the form described in the preceding paragraph. However, the number of distinct nth-order moments that contribute also increases rapidly with n. That number is determined by the branching properties of (13) under the iteration that yields the R_0 expansion. Thus the total number of terms in the final expression for $U_{ij}^{(n)}$ rises much more rapidly than $n!/[2^{n/2}(n/2)!]$. A further increase is due to the summations over tensor indices.

The incomplete description just given is sufficient to suggest much about the possible domain of usefulness of the expansion in powers R_0. If R_0 is very small, the nonlinear terms in the Navier-Stokes equation plausibly can be treated as small perturbations in the range of spatial scales (wave numbers) which are directly excited by the stirring forces or for which the initial excitation is substantial in freely decaying flows. If so, the leading term in the R_0 expansion should provide a valid asymptotic expansion for these wavenumbers in the limit $R_0 \to 0$. The argument does not apply to wave numbers whose excitation depends principally on the transfer process. For the latter wave numbers, the nonlinear terms mean the difference between excitation and nonexcitation and are not a small perturbation no matter how small R_0 becomes.

The case of most interest is large R_0. Here it is clear physically, and easily verified analytically, that the quantities $R_0{}^n U_{ij}^{(n)}(\mathbf{x}, t; \mathbf{x}', t')$ grow with n for small n, unless $t - t_0$ and $t' - t_0$ are small compared with characteristic correlation times of the turbulence. If the R_0 expansion converges at all, it does so in such a way that the number of terms which must be included to obtain a valid approximation becomes infinite as $R_0 \to \infty$. This fact, together with the enormously rapid proliferation of terms as n increases, is sufficient to show that the expansion cannot be used to compute $U_{ij}(\mathbf{x}, t; \mathbf{x}', t')$ at large R_0, unless $t - t_0$ and $t' - t_0$ are very small.

The fact of convergence or divergence in itself does not determine whether the expansion is useful. Divergent series can provide excellent asymptotic approximations, and convergent series can converge so slowly that they are useless. What counts is how much must be computed to obtain a good approximation. Suppose that the R_0 expansion converges and that terms through order $n = 40$ must be retained to give an adequate approximation at some moderate R_0. The number of terms which must be computed is larger than $40!/(2^{20}20!) = 3.2 \times 10^{23}$ by an enormous factor. The typical term is a manyfold space-time integral over a manyfold sum on tensor indices. More significant than the staggering size of the computing task in itself is the fact that it may exceed the work required to approximate U_{ij} by direct numerical integration of the Navier-Stokes equation for a sufficient ensemble of flows. It is hard to see value in a statistical approximation that requires more labor than doing the whole problem without approximation.

Actually, the expansion probably has zero radius of convergence in R_0 no matter how small $t - t_0$ and $t' - t_0$ are. If $t - t_0$ and $t' - t_0$ are not small, valid approximations for large R_0 probably cannot be obtained by truncating the expansion no matter how many terms are computed. Some evidence favoring this conjecture is provided by the behavior

of the system

$$(\partial/\partial t + \mu)y_1 = R_0 C_1 y_2 y_3, \qquad (\partial/\partial t + \mu)y_2 = R_0 C_2 y_3 y_1,$$
$$(\partial/\partial t + \mu)y_3 = R_0 C_3 y_1 y_2, \tag{17}$$

where the coefficients obey

$$C_1 + C_2 + C_3 = 0 \tag{18}$$

and μ is a nonnegative damping factor. This system has the same degree of nonlinearity as the Navier-Stokes equation but can be solved. The substitutions

$$y_n(t) = e^{-\mu t} z_n(t_*), \qquad t_* = (1 - e^{-\mu t})/\mu, \qquad (n = 1, 2, 3) \tag{19}$$

transform (17) into

$$\partial z_1/\partial t_* = R_0 C_1 z_2 z_3, \qquad \partial z_2/\partial t_* = R_0 C_2 z_3 z_1,$$
$$\partial z_3/\partial t_* = R_0 C_3 z_1 z_2, \tag{20}$$

which has the constant of motion $z_1^2 + z_2^2 + z_3^2$.

The general solution of (20) has been given by Lorentz [14]. It has the form

$$z_n(t_*) = g_n(R_0 q_n t_*) \qquad (n = 1, 2, 3), \tag{21}$$

where the g_n are elliptic functions and the q_n are expressions homogeneous of degree 1 in the initial amplitudes $|y_1(0)|$, $|y_2(0)|$, $|y_3(0)|$ and homogeneous of degree 1 in the C's.

Now let g_n be expanded as a power series in R_0. The elliptic functions have poles within the periodicity parallelogram in the complex plane. Hence the domain of convergence of the series is given by

$$R_0 < \tau_n/(q_n t_*), \tag{22}$$

where τ_n is the distance of the nearest pole from the origin. By (19), $t_* \approx t$ for small t, $t_* \approx \mu^{-1}$ for large t, and t_* increases monotonically with t for all t. Hence, if $R_0 < \tau_n \mu/q_n$, the power series in R_0 converges for all t. If $R_0 \gg \tau_n \mu/q_n$, the series converges only if $t < \tau_n/(q_n R_0)$. Now consider a statistical ensemble of realizations and suppose that $\langle y_n(t)y_n(t')\rangle$ is expanded in powers of R_0 by expanding (21), multiplying the series, and averaging. To make a correspondence with the nondimensionalized Navier-Stokes equation, take $\mu = 1$, the C's of order unity, and the initial variances $\langle |y_n(0)|^2\rangle$ of order unity. The τ_n in (22) are determined only by the ratios of the C's and the ratios of the initial amplitudes. However, the q_n are homogeneous of order 1 in the initial amplitudes. In a Gaussian statistical ensemble, or in any distribution without a high-amplitude cutoff, there will be a finite statistical weight to every value

of the initial amplitudes, no matter how large. Hence there will be contributions to $\langle y_n(t)y_n(t')\rangle$ from realizations in which the right-hand side of (22) is smaller than any given value, no matter how small. Regardless of how small t and t' are taken, there will be contributions to the covariance whose power series in R_0 have indefinitely small radii of convergence. In other words, $\langle y_n(t)y_n(t')\rangle$ is a nonanalytic function of R_0 at $R_0 = 0$. However, $y_n(t)y_n(t')$ is analytic at $R_0 = 0$ in any realization, which implies that the nonanalytic part of the covariance goes to zero as $R_0 = 0$ is approached along the positive real axis.

As an example to show the significance of these properties, consider the function

$$Q(R) = \int_0^\infty (1 + aR^2)^{-1}e^{-a}\,da\,, \tag{23}$$

which can be written

$$Q(R) = Q_1(R, A) + Q_2(R, A)\,, \tag{24}$$

where $Q_1(R, A)$ is the integral over $(0, A)$ and $Q_2(R, A)$ is the integral over (A, ∞). The formal expansion in powers of R is easily obtained by expanding the integrand and then integrating each term. $Q_1(R, A)$ has a convergent expansion for $R < A^{-1/2}$, whereas $Q_2(R, A)$ has zero radius of convergence. The integrand is a monotone decreasing function of a, and $Q_2(R, A) \to 0$ as $A \to \infty$. Thus $Q(R)$ can be represented as the sum of a function analytic at $R = 0$ and an arbitrarily small function nonanalytic at $R = 0$. For $R \ll 1$, the integrand in (23) is well approximated by finite truncations of its power series for all a that contribute appreciably to the integral. Thus the power series representation of $Q(R)$ is divergent at all R and yields asymptotically valid approximations for $R \ll 1$. For $R \gg 1$, truncations of the power series give bad approximations, which worsen with increase of order.

It is important to note that $Q(R)$ is not uniquely determined by its formal power series. The latter is expressed in closed form by (23), but it is equally well expressed by other functions that differ from $Q(R)$ by a nonanalytic part whose power series vanishes. For example,

$$Q'(R) = Q(R) + R^{-1}e^{-1/R} \tag{25}$$

has precisely the same power series as $Q(R)$. It differs negligibly from $Q(R)$ for small R but has a completely different behavior for large R.

The model differential equation introduced by Burgers [15] is an exactly soluble system [16] much closer to the Navier-Stokes equation than the three-degrees-of-freedom system just considered. A convergence investigation of R_0 expansions for Burgers' equation would be of great interest.

II. SUMMATION SCHEMES AND CRITERIA FOR VALID APPROXIMATIONS

It is possible to set up equations that sum in closed form certain infinite classes of terms from the R_0 expansion of $U_{ij}(\mathbf{x}, t; \mathbf{x}', t')$. This is the basis for several expansion schemes that have been suggested to deal with the case of large R_0 [3, 5, 10]. The common feature of these expansions is that truncation retains classes of terms from all orders of the R_0 expansion. They will be called consolidated expansions in this paper. The natural hope is that the consolidated expansions yield valid approximations even for large R_0.

There are two serious troubles with the consolidated expansions. First, the radius of convergence of the R_0 expansion probably is zero. If so, there is not enough information to determine $U_{ij}(\mathbf{x}, t; \mathbf{x}', t')$ unambiguously. Even if the series could be summed completely in closed form, the sum is nonunique, as illustrated at the end of Section I. In fact, even if the expansion should turn out to have a nonzero radius of convergence, its sum could not be asserted to give $U_{ij}(\mathbf{x}, t; \mathbf{x}', t')$, unless there is proof, *independent of the power series representation*, that U_{ij} is an analytic function of R_0 within the circle of convergence. It must be remembered that U_{ij} is defined as an average over an ensemble of solutions of a differential equation, not as a power series. The power series representation, taken alone, always leaves U_{ij} undetermined to the extent of a nonanalytic part that vanishes strongly as $R_0 \rightarrow 0$ [cf. (25)]

The second major trouble with the consolidated expansions is that they yield puny summations. Truncation at any finite order gives equations that omit almost all the terms of very high order in the R_0 expansion. More precisely, if the consolidated expansions are truncated at order n, almost all terms in any order m of the R_0 expansion are omitted if $m \gg n$.[2]

---

[2] A connected diagram consisting of lines and vertices (each vertex is the intersection of three lines) may be associated with each term of the R_0 expansion in a way explained in Refs. [3] and [5]. If either of the consolidated expansions is truncated at order n, it includes all terms in the R_0 expansion through order n. Above order n, it includes only those terms in the R_0 expansion whose diagrams have certain degenerate topological properties: they can be decomposed according to definite rules into subdiagrams whose order does not exceed n. When $m \gg n$, almost all diagrams of order m in the R_0 expansion are not so decomposable. This can be seen by induction. A diagram of order m may be constructed by taking a diagram of order $m - 2$ and connecting the middles of two lines (call them A and B; A and B may be the same line) by a new line so as to add two vertices. All the order m diagrams are constructed by doing this in all possible ways to all the order $m - 2$ diagrams, subject

Clearly it is an act of great faith to expect valid approximations from the consolidated expansions for values of R_0 where simple truncations of the power series in R_0 do not yield good approximations. Success requires that it be possible to pick a tiny subset of the terms of a probably divergent expansion, sum them, and get an answer close to a function that the entire expansion may not even determine uniquely. The situation would not be a happy one at large R_0 even if the R_0 expansion were convergent. At best, the R_0 expansion would have to be carried to an order n yielding impracticably many terms. The consolidated expansions would have to be carried to a comparable order if they were not to omit most of these terms. The unacceptably large computation task would remain unacceptably large, although changed in nature.

The preceding remarks suggest that the mere fact of summing infinitely many terms from the R_0 expansion is no reason for expecting a valid approximation, a conclusion supported by some explicit results cited below. Most infinite partial sums so far investigated turn out to yield nonsense at large R_0, not just bad answers. However, the possibility of good high-R_0 approximations from low-order truncations of consolidated expansions is not ruled out. It may be possible, although very improbable a priori, that some particular choices of summable terms give answers happily close to the truth, even though most of the R_0 expansion is omitted. All the omitted terms may turn out to represent an unimportant net contribution.

A natural question is how to choose summations so as to optimize the slim chances of getting good answers. One obvious criterion is that the approximations should not destroy the fundamental invariance properties of the exact flow equations. The latter include the conservation of energy and momentum by the nonlinear interaction and, in two-dimensional flows, the conservation of total vorticity by the nonlinear interaction. These properties are basic qualitative features of the interaction.

A further basic property, related to energy conservation, is the existence of formal inviscid equipartition ensembles and the associated fluctuation-dissipation relations. The equilibrium behavior can be described as follows. Transform the inviscid Navier-Stokes equation to equations for spatial Fourier amplitudes, and then make a cutoff by eliminating all terms that contain a wave number greater than an arbitrarily chosen magnitude. The resulting system conserves kinetic energy, has a finite

---

to certain rules for avoiding redundancy. Suppose that a given order $m - 2$ diagram is degenerate in the desired sense. For a given choice of line A, the order m diagram created by connecting lines A and B is degenerate only for very restricted choices of line B, if $m \gg n$.

number of degrees of freedom per unit volume, and obeys a Liouville theorem. The Liouville theorem was first demonstrated by Burgers [17] and later discussed by other authors [18–20]. It follows that the canonical ensemble of Gibbs is an equilibrium ensemble, invariant under the equations of motion, and that the time-correlation functions of the Fourier amplitudes are proportional, in equilibrium, to the functions that give the average decay of infinitesimal externally imposed perturbations of the system (fluctuation-dissipation theorem [20]).

The canonical ensemble for the truncated inviscid Navier-Stokes system yields equipartition of kinetic energy among the wave-vectors that remain in the equations. This spectral distribution is very far from that encountered in actual turbulence, where viscosity acts and there is no cutoff. Therefore it might seem irrelevant to demand that statistical approximations preserve the inviscid equipartition property. Actually, it is as relevant as to demand conservation of energy by the nonlinear interaction. In actual turbulence, there always is strong dissipation of energy by viscosity, even at high Reynolds numbers, so that the inviscid property of invariance of total energy under the equations of motion is not realized. The importance of both the conservation and equipartition properties is that they express intrinsic characteristics of the nonlinear interaction. If they are lost, the nonlinear dynamics is badly represented. There is little reason to expect that the consequences of the misrepresentation would be less serious for actual turbulence than in inviscid equilibrium. This is an opinion, not a theorem, and must remain so, since the class of unexplored nonconservative approximations is inexhaustible.

All of the conservation properties, together with the inviscid equilibrium-fluctuation-dissipation property, are preserved exactly if the expansion of U_{ij} in powers of R_0 is truncated at any order. The reason is that the R_0 expansion was obtained by demanding that the exact equations of motion be formally satisfied for each power of R_0. It does not follow that the properties hold for truncations of the consolidated expansions, equivalent to infinite partial summations of the R_0 expansion. The terms selected from a given order of the R_0 expansion may or may not form a conservative subset.

The simpler of the proposed consolidated expansion schemes yields all the consistency properties named in the preceding paragraphs [3]. This expansion will be called the irreducible covariance expansion hereafter because it expresses third-order and higher moments as functional power series in the exact covariance tensor U_{ij}. The scheme of Wyld and Lee [5, 10], which involves more comprehensive summations, appears not to assure the energy-conservation and equipartition fluctuation-dissipation

properties. However, the summations attempted by Wyld and Lee can be carried out so as to incorporate all these properties. The restriction by Wyld and Lee to stationary turbulence is removable also. These changes will be assumed hereafter, and the resulting expansion will be called the vertex expansion, in allusion to the associated diagram representation [3, 5, 10].

Preservation of the basic invariance properties of the Navier-Stokes equation may be necessary to good turbulence approximations, but it is not sufficient. This is clear from the fact that truncations of the R_0 expansion yield all the invariance properties but give bad approximations at high R_0. The most striking failure of these truncations at high R_0 is that they yield unbounded values for $U_{ij}(\mathbf{x}, t; \mathbf{x}', t')$ which are physically impossible. That is to say, these values cannot be realized as an ensemble average $\langle u_i(\mathbf{x}, t) u_j(\mathbf{x}', t) \rangle$ no matter what real, finite values are assumed for the velocity field. For example, truncations of the R_0 expansion for isotropic turbulence decay predict negative values for the wave number energy-spectrum $E(k, t)$ at some values of k, although the total energy is conserved. The negative spectrum values appear after a time $t - t_0$ of the order of one circulation time of the energy-containing eddies. Eventually, the total energies in the negative and positive parts of the spectrum become very large in magnitude, although their sum remains bounded. The truncations also yield a related unphysical behavior: the time-correlation functions grow indefinitely, instead of falling toward zero as difference time increases.

Boundedness appears to be much more elusive than the invariance properties. Truncations of both of the cited consolidated expansions yield unphysical results of the same kind as the R_0 expansion truncations. For a given order of truncation, the unphysical behavior is delayed to slightly longer values of $t - t_0$ with the consolidated expansions, but develops more explosively once it occurs. There appear to be two exceptions: the lowest nontrivial truncation of each consolidated expansion seems to give physically acceptable behavior free of obvious violations of realizability.[3]

---

[3] Explicit results of a variety of truncations are obtained in Ref. [3] for an asymptotic situation. The results include the lowest nontrivial truncation of the energetically consistent version of the vertex expansion attempted in Refs. [5] and [10]. This truncation includes infinitely iterated vertex corrections. Some further properties of it are described in Ref. [23]. (This truncation should not be confused with either of the two approximations described in Refs. [5] and [10]. The first of these [Chandrasekhar's approximation] does not conserve energy and is not a truncation of the energetically consistent vertex expansion. The second is a trivial, zeroth-order truncation of the vertex expansion and is identical with the lowest nontrivial truncation [direct-interaction approximation] of the irreducible covariance expansion.

It seems difficult to avoid concluding that the consolidated expansions are failures. They do not represent a real improvement over the simpler R_0 power series because successive truncations yield increasingly violent unphysical behavior instead of progressively more faithful approximations to high R_0 turbulence. The two exceptional truncations that have been found do not alter this judgment. The success of these approximations cannot be predicted because they are truncations of the consolidated expansions; reasons must be sought elsewhere. Nor are the consolidated expansions necessary in order to construct the approximations.

The first truncation of the irreducible covariance expansion has been called the direct-interaction approximation [21]. It was originally constructed by physical arguments, without invoking formal expansions. The approximation preserves boundedness and realizability properties because it happens to be an exact description, not an approximation, for the behavior of a model dynamical system that has the same conservation and inviscid equilibrium properties as the Navier-Stokes system. The covariance U_{ij} predicted by the approximation is exactly the covariance of a real field $\mathbf{u}(\mathbf{x}, t)$ that obeys the model dynamical equation [3]. This can be demonstrated by means that do not involve perturbation expansions at all [22].

No such clear reason is known why the first truncation of the vertex expansion gives sensible results. The only evidence is the results themselves, which so far are limited to the high-wave-number part of the turbulence. It cannot be asserted that this approximation will continue to give sensible, realizable results when applied more generally.

III. KOLMOGOROV'S THEORY AND GALILEAN INVARIANCE

Kolmogorov's hypothesis of the statistical independence of high and low wave numbers in large R_0 turbulence is associated with a further invariance property of the Navier-Stokes equation, in addition to those cited in Section II. Suppose that each realization in an ensemble describing homogeneous isotropic turbulence is subjected to a translating

---

An energetically inconsistent approximation that includes vertex corrections is described in Ref. [8]). The higher truncations of the energetically consistent vertex expansion are not treated in the cited references, but the methods of Ref. [3] show that they are invalid. In particular, it can be seen that the vertex expansion for the response and correlation times at high wave numbers diverges: all terms in any given order have the same sign, and the number of terms increases enormously fast with order.

velocity **v** that is constant in space but that has a Gaussian distribution over the ensemble. That is, **v** changes randomly from realization to realization. The translations produce no distortion of the flow fields, and therefore they cannot affect the turbulent energy-transfer process. The ensemble-averaged rate of energy transfer into wave number k at time t must be invariant under this random Galilean transformation. Thus, a weakened form of Kolmogorov's hypothesis surely is true: zero-wave-number excitation does not affect the energetics of finite wave numbers in homogeneous turbulence.

Invariance to random Galilean transformation is preserved in each order of the R_0 expansion, like every other exact property of the turbulence. But it does not survive in any order of either of the consolidated expansions cited in Section II. This is because truncations of the latter expansions include some of the terms from each order of the R_0 expansion but discard others. In particular, the lowest truncations of the two expansions, which appear to be satisfactory in other respects, do not incorporate this invariance. A consequence is that neither approximation can give Kolmogorov's inertial-range spectrum law [23]. Regardless of whether Kolmogorov's law is exactly correct, a necessary condition for an approximation to describe properly the energetics of the small scales of turbulence would appear to be preservation of the Galilean invariance property. This invariance should therefore be added to the list of fundamental properties in Section II.

An apparently self-consistent statistical approximation that incorporates the Galilean invariance property has been developed recently by modification of the direct-interaction approximation [24]. It predicts both Eulerian and Lagrangian velocity covariances. Two characteristics of the approximation are of interest here. First, its construction involved heuristic procedures of which a crucial part was to require simultaneously all the fundamental qualitative properties cited previously: energy-momentum conservation, inviscid equipartition and fluctuation-dissipation relation, and Galilean invariance. Requiring all these properties served to determine the approximation uniquely within the general analytical framework used. Second, the final results do not appear to be describable as a partial sum of terms from the R_0 expansion. As $R_0 \rightarrow 0$, the predictions of the approximation become indistinguishable from those of the lowest truncation of the R_0 expansion, but no further simple relationship has appeared. Certain asymptotic predictions of the approximation are exact [24], and therefore exact to all powers of R_0. This suggests that the inaccuracies of the approximation under non-asymptotic conditions cannot be described as the omission of classes of terms from the R_0 expansion.

IV. CONCLUDING REMARKS

The expansion of the velocity covariance $U_{ij}(\mathbf{x}, t; \mathbf{x}', t')$ in powers of turbulent Reynolds number R_0 probably has zero radius of convergence and constitutes, at best, an asymptotic expansion about $R_0 = 0$. Even if the radius of convergence were infinite, an impracticably large number of terms would be needed to obtain valid approximations at moderate or large R_0.

Several consolidated expansion schemes have been proposed whose truncations represent the summation of infinite classes of terms from the R_0 expansion. These schemes seem so far to have little value. The summed classes of terms, although infinite, still omit most of the R_0 expansion. Moreover, it appears that most truncations of the consolidated expansions exhibit the same kind of unphysical behavior [unbounded $U_{ij}(\mathbf{x}, t; \mathbf{x}', t')$] as truncations of the simpler R_0 expansion.

The expansions recently proposed by Edwards [7] and Herring [13] have not been examined here because their consistency properties are not yet sufficiently investigated.

The exceptional truncations of the consolidated expansions which yield bounded U_{ij} do not succeed for any reasons apparent from the consolidated expansions. These approximations must be justified on other grounds, and the fact that they formally represent well-defined classes of terms from the R_0 expansion cannot defensibly be called a virtue. Moreover, the successful approximations are more directly and clearly derived by physical arguments rather than by appeal to formal expansions.

In the author's opinion, strong emphasis should be placed on the fundamental boundedness and invariance properties of the exact dynamics when seeking new turbulence approximations. These properties include conservation of energy-momentum by the nonlinear interaction, conservation of vorticity in two-dimensional flow, inviscid equipartition and fluctuation-dissipation properties, and invariance to random Galilean transformation. An approximation that ignores these properties would seem to offer little hope of coping with high R_0 turbulence.

The basic invariance properties are shared by the Navier-Stokes equation with many other systems that exhibit quite different nonequilibrium statistical behavior. Clearly then, inclusion of these properties is not enough. There also must be some *quantitative* contact with the Navier-Stokes equation. The direct-interaction approximation, the simpler of the successful approximations cited previously, has two such contacts. First, it presumably gives some asymptotically correct predictions as $R_0 \to 0$. The second contact is provided by the model dynamical system

for which this approximation is an exact description. In the case of homogeneous turbulence, the model dynamical system exhibits precisely the same strengths of interaction within each interacting wave-vector triad as does the Navier-Stokes equation. The difference is in the relative phasing of the interactions of different triads.

This appears to be scanty contact with reality. However, the numerical results obtained from the approximation show fair agreement with experiment at moderate R_0 [25]. The Lagrangian modification of the approximation, which incorporates Galilean invariance, seems in fair agreement with experiment without restriction on R_0 [24]. The agreement may be fortuitous, but it may indicate instead that the turbulence problem is not wholly perverse. Perhaps the basic invariance and boundedness properties, together with relatively few points of quantitative contact to reality, restrict the behavior sufficiently that there is really a sporting chance of avoiding big errors.

The partial success of known approximations suggests that further exploration of this possibility is worthwhile. Rewarding improvement might come if quantitative contact with the Navier-Stokes equation could be made for some asymptotic condition more directly relevant than small R_0. Such a condition need not be describable by the R_0 expansion at all.

However, unless some convergent, and practicable, sequence of systematic approximations is discovered, the prediction of turbulence properties must rely to an uncomfortable extent on intuition and guesswork. The quantitative validity of an approximation cannot now be assayed in advance. It can be determined only by numerical calculations that are compared with experiment. Such calculations are mandatory. In the present situation, a very accurate quantitative prediction from an approximation would have to be considered a miracle or accident, not a triumph of the approximation.

A convergent, but impracticable, approximation sequence possibly can be constructed by finite-difference integration of the Navier-Stokes equation in time. To illustrate this kind of procedure, suppose that $U_{ij}(\mathbf{x}, t; \mathbf{x}', t')$ is wanted for the time range $(t_0, t_{\max})$. The range can be divided into M equal intervals $\Delta t = (t_{\max} - t_0)/M$, and the values of $\mathbf{u}(\mathbf{x}, t_m)$ at the times $t_m = t_0 + m\Delta t$ $(m = 1, 2, \ldots, M)$ can be approximated by the finite-difference form of (13):

$$\mathbf{u}(\mathbf{x}, t_m) = \mathbf{u}^{(0)}(\mathbf{x}, t_m) - R_0\Delta t \sum_{n=0}^{m-1} \int G^{(0)}(\mathbf{x}, t_m; \mathbf{y}, t_n)[\mathbf{u}(\mathbf{y}, t_n) \cdot \nabla\mathbf{u}(\mathbf{y}, t_n)$$

$$+ \nabla p(\mathbf{y}, t_n)] \, d^3y. \tag{26}$$

Equations (26) can be solved by recursion, starting with $m = 1$, so as to express the $\mathbf{u}(\mathbf{x}, t_m)$ in terms of $\mathbf{u}^{(0)}$. Finally, the result can be substituted into (4), and the averages over the Gaussian $\mathbf{u}^{(0)}$ carried out to give explicit results for the functions $U_{ij}(\mathbf{x}, t_m; \mathbf{x}', t_{m'})$. Successive approximations would be constructed by increasing M in an appropriate fashion; for example, by doubling M at each stage.

For some realizations in the ensemble, (26) will be a bad approximation and will give unstable answers, no matter what fixed value of Δt is used. This is because nonzero statistical weight is given to realizations with velocity fields whose magnitude exceeds any given value. However, if $\mathbf{u}^{(0)}$ is Gaussian, the consequent error in $U_{ij}(\mathbf{x}, t_m; \mathbf{x}', t_{m'})$ may be bounded and go to zero as M approaches infinity because the weight given exceptional velocities is sufficiently small.

These finite-difference approximations to U_{ij} are even more unwieldy than truncations of the R_0 expansion. In fact, they represent complicated, finite, weighted, partial sums of the R_0 expansion, if the time-integrals in the latter are replaced by rectangular-rule sums. However, they can be used, like the R_0 expansion, to analyze approximations like the direct-interaction approximation, and may provide a sounder basis for such analysis.

Other impracticable convergent approximation sequences conceivably are associated with expansions of the Gram-Charlier type [6] or the Wiener-Hermite expansion [11]. A warning should be sounded, however. A convergent expansion for the probability functional need not mean a convergent approximation sequence when truncations of this expansion are used in the dynamical equations. The physically tiny effects of very-high-order statistical properties may be expressed in the equations by cancellations among large numbers of high-order terms, and these cancellations may be spoiled by the truncation procedure.

Acknowledgment

This work was supported by the Fluid Dynamics Branch of the Office of Naval Research under Contract Nonr 4307(00).

References

1. Batchelor, G. K., "The Theory of Homogeneous Turbulence," Chapter V. Cambridge Univ. Press, London and New York, 1953.
2. Deissler, R. G., *Phys. Fluids* **2**, 111 (1958).
3. Kraichnan, R. H., *J. Math. Phys.* **2**, 124 (1961); Erratum, *ibid.* **3**, 205 (1962).
4. Roberts, P. H., *J. Fluid Mech.* **11**, 257 (1961).
5. Wyld, H. W., *Ann. Phys.* **14**, 143 (1961).
6. Hopf, E., *Proc. Symp. Appl. Math.* **13**, 157 (1962).
7. Edwards, S. F., *J. Fluid Mech.* **18**, 239 (1964).

8. Shut'ko, A. V., *Dokl. Akad. Nauk SSSR* **158**, 1058 (1964); translated in *Soviet Phys. Dokl.* **9**, 857 (1965).

9. Mikhailovsky, A. B., *Nucl. Fusion* **4**, 321 (1964).

10. Lee, L. L., *Ann. Phys.* **32**, 292 (1965).

11. Siegel, A., Imamura, T., and Meecham, W. C., *J. Math. Phys.* **6**, 707 (1965).

12. Kadomtsev, B. B., "Plasma Turbulence." Academic Press, New York, 1965.

13. Herring, J., *Phys. Fluids* **8**, 2219 (1965).

14. Lorentz, E., *Tellus* **12**, 243 (1960). This system has been investigated also by D. K. Lilly in unpublished work. Dr. Lilly's analysis helped lead to the present application.

15. Burgers, J. M., *Adv. Appl. Mech.* **1**, 171 (1948).

16. Cole, J. D., *Quart. Appl. Math.* **9**, 225 (1951).

17. Burgers, J. M., *Verhandel. Koninkl. Akad. Ned. Wetenschap.* **32**, 643 (1929); *ibid.* **36**, 620 (1933); *ibid.* **43**, 936, 1153 (1940).

18. Hopf, E., *J. Ratl. Mech. Anal.* **1**, 87 (1952); also Hopf, E. and Titt, E. W., *J. Ratl. Mech. Anal.* **2**, 587 (1953).

19. Lee, T. D., *Quart. Appl. Math.* **10**, 69 (1952).

20. Kraichnan, R. H., *Phys. Rev.* **109**, 1407 (1958).

21. Kraichnan, R. H., *J. Fluid Mech.* **5**, 497 (1959).

22. Kraichnan, R. H., *J. Math. Phys.* **3**, 496 (1962).

23. Kraichnan, R. H., *Phys. Fluids* **7**, 1723 (1964). In Ref. [8], it was erroneously concluded that an (energetically inconsistent) approximation including vertex corrections gave Kolmogorov's law. The error arose from confusing Eulerian and Lagrangian response functions.

24. Kraichnan, R. H., *Phys. Fluids* **8**, 575, (1965); *ibid.* **9**, 9 (1966).

25. Kraichnan, R. H., *Phys. Fluids* **7**, 1030 (1964).

Space-Time Correlations in Turbulence

FRANÇOIS N. FRENKIEL

APPLIED MATHEMATICS LABORATORY, DAVID TAYLOR MODEL BASIN
WASHINGTON, D.C.

AND

PHILIP S. KLEBANOFF

NATIONAL BUREAU OF STANDARDS
WASHINGTON, D.C.

Space-time correlations of the component of turbulent velocities along the direction of mean velocity were measured in a turbulent field downstream of a grid using high-speed computing techniques. These results provide new information in that the space-time evaluation is carried out to much higher orders than has previously been measured. Space-time correlations of even order up to the eighth and of odd order up to the fifth are presented. The applicability of Taylor's space-time approximation, i.e., the concept of a frozen pattern of turbulence moving with the mean velocity, to these higher-order correlations is examined. The higher even-order correlations are compared with the results obtained from the second-order correlation assuming a Gaussian distribution for the turbulent velocities, and the different behavior of the various odd-order correlations is demonstrated.

I. INTRODUCTION

The use of high-speed computing methods for experimental measurements of turbulence was initiated some time ago [1]; however, the equipment available at that time was too limited to attempt an extensive study of the statistical characteristics of turbulence. The development and the availability of more advanced computers and computing techniques now permit a more extensive application of high-speed computing methods to the experimental study of turbulence. The digital computer is used as an extremely versatile voltmeter capable of performing the many complex operations required which, because of their difficulty, were not, hitherto, made by analog methods. Moreover, the use of digital techniques provides for considerable improvement in the statistical sampling of turbulence data. More recently, the present authors

have been able to obtain significant results for the correlations between velocities at a single point [2] as well as for two-dimensional probability density distributions [3] by these methods. The results demonstrated the great potentialities of high-speed computing techniques in determining the statistical characteristics of turbulence which are of interest in turbulence studies and which have not previously been measured. With this capability, it seemed desirable to extend the basic experimental information on space-time correlations to higher-order correlations and to evaluate the applicability of Taylor's space-time approximation [4] in more detail.

In the present paper, some results will be presented on space-time correlations between the components of the turbulent velocities at two points located along the direction of the mean velocity taken at two different times. These results provide new information, since the space-time evaluation is carried out to much higher orders, both even and odd, than had previously been done.

II. TAYLOR'S APPROXIMATION

Let us consider the turbulent velocity component $u(0, 0, 0, t)$ and $u(x, 0, 0, t)$ parallel to the mean velocity U at two points located along the direction of U and separated by a distance x. The space-time correlation coefficients $R_{x,t}$ between the velocity components at the two points is defined by the expression

$$R_{x,t}(x, h, t) = \frac{\overline{u(0, 0, 0, t)u(x, 0, 0, t + h)}}{[\overline{u^2(0, 0, 0, t)}]^{1/2}[\overline{u^2(x, 0, 0, t + h)}]^{1/2}},$$

where h is a time interval. It should be noted that in theoretical studies of nonstationary turbulence it is necessary to use ensemble averages, in which case the foregoing correlation coefficient would be a function not only of the distance x between the two points and of the time interval h, but also of the time t. Ensemble averages cannot, however, be measured experimentally, and in what follows we shall use time averages and assume a stationary turbulence. Since the statistical characteristics of the turbulent field are independent of the time t, the time averages are taken to be equal to the ensemble averages. Thus we have, for the space-time correlations, the expression

$$R_{x,t}(x, h) = \frac{\overline{u(0, 0, 0, t)u(x, 0, 0, t + h)}}{[\overline{u^2(0, 0, 0)}]^{1/2}[\overline{u^2(x, 0, 0)}]^{1/2}}$$

where $\overline{u^2}(0, 0, 0)$ and $\overline{u^2}(x, 0, 0)$ are the variances of the u-components of the turbulent velocities at each of the two points, respectively.

In studying the relation between a spectrum of turbulence at a single point and the correlation between the simultaneous velocity components at two points along the direction of the mean velocity, Taylor [4] assumed that the fluctuations of the turbulent velocity component u at the downstream point $(x, 0, 0)$ are simply due to the passage of a frozen pattern of turbulence over that point; therefore, the turbulent velocity component $u(x, 0, 0, t)$ at time t can be expressed as a function of the turbulent velocity at the upstream point by

$$u(x, 0, 0, t) = u\left(0, 0, 0, t - \frac{x}{U}\right).$$

Thus, the turbulence is considered to be homogeneous, with

$$\overline{u^2}(0, 0, 0) = \overline{u^2}(x, 0, 0),$$

and Taylor found that the (space) longitudinal correlation coefficient

$$R_x(x) = \frac{\overline{u(0, 0, t)u(x, 0, 0, t)}}{\overline{u^2}(0, 0, 0)}$$

between the simultaneous components of the turbulent velocities at two points located along the direction of the mean velocity and separated by a distance x and the time spectrum of turbulence $f_t(\omega)$ at a single point can be obtained from one another by the Fourier transforms

$$\begin{aligned}
f_t(\omega) &= \frac{2}{\pi U} \int_0^\infty \cos\left(\frac{\omega x}{U}\right) R_x(x)\, dx, \\
R_x(x) &= \int_0^\infty \cos\left(\frac{\omega x}{U}\right) f_t(\omega)\, d\omega,
\end{aligned} \tag{1}$$

where $\omega = 2\pi n$ is the cyclic frequency (n being the frequency). Taylor verified [4] these equations for the experiments performed by Simmons and Salter [5].

Similarly, the relation between the time spectrum of turbulence $f_t(\omega)$ and the time correlation coefficient

$$R_t(h) = \frac{\overline{u(0, 0, 0, t)u(0, 0, 0, t + h)}}{\overline{u^2}(0, 0, 0)},$$

where h is a time interval, is given by the Fourier transforms

$$f_t(\omega) = \frac{2}{\pi} \int_0^\infty \cos (\omega h) R_t(h)\, dh,$$

$$R_t(h) = \int_0^\infty \cos(\omega h) f_t(\omega)\, d\omega. \tag{2}$$

Although Eq. (1) corresponds to Taylor's approximation, Eq. (2) is not an approximation. Thus, an experimental verification of Eq. (1) would show that the time correlation can be expressed by the longitudinal correlation through the relations [6]

$$R_t(h) = R_x(hU), \qquad R_x(x) = R_t(x/U), \tag{3}$$

which are not sufficiently sensitive to evaluate Taylor's approximation. A more complete evaluation requires the measurement of space-time correlations, and, in fact, if we assume Taylor's approximation, we find for the space-time correlation

$$R_{x,t}[x, h - (x/U)] = R_t(h) \tag{4}$$

which shows that the space-time correlation curve $R_{x,t}[x, h - (x/U)]$ for a given value of x can be obtained by shifting the time correlation curve $R_t(h)$ along the axis of ordinates by a distance x/U. Similarly, we have the relation

$$R_{x,t}(x - hU, h) = R_x(x) \tag{5}$$

between the space-time correlation and the longitudinal correlation curve.

III. EXPERIMENTAL ARRANGEMENT

The measurements were performed in the National Bureau of Standards 1.37-m wind tunnel downstream of a square mesh grid placed perpendicularly to the direction of the mean velocity. The mesh length M was 2.54 cm, and the wind velocity U was 15.4 m/sec. The Reynolds number based on the mesh length was 25,600.

Compensated hot-wire equipment with two wires was used to measure the fluctuating velocity components at two points. No correction for the nonlinear response of the hot-wire has been applied. The upstream wire was located at a fixed point at a distance $X = 48.5\,M$ from the grid. The downstream wire was movable and was placed at variable distances x from the fixed wire. The largest distance x for which experiments were performed was equal to 4.56 times the mesh length M. Thus, the measurements were conducted in the region between $X/M = 48.5$ and

$X/M = 53.06$. The longitudinal intensity of turbulence $(\overline{u^2})^{1/2}/U$ (where u is the instantaneous turbulent velocity component parallel to U) was 0.018 at 48.5 mesh lengths downstream of the grid. The decay of the longitudinal intensity of turbulence with increasing distance from the grid is shown in Fig. 1 and illustrates that the measurements were made in the initial stage of decay. To reduce the influence of the wake of the upstream wire on the downstream wire, the latter was shifted

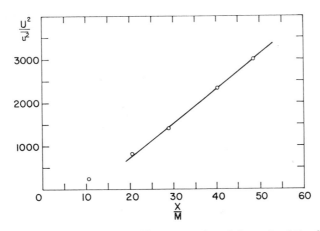

FIG. 1. The measured values of $U^2/\overline{u^2}$ as a function of the ratio of the downstream distance X from the grid to the mesh length M illustrate the decay of the longitudinal intensity of turbulence $(\overline{u^2})^{1/2}/U$.

from the point $(x, 0, 0)$ by a small distance y in a direction perpendicular to the mean velocity. This distance was determined by repetitive measurements of the intensity of turbulence with the downstream wire while placing it at variable distances y from the point $(x, 0, 0)$. Table I lists the distances y selected for the different values of x at which the measurements were made. The angle between the plane of the two wires and the direction of the mean velocity was small, particularly for large distances, and therefore no correction has been made to the measured correlations.

TABLE I

THE LOCATION OF THE DOWNSTREAM HOT
WIRE IN RELATION TO THE UPSTREAM
WIRE EXPRESSED IN MESH
LENGTHS M

x/M	0.2	1.06	2.06	4.56
y/M	0.020	0.050	0.100	0.1625

The simultaneous turbulent velocity components at the two points were recorded on two channels of a magnetic tape with a time signal of frequency 12,800/sec recorded on a third channel. These recordings are illustrated in Fig. 2, which represents the case where the correlation

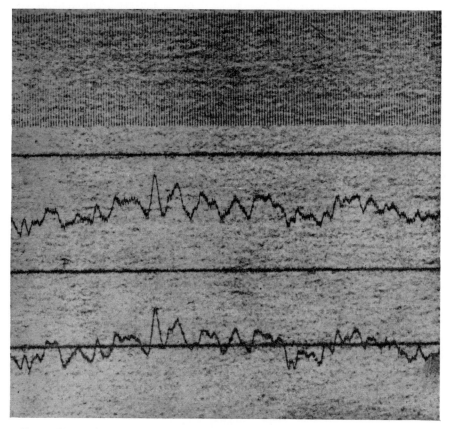

FIG. 2. Example of data recorded on magnetic tape. The recording at the top is a sinusoidal time signal with a frequency of 12,800/sec. The other two signals correspond to fluctuating turbulence velocities at two points. In this case, the correlation between the velocities is very high.

between the velocity components at the two points was very large, and therefore the recordings for the two wires are very similar.

After recording the fluctuating velocities and the time signal on an analog magnetic tape, the analog data were digitized using the time signal as a trigger for the digitizing of simultaneous measurements for each succeeding 1/12,800 sec of real time.

The digital tape obtained as a result of this conversion from analog to digital data was then used as an input to the high-speed computer, which in most cases was an IBM 7090. More detailed information concerning the computing methods is given in reference [2].

IV. SPACE-TIME CORRELATIONS OF EVEN ORDER

The experimental results for the second-order space-time correlation $R_{x,t}(x, h)$ are presented in Fig. 3, where the correlation is given as a

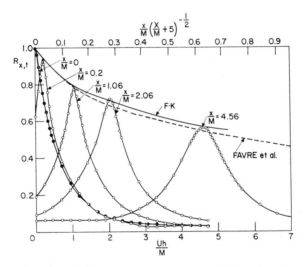

FIG. 3. Space-time correlation curves $R_{x,t}$ are presented as functions of the non-dimensional time delay Uh/M by open points. The time correlation R_t ($R_{x,t}$ for $x/M = 0$) is represented by closed points. The curve F–K representing the correlation coefficient following the mean motion corresponding to the present measurements is compared with the similar curve obtained by Favre et al. [7].

function of the nondimensional time delay Uh/M for the values of $x/M = 0, 0.2, 1.06, 2.06,$ and 4.56. For each of the last four values of x/M, $R_{x,t}$ was determined using one sample of the simultaneous recordings of turbulent velocities at two points taken during time intervals of about 12.5 sec. Thus, the measured values of $R_{x,t}$ represented in Fig. 3 by open points correspond to sample correlations for each of these four values of x/M. The experimental points for $x/M = 0$ represent average values obtained from the four samples of the recorded data measured at the upstream wire for $x/M = 0.2, 1.06, 2.06,$ and 4.56. It should be

noted that, when $x/M = 0$, the corresponding results, represented in Fig. 3 by closed points, give the time correlation $R_t(h) = R_{x,t}(0, h)$.

As shown previously [2], sample correlations deviate from an average correlation obtained using a large number of samples; however, the sample correlations shown are fairly representative. The time T over which each sample of recorded data was taken (used to determine a sample correlation) is very large compared to h; thus, for $T = 12.5$ sec, $UT/M = 7500$ which is considerably larger than the values of Uh/M for which correlation curves are presented.

The conditions for a frozen pattern of turbulence moving downstream with the mean velocity would require that the correlation curve $R_{x,t}$ for each value of x/M be obtained by shifting the time-correlation curve R_t ($R_{x,t}$ for $x/M = 0$) using the corresponding value $Uh/M = x/M$. The maxima for the measured $R_{x,t}$ curves are located very close to the appropriate values of Uh/M; however, the values of $R_{x,t}$ at these locations are 0.94, 0.78, 0.72, and 0.57, respectively, instead of being equal to 1, which would have corresponded to the frozen pattern of turbulence. The curve designated as F–K in Fig. 3 was traced through the values of $R_{x,t}$ at which $Uh/M = x/M$. It should be noted that such a curve represents, therefore, the time correlation curve following the mean motion

$$R_m(h) = \frac{\overline{u(0, 0, 0, t)u(hU, 0, 0, t + h)}}{[\overline{u^2(0, 0, 0)}]^{1/2}[\overline{u^2(hU, 0, 0)}]^{1/2}} = R_{x,t}\left(x, \frac{x}{U}\right). \tag{6}$$

For comparison, we have traced a similar curve R_m obtained by Favre et al. [7, 8]. Since their measurements were made under somewhat different conditions, their curve was traced using the top scale of Fig. 3 and presenting R_m as a function of the empirical parameter $(x/M)[(X/M) + 5]^{-1/2}$, which was introduced by Stewart [9] to compare measurements of correlations in turbulent flows under different conditions, particularly for different ratios of the distance from the grid to its mesh length. It should be noted that the time-correlation curve following the mean motion for our measurements is relatively close to the similar curve for Favre et al. and supports the fact that the sample correlations are fairly representative.

Figures 4–6 are measurements of space-time correlations of higher orders

$$R_{x,t}^{m,n}(x, h) = \frac{\overline{u^m(0, 0, 0, t)u^n(x, 0, 0, t + h)}}{[\overline{u^2(0, 0, 0)}]^{m/2}[\overline{u^2(x, 0, 0)}]^{n/2}}, \tag{7}$$

where $m = n = 2, 3,$ and 4, respectively. As for the second-order correlations, the curves for $x/M = 0$ were obtained by taking averages for

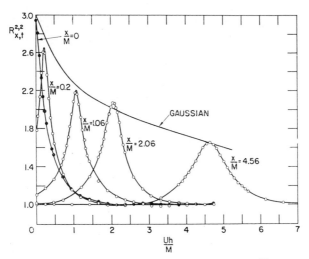

FIG. 4. Space-time correlation curves of the fourth-order $R_{x,t}^{2,2}$ are represented by open points, and the time correlation of the same order $R_t^{2,2}$ ($R_{x,t}^{2,2}$ for $x/M = 0$) is represented by closed points. The curve marked "Gaussian" is the fourth-order correlation following the mean motion obtained from the second-order correlation $R_{x,t}$ (indicated in Fig. 3 by F–K) when assuming the turbulent velocities to be distributed according to a Gaussian law.

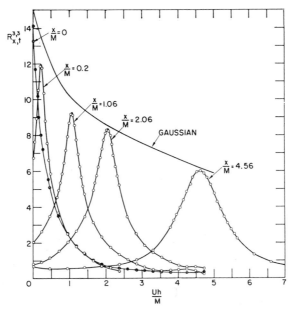

FIG. 5. Space-time correlations, time correlation, and correlation following the mean motion of the sixth order similar to those in Fig. 4.

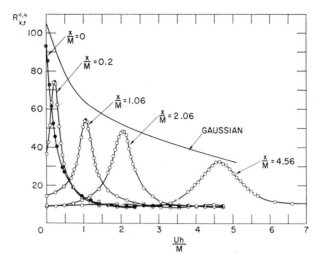

FIG. 6. Space-time correlations, time correlation, and correlation following the mean motion of the eighth order similar to those in Fig. 4.

four sample correlations and are represented by closed circles, whereas the results for each of the other four values of x/M which were determined for single samples of recorded data are represented by open circles.

Now let us assume that the fluctuating turbulent velocity components $u[x, 0, 0, t + (x/U)]$ are distributed according to a Gaussian law. Taking the correlation curve following the mean motion R_m, as marked by F–K in Fig. 3, we can determine the corresponding higher-order correlation curves such as $R_m^{2,2}(h)$, $R_m^{3,3}(h)$, and $R_m^{4,4}(h)$ from the following relations (cf. [2]):

$$
\begin{aligned}
R_m^{2,2} &= 1 + 2(R_m)^2, \\
R_m^{3,3} &= 3R_m[3 + 2(R_m)^2], \\
R_m^{4,4} &= 3[3 + 24(R_m)^2 + 8(R_m)^4].
\end{aligned}
\tag{8}
$$

Thus $R_m^{2,2}(0)$, $R_m^{3,3}(0)$, and $R_m^{4,4}(0)$ will be equal to 3, 15, and 105, respectively; the curves calculated from Eqs. (8) are also included in Figs. 4–6. The departures of these curves from the measured values increase with increasing order of the correlations. It is difficult to attach particular significance to the departures being larger in the vicinity of $Uh/M = 1$, since this may be the sample effect. The departures are relatively small with an average value of about 2, 6, and 11% for $R_m^{2,2}$, $R_m^{3,3}$, and $R_m^{4,4}$, respectively. The fact that they are small may reflect the insensitivity of the even-order correlations to the non-Gaussianity of the turbulent velocities.

A more accurate evaluation of the space-time transformation can be made by comparing $R_{x,t}$ with R_t when both are obtained using the same sample of recorded data rather than using the average value of R_t. For example, a comparison of $R_x(x)$, i.e., $R_{x,t}$ at $h = 0$, with $R_t(h)$ at the appropriate time delay $h = x/U$ for the different values of x/M shows better agreement when compared with its individual sample (see Fig. 7) rather than with the average (see Fig. 3). The present method does make possible comparisons of various statistical characteristics using a well-defined sample of turbulence with both positive and negative time delays being used. Such comparisons are made in Fig. 7 for the four different values of x/M. The time correlation coefficients R_t measured

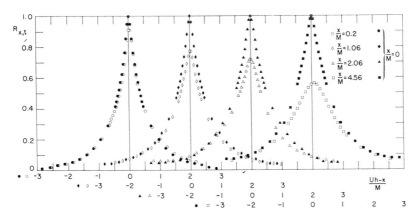

FIG. 7. Space-time correlation coefficients $R_{x,t}$ compared with the frozen pattern of time correlation coefficients R_t obtained from the same sample for each value of x/M.

with the upstream wire are represented by closed points, and the space-time correlations measured with the two wires are represented by the open points. Points having the same shapes (circles for $x/M = 0.2$, diamonds for $x/M = 1.06$, etc.) represent the results for R_t and $R_{x,t}$ obtained using the same samples of recorded data. It should be noted that the values of R_t in Fig. 7 differ from those on Fig. 3 because the latter were given as averages over the four different samples of data from the upstream wire.

The comparisons of Fig. 7 are made according to Eq. (4) to show directly the deviations of $R_{x,t}$ from the frozen patterns R_t for the entire correlation curves. On this basis, if the frozen pattern were conserved exactly, $R_{x,t}$ and R_t would be identical. The departure from the frozen pattern occurs mainly in the small eddy region and, with increasing x/M,

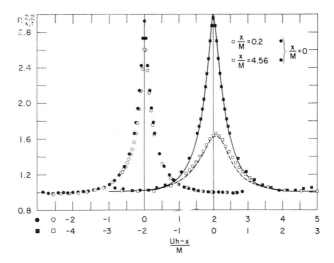

FIG. 8. Space-time correlations of the fourth-order $R_{x,t}^{2,2}$ compared with the corresponding time correlations $R_t^{2,2}$, the dashed and solid curves were obtained from the corresponding curves $R_{x,t}$ and R_t (of Fig. 7) assuming the turbulent velocities to be distributed according to a Gaussian law.

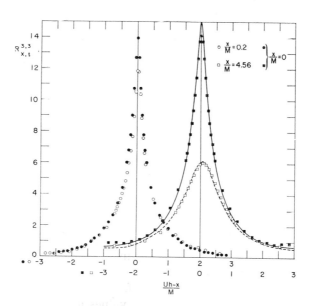

FIG. 9. Correlations of the sixth order similar to those in Fig. 8.

slowly penetrates into a larger eddy region. This behavior appears to be quite natural, since during the process of decay smaller eddies are destroyed by viscosity, whereas newly produced small eddies do not have a large (if any) correlation with the larger eddies from which they derive.

Similar comparisons are made between the higher-order space-time correlations $R_{x,t}^{2,2}$, $R_{x,t}^{3,3}$, and $R_{x,t}^{4,4}$ and the corresponding time correlations $R_t^{2,2}$, $R_t^{3,3}$, and $R_t^{4,4}$ in Figs. 8–10, respectively. In these figures, we have presented the correlations as measured for the values of $x/M = 0.2$ and $x/M = 4.56$, which are the smallest and the largest distances for which data are presented.

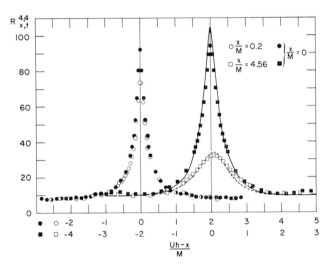

FIG. 10. Correlations of the eighth order similar to those in Fig. 9.

If we now assume that the probability distribution of turbulent veloci-ties at the upstream wire is Gaussian, then the higher-order time correla-tions can be obtained in the same manner as previously, using equations similar to Eqs. (8). These are represented by the solid-line curves as shown in Figs. 8–10. Similarly, assuming the Gaussianity of the appro-priate probability distributions for the space-time correlation $R_{x,t}$ (cf. Fig. 7), the higher-order space-time correlations represented by the dashed curves are obtained. From these figures, it is seen that the curves are in good agreement with the experimental points, again reflecting the insensi-tivity of the even-order correlations to the non-Gaussianity of the turbu-lent velocities. The greatest departures from the time-correlation curves is found for $h = 0$, where the measured values are 2.96, 14.3, and 94.2 instead of 3, 15, and 105, respectively.

V. SPACE-TIME CORRELATIONS OF ODD ORDER

In the previous section, it was shown that the correlation coefficients of even orders are not too sensitive to departures of the distribution of turbulent velocities from a Gaussian law. The correlation coefficients of odd order must, however, be zero for a Gaussian distribution, and therefore their very existence proves that distribution of the turbulent velocities is non-Gaussian. Indeed, the measured data have shown that the various moments of odd order

$$\overline{u^m(0,0,0,t)u^n(0,0,0,t+h)}, \qquad (m+n) \qquad \text{odd}$$

are not negligible compared to the products of standard deviations elevated to the appropriate powers, i.e.,

$$[\overline{u^2(0,0,0)}]^{m/2}[\overline{u^2(x,0,0)}]^{n/2}$$

and that the resulting space-time correlations $R_{x,t}^{m,n}$ provide very significant information concerning the non-Gaussianity of the turbulent velocities. We discuss this question more extensively in other papers [2, 3], where non-Gaussian laws are presented for which the correlation coefficients of odd orders do not have to be equal to zero.

Although the experimental results on space-time correlation of odd order presented here are rather limited, and more extensive measurements and analysis are in progress, it is felt that they may be of some interest and do provide additional information as to the nature of Taylor's approximation.

In Fig. 11, results are presented for the expression

$$\mathcal{R}_{x,t}^{2,1} = \frac{1}{2}(R_{x,t}^{2,1} - R_{x,t}^{1,2}) = \frac{1}{2}\left\{ \frac{\overline{u^2(0,0,0,t)u(x,0,0,t+h)}}{\overline{u^2(0,0,0)}[\overline{u^2(x,0,0)}]^{1/2}} \right.$$
$$\left. - \frac{\overline{u(0,0,0,t)u^2(x,0,0,t+h)}}{[\overline{u^2(0,0,0)}]^{1/2}\overline{u^2(x,0,0)}} \right\}$$

as a function of $(Uh - x)/M$. As for the even-order correlations, these measured values are compared with the corresponding time correlations obtained from the same samples of recorded data. The comparison of $\mathcal{R}_{x,t}^{2,1}$ with the frozen pattern $\mathcal{R}_t^{2,1}$ shows that the maximum values obtained with positive time delays corresponds rather well with no systematic deviations for increasing x/M, in contrast with the even-order correlations (cf. Fig. 7). We thus conclude that in the space-time transformation the values of $\mathcal{R}_{x,t}^{2,1}$ are conserved to a greater degree than the values of

the even-order correlations. However, their locations relative to the positions of the frozen pattern in the vicinity of $h = 0$ show greater departures than those for the even-order correlations. For negative time delays, the $\Re_{x,t}^{2,1}$, although not too different in magnitude from the frozen pattern, are indicative of an asymmetry that may be related to the nonisotropy of these third-order correlations. This asymmetry appears to increase with increasing distance x between the two points.

It is interesting to note that the departures of the odd- and even-order correlations from the position of the frozen pattern are not in correspondence. For example, at $x/M = 4.56$, the even-order correlations (see

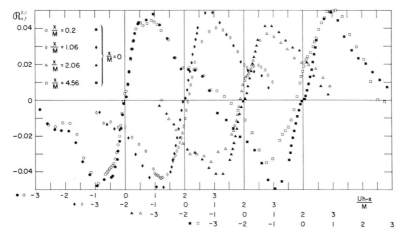

Fig. 11. Space-time correlations of odd order $\Re_{x,t}^{2,1} = \frac{1}{2}(R_{x,t}^{2,1} - R_{x,t}^{1,2})$ compared with the time-correlations $\Re_t^{2,1} = \frac{1}{2}(R_t^{2,1} - R_t^{1,2})$.

Figs. 7–10) are displaced downstream, indicating that for this particular sample the apparent translational velocity is smaller than U, whereas for the same sample the odd-order correlations (see Fig. 11) are shifted upstream, indicating a velocity somewhat greater than U. Although in averaging over several sample correlations such differences may disappear, the fact that they are observed for the same sample indicates that these differences are not due to the variation of the "mean velocity." It seems reasonable to infer that the odd-order correlations are governed by a different range of eddy sizes (weighted toward the larger eddies) than the even-order correlations, and that the eddies of various sizes may propagate with different velocities.

In passing, it should be noted that, if it is assumed that the turbulence is homogeneous and stationary with

$$\overline{u^3(0, 0, 0, t)} = \overline{u^3(x, 0, 0, t + h)},$$

then the skewness is

$$S_{x,t}^{(3)} = \frac{\overline{[u(x,0,0,t+h) - u(0,0,0,t)]^3}}{[\overline{u^2}(0,0,0)]^{3/2}} = 3(R_{x,t}^{2,1} - R_{x,t}^{1,2}) = 6R_{x,t}^{2,1}.$$

Since the role of the odd-order correlations is intrinsic to the dynamics of turbulence, we felt that it would be of interest to extend the measurements to the space-time correlations of the fifth order. In Ref. [2], the different behavior of the time-correlations

$$\mathfrak{R}_t^{4,1} = \tfrac{1}{2}(R_t^{4,1} - R_t^{1,4}), \qquad \mathfrak{R}_t^{3,2} = \tfrac{1}{2}(R_t^{3,2} - R_t^{2,3})$$

was observed, and we shall now consider the similar space-time correlations

$$\mathfrak{R}_{x,t}^{4,1} = \tfrac{1}{2}(R_{x,t}^{4,1} - R_{x,t}^{1,4}), \qquad \mathfrak{R}_{x,t}^{3,2} = \tfrac{1}{2}(R_{x,t}^{3,2} - R_{x,t}^{2,3})$$

which are presented in Figs. 12 and 13, respectively.

In Fig. 12, the curves for $\mathfrak{R}_{x,t}^{4,1}$ are similar in shape to the curves $\mathfrak{R}_{x,t}^{2,1}$ of Fig. 11, but their magnitude is about five times larger. It will be of interest to note that $\mathfrak{R}_{x,t}^{4,1}$ for positive time delays corresponds much better to the frozen pattern than for negative time delays, again reflecting a nonisotropy of the odd correlation coefficients. A comparison of $\mathfrak{R}_{x,t}^{4,1}$ and $\mathfrak{R}_{x,t}^{2,1}$ with respect to their positions relative to their frozen patterns shows that they are not always in correspondence. For example, at $x/M = 1.06$, $\mathfrak{R}_{x,t}^{2,1}$ departs downstream from the frozen pattern, whereas $\mathfrak{R}_{x,t}^{4,1}$ departs in the upstream direction, thus indicating the possibility that the different odd-order moments may be governed by a different range of eddy sizes.

The correlation curves $\mathfrak{R}_{x,t}^{3,2}$ in Fig. 13 present very characteristic irregularities near $(Uh - x)/M = 0$. Comparing the amplitudes of these irregularities for increasing distances x/M, it can be seen that their magnitude decreases. It should be noted that the noise (superposed with the turbulent signal) will affect the shape of the curves $\mathfrak{R}_{x,t}^{3,2}$, but this effect is small and cannot account for the magnitude of the irregularities and their variation with x/M. The effect of a low-frequency fluctuation (influenced by the finite length of samples) on the curves may be responsible for some irregularities, but again an estimate shows that their magnitude should be considerably smaller than observed. In fact, we have determined the time correlations $\mathfrak{R}_t^{3,2}$ and $\mathfrak{R}_{x,t}^{3,2}$ by interposing a filter that cuts out frequencies below 4/sec and obtained the same irregularity. This characteristic shape of the $\mathfrak{R}_{x,t}^{3,2}$ curves is therefore regarded as inherent and not necessarily anomalous, for as shown in [2] it can be consistent with the non-Gaussian nature of the turbulent field.

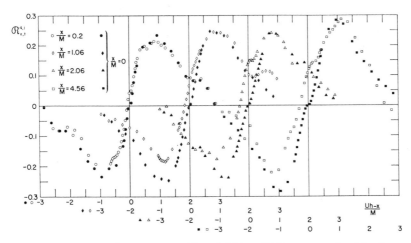

FIG. 12. Space-time correlations $\mathfrak{R}_{x,t}^{4,1} = \frac{1}{2}(R_{x,t}^{4,1} - R_{x,t}^{1,4})$ compared with time correlations $\mathfrak{R}_{t}^{4,1} = \frac{1}{2}(R_{t}^{4,1} - R_{t}^{1,4})$.

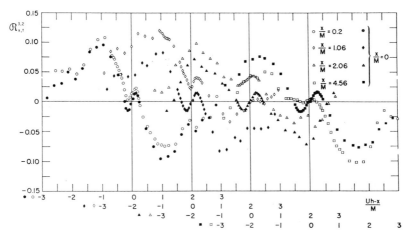

FIG. 13. Space-time correlations $\mathfrak{R}_{x,t}^{3,2} = \frac{1}{2}(R_{x,t}^{3,2} - R_{x,t}^{2,3})$ compared with time correlations $\mathfrak{R}_{t}^{3,2} = \frac{1}{2}(R_{t}^{3,2} - R_{t}^{2,3})$.

ACKNOWLEDGMENTS

The authors wish to express their gratitude to Dr. Elizabeth H. Cuthill for her aid in connection with the high-speed computing, and to Mr. K. D. Tidstrom for his assistance in the recording of analog data and the hot-wire instrumentation. They also wish to thank Mr. E. G. Robinson for his assistance in the conversion from analog to digital data.

REFERENCES

1. Frenkiel, F. N., The Comparison between the Longitudinal Correlation and the Time Correlation in a Turbulent Flow. *Phys. Rev.* **88,** 1380 (1952).
2. Frenkiel, F. N. and Klebanoff, P. S. (to be published).
3. Frenkiel, F. N. and Klebanoff, P. S., Two-Dimensional Probability Distribution in a Turbulent Flow. *Phys. Fluids* **8,** 2291 (1965).
4. Taylor, G. I., The Spectrum of Turbulence. *Proc. Roy. Soc. (London)* **A164,** 476 (1938).
5. Simmons, L. F. G. and Salter, C., An Experimental Determination of the Spectrum of Turbulence. *Proc. Roy. Soc. (London),* **A165,** 73 (1938).
6. Frenkiel, F. N., Étude statistique de la turbulence; corrélation et spectres dans un écoulement homogène. *Compt. Rend.* **222,** 367 (1946).
7. Favre, A., Gaviglio, J., and Dumas, R., Quelques mesures de corrélation dans le temps et l'espace en soufflerie. *Rech. Aéron* **32** (1953); transl. as NACA Tech. Memo. 1370 (1955).
8. Favre, A., Review on Space-Time Correlations in Turbulent Fluids. *J. Appl. Mech.* **32,** 241 (1965).
9. Stewart, R. W., Triple Velocity Correlations in Isotropic Turbulence. *Proc. Cambridge Phil. Soc.* **47,** 146 (1951).

Computer Experiments on Random Walks
with Both Eulerian and Lagrangian Statistics

G. S. PATTERSON, JR., AND S. CORRSIN

DEPARTMENT OF MECHANICS
THE JOHNS HOPKINS UNIVERSITY
BALTIMORE, MARYLAND

Random walk experiments have been made with a digital computer on several ensembles of random, binary, homogeneous "velocity" fields. The field properties are Eulerian, and those experienced by walking particles are Lagrangian. Of heuristic interest for turbulent dispersion research are the Eulerian two-point velocity correlations with separation in both space and time, and the Lagrangian velocity correlation with separation in time only, the autocorrelation following a material point. In particular, it was hoped that some empirical connection might be discovered between these two kinds of functions. The results show that no single Eulerian two-point correlation function is a good approximation to the Lagrangian function, but the Eulerian integral scale along a "particular" space-time diagonal ($\Delta x = V\Delta t$) is close to the Lagrangian integral time scale. Experiments were also done on walks with a kind of "inertia," i.e., walks that reverse direction only after traveling a specified number of steps into a region of reversing velocity field. With increasing inertia, the particles have increasing Lagrangian integral scale, a behavior qualitatively consistent with that of small spheres in turbulent fluid. With only one space dimension, the "flow" must be compressible. "Shock waves" develop and merge. The rate of coalescence of shocks with time agrees roughly with that estimated by Burgers for his one-dimensional fluid model equation.

I. INTRODUCTION

A. The Turbulent Dispersion Problem

The statistical properties of turbulent motion are more accessible both theoretically and experimentally in Eulerian representations, "laboratory" or "spatial" coordinates. On the other hand, the description of turbulent dispersion is the description of fluid point displacement statistics and hence is more naturally described in a Lagrangian frame, "material" coordinates.

275

Since mean square displacement of fluid particles passing a fixed point is the simplest statistical measure of dispersion, it is instructive to recall Taylor's (1921) original formulation in terms of velocity. The fluid point (or particle) position at any time is

$$X(a, t) = a + \int_0^t V(a, t_1) \, dt_1, \tag{1}$$

where $a \equiv X(a, 0)$ is initial position. Essentially by squaring and averaging, Taylor showed that the mean square particle displacement is a simple integral function of the Lagrangian velocity autocorrelation. For a single component, and taking $a = 0$ for simplicity, Taylor's result can be written in terms of the Lagrangian velocity correlation of a single particle,

$$R_{11} \equiv \overline{V_1(0, t) V_1(0, t + \tau)},$$
$$\overline{X_1^2}(t) = 2 \int_0^t \int_0^{t_1} R_{11}(t_1, - \tau) \, d\tau \, dt_1, \tag{2}$$

or, as slightly modified by Kampé de Fériet (1939) [for the special case in which the velocity following the particle is a stationary random variable so that $R_{11}(t, \tau) - \rho_{11}(\tau)$ only],

$$\overline{X_1^2}(t) = 2 \int_0^t (t - \tau) \rho_{11}(\tau) \, d\tau. \tag{3}$$

Restricting the discussion to this stationary case for simplicity, we can display some of the mathematical complexity by replacing the Lagrangian autocorrelation in terms of its explicit expression in Eulerian velocity, $u(x, t)$:

$$\overline{X_1^2}(t) = 2 \int_0^t (t - \tau) \overline{u_1[X(0, t), t] u_1[X(0, t + \tau), t + \tau]} \, d\tau. \tag{4}$$

From this we see that, even if the statistical properties of $u(x, t)$ are known, the solution of Eq. (4) for the mean square displacement is complicated by the fact that the unknown displacement occurs in the arguments of the velocities as well.

Lumley (1957) has shown that the statistical properties of the velocity fields expressed in the Eulerian and Lagrangian frames are uniquely connected only at the level of functional probabilities. These contain much more information than we care to cope with, and so experimental and theoretical research is directed at the search for approximate connections between the lower-order moments in the two frames. From the foregoing equations, we can see that it would be helpful to be able to predict the Lagrangian velocity autocorrelation function in terms of some Eulerian

correlation functions, preferably of fairly low order.   A detailed review covering the period up to the end of 1961 is available (Lumley, 1962; Corrsin, 1962).   Some additional work has been done since that time (for example, Corrsin, 1963; Kraichnan, 1964a, 1964b), but the problem is far from solved.

B. The Walk on a Random Field

In the hope of providing partial kinematic insight into possible connections between low-order correlations in Eulerian and Lagrangian representations, a new kind of random walk was invented, possessing both representations (Lumley and Corrsin, 1959).   In classical random walks, the transition instructions after each step are given directly to the walking particle.   In this new kind of walk, a random field of instructions (velocities) is defined over a space-time lattice.   The walk is then done by having the particle obey whatever instruction it finds at a lattice point when it arrives there.   With a suitable ensemble of such random fields, we can perform a single walk on each, from the same starting point.   We then have a system that displays one of the complications present in the turbulent dispersion problem.   The statistical properties of the ensemble of random fields in space-time are Eulerian, and those computed following the ensemble of walking "material points" in time are Lagrangian.

In the original paper proposing this game, an analytical result was desired, and so the Eulerian field was restricted to being generated by two Markov chains.[1]   With sufficient computational help, no such degeneracy need be assumed here.   On the other hand, the ensembles to be explored will all be binary velocity fields and will be restricted to one space dimension plus time.

A hypothetical realization of such a field with a single particle track drawn on it is sketched qualitatively in Fig. 1.   In this space-time domain, the trajectory proceeds at an angle of 30° to the left of the time axis when the particle is in the light areas ($V = -1$) and 30° to the right of the time axis when the particle is in the shaded areas ($V = +1$).   Because of the rules of the game, the trajectory occasionally hugs a boundary between the positive and negative velocity regions.

Obviously, there is no reason in principle to restrict the Eulerian velocity field to be binary.   It can be a continuous function of position and time.   Furthermore, it can encompass any number of space dimensions.   When it is a random vector field in three space dimensions plus time, the problem can be as complicated as that of the turbulence itself.   In fact, with the appropriate fluid-mechanical constraints, it will be turbulence.

[1] An error in that paper has been corrected.   See Patterson (1966).

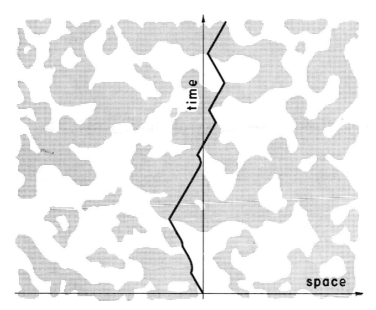

Fig. 1. Qualitative sketch of a binary velocity field with a trajectory.

II. THE BINARY WALK IN 1 + 1 DIMENSIONS

A. Some Qualitative Notions

A bit of light can be shed on the character of the trajectories by considering two extreme cases. When the Eulerian velocity field is very well correlated in space but changes relatively rapidly in time (Fig. 2), a typical trajectory in the ensemble will be a series of straight line segments in the (+) and (−) directions. The asymptotic limit of this kind of field would be one in which the entire fluid oscillates randomly as a rigid body, having perfect correlation in the space direction. When the Eulerian field shows a high degree of correlation in the time direction and relatively little in the space direction (Fig. 3), a typical trajectory will contain long segments that are trapped on the interface between the $V = +1$ and $V = −1$ regions in space-time. The asymptotic limit of this kind of field is evidently one in which each space point has a velocity independent of time in the Eulerian frame: essentially a cellular motion, if we have more than one space dimension. In these, the walking particle gets trapped permanently and does not diffuse.

Qualitative diagrams of Lagrangian velocity history for the kinds of cases displayed in Figs. 2 and 3 are sketched in Fig. 4. Figure 4a looks

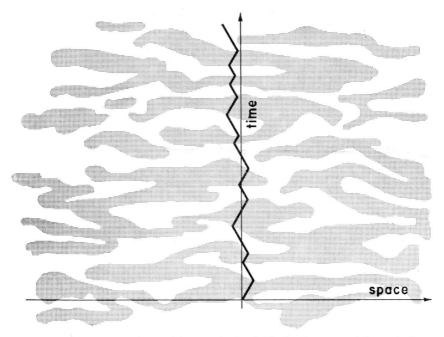

Fig. 2. Qualitative sketch of a binary velocity field: dominant spatial correlation.

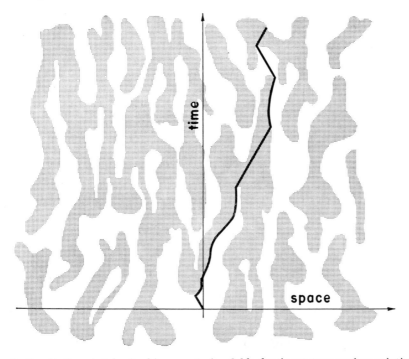

Fig. 3. Qualitative sketch of a binary velocity field: dominant temporal correlation.

very much like a traditional "random telegraph signal," whereas Fig. 4b has a somewhat more general appearance.

What is the measure of whether a field is relatively highly correlated in space as in Fig. 2 or relatively highly correlated in time as in Fig. 3? Evidently, it depends on the ratio of the velocity of the fluid (with which the particle walks) to the average slope of the interfaces between the positive and negative velocity regions. If we increase the velocity magnitude sufficiently in Fig. 2, i.e., increase the angle between the particle path and the time axis, we can reach a condition where this field, too, will have a boundary-hugging trajectory.

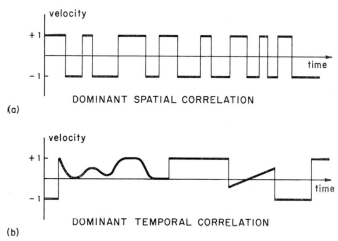

FIG. 4. Lagrangian (particle) velocity histories for Figs. 2 and 3.

A simple measure of the foregoing behavior is the magnitude of the dimensionless quantity VT/L, where V is the magnitude of the velocity, L is the Eulerian integral length scale, and T is the Eulerian integral time scale. When this ratio is very small compared to 1, the trajectory will be of the type sketched in Fig. 2. When the ratio is very large compared to 1, it will be of the type sketched in Fig. 3. Parenthetically, it appears that the corresponding quantity in nearly isotropic turbulence is of order 1.[2]

Although it is not immediately obvious, one of the unfortunate consequences of confining the velocity field to one space dimension is that the Lagrangian velocity of a particle cannot be statistically stationary (except in some very special cases). This can be demonstrated easily in a case like Fig. 3; although the particle spends perhaps half of its time hugging a boundary between positive and negative velocity regions, the probability that the arbitrarily chosen starting point will lie exactly on such a bound-

[2] G. Comte-Bellot and S. Corrsin, report in preparation.

ary is essentially zero.   In the actual experiment, approximate stationarity was reached after a number of steps larger than the time interval for appreciable correlation.   This is discussed briefly in Section III.B.

B. The Discrete Case in Digital Computation

This game, even with continuous rather than merely binary velocity fields, would lend itself well to analog computation with combined optical and electronic devices.   But because of operational and data reduction difficulties, it was decided to proceed with a high-speed digital computer. This required that the space and time dimensions be discretized.   Figure 5 shows four realizations from one of the actual ensembles.   In the experiment, it was not necessary to print out the fields, but occasional visual inspection can be instructive.

In this computer printout, a lattice point with unit velocity in the $+x$-direction is indicated by an X, and one with unit velocity in the $-x$-direction is left blank.   It is an unfortunate consequence of the discretization of space and time that the boundary-hugging segments of the trajectories appear as zig-zag lines with a single step each for a zig and a zag.   In the Lagrangian autocorrelation functions, this zig-zag behavior introduces an oscillation that is irrelevant to the general investigation.

The ensemble from which Fig. 5 is selected is one in which the Eulerian correlation functions in space and in time are identical in terms of steps. The appearance of greater extension in the time direction results simply from the fact that the printout lattice of the computer has a five-to-three length ratio.   All ensembles generated were statistically homogeneous in both space and time.

Integer values are assigned to the distances along the space and time directions.   The two-point velocity correlation function for any pair of points on the lattice is defined as

$$E(m,n) \equiv \overline{u(x,t)u(x+m,t+n)}/\overline{u^2} ; \qquad (5)$$

$u(x, t)$ is the binary, random velocity field.   Due to the Eulerian space and time homogeneity, this correlation depends only on the separations between the two field points.   Furthermore, the mean square velocity is the same everywhere so that no argument is indicated in the denominator.   The overbar denotes ensemble average.   (For stationary variables it can, with relatively weak restrictions, be an average taken over the field of a single realization, i.e., we could have ergodicity.)   Since the velocity is a binary variable, its probability density function consists simply of two Dirac functions.   We restrict to fields in which the positive and negative constant velocities are equal in magnitude and in probability, and so the two Dirac functions are equal in "strength" and are symmetri-

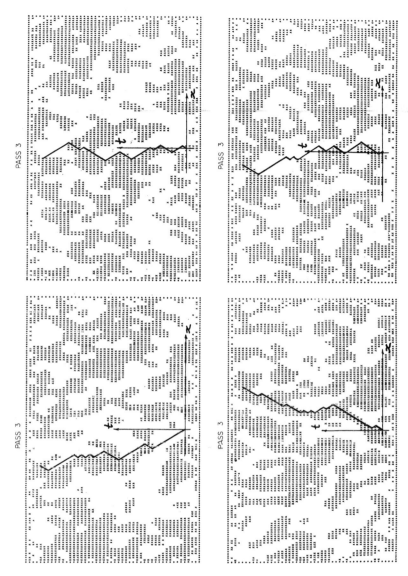

FIG. 5. Four realizations of a discrete binary velocity field (3 × 3 filter) with particle trajectories.

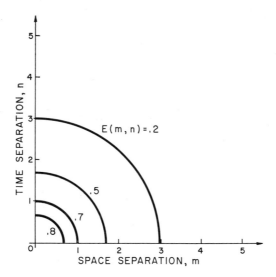

FIG. 6. Two-point Eulerian isocorrelation contours: 3×3 filter (see Table I, page 301).

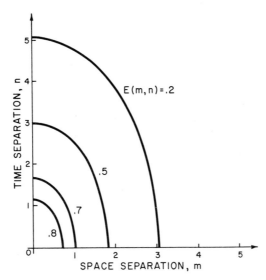

FIG. 7. Two-point Eulerian isocorrelation contours: 3×5 filter (see Table I, page 301).

cally disposed about the origin in probability space.   The *joint* probability density function for velocity at two points in space-time is, correspondingly, an array of four Dirac functions.   From this, it is not difficult to deduce an alternative expression for the double correlation function:

$$E(m, n) = P_s - P_0, \tag{6}$$

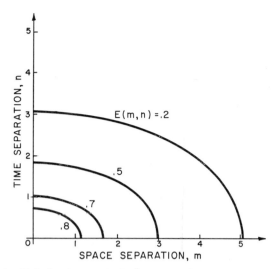

FIG. 8. Two-point Eulerian isocorrelation contours: 5×3 filter (see Table I, page 301).

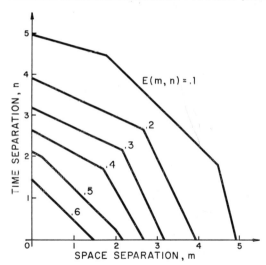

FIG. 9. Two-point Eulerian isocorrelation contours: nine-point "plus" filter (see Table I, page 301).

where P_s is the probability that the velocities separated by (m, n) are equal, and P_0 is the probability that they are opposite.

The exact method by which the different Eulerian ensembles were generated is not relevant at this point. The Appendix contains the outline of this procedure. What is relevant is the statistical nature of each of the ensembles. Figures 6–9 show empirical isocorrelation contours in

space and time for four of the ensembles. For these figures and later ones, the sizes of the steps in the space and time directions are taken equal. Although the correlation has values only at the lattice points, continuous curves have been drawn to represent the constant correlation contours.

A number of the ensembles showed isocorrelation contours that were ellipses within the accuracy of measurement. It was found that these could be made identical by a simple affine transformation, a scaling dependent on the spatial filter geometry used in the generation (Appendix). The result was a radially symmetric two point correlation function for

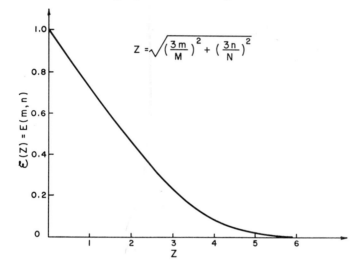

$$Z = \sqrt{\left(\frac{3m}{M}\right)^2 + \left(\frac{3n}{N}\right)^2}$$

FIG. 10. Normalized two-point Eulerian correlation functions (5×5, 5×3, 3×5, and 3×3 filters).

this class of ensembles. A smooth curve drawn through the discrete values of four such scaled correlation functions is presented in Fig. 10.

The number of realizations required in an ensemble to get sufficiently consistent results must depend, of course, on the particular statistical property under study. For these two-point correlation functions, ensembles of 20,000 turned out to be more than adequate.

III. EXPERIMENTAL RESULTS FOR THE BINARY WALK

A. Nonstationarity of the Lagrangian Velocity

It was pointed out in the previous section, primarily by example, that with a single space dimension a homogeneous and stationary Eulerian

velocity field does not generally give a stationary Lagrangian velocity history. If we place the (x, t) [or (m, n)] origin at the starting point of the walks, the Lagrangian velocity at the nth time step (for the particle that started at $x = 0$) can be expressed as

$$V(0, n) = u[X(0, n), n], \tag{7}$$

where $X(a, n)$ is the position after n time steps of the particle that was at a at $t = n = 0$:

$$X(0, s) = \sum_{j=0}^{s-1} V(0, j). \tag{8}$$

Evidently, the mean square displacement in "diffusion by discontinuous movements" can be expressed in terms of Lagrangian correlation in the same way as in G. I. Taylor's theory of "diffusion by continuous movements." The result analogous to Eq. (2) is gotten after some manipulation:

$$\overline{X^2}(n) = \sum_{k=0}^{n-1} \left\{ 2 \sum_{j=0}^{k} R(-j; k) - 1 \right\}, \tag{9}$$

where

$$R(s; p) \equiv \overline{V(a, p)V(a, p+s)}$$

is the Lagrangian autocorrelation. The 1 subtracted in the braces in Eq. (9) prevents counting the diagonal terms twice when we square Eq. (8).

The possibility of analyzing dispersion in a discrete random walk with correlation between successive steps was pointed out by Taylor (1921) as a prelude to his presentation of the continuous case. It is a generalization of the classical (uncorrelated) random walk and was examined in great detail by Goldstein (1951). For the walk on a random field, the problem has the additional facet that Eq. (7) can be substituted into Eq. (8) to express the displacement $X(0, n)$ of the walking particle in terms of the Eulerian velocity field:

$$X(0, n) = \sum_{j=0}^{n-1} u[X(0, j), j]. \tag{10}$$

In principle, the value of the Lagrangian velocity autocorrelation function can be written in terms of Eulerian correlation functions. Considering all possible trajectories for the first two steps on a lattice (Fig. 11) and remembering that the Lagrangian velocity is written $V = V(a, n)$, whereas the Eulerian velocity is $u = u(m, n)$, the sequence of Lagrangian velocities can be written in terms of the Eulerian ones by inspection as

follows:

$$V(0,0) = u(0,0) \tag{11}$$
$$V(0,1) = \tfrac{1}{2}[u(0,0) + 1]u(1,1) - \tfrac{1}{2}[u(0,0) - 1]u(-1,1) \tag{12}$$
$$V(0,2) = \tfrac{1}{2}[u(0,0) + 1] \cdot \tfrac{1}{2}[u(1,1) + 1]u(2,2)$$
$$- \tfrac{1}{2}[u(0,0) + 1] \cdot \tfrac{1}{2}[u(1,1) - 1]u(0,2)$$
$$- \tfrac{1}{2}[u(0,0) - 1] \cdot \tfrac{1}{2}[u(-1,1) + 1]u(0,2)$$
$$+ \tfrac{1}{2}[u(0,0) - 1] \cdot \tfrac{1}{2}[u(-1,1) - 1]u(-2,2) \tag{13}$$

etc.

With a fair amount of manipulation, the sequence of Lagrangian correlation functions $R(j; n)$ can be computed in terms of the Eulerian ones.

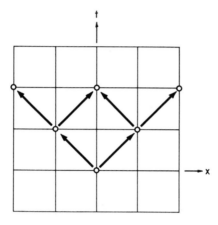

FIG. 11. Possible trajectories for the first two steps of a walk.

The first three are the following:

$$R(1; 0) = E(1,1) \tag{14}$$
$$R(2; 0) = \tfrac{1}{2}[E(0,2) + E(2,2)] \tag{15}$$
$$R(1; 1) = E(1,1) - \tfrac{1}{2}[E(0,2) - E(2,2)] \tag{16}$$

The nonstationarity of the Lagrangian correlation function is immediately obvious from the fact that $R(1; 1) \neq R(1; 0)$. Furthermore, it turns out that the general two-point Lagrangian correlation $R(j; n)$ depends on Eulerian correlations involving $(n + j + 1)$ points (Patterson, 1966).

An experimental demonstration of the degree of nonstationarity is given in Fig. 12. This particular ensemble is the one whose Eulerian correlation function is displayed in Fig. 7. When the value of time (not time separation) exceeds the interval over which there is appreciable

Eulerian correlation in time, the Lagrangian functions seem to be approaching an asymptotic shape. For the comparison with Eulerian functions, we have presented $R(-j; 9)$, which has reached the range of n where R is rather insensitive to n.

There would be an important simplification if we could devise a walk on a random field such that the Lagrangian velocity is statistically stationary. This may be possible with two space dimensions plus time, but it may require three space dimensions plus time. The subject has not yet been investigated. In the (later) discussion on the occurrence of "shock waves" in the present field, further desirability of two- and three-

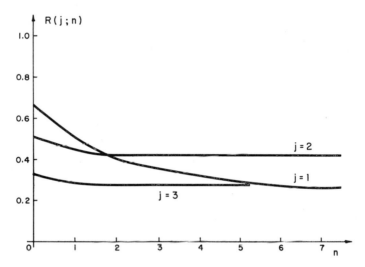

Fig. 12. Nonstationarity of the Lagrangian velocity autocorrelation (3×5 filter).

dimensional cases will become apparent. Of course the computing time and, therefore, the cost rise rapidly with increases in the number of dimensions.

B. Probability Density Function for Particle Displacement

In a dispersion problem, the result of central interest is the time development of the probability density function for the displacement in the ensemble of walking particles. For many problems, this function is more information than is required, and so the minimum goal is the second moment of this probability density function, the mean square displacement identified earlier. Since Eulerian statistical information in turbulence is more easily available than Lagrangian information, it is reasonable to ask what statistical information on the Eulerian representation is

required for a prediction of the one-point probability density function of particle displacement in turbulence. On rewriting Eq. (1) for $a = 0$ in the form

$$X(0, t) = \int_0^t u[X(0, t_1), t_1] \, dt_1, \tag{17}$$

we see that the *functional* probability of the Eulerian velocity fields is required.

For the binary walk on a random field, the situation is considerably simpler. Considering once more just the first two steps on a lattice, we can write Eq. (8) for $s = 1$ and 2:

$$X(0, 1) = V(0, 0) \tag{18}$$
$$X(0, 2) = V(0, 0) + V(0, 1) \tag{19}$$

The mean square displacements are

$$\overline{X^2}(1) = 1 \tag{20}$$
$$\overline{X^2}(2) = 2[1 + R(1 ; 0)], \tag{21}$$

which can be shown to agree with Eq. (9).

From Fig. 11, we can see that the probability density function $p_X(X; t)$ for $X(0, t)$ has the value $\frac{1}{2}$ for $X = \pm 1$ at $t = 1$ in an Eulerian field for which positive and negative unit velocities are equally probable. This is just equal to the probability density for the Lagrangian velocity at the starting point. On the other hand, after two time steps, we have

$$p_X(2 ; 2) = p_{V_0, V_1}(1, 1) \tag{22}$$
$$p_X(-2 ; 2) = p_{V_0, V_1}(-1, -1) \tag{23}$$
$$p_X(0 ; 2) = p_{V_0, V_1}(-1, 1) + p_{V_0, V_1}(1, -1). \tag{24}$$

But, for a binary random variable like V, it can be shown that the two-element joint probability density and the correlation are related by

$$\begin{aligned} p_{V_0, V_1}(1, 1) &= p_{V_0, V_1}(-1, -1) = \tfrac{1}{4}[1 + R(1 ; 0)] \\ p_{V_0, V_1}(1, -1) &= p_{V_0, V_1}(-1, 1) = \tfrac{1}{4}[1 - R(1 ; 0)]. \end{aligned} \tag{25}$$

Therefore, the particle displacement probability can be written in terms of the Lagrangian correlations. These, in turn, can be written in terms of the Eulerian correlation functions as we saw in the previous section.

The complexity of these explicit relationships is sufficiently great that the experimental approach with the digital computer seems more reasonable for studying the walk on the random field than does the scrutiny of a vast hierarchy of ever more complex analytical relationships. The experimental result for the probability density function of a particular case (that whose Eulerian isocorrelation contours are presented in Fig. 6)

is shown in Fig. 13 for a small number of time steps. Although the results look little like a "binomial distribution" for this small number of steps, they do appear to approach that familiar result eventually. A behavior somewhat like that in Fig. 13 can be observed in a classical random walk if we assign the particle a probability of continuing in whatever direction it is traveling higher than that of reversing itself (Goldstein 1951). In the classical walk, this may be viewed as a variety of "inertia."

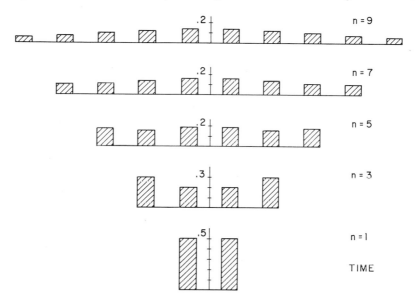

FIG. 13. Displacement probability density function for a particle (3 × 3 filter).

C. Some Lagrangian Autocorrelation Functions

Since the Lagrangian velocity autocorrelation function is a property central to mean square displacement, the simplest measure of dispersion, some typical results are presented in Figs. 14–16. These are three representative ensembles, varying from one that is more highly correlated in space than in time (Fig. 14) to one that is more highly correlated in time than in space (Fig. 16). The Eulerian correlation functions are represented by smooth curves drawn through their discrete values in order to provide contrast with the Lagrangian points. The initial oscillation of the Lagrangian correlations (evidenced by the pathologically low value of R at $n = 1$) is a behavior irrelevant to the objectives of the present study. It results from the zig-zag nature of the boundary-hugging phenomenon in the discretized field, as remarked in Section II.B. It is therefore most dramatically seen in the case with relatively strong persistence in time.

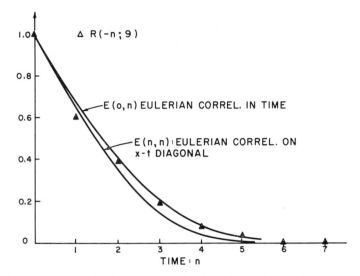

FIG. 14. Asymptotic Lagrangian velocity autocorrelation: 5×3 filter.

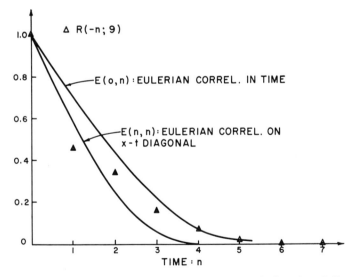

FIG. 15. Asymptotic Lagrangian velocity autocorrelation: 3×3 filter.

In these three figures, the Lagrangian autocorrelation functions are moderately well bracketed by the particular Eulerian functions presented [correlation in time alone, $E(0, n)$, and correlation along a space-time diagonal, $E(n, n)$], but no close equality was observed for any ensemble between the Lagrangian correlation function and any simply selected

Eulerian function defined along a straight line in the Eulerian correlation space.

An attempt was also made to discover a "universal" trajectory in the Eulerian correlation space such that the Lagrangian autocorrelation is equal to the Eulerian space-time correlation sampled along that trajectory $\{X(0, n)$ such that $E[X(0, n), n] = R(-n; \infty)\}$. It was immediately obvious that there can be no universal result simply because the Eulerian correlations in these ensembles are all positive, whereas some of the Lagrangian correlations have negative regions. There were also one or

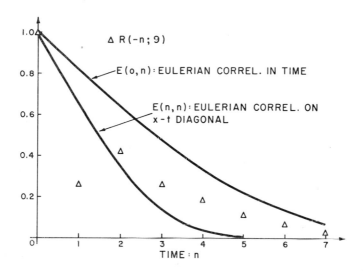

Fig. 16. Asymptotic Lagrangian velocity autocorrelation: 3×5 filter.

two cases in which the magnitude rather than the sign proved impossible to match. In the cases where such a trajectory existed, however, there was a qualitatively common behavior: the trajectories tended to start off for small times at roughly a 45° angle, and at large times turned gradually parallel to the time axis.

It is interesting to note that the Lagrangian functions lie largely below the Eulerian ones with time separation only. This is contrary to a conjecture once suggested for the turbulence problem (Corrsin, 1963). It is consistent with the opposite conjecture offered by Kraichnan (1964a).

D. Integral Scales

Since the asymptotic diffusion coefficient in the turbulent case depends on the Lagrangian integral scale, we were particularly interested in seeing

whether the walk on a random field shows a Lagrangian "integral scale" nearly equal to any of the simple Eulerian integral scales. The closest approximation for all the ensembles was found to be the Eulerian integral scale along the diagonal in space-time. This is presented in Fig. 17. It is perhaps the most concrete outcome of this experimental investigation.

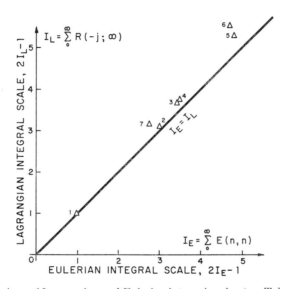

Fig. 17. Comparison of Lagrangian and Eulerian integral scales (see Table I, page 301).

For the turbulent case, with stationary Lagrangian velocity, the asymptotic mean square displacement grows like

$$\overline{X^2}(t) \to 2\overline{V^2}T_L t, \qquad (26)$$

where $\overline{V^2}$ is the (constant) mean square Lagrangian velocity fluctuation, and T_L is the integral scale:

$$T_L = (1/\overline{V^2}) \int_0^\infty R(\tau)\, d\tau. \qquad (27)$$

$R(\tau)$ is the Lagrangian correlation function.

The corresponding forms for discrete cases with $V = \pm 1$ are

$$\overline{X^2}(n) \to [2I_L - 1]n, \qquad (28)$$

where

$$I_L = \sum_{j=0}^\infty R(-j;\ \infty). \qquad (29)$$

IV. THE BINARY WALK WITH "INERTIA"

The Choice of "Inertia"

A turbulent dispersion problem of considerable interest is the diffusion of small suspended solid particles whose densities are different from that of the fluid medium.   In addition to the superimposed "drift" effect of gravity or other steady body forces, the density difference prevents the suspended particle from following precisely the random motion of the fluid material, thereby leading to a different effective turbulent diffusivity. The problem has a long investigative history.   For the relatively simple case of a sphere smaller than the Kolmogorov microscale, wandering at a Reynolds number of order 1 or smaller, Lumley (1957) has presented the first clear statement of the theoretical problem.   Up to now, the only significant theoretical results seem to be asymptotic forms.   The first well-defined experiments on such a problem are those of Kennedy (1965), although equipment limitations forced him to use sphere sizes and Reynolds numbers slightly larger than the limits just mentioned.

If the suspended particle is denser than the surrounding medium, for example, the particle does not follow the most rapid accelerations of the fluid surrounding it.   It is a "low pass filter."   The velocity of the suspended particle at any instant depends on an integral over previous time with a suitably decaying weighting function or "memory."   To set up an analogous inertia for the case of a walk on a random field would require a program more complex than we wanted to use.   Consequently, "inertia" was introduced by requiring that the "heavy" particle encounter a particular number of successive reversed velocity instructions before it obeyed.   This is sketched qualitatively in Figs. 18a and 18b.

The two trajectories are for particles with different amounts of inertia and should be compared with the strictly Lagrangian trajectory sketched for the same field in Fig. 1.

Figure 19 shows a comparison of the roughly asymptotic velocity auto-correlation functions following the particles with transition delays of one, two, and three steps.   This means that to change direction these particles had to encounter two, three, and four successive instructions to change. These autocorrelations have been drawn in as solid curves; the strictly Lagrangian case for the same Eulerian field is represented by the actual experimental points.   As can be expected, an increase in the inertia generally increases the persistence of the motion, as evidenced by a slower drop rate in the velocity autocorrelation function.   A bit surprising is the fact that the one-step delay gives an autocorrelation that lies below the Lagrangian (zero delay) case for $n > 2$.   It lies well above for $n = 1$

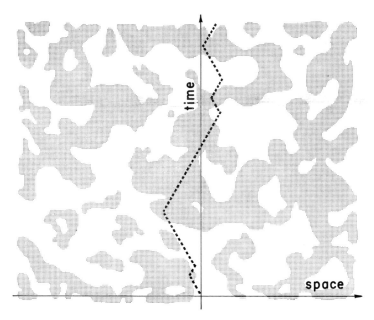

FIG. 18a. Qualitative sketch of walk with some "inertia" (Eulerian field same as Fig. 1).

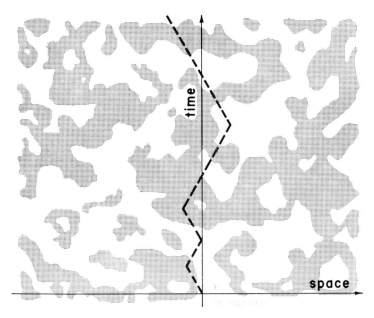

FIG. 18b. Qualitative sketch of walk with "inertia" twice as large as in Fig. 18a.

simply because the one-step zig-zag motion on the interfaces between the regions of positive and negative velocities is eliminated by the inertia. The integral scales of these two cases are equal.

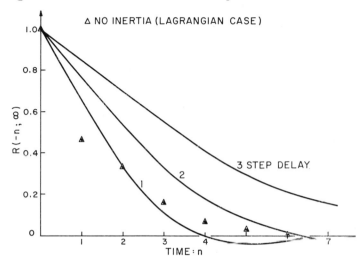

Fig. 19. Asymptotic Lagrangian velocity autocorrelation for walks with inertia (3 × 3 filter).

V. "SHOCK WAVES" AND THEIR COALESCENCE IN THE EULERIAN FRAME

Up to this point, we have studied the ensemble of trajectories of single particles departing from the identical space-time point in each ensemble of Eulerian fields. Some light is shed on the Eulerian fields by examining instead the trajectories of *all* "fluid material points," beginning at $t = 0$. A single realization is shown in Fig. 20. The dominant aspect of this collection of trajectories is their coalescence into "shock waves." After two particles come together, they see the same instructions on the field, and therefore they follow the same trajectory.[3] This is the most dramatic demonstration that we are dealing with a compressible motion.

[3] For people interested in the relative dispersion of two fluid points in turbulence, this statistical behavior is distressing: the mean square distance between two material points decreases with time instead of increasing. The $1 + 1$ dimensional game is apparently not relevant for the turbulent relative dispersion problem. At least two and possible three space dimensions will be required to achieve increasing separation with time. Two space dimensions are necessary also to permit a "constant density fluid." Aside from the vast increase in computing time this would bring, considerable complication is added by the application of the "incompressibility" condition to each realization.

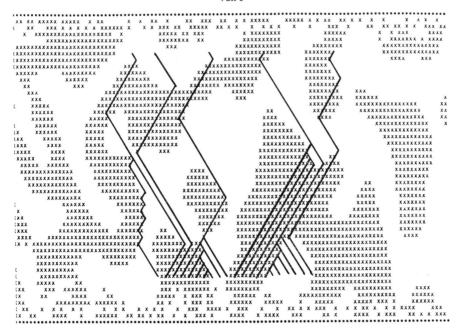

FIG. 20. Coalescence of trajectories in a typical one-dimensional binary velocity field.

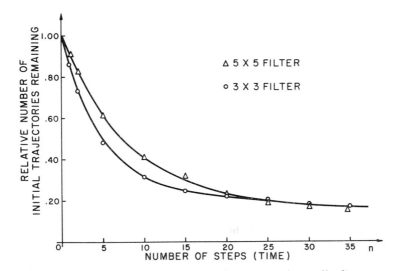

FIG. 21. Trajectories remaining after n steps (normalized).

For two different ensembles, a count was made of the relative number of distinct trajectories remaining after any number of steps, i.e., after any period of time.   This function is presumably some measure of the structure in the fields.   The results are shown in Fig. 21.   The data from the two different ensembles could be put into rough agreement by normalizing the time (number of steps) with some measure of the integral scale.

The shock coalescence phenomenon is distinctly reminiscent of that which occurs in random motions governed by the Burgers equation:

$$\frac{\partial u}{\partial t} + u\,\frac{\partial u}{\partial x} = \nu\,\frac{\partial^2 u}{\partial x^2}. \tag{30}$$

u is "velocity," ν is "kinematic viscosity."

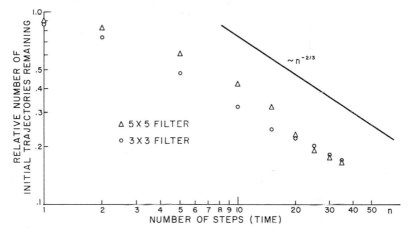

FIG. 22. Trajectories remaining after n steps (normalized).

He proposed it (Burgers, 1948) as a relatively simple model constraint to replace the Navier-Stokes equations in the study of random hydrodynamics, i.e., turbulence.   It is the Navier-Stokes equation for one-dimensional motion with the pressure gradient term omitted.   In a sense, therefore, it is a bit better model of shock wave development than of turbulence. In a lecture course on turbulence (Burgers, 1951), he made a simple estimate of the average number of shock waves remaining as a function of time, a quantity of the same type as that presented here for the walk on a random field in one space dimension.   His result was

$$N/N_0 \sim t^{-2/3}. \tag{31}$$

The experimental results of Fig. 21 have been replotted on log paper (Fig. 22) in order to bring out the power law behavior, if any.   The degree of agreement with Burgers' estimate for his model equation is noteworthy.

APPENDIX: METHOD OF GENERATION OF THE EULERIAN FIELDS

In order to generate Eulerian fields that were homogeneous in both space and time and had varying degrees of coherence, we began with a "completely random" binary field, and then operated on that with a spatial filter. Initial fields of size M by N were generated in which every possible configuration (2^{MN} in all) had equal probability of occurring.

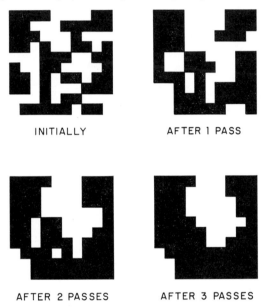

INITIALLY   AFTER 1 PASS

AFTER 2 PASSES   AFTER 3 PASSES

Fig. 23. Applying a 3 × 3 filter to a "completely random" field. (Only a portion of the field is shown.)

The correlation between any two lattice points is zero. A useable ensemble resulted by filtering each member of an ensemble of "completely random" fields with the same filter the same number of times.

The initial, equal probability, binary fields were generated from a sequence of 35 bit binary pseudo-random numbers where the ith member of the sequence was the product of the $(i-1)$ member and a "generator," 5^{15}. Only the least significant 35 bits of the 70-bit product were retained. However, 36 bits of the product (bits 16–51) were used to represent 36 realizations of the velocity (1 means $V = +1$, 0 means $V = -1$). MN members of the sequence were then used to generate 36 of the initial fields of size M by N. The use of 5^{15} as a pseudo-random number generator

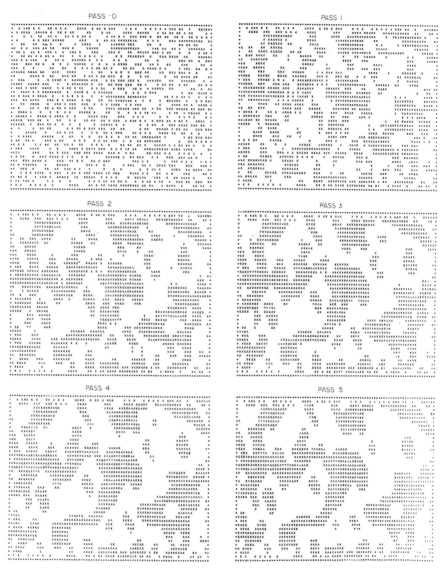

FIG. 24. Successive passes with a 3 × 3 filter on an 81 × 40 discrete binary velocity field (note "edge effect").

has been extensively tested, as was the use of more than one bit from the product (Patterson, 1966).

The spatial filtering was done by taking the arithmetic mean of a grouping of lattice points and assigning the value +1 or −1 to the velocity at the central location in the next generation of realizations.   This opera-

tion was repeated with the center point of the filter "window" set in turn on each point of each initial realization. This is illustrated with a 3 × 3 filter on a small sample realization in Fig. 23.

It is clear from this procedure that each time the filtering operation is performed an inhomogeneous edge effect diffuses further inward from the boundary. Care was taken to avoid this inhomogeneous region in performing the walks, and it is not shown in the figure.

Although we have not explored the question theoretically, there is some empirical indication that the filtered fields approach asymptotic states after several "passes" with the filter. Simple linear filters, as used in

TABLE I

THE FILTERS USED TO GENERATE EULERIAN FIELDS

	FILTER	POINTS USED IN AVERAGING	SHAPE
1	1 X 3	3	
2	3 X 3	9	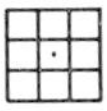
3	3 X 5	15	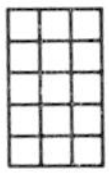
4	5 X 3	15	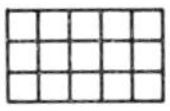
5	5 X 5	25	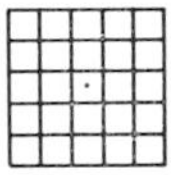
6	"CROSS"	9	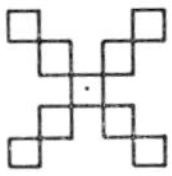
7	"PLUS"	9	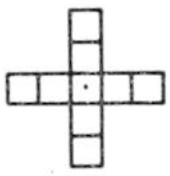
8	"TRIANGLE"	9	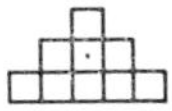
9	"TRIANGLE"	9	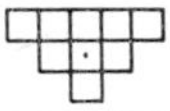

many electrical circuits, for example, change the function at each pass. Figure 24 is a photograph of a typical realization after increasing numbers of passes.

Table I illustrates the particular filter shapes used in generating ensembles for the experiments reported here. In each filter window, a dot denotes the lattice position at which the "average" is plotted in the output ("filtered") field. The first seven of these were computed sufficiently that

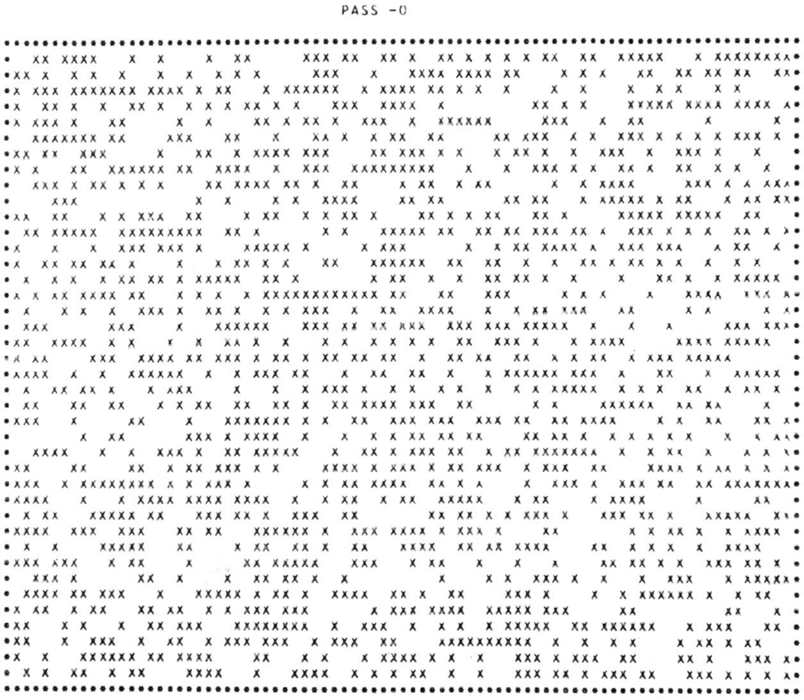

FIG. 25. A typical realization from each of several ensembles: (a) initial field, (b) 1 × 3 filter (see Table I, page 301), (c) 3 × 3 filter, (d) 3 × 5 filter, (e) 5 × 3 filter, (f) 5 × 5 filter, (g) "cross," and (h) "plus."

their Lagrangian integral scale values are included in Fig. 17. The remaining ones were carried out simply to see what sorts of Eulerian fields resulted. Figure 25 shows typical members of each of the first seven ensembles. All ensembles used for walking experiments were generated by only three passes with the appropriate filter in order to avoid too much shrinkage of the useable Eulerian space. All realizations shown in Fig. 25 began with the same "completely random" realization, shown as Fig. 25a.

Fig. 25b.

Fig. 25c.

FIG. 25d.

FIG. 25e.

Fig. 25f.

Fig. 25g.

FIG. 25h.

ACKNOWLEDGMENT

This work was supported by the Fluid Dynamics Branch, Office of Naval Research.

REFERENCES

BURGERS, J. M. (1948). A Mathematical Model Illustrating the Theory of Turbulence, *in* "Advances in Applied Mechanics" (R. von Mises and T. von Kármán, eds.), Vol. 1, p. 171. Academic Press, New York.

BURGERS, J. M. (1951). On Turbulent Fluid Motion. Report E-34.1, Hydrodynamics Lab., Calif. Inst. Tech., Pasadena, California, p. 125 et seq.

CORRSIN, S. (1962). Theories of Turbulent Dispersion, *in* "Mécanique de la Turbulence," p. 27. C.N.R.S., Paris.

CORRSIN, S. (1963). Estimates of the Relations between Eulerian and Lagrangian Scales in Large Reynolds Number Turbulence. *J. Atmos. Sci.* **20,** 115.

GOLDSTEIN, S. (1951). On Diffusion by Discontinuous Movements, and on the Telegraph Equation. *Quart. J. Mech. Appl. Math.* **4,** Pt. 2, 129.

KAMPÉ DE FÉRIET, J. (1939). Les Fonctions Aléatoires Stationnaires et la Théorie Statistique de la Turbulence Homogène. *Ann. Soc. Sci. Bruxelles* **59,** 145.

KENNEDY, D. A. (1965). Some Measurements of the Dispersion of Spheres in a Turbulent Flow. Dissertation for Ph.D. degree, The Johns Hopkins Univ., also *J. Fluid Mech.* (in press).

KRAICHNAN, R. H. (1964a). Relation Between Lagrangian and Eulerian Correlation Times of a Turbulent Velocity Field. *Phys. Fluids* **7,** 142.

KRAICHNAN, R. H. (1964b). Mixed Lagrangian-Eulerian Approach to Turbulent Dispersion. *Phys. Fluids* **7,** 1717.

LUMLEY, J. L. (1957). Some Problems Connected with the Motion of Small Particles in a Turbulent Fluid. Dissertation for Ph. D. degree, The Johns Hopkins Univ., Baltimore, Maryland.

LUMLEY, J. L. (1962). The Mathematical Nature of the Problem of Relating Lagrangian and Eulerian Statistical Functions in Turbulence, *in* "Mécanique de la Turbulence," p. 17. C.N.R.S., Paris.

LUMLEY, J. L. and CORRSIN, S. (1959). A Random Walk with Both Lagrangian and Eulerian Statistics. *Adv. Geophys.* **6,** also *in* "Proceedings of Symposium on Atmospheric Diffraction and Air Pollution" (F. N. Frenkiel and P. A. Sheppard, eds.), p. 179. Academic Press, New York.

PATTERSON, G. S., JR. (1966). Dissertation for Ph.D. degree, The Johns Hopkins Univ.

TAYLOR, G. I. (1921). Diffusion by Continuous Movements. *Proc. London Math. Soc.* **A20,** 196.

Investigations of Stability and

Transition in Rotating Boundary Layers

ALAN J. FALLER AND ROBERT E. KAYLOR

INSTITUTE FOR FLUID DYNAMICS AND APPLIED MATHEMATICS
UNIVERSITY OF MARYLAND
COLLEGE PARK, MARYLAND

The Ekman boundary layer is a rather simple example of a class of boundary-layer flows in which the direction of the flow varies with distance from the boundary. For this flow, we have identified two distinct modes of boundary-layer instability, each of which consists of two-dimensional roll vortices superimposed upon the basic boundary-layer flow. The first (type 1) have their axes oriented about 14° to the left of the direction of the basic flow, are stationary or nearly so, and have a relatively short wavelength. In the second (type 2), the angle observed is more variable and lies from 20° to the right to 5° to the left of the basic flow, the vortices move rapidly (dependent upon their orientation), and their spacing is two to three times that of the first type. From numerical integrations, it has been found that with no curvature to the basic flow type 2 has a lower critical Reynolds number, Re_c. The laboratory experiments, conducted in a cylindrical tank, indicate that curvature of the basic flow as measured by a Rossby number, Ro, inhibits both types of instability, but type 2 is more strongly affected. Consequently, four regimes of regular flow may be identified in the experimental results: completely stable, unstable to type 1, unstable to type 2, and unstable to both types of disturbances. Photographic examples of dye patterns in the various regimes illustrate each of the separate waves and their interaction when they occur simultaneously. The stationary type 1 disturbances have been observed to rather high values of Re without transition to turbulence. Although these vortices become somewhat irregular at large Re (e.g., three times the value at instability), the apparent transition to turbulence has not been observed except following incidence of the rapidly moving type 2 disturbances. Experiments similar to the flow over a rotating disk in a stationary fluid also have indicated that both types of waves exist in this boundary-layer flow, as well. Photographic examples of the simultaneous existence of the two wave types are suggestive that the rapidly moving type 2 waves, not identified in previous studies of rotating disk flow, are important for the transition to turbulence which is observed.

I. INTRODUCTION

When the equations of motion are written so that velocity is taken with respect to a rotating coordinate system, Coriolis accelerations appear as additional terms in the equations. Because many of the large-scale motions in the free atmosphere and in the oceans (far from the boundaries) are slow compared to the speed of rotation of the earth and are relatively steady, for many purposes it is possible to neglect the nonlinear inertial accelerations and the viscous forces compared to the Coriolis acceleration. The remaining terms in the equations represent hydrostatic balance (in the vertical direction) and a balance of the horizontal pressure gradient force with the Coriolis force. Meteorologists, oceanographers, and others concerned with geophysical fluid dynamics are accustomed to thinking in such terms and refer to this balanced state of motion, in which the velocity is normal to the horizontal component of the pressure gradient, as that of "geostrophic flow."

Near a horizontal boundary, e.g., the earth's surface or the bottom of the ocean, viscous stresses become important, and there is a component of flow toward low pressure. The flow changes both direction and speed with distance from the boundary and approaches geostrophic flow. This type of spiral boundary layer was first investigated by Ekman (1905) as an approximation of the wind drift in the surface layer of the oceans. His analytical solution (applicable to laminar flow or to a constant "turbulent viscosity") is referred to as the Ekman spiral or as Ekman boundary-layer flow. As may be seen from Fig. 1, the cross-stream component of the Ekman spiral has many characteristics in common with the boundary-layer flow over a rotating disk as well as with other secondary flows where the direction of the velocity changes with distance from the boundary. Because the Ekman spiral is a particularly simple example of rotating boundary-layer flows, it is suitable for theoretical studies of stability, and, indeed, it is easily generated in the laboratory for experimental investigation.

In an earlier study, laminar Ekman flow was found to be unstable above a critical value of a suitably defined Reynolds number, Re (Faller, 1963). The "preferred" unstable mode was identified as horizontal roll vortices superimposed upon the basic boundary-layer flow, an example of instability associated with the inflection in the profile of the component of flow normal to the bands (Fig. 1). Lilly (1966) has confirmed this fact through a numerical solution of the equivalent of the Orr-Somerfeld

equation, where he showed that the Coriolis forces are not very important for determination of the minimum Re nor for the general characteristics of the unstable motions. This result is in essential agreement with the earlier deduction of Barcilon (1965) for Ekman flow and of Stuart (Gregory et al., 1955) for the instability of flow over a rotating disk.

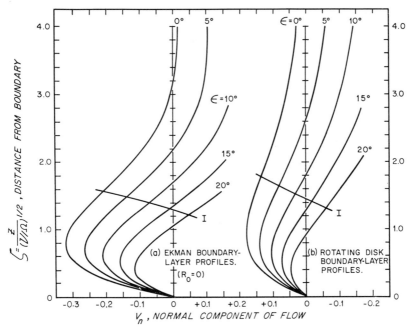

FIG. 1. Boundary-layer components of flow normal to the direction at angle ϵ with the tangential direction: (a) Ekman boundary-layer profiles for Ro = 0; (b) rotating disk boundary-layer profiles. Inflection points relevant to the type 1 instability are indicated by the curves I.

It now appears, however, that there is an additional mode of instability in which the Coriolis forces play an essential role. This mode was identified in the experimental studies (Faller, 1963), but, because of the apparent irregularity of its behavior, detailed studies of its characteristics were postponed. Lilly (1966) has now shown that this mode is similar to a viscous instability in the sense that a normally stabilizing influence (rotation) is the source of the instability through the action of the Coriolis forces. Moreover, both Lilly (1966) and the present authors (Faller and

Kaylor, 1966) have shown that this second mode (here designated as type 2) has a critical Re lower than was found for the mode previously described (type 1).   These modes of instability are variously referred to as waves, bands, vortices, or circulations, as may seem appropriate.   In this paper, experiments and numerical results illustrating the nature of the type 2 vortices as compared to those of type 1 are presented.

II. EXPERIMENTAL APPARATUS AND THE BASIC CIRCULATION

The experiment to which most of the observational results apply may be described most simply as a vortex flow in water generated by withdrawing fluid from the axis of a cylindrical rotating tank and resupplying

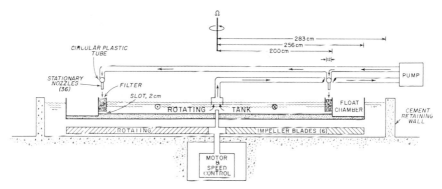

Fig. 2. A schematic diagram of the 4-meter rotating tank formerly in use at Woods Hole Oceanographic Institution for these studies.   Water was pumped from the center to the rim to generate a steady-state vortex flow.   The experiments illustrated in Figs. 3–6 were performed in this apparatus.

the fluid at the rim.   Figure 2 is a schematic diagram of rotating apparatus of this type formerly in use at the Woods Hole Oceanographic Institution. A smaller rotating tank with a similar pumping system is currently in use at the University of Maryland for these studies.

Under the conditions of these experiments, the unperturbed flow in the main body of the fluid is pure circular motion.   The radial flow that accomplishes the required steady-state transport from the rim to the center is confined to the thin boundary layer at the bottom of the tank.

NOMENCLATURE

S	forced flow rate in the Ekman boundary-layer experiments, $cm^3\text{-}sec^{-1}$
Ω	angular speed of the rotating tank, sec^{-1}
ν	kinematic viscosity, $cm^2\text{-}sec^{-1}$
$D = (\nu/\Omega)^{1/2}$	characteristic depth of rotating boundary layers, cm
z	vertical coordinate, dimensionless with respect to D
H	average depth of water, cm
V	theoretical tangential speed of the basic flow, $cm\text{-}sec^{-1}$
v_r	radial component of flow, dimensionless with respect to V
v_θ	tangential component of flow, dimensionless with respect to V
$Re = VD/\nu$	Reynolds number based on the tangential flow and the depth D
$Ro = V^2 r^{-1}/\Omega V$	Rossby number, the ratio of centrifugal to Coriolis accelerations
$\Delta\Omega$	change of angular speed of rotation, sec^{-1}
$L(1, 2)$	wavelength of the type 1 and type 2 instabilities, cm
$r_c(1, 2)$	critical radius at which instability was first observed, cm
ϵ	angle of the axes of unstable vortices, to the left of the tangential direction, deg

The boundary-layer thickness, as in other rotating systems, is characterized by the depth $D = (\nu/\Omega)^{1/2}$, where ν is the kinematic viscosity and Ω is the rotation rate of the tank. For the typical values $\nu = 0.01$ $cm^2\text{-}sec^{-1}$ and $\Omega = 1.0\ sec^{-1}$, we find $D = 0.1$ cm, a value small compared with the total depth of fluid, usually about $H = 20$ cm. If the pumping rate S is sufficiently slow, the basic flow is given by the equations of the Ekman spiral

$$v_\theta = 1 - e^{-z} \cos z \qquad (1)$$
$$v_r = e^{-z} \sin z \qquad (2)$$

where the velocity components v_θ and v_r and the height z have been made dimensionless with respect to the basic tangential flow V and the depth D, respectively. (Please refer to the Table of Nomenclature, above, for explanation of the nondimensionalization, and to previous publications for the derivation of these results.) The corresponding tangential flow above the boundary layer is given by

$$V = S/\pi r D. \qquad (3)$$

Note that, although this is a $Vr = $ const vortex, it does not correspond to conservation of angular momentum, since V is relative to the rotating tank. Note also that the entire radial dependence of the flow is determined by the requirement of a constant radial mass transport in the boundary layer. Therefore, since the boundary flow controls the entire

circulation, it should not properly be considered a secondary flow as such boundary currents are frequently designated.

At the rim, there is a thin vertical viscous boundary layer and a region in which the entering flow becomes adjusted to the balanced condition of Eq. (3). This region of adjustment is generally wide compared to the viscous boundary layer and may extend halfway or more to the center of the tank. Observations of the tangential flow have resulted in an empirical dependence of the width of the rim effect upon certain nondimensional parameters, and all observations quoted below either have been made outside the region of rim effect or the influence of the rim is specifically mentioned. Toward the center of the tank the vortex becomes intense, curvature of the flow is no longer negligible, and Eqs. (1)–(3) become less satisfactory approximations.

Ignoring the influence of side walls and regarding the depth of water as essentially infinite, the independent parameters of this problem are only ν, Ω, and S. It follows that some dependent variable, say r_c, the critical radius at which instability occurs, may be expressed by

$$r_c = f_0(\nu, \Omega, S). \tag{4}$$

From these four variables, we form the following two independent non-dimensional numbers: the Reynolds number at the critical radius, $\mathrm{Re}_c = S/(\pi r_c \nu)$, and the Rossby number at the critical radius, $\mathrm{Ro}_c = S/(\pi r_c^2 (\Omega \nu)^{1/2})$. It follows that expression (4) may be written as $\mathrm{Re}_c = f_1(\mathrm{Ro}_c)$. Similarly, any property of the flow may be expressed as some function of Re and Ro where $\mathrm{Re} = S/\pi r \nu$ and $\mathrm{Ro} = S/\pi r^2 (\Omega \nu)^{1/2}$. In the region where Eq. (3) is valid, it follows that $\mathrm{Re} = VD/\nu$, a Reynolds number based upon the basic flow V and the Ekman depth D. In the same way, $\mathrm{Ro} = V^2 r^{-1}/\Omega V$, the ratio of the centrifugal and Coriolis accelerations. Hence, Ro may be interpreted as a measure of the influence of the curvature of the flow in the cylindrical tank, and for $\mathrm{Ro} = 0$ we would have straight geostrophic flow with the pure Ekman spiral boundary layer. But, regardless of the adequacy of Eqs. (1)–(3) as approximate expressions for the flow, Re and Ro are suitable nondimensional parameters that characterize the circulation apart from the influence of the vertical boundaries.

The method of observation of instability was to sprinkle crystals of potassium permanganate dye into the tank near the rim. The crystals fell to the bottom, and in the region of laminar flow near the rim they gave off plumes of dye which flowed inward and merged into a thin sheet of dye at the bottom of the Ekman layer (Fig. 3). When instability occurred, usually within some critical radius r_c, the dye assumed a banded

FIG. 3. An example of type 1 instability. Conditions: $S = 568$ cm^3-sec^{-1}, $\Omega = 0.0273$ sec^{-1}, $\nu = 1.11 \times 10^{-2}$ cm^2-sec^{-1}, $H = 25$ cm. Results: $r_c = 130$ cm, Re$_c = 126$, Ro$_c = 0.614$, $L = 13D$. The circles are at radial intervals of 20 cm.

structure that indicated organized regions of horizontal convergence and divergence at the bottom of the boundary layer. An example of these may be seen in Fig. 3 within the radius $r_c = 130$ cm.

III. EXPERIMENTAL RESULTS

Two general types of banded disturbances have been found. The waves designated type 1 were stationary, or nearly so, and were quite reproducible in all respects. These had a band spacing $L(1) = 11D$ and occurred above Re = 130 with a slight dependence of Re$_c$ upon Ro$_c$. They were oriented approximately 14° to the left of the tangential direction with a standard deviation of spread of angle of 2.5°. The type 2 waves seemed to occur sporadically and move rapidly, and their wavelength was two to three times that of the type 1 waves. The radius at which they were first observed was not always well defined, their range of

angle was from 5° to the left of the tangential direction to 20° to the right, and there was no clear relation between the observed values of Re_c and Ro_c nor between any other nondimensional combination of parameters that was tried.

The type 1 waves already have been considered in some detail (Faller, 1963; and Faller and Kaylor, 1966), and several photographic examples

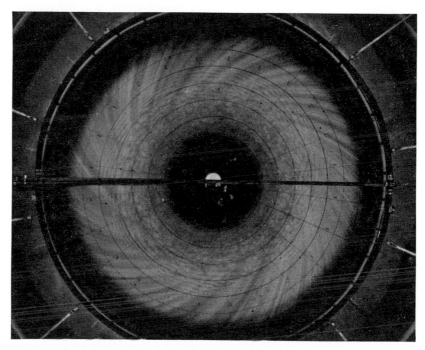

Fig. 4. An example of type 2 instability and turbulence. Conditions: $S = 694$ cm³-sec⁻¹, $\Omega = 0.510$ sec⁻¹, $\nu = 1.16 \times 10^{-2}$ cm²-sec⁻¹, $H = 18$ cm. Results: $r_c = 140$ cm, $Re_c = 136$, $Ro_c = 0.146$, $L = 25D$. Turbulence appears to begin at $r_t = 100$ cm, $Re_t = 190$.

of these have been presented. Figure 3 is an example of type 1 waves where the depth of the boundary layer was quite large and the bands had a proportionately large spacing. In that experiment, even though the type 1 waves became somewhat irregular at large Re (near the center of the tank), there was no evidence of the type 2 waves as just described.

In Fig. 4, only type 2 waves appear. These may be recognized as such by their orientation and by their relatively large spacing, which in this example averaged $L(2) = 25D$. Figures 5 and 6 are examples of the

simultaneous occurrence of both types. The interference patterns of the two sets of vortices is particularly evident in Fig. 6, where the type 1 vortices were established before those of type 2. In Fig. 5, both banded structures are first apparent at about the same radius, but the type 2 bands dominate the pattern.

Here it is pertinent to clarify the uncertainty in the method of observation of the two forms of instability, i.e., by dye introduced into the boundary layer. For the experiment of Fig. 6, dye dissolved from crystals near the rim showed only the type 1 bands. The type 2 bands were clearly observed (as in Fig. 6) only after a solution of dye was injected into the inflowing water near the rim so that dye extended through the entire depth of the boundary layer. Thus, the advantages of dye in showing the spatial pattern of flow may sometimes be offset by the selectivity that occurs due to its distribution. It is clear from elementary considerations that rapidly moving vortices would not distort a thin layer of dye close to the boundary to the same extent as would stationary vortices. The relative distortion of the dye would depend upon other factors as well, including the ratio of the depth of the dye layer to D. Because of uncertainties such as these, it is realistic to assume that the true critical radius of instability was always larger than that for which regular bands were observed.

Figure 7 is a diagram of observed Re_c versus Ro_c for the type 2 waves. [Note that the definition of Ro used here is twice the value as previously defined (Faller, 1963).] The points V represent valid observations, the points X are those in which the waves first appeared within the influence of the rim, and the points D are those cases in which it was not clear whether type 1 waves were becoming irregular or whether type 2 waves were forming. Open circles are experimental points where no waves of type 2 were observed. The dashed line is a regression line through the points of instability for the type 1 waves (Faller, 1963), but the solid line for the type 2 waves is an envelope of the observed points. The envelope is preferred because of the lesser reliability of observation of the type 2 waves as just noted. In particular, the points X in comparison to the points V indicate that the effect of the rim was to delay the onset of instability significantly. This is in qualitative agreement with the fact that the tangential flow near the rim was always less than the balanced flow given by Eq. (3).

The two straight lines in Fig. 7 define four regions corresponding to stability or instability of the two distinct modes. These two lines extrapolated to $Ro_c = 0$ show that for linear Ekman flow the type 2 waves are unstable at a significantly lower value of Re, approximately $Re_c = 70$. This is in agreement with our numerical integrations of the equations of

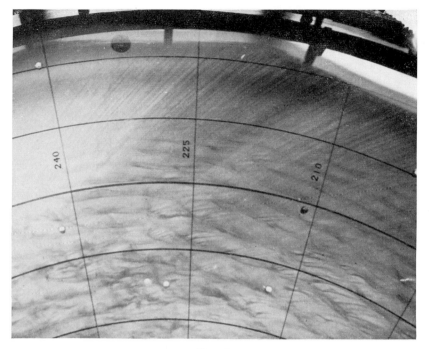

Fig. 5.

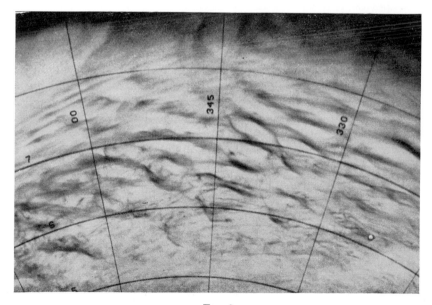

Fig. 6.

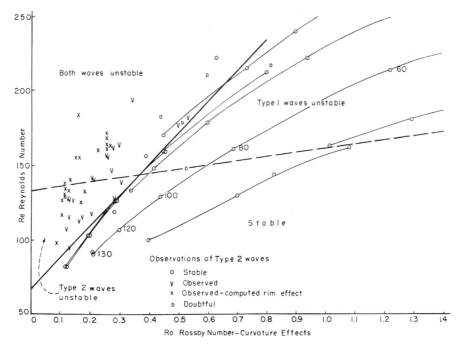

FIG. 7. Observations of Re$_c$ versus Ro$_c$ for the type 2 waves. The dashed line is a regression line for observations of the type 1 waves. The solid line is an envelope of observations of the type 2 waves. The curves connect points for experiments in which no type 2 waves were observed. On one of these curves, the radii (centimeters) in the 200-cm radius tank are denoted to show the simultaneous variation of Re and Ro with radius.

motion (Faller and Kaylor, 1966) and with Lilly's numerical solutions of the eigenvalue problem for the linearized perturbation equations (Lilly, 1966), both of which give the minimum critical value Re$_c$ = 55.

FIG. 5. An example of type 2 instability with intermittent type 1 bands. Conditions: $S = 836$ cm^3-sec^{-1}, $\Omega = 0.465$ sec^{-1}, $\nu = 1.19 \times 10^{-2}$ cm^2-sec^{-1}, $H = 23$ cm. Results: r_c (both instabilities) = 180 cm, Re$_c$ = 124, Ro$_c$ = 0.110, $L(1) = 10D$, $L(2) = 28D$. Band spacings were measured close to r_c. The spacings at lesser radii were quite variable.

FIG. 6. An example of the simultaneous occurrence of type 1 and type 2 instabilities. Conditions: $S = 872$ cm^3-sec^{-1}, $\Omega = 0.249$ sec^{-1}, $\nu = 1.16 \times 10^{-2}$ cm^2-sec^{-1}, $H = 8.0$ cm. Results: $r_c(1) = 180$ cm, Re$_c(1) = 133$, Ro$_c(1) = 0.160$, $L(1) = 11D$; $r_c(2) = 164$ cm, Re$_c(2) = 145$, Ro$_c(2) = 192$, $L(2) = 31D$.

IV. IRREGULARITIES AND APPARENT TURBULENCE

In each case shown, the type 2 waves are regularly spaced and are at a fairly large angle to the basic flow. These are some of the better examples of the type 2 waves and do not illustrate the irregularity and the uncertainty of angle and spacing that were often encountered. The numerical results show that the values of L and ϵ for instability are not sharply defined, and as a result one might expect some variability of these observed quantities according to the perturbations present in the initial flow field. For example, when the type 1 waves were already well established before the occurrence of the type 2 variety (at large Ro), there seemed to be a tendency for the type 2 waves to occur more parallel to the basic flow or even at positive angles. In those cases, it seemed that the type 2 waves were strongly influenced by the prior occurrence of the type 1 waves, both in angle and wavelength. The "doubtful" cases in Fig. 7 are examples where this selection seemed to be effectual and where it was not clear whether type 2 instability was occurring or the type 1 waves were becoming irregular.

The question of transition to turbulence is particularly interesting in this experiment because of the possibility that the interaction of the two types of waves may be an essential mechanism for transition. [Some of the extensive debate on this subject with respect to the transition of Blasius flow has been reviewed by Hama and Nutant (1963).] Figure 3 is an example where only type 1 bands were observed because of large Ro and where they persisted in a fairly regular form to values of Re as large as 500 or more. It was clear in those cases that the dye was confined to the boundary layer and gave no indication of turbulence, even though the bands became somewhat irregular and transient. Unfortunately, the lack of an observable transition could have been associated with some other stabilizing effect at large Ro as well as the mere absence of the type 2 waves.

In the experiments of Figs. 4–6, the bands of dye which indicated the type 2 waves became disorganized and indicated the probable existence of turbulence well below Re = 200. Again it is tempting to assume that transition was brought about by the interaction of the two wave systems. However, the arrangement of dye into an apparently disorganized pattern does not necessarily indicate turbulence, since a superposition of two vortices, one stationary and the other moving, could lead to a complex dye pattern without significant dynamical interaction. A definitive

investigation of the mechanism of transition will require extremely well-controlled experiments and careful observations, but the possibility of systematically producing two distinct wave systems for transition studies is an intriguing one. Further comments on transition, for the flow over a rotating disk, are given in Section VI.

V. NUMERICAL RESULTS

Our numerical studies have extended the experimental data to give quantitative patterns of the circulations in the vortices and their interactions with the basic Ekman flow. In brief, the method has been to solve the Navier-Stokes equations numerically for a uniform fluid as an initial value problem under the assumption that the flow was independent of the x-coordinate, taken along the axes of the cells. This permitted a reduction of the equations of motion and continuity to two equations, one for vorticity in a vertical plane normal to the axes of the vortices, and one for the component of flow normal to this plane. Conditions of the problem were no slip at the lower boundary, no stress at the upper boundary, periodicity at the side boundaries of the grid, and an applied horizontal pressure gradient. The corresponding initial basic flow was an Ekman spiral with geostrophic flow above the boundary layer. The complete initial conditions consisted of the basic flow plus a perturbation that varied from random numbers on the grid to various organized patterns of flow contrived to resemble the anticipated solution. The only difference due to different initial conditions was the length of time required for transient motions to dissipate.

The data presented here are for steady-state finite-amplitude solutions at Re = 150. Figure 8 corresponds to type 1 waves with a wave length $L = 11D$ and $\epsilon = 14°$. Figure 9 corresponds to type 2 waves with $L = 24D$ and $\epsilon = -15°$. In each case, the grid extended vertically to twice the height shown in the figures, and the development of the vortices could not have been severely limited by the upper boundary.

From Figs. 8 and 9, it is apparent that at Re = 150 (Ro = 0) the type 2 vortices are significantly more intense than those of type 1. This is in agreement with the experimentally observed fact that for small Ro the type 2 waves definitely predominated (Figs. 4–6), and it is in accord with the numerical results that the minimum critical Re is much lower for the type 2 instability.

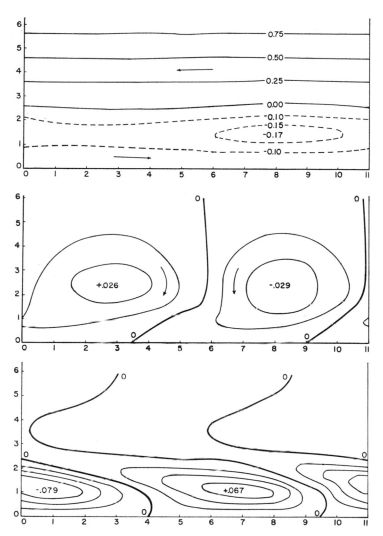

FIG. 8. Results of a numerical integration of the equations of motion for Ekman boundary-layer instability. These patterns correspond to the type 1 vortices for $\epsilon = 14°$, $L = 11D$, and Re = 150, and the pattern is stationary. The total stream function in the plane normal to the axes of the vortices (upper). Departure of the stream function from its horizontally averaged value (middle). The component of flow, u, along the axes of the vortices; departure from the horizontal mean (lower).

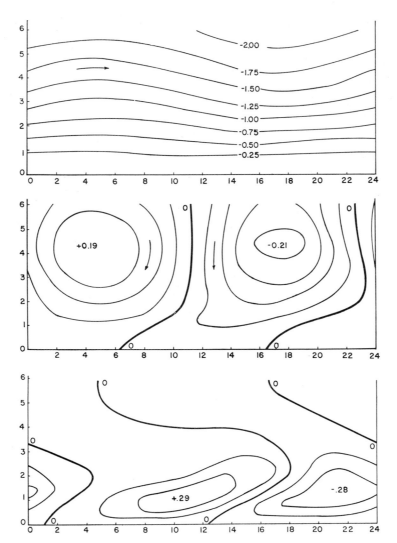

Fig. 9. Results of a numerical integration of the equations of motion for Ekman boundary-layer instability. These patterns correspond to the type 2 vortices for $\epsilon = -15°$, $L = 24D$, and Re $= 150$, and the patterns move to the right at the phase speed $v_n = 0.41$ (dimensionless). The total stream function in the plane normal to the axes of the vortices (upper). Departure of the stream function from its horizontally averaged value (middle). The component of flow u along the axes of the vortices; departure from the horizontal mean (lower).

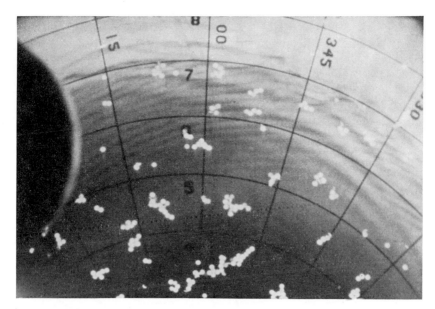

FIG. 10.

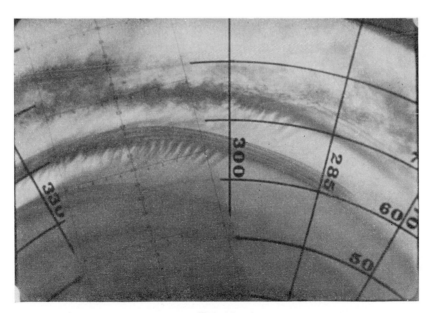

FIG. 11.

VI. INSTABILITY OVER A ROTATING DISK

Because of the similarity of the Ekman spiral flow and that due to a rotating disk, it is interesting to inquire whether both types of instability also occur in the latter case. The experiments of Gregory *et al.* (1955) clearly demonstrated an inflectional instability equivalent to the type 1 vortices, but their technique of observation did not allow the detection of a rapidly moving mode. By changing the rate of rotation of a cylindrical tank of water, it is a relatively simple matter to study the profile of flow due to a rotating disk and, indeed, to make a continuous transition to the Ekman spiral.

Although there are transient boundary-layer circulations when the speed of the tank is altered, these have a time scale of the order of Ω^{-1}, so that after 1 rev most of the transients have disappeared. There is also the transient response of the main body of the fluid with the characteristic time $(H/D)\Omega^{-1}$, where H is the total depth of fluid. Therefore, by making H/D large, there can be a time interval of several revolutions during which the tangential flow is relatively constant and the boundary-layer flow is correspondingly steady.

For this experiment, we define Re and Ro as before: $\mathrm{Re} = VD/\nu$ and $\mathrm{Ro} = V^2 r^{-1}/\Omega V$. Because of a change of rotation speed, the relative tangential speed is $V = -\Delta\Omega r$, so that we obtain $\mathrm{Re} = |\Delta\Omega r/(\Omega\nu)^{1/2}|$ and $\mathrm{Ro} = -\Delta\Omega/\Omega$, where Ω is taken as the rotation rate after acceleration, and Re is always considered to be positive. For increasing Ω, the boundary-layer flow is radially outward, and instabilities are easily observed by injecting dye near the axis of rotation, although the same difficulties as before, concerning the distribution of dye in the boundary layer, are encountered.

FIG. 10. An example of the simultaneous appearance of both type 1 and type 2 instabilities. Circles in the photograph are at 10-cm intervals. White spots are paper disks used to indicate the motion at the free surface. Conditions: $\Omega_1 = 0.624$ sec^{-1}, $\Omega_2 = 1.100$ sec^{-1}, $\Delta\Omega = 0.476$ sec^{-1}, $\nu = 0.948 \times 10^{-2}$ cm^2-sec^{-1}, $H = 12$ cm. Results: $r_c(1) = 45$ cm, $\mathrm{Re}_c(1) = 210$, $L(1) = 15D$; $r_c(2) = 50$ cm, $\mathrm{Re}_c(2) = 234$, $L(2) = 38D$.

FIG. 11. An example of the type 2 bands, the gill-type instability, and transition to turbulence in the case of acceleration from rest, the equivalent of the rotating disk experiment. Conditions: $\Omega_1 = 0$, $\Omega_2 = 0.325$ sec^{-1}, $\nu = 0.99 \times 10^{-2}$ cm^2-sec^{-1}, $H = 15$ cm. Results: $r_c(2) < 40$ cm, $\mathrm{Re}_c(2) < 230$, $L(2) = 44D$; $r_c(g) = 62$ cm, $\mathrm{Re}_c(g) = 356$, $L(g) = 7D$. Transition to turbulence followed soon after the appearance of the gill instability at approximately $\mathrm{Re}_t = 400$.

These experiments are still in the preliminary stage, but there is rather definite evidence of the existence of both instabilities from Ro = −1.0 (the rotating disk in a stationary fluid) to Ro = 0 (the Ekman boundary layer) and into the range of positive Ro. Figure 10 shows a single frame (selected from a ciné film) that contains a clear example of the simultaneous existence of both instabilities for Ro = −0.433. This photograph was taken 1.32 rev after acceleration of the tank, and it may be assumed that transient boundary-layer processes were not an important factor for the observed pattern. Moreover, both types of bands persisted for several revolutions, although the type 2 bands were somewhat obscured at later stages in the experiment. Detailed data on the two instabilities are given in the figure legend.

Figure 11 is a particularly interesting experiment for Ro = −1.0, acceleration from rest, the equivalent of a rotating disk in a stationary fluid. There the type 2 bands were quite regular until their disruption by turbulence. Inspection of the ciné films shows clearly that turbulence in the type 2 bands quickly followed the appearance of a small-scale structure, referred to as "gills," between the bands. In Fig. 11, the left-hand portion of the outer type 2 band is almost completely disorganized by turbulence, whereas some of the gills still may be seen to the right of center. Across the middle of Fig. 11 the gills appear along the entire left side of the band. From one band to another, there was some variation of the exact radius at which the gills appeared, presumably caused in part by the dye distribution and in part by true variations in their occurrence. The gills clearly were not the same phenomenon as the type 1 instability. For the rotating disk, the type 1 bands have a wavelength $L(1) = 22D$ compared to the gill spacing $L(g) = 7D$ and compared to the type 2 bands, $L(2) \approx 44D$. In addition, the gills formed nearly perpendicular to the type 2 bands, but, because of differential shearing motions associated with circulations in the type 2 vortices, they were rapidly advected and distorted.

We do not have numerical solutions for the flow over the rotating disk, but the solutions for the Ekman boundary layer (Fig. 9) may serve to illustrate some of the characteristics of the type 2 vortices and the distribution of dye within them. Figure 12 is the total stream function corresponding to Fig. 9a but with the average horizontal speed of the type 2 vortices subtracted out so that the pattern represents the flow relative to the moving vortices. Since Fig. 12 is a stationary stream-line pattern, it can be used to determine trajectories of fluid particles. In particular, dye that does not significantly diffuse will remain confined between streamlines. The hatched area of Fig. 12 denotes the probable distribution of dye (that is, confined mostly to the closed streamlines)

after the vortices have moved from the source of dye. We believe that the large bands of dye in Fig. 11 correspond to the hatched area of Fig. 12 and that the gills are an instability at very low levels which converge dye from the very bottom of the boundary layer. From the ciné films, it is clear that the gill-type bands represent an instability of the total flow produced by the interaction of the type 2 vortices and the mean flow. The gill instability in turn appears to interact with the type 2 vortices (and the mean flow) to lead directly to the chaotic motions of turbulence.

The type 1 vortices seem to have had no role in the transition pictured in Fig. 11. In fact, they were not observed at all in that experiment since transition to turbulence had already occurred below the critical

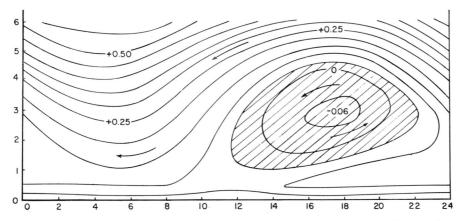

FIG. 12. The pattern of stream function for type 2 vortices corresponding to the upper part of Fig. 9 but with respect to the moving vortices. The phase speed of the vortices, $v_n = 0.41$, was subtracted from the upper part of Fig. 9 to obtain this stationary pattern. The hatched area represents the region of retention of dye by the rapidly moving vortex.

value of Re for the type 1 instability. However, if the rotating disc experiment is performed so as to carefully minimize disturbances, as reported by Gregory et al. (1955) and as confirmed in our studies, the type 1 bands are the first to be observed while the type 2 bands and transition occur at greater Re. Accordingly, finite disturbances seem to be necessary in order to produce the type 2 instability at low Re.

The requirement of finite disturbances in the flow for observations of the type 2 vortices at low Re suggests 3 possible interpretations: (1) the disturbances affect the distribution of dye and render the type 2 vortices more readily visible; (2) the type 2 vortices result from a finite-amplitude instability; or (3) the rapidly moving type 2 vortices require a finite

initial perturbation in order to grow to observable amplitude before they have moved radially too far out.   The first suggestion is rendered invalid from the observations that transition may be accelerated or retarded according to the presence or absence of disturbances, and transition is dependent upon the amplitude of the type 2 vortices but not upon the dye distribution.   In all probability we may dismiss the argument for a finite-amplitude instability by reference to the numerical solutions for the Ekman boundary layer since there it was found that both types of instability could be grown from computer round-off error.   It is not likely that there is a substantial difference in the rotating disc and the Ekman boundary layers in this respect since experimentally, the latter showed the same type of dependence of the type 2 bands upon finite disturbances (Faller and Kaylor, 1966).   On the other hand, the numerical results show that the type 2 vortices may move several times their wavelength during the characteristic time period for their growth by the factor e. Therefore, the level of perturbations at the true critical radius should be a governing factor for the radius at which the vortices are first observable. It follows that in experiments where great care is taken to provide smooth initial conditions the type 1 vortices may reach finite amplitude before the appearance of finite type 2 disturbances, and in such a case the mechanism of transition may be significantly different from that pictured in Fig. 11.

VII. CONCLUDING REMARKS

Clarification of the respective rolls of the two types of instability of the basic flow will require further well-controlled experiments.   Clearly, there would be considerable advantage in an observational technique that did not require the introduction of foreign material into the boundary layer, but the use of dye or a similar tracer has unique advantages in its ability to show patterns of flow in a rather simple way.

From the preceding examples of instability, we may draw some tentative conclusions.   First, two distinct types of shear-flow instability occur generally in rotating boundary layers, and the large, rapidly moving type 2 vortices are unstable at Reynolds numbers lower than for the commonly observed stationary waves.   This is certainly the case for the Ekman boundary layer, as indicated both by the experiments and by the numerical results, and seems to be true for the flow over a rotating disk as well.

Second, because the type 2 waves move rapidly, they may or may not be observable in any given situation.   Their relative importance will depend upon the amplitudes of perturbations which excite this mode of

instability, their radial phase speed, the radial gradient of Re, and their growth rate. It has been observed for the flow over a rotating disk that delay in the attainment of finite-amplitude of the type 2 vortices allows the type 1 bands to appear first and probably makes a significant difference in the detailed mechanism of transition to turbulence.

Third, when the type 2 vortices attain finite amplitude before the type 1 mode becomes important (as for the case in Fig. 11), the combined circulation of the basic flow and the type 2 vortices becomes unstable to a small-scale mode, referred to here as gills. The gill-type instability then interacts with the previously established flow to produce an abrupt transition to turbulence. On the other hand, when the type 1 vortices reach finite amplitude at lower Re than those of type 2, it appears that transition to turbulence occurs in a less dramatic fashion from interaction of the two independent modes of instability of the basic flow. From these results, we infer that other boundary-layer flows may have similar uncertainties in the mechanism of transition according to the nature and magnitude of perturbations in the basic flow.

Acknowledgment

The research reported here has been supported in part by the National Science Foundation under Grant NSF-GP-3443. Computer time for the numerical studies was made available by the Computer Science Center of the University of Maryland under NASA Research Grant NsG-398.

References

Barcilon, V. (1965). Stability of a Non-Divergent Ekman Layer. *Tellus* **17**, 53–68.

Ekman, V. W. (1905). On the Influence of the Earth's Rotation on Ocean Currents. *Arkiv Mat. Ast. Fysik.*, **2**, No. 11.

Faller, A. J. (1963). An Experimental Study of the Instability of the Laminar Ekman Boundary Layer. *J. Fluid Mech.* **15**, 560–576.

Faller, A. J. and Kaylor, R. E. (1966). A Numerical Study of the Instability of the Laminar Ekman Boundary Layer. *J. Atmospheric Sci.* **23**, No. 5 (Sept.).

Gregory, N., Stuart, J. T., and Walker, W. S. (1955). On the Stability of Three-Dimensional Boundary Layers with Application to the Flow Due to a Rotating Disc. *Phil. Trans. Roy. Soc. London* **A248**, 155–199.

Hama, F. R. and Nutant, J. (1963). Detailed Flow-Field Observations in the Transition Process in a Thick Boundary Layer *in* "Proceedings of the 1963 Heat Transfer and Fluid Mechanics Institute" (Roshko, Bradford, and Bartz. eds.). Stanford Univ. Press, Stanford, California.

Lilly, D. K. (1966). On the Instability of Ekman Boundary Flow. *J. Atmospheric Sci.* **23**, No. 5 (Sept.).

SECTION V

Theoretical Plasma Physics

edited by

D. A. TIDMAN

Resistive Instabilities in Toroidal Hydromagnetic Systems[1]

RUSSELL M. KULSRUD

PRINCETON PLASMA PHYSICS LABORATORY
PRINCETON UNIVERSITY
PRINCETON, NEW JERSEY

The general behavior of hydromagnetic systems to the interchange instability with and without resistivity is discussed. The remarks are illustrated on a model system which, it is felt, is typical.

I. INTRODUCTION

The purpose of this paper is to discuss a situation in which the inclusion
of even a small resistance of a plasma makes a drastic change in its
stability from that of a zero resistance plasma. The situation considered
is basically the so-called min-B system in a torus or minimum $\bar{B}$ systems.
The instability in question is the interchange instability.

Toroidal magnetic devices for confining hot plasma are almost all
unstable to some extent to the interchange instability. This is an instability that effectively interchanges two magnetic tubes of force of equal
flux as well as the plasma contained in them. If such an interchange can
be carried out, it will be stable if, and only if, the volume containing
higher pressure plasma is larger [1], at least near the plasma boundary.
(Internally the change in volume must be less than the change in $p^{1/\gamma}$
where γ is the ratio of specific heats.) Since for a sufficiently small
β plasma, where β is the ratio of plasma pressure to magnetic pressure,
the magnetic field energy is essentially unperturbed, this gives a necessary
and sufficient stability condition at low β for the interchange instability
on the basis of zero-resistivity equations. For a closed device such as a
torus, the volume per flux is given by

$$U = \int dl/B \tag{1}$$

where the integral is taken along a magnetic line of force. [If the line

---

[1] This work is essentially a summary of the material included in more detail in
Paper CN 21/113 of the Proceedings of the International Conference on Plasma
Physics and Controlled Nuclear Fusion at Culham, England, 1965.

closes on itself, the integration path is simply the closed line of force.   If
the line does not close on itself but instead ergodically covers a magnetic
surface, one should replace the line integral by the limit $(1/n) \int dl/B$
taken over a length of the line n times around the torus as n goes to
infinity.   This limit is $dV/d\Psi$, where V is the volume and Ψ the flux
inside a magnetic surface.   Since only relative variations of U are important, these definitions are not critical.]   In terms of U, the criterion for
stability against the interchange is simply

$$\delta U \, \delta p > 0 . \tag{2}$$

For nonclosed lines, the criterion is $(dp/d\Psi) \, d^2V/d\Psi^2 = p'V'' > 0 .$

Since most simple confinement schemes fail to satisfy criterion (2),
the method employed until recently to obtain stability against the interchange was to prevent it from occurring by shearing the lines of force.
Thus, a pure interchange could not occur without perturbing the lines of
force, which leads to a stabilizing action.   It was shown that in toroidal
systems such as the stellarator one could achieve sizable β's that were
stable if one assumed that the plasma was described sufficiently well by
equations assuming zero resistivity [2].   This was felt to be a satisfactory
assumption because the resistive time scale was of the order of the classical
diffusion time scale,

$$\tau_{\mathrm{class}} = 4\pi a^2/\beta\eta \tag{3}$$

where a is the radius of the plasma and η the resistivity, and it was felt
that instabilities on such a slow time scale would be unimportant.   However, it was shown by Furth et al. [3] that such an expectation was unjusti-
fied and that the interchange could take place on such a small length
scale that resistance would be important on seriously short-time scales.
Thus, the results of Johnson et al. [2] were thrown in doubt, and one could
not be sure that sheared magnetic fields would give a sufficient stability.

However, shortly afterward, it was shown by Furth and Rosenbluth
[4] that one could find closed systems for which criterion (2) for stability
against the interchange was satisfied, and thus the other line of attack
against it could be pursued.   Still, the first systems of Rosenbluth and
Furth were rather complicated, and therefore it was of interest that
Lenard [5] and Johnson [6] were able to achieve a significant simplication
by considering systems with nonclosed lines of force.   These systems are
referred to as negative V'' systems.   (It should be mentioned that, so far,
these systems are not closed in any physical sense, but are all straight
systems with the closure obtained mathematically by identifying the two
ends mathematically, as in Ref. [2].)   Building on these systems, Furth
and Rosenbluth [7] were able to find systems of greater simplicity, whereas

the simplest of all so far was achieved by Taylor [8] and independently by Yoshikawa [9]. The last system is actually a torus and is physically closed.

The closed systems are stable if U is a maximum on the line of maximum pressure, the magnetic axis. If U is regarded as a harmonic average of B, i.e., $U = L/\bar{B}$, then the latter statement is equivalent to $\bar{B}$ being minimum on the magnetic axis. This condition is analogous to the condition for an open-ended system such as a mirror machine of the Ioffe type, namely, that B be a minimum at the center of the machine [10]. It is the very encouraging experimental results on long confinement in such systems that have stirred such great interest in the corresponding closed systems, although no successful test in a toroidal system has yet been carried out.

II. THE PHYSICAL PICTURE

Equation (2) is the condition for small-β intrinsic stability of a closed system. However, for $\beta > 0$, this condition is only necessary. What happens to these systems when $\beta > 0$?

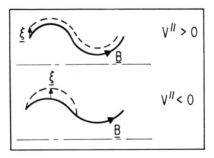

FIG. 1. The interchange for $\eta = 0$. The system is represented by a single line of positive and negative curvature. For the upper curve, the average curvature is unstable, and the line is displaced uniformly to the dashed line by the interchange. For the lower curve, the average curvature is stable, and only the unstable part of the line is displaced.

We consider systems where the magnetic lines of force have no shear. The situation is illustrated in Fig. 1. First set η, the resistivity, equal to zero. We represent the systems by a curved line of force whose average curvature toward axis of the plasma we imagine to be positive if V'' is, and negative if V'' is. For $V'' > 0$, the perturbation is uniform along the line as indicated in the top picture. ξ is the displacement of the plasma,

and the dashed line represents the displaced line of force.   For $V'' < 0$, the perturbation concentrates in the bad region of positive curvature of the line to the extent that the material can bend the lines.   This is the ballooning mode, and it is clear there will be a competition between the plasma forces attempting to carry out an interchange and the magnetic forces from the bent lines so that a β_c exists for this mode, where β_c is the critical value β for stability with $\eta = 0$.

Now let $\eta > 0$, $\beta < \beta_c$.   Then the corresponding situation for the $V'' < 0$ system is shown in Fig. 2.   There are two cases according to whether the growth rate of the instability is fast compared to the reciprocal

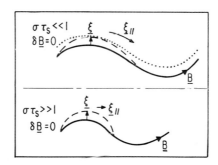

FIG. 2. The interchange for $\eta \neq 0$, $V'' < 0$. σ is the growth rate, and τ_s $= L/(\text{velocity of sound})$. For the lower curve, the sound speed is slow so that the displacement can be localized to the unstable part of the line. For the upper curve, the sound speed is large, and, although the perturbation would like to carry out the displacement leading to the dashed line, the sound wave spreads it out to the dotted line. In both cases, the line of force is relatively undisplaced, the plasma crossing it by finite resistivity.

of the time for a sound wave to travel between the two regions, i.e., whether $\sigma\tau_s \gg 1$, or not, where σ is the growth rate, $\tau_s = L/(\text{velocity of sound})$, and L is the length of the region of positive curvature.   If $\sigma\tau_s \gg 1$, then the perturbation takes the form shown in the lower part of Fig. 2. Because $\eta > 0$, matter crosses the lines and δB, the perturbed magnetic field, is small, although the lines are bent slightly.   The growth rate is determined by the rate at which material can cross lines.   The flow of matter along lines is relatively small because $\sigma\tau_s \gg 1$.

The other limiting case, $\sigma\tau_s \ll 1$, is shown in the top picture.   Here the flow along the lines is fast.   This flow tends to even out ξ along a line of force, so that the dashed displacement of the ordinary resistive ballooning mode should be replaced by the dotted one.   Since $V'' < 0$, the situation is intrinsically stable, and the sound wave leads to stability. Thus, no slow unstable mode satisfying $\sigma\tau_s \ll 1$ is possible.   However,

Rosenbluth *et al.* [11] have shown that the stabilization by flow along lines is too strong, and one gets overstability, σ having a large oscillatory part so that $\sigma\tau_s$ is not small for this overstability.   It is possible that the sound wave could be Landau damped, restoring stability if the mean free path for ion-ion collisions is as large as L.

These pictures represent the physical conclusions of this paper, and I turn now to describe the calculation I made to justify them.

III. THE MATHEMATICAL ANALYSIS

In this calculation, a specific magnetic configuration was analyzed rather than simply one in which the curvature of the line is replaced by merely a periodic gravitational field.   The system analyzed was the negative V'' configuration of Johnson [6].   Since β is small, one can specify this system by giving the vacuum magnetic field

$$\mathbf{B} = \mathbf{B}_0 + B_0 \nabla \phi \tag{4}$$

where

$$\phi = \frac{\epsilon_1}{h + \gamma} I_1[(h + \gamma)r] \sin (u - hz) + \frac{\epsilon_3}{h + 3\gamma} I_3[(h + 3\gamma)r] \sin (3u - hz)$$
$$+ \delta_2 \gamma r^2 \sin 2u , \tag{5}$$

$$u = \theta - \gamma z . \tag{6}$$

A small pressure with a parabolic profile is added to this field.   The configuration is a long straight system with the ends identified (thus representing the toroidal curvature), and it consists of a uniform magnetic field plus three small-amplitude helical fields with periods arranged to beat against each other to produce a negative value of V''. ϵ_1, ϵ_3, and γ are small quantities.   The magnetic surfaces are given by $\psi = $ const, where

$$\psi = \frac{\gamma r^2}{2} (1 - 2\Delta \cos 2u) , \tag{7}$$

$$\Delta = \frac{\delta_2 + h\epsilon_1\epsilon_3/32\gamma}{1 - h\epsilon_1^2/8\gamma} , \tag{8}$$

and are of elliptical cross section.   These are also the surfaces of constant plasma pressure.   The well depth for U (the relative variation of U from the axis to the plasma radius a) is

$$\frac{\Delta U}{U} = \frac{h^2 a^2}{8(1 - 4\Delta^2)^{1/2}} \left(2\epsilon_1^2 + \Delta \epsilon_1 \epsilon_3 + \frac{32\gamma^2 \delta_2^2}{h^2} \right) \tag{9}$$

and can be made negative if ϵ_1 and ϵ_3 have opposite signs.

The stability of this system from the ideal fluid equations with resistivity was analyzed in a manner similar to that previously used in showing the shear stabilization of helical fields [2]. These equations are

$$(\nabla \times \delta B) \times B + j \times \delta B + \nabla(\xi \cdot \nabla p + \gamma p \nabla \cdot \xi) = \rho \sigma^2 \xi, \quad (10)$$

$$\delta B = \nabla \times (\xi \times B) - \frac{\eta c}{4\pi\sigma} \nabla \times (\nabla \times \delta B), \quad (11)$$

$$Q = \nabla \times (\xi \times B). \quad (12)$$

Equation (10) is simply the perturbed force equation, B and δB are the equilibrium and perturbed magnetic field, respectively; j, p, and ρ are the equilibrium current, pressure, and density; γ is the ratio of specific heats; σ the growth rate (so that $\delta B \sim \exp \sigma t$), and ξ the displacement of the plasma. The first two terms in Eq. (10) are the perturbed magnetic force, whereas the next two are the perturbed pressure force. The right-hand side is the inertial term. δB is found from solving Ohm's Law, which can be written as Eq. (11).

These equations were solved in three cases: (a) For $\eta = 0$, σ was set equal to 0 to obtain the zero resistivity β_c. (b) For $\eta \neq 0$, $\sigma\tau_s \gg 1$, the inertia along the lines is large and one can have any perturbed force parallel to B balanced by this inertia. Thus we drop the parallel part of Eq. (10). This leads to the so-called resistive ballooning mode. (c) For $\eta \neq 0$, $\sigma\tau_s \ll 1$, the inertia is small, and the parallel force must vanish. Thus the parallel part of Eq. (10) must be satisfied with $\sigma = 0$. (In all three cases, the perpendicular part of the inertia can be neglected as small.)

These equations were reduced to an ordinary differential equation for the equilibrium of Eq. (5) in the limit of large m, the azimuthal mode number. Surprisingly, in all three cases one gets essentially the same eigenvalue equation with different eigenvalues, namely,

$$(dy^2/du^2) + \alpha g(u)y = 0, \quad (13)$$

where u is defined by Eq. (6); the derivative is taken along a line of force; y is any perturbed quantity; the function $g(u)$ is related to U by

$$U = \text{const} + (\psi/2B_0) \int g \, du \quad (14)$$

and represents the curvature of the line; and α is the eigenvalue that is different in the three cases. Its value is given in Table I in the three cases.

The results of a rough solution of Eq. (13) are, for $\eta = 0$,

$$\beta_c \approx \frac{\pi^2}{2L^2} \frac{a^2}{(\delta U/U)_{\text{bad}}}. \quad (15)$$

TABLE I

THE EIGENVALUE α

	$\eta = 0$	$\eta \neq 0,\ \beta < \beta_c$
$\sigma\tau_s \gg 1$	β_c	$m^2\beta\eta/4\pi a^2\sigma$
$\sigma\tau_s \ll 1$	—	β

It is seen that β_c depends on L and $(\delta U/U)_{\text{bad}}$, where the subscript "bad" indicates that in evaluating U and δU by Eq. (1) the integral is taken only over the region of unstable curvature, that is, the length and well depth of the bad region. For $\eta \neq 0$, the growth rate of the resistive ballooning mode can be expressed in terms of the classical diffusion time if $\sigma\tau_s \gg 1$,

$$\sigma = m^2/\beta_c\tau_{\text{class}}. \tag{16}$$

If $\sigma\tau_s \ll 1$, the growth rate is zero, but, as mentioned in Section II, this case is impossible, and one has an overstability instead.

In conclusion, we find that by choosing $(\delta U/U)_{\text{bad}}$ and L small enough β_c can be made significantly large, and this is actually the case for the Johnson system. The resistive ballooning mode is the worst instability. The growth time of the resistive ballooning mode for $\beta < \beta_c$ can be made a sufficiently large fraction of the classical diffusion time to be useful experimentally if m is not much larger than 10, but an upper limit to m can only be found by going to a more sophisticated treatment of the plasma than the fluid Eqs. (10) and (11).

IV. CONCLUSION

Although the problem considered, namely, the stability of a given class of systems against the interchange instability, is rather specific, certain general features emerge which I believe are typical of the stability of all toroidal hydromagnetic systems:

First, the interchange of lines of force will always try to occur. Furthermore, certain parts of a line will be unstable, whereas other parts will not.

Now if the average curvature is unstable, the situation is intrinsically unstable. In this case, shear will inhibit the instability, but even a small resistance will weaken the shear effect so that stability achieved by shear is doubtful.

On the other hand, if the average is stable, then the stability is reduced to a question of the connection between these two regions. We can

distinguish two subcases.   If β is large, the plasma can bend lines and the connection is poor.   Thus a critical β exists even for $\eta = 0$.   If β is small, the plasma cannot bend the lines but can cross them by finite resistivity. That is, resistivity weakens the connection, and an instability occurs at the rate at which matter can cross lines.   However, the connection is restored by the flow of sound waves along lines of force, but these can lead to overstability unless Landau damped.

It seems clear that the final resolution of the question of stability will hinge on the question of the connection of the good and bad regions.

ACKNOWLEDGMENT

This work was supported under the auspices of the U.S. Atomic Energy Commission, Contract No. AT(30-1)-1238.

REFERENCES

1. Bernstein, I. B., Frieman, E. A., Kruskal, M. D., and Kulsrud, R. M., *Proc. Roy. Soc. (London)* **A244,** 17 (1958); also Longmire, C. I. and Rosenbluth, M. N., *Ann. Phys.* **1,** 120 (1957).
2. Johnson, J. L., Oberman, C. R., Kulsrud, R. M., and Frieman, E. A., *Phys. Fluids* **1,** 281 (1958).
3. Furth, H. P., Killeen, J., and Rosenbluth, M. N., *Phys. Fluids* **6,** 459 (1963).
4. Furth, H. P. and Rosenbluth, M. N., *Phys. Fluids* **7,** 764 (1964).
5. Lenard, A., *Phys. Fluids* **7,** 1875 (1964).
6. Johnson, J. L., *Phys. Fluids* **7,** 2015 (1964).
7. Furth, H. P. and Rosenbluth, M. N., *Bull. Am. Phys. Soc.* **10,** 198 (1965).
8. Taylor, J. B., *Phys. Fluids* **8,** 1203 (1965).
9. Yoshikawa, S., private communication.
10. Gott, Y. B., Ioffe, M. S., and Telkovsky, V., *Nucl. Fusion Suppl.* **3,** 1045 (1962); also Taylor, J. B., *Phys. Fluids* **7,** 767 (1964).
11. Furth, H. P., Killeen, J., Rosenbluth, M. N., and Coppi, B., Paper CN 21/106, *Proc. Intern. Conf. Plasma Phys. Controlled Nucl. Fusion,* Culham, England (1965).

The Physical Foundations of Modern Kinetic Theory

G. SANDRI

AERONAUTICAL RESEARCH ASSOCIATES OF PRINCETON, INC.
PRINCETON, NEW JERSEY

Modern kinetic theory is based on a physical analysis of systems describing many interacting particles which is markedly different from the classical (Boltzmann) analysis. The classical analysis of Boltzmann is based on the notion that collisions are sharply localized in space and time, a picture well suited to hard molecules. The modern development emphasizes, instead, the sharp separation that exists between the time scale over which purely dynamical phenomena occur and the much longer time scale over which statistical phenomena develop. In this paper, we first show that the gaseous regimes are characterized by the two dimensionless parameters ϕ_0/kT and nr_0^3 (ϕ_0 and r_0 are the depth and range of the interparticle potential, k is Boltzmann's constant, T the kinetic temperature, and n the mean density of the gas). After a review of the modern theories of irreversibility, we show, by a physical analysis of the basic gaseous regimes, that the Liouville equation, in a particularly suitable form (the BBGKY hierarchy), is best interpreted in terms of the time scales appropriate to the system. We conclude by a brief summary of the kinetic equations that result from a systematic expansion in the ratio of the time scales and compare the various forms that appear in the literature. The state of the art is surveyed by comparing the various expansion techniques currently employed and by reviewing the recent developments in the N-body problem for hard spheres.

I. THE PHYSICAL REGIMES OF GAS THEORY

A. Introduction

The purpose of nonequilibrium statistical mechanics is to determine the time evolution of systems that contain a large number of particles. The behavior of systems over long periods of time is of particular interest. We believe, in virtue of Gibbs' general H-theorem [1], that almost all isolated systems will tend to thermodynamic equilibrium. We are interested, therefore, in obtaining solutions of the fundamental equations of motion which are valid for times comparable to that needed for the system to reach thermodynamic equilibrium. As a consequence, the irre-

versible behavior of the system has to play a very prominent role in the discussion of nonequilibrium statistical mechanics.

The description of systems that are not in thermodynamic equilibrium requires probing into the microscopic structure of the macroscopic portion of matter under consideration. It is our task to deduce the behavior of a large aggregate of particles starting from the laws of motion for the particles themselves. To make the deductive procedure more transparent, we shall review the phenomenological description of macroscopic portions of matter. This description is based on the most general laws applicable, that is, the conservation laws (for particles, momentum, and energy).

Consider as a simple example a system consisting of identical particles totally isolated from the rest of the world. In particular, consider a system that is in thermodynamic equilibrium so that we can characterize all of its possible states by means of the two independent state variables N and T, defined as follows

$$N = \int M_0(\mathbf{v}) \, d\mathbf{v} \tag{1.1}$$

$$T = \frac{2}{3Nk} \int \frac{mv^2}{2} M_0(\mathbf{v}) \, d\mathbf{v} \tag{1.2}$$

where

$$M_0(\mathbf{v}) = \frac{N}{(2\pi RT)^{3/2}} \exp\left\{ -\frac{v^2}{2RT} \right\}$$

In Eq. (2),[1] N is the number density of the gas and $(\frac{3}{2}RT)$ is the mean kinetic energy of a particle in the gas. The reference frame for the gas, described by Eqs. (1) and (2), is the one in which the gas, as a whole, is at rest. The laws of thermodynamics govern the transition among equilibrium states.

B. Nonequilibrium Descriptions

1. *Fluid Mechanical.* In order to consider nonequilibrium situations, we shall have to generalize our description of the system. The characterization of the thermodynamic equilibrium states, in terms of density and kinetic energy, is so fundamental that it is useful to characterize the nonequilibrium states in terms of density and kinetic energy as well.

In the equilibrium state, the gas is spatially homogeneous. The simplest generalization of this situation arises when there are small spatial inhomogeneities. The state of a slightly inhomogeneous gas is charac-

---

[1] Equations referred to in the text will be denoted by the equation number only (no section number) if the equation appears in the same section. The full equation number is employed only when the equation referred to appears in another section.

terized by local thermodynamic equilibrium, and the fundamental variables N, T, and $\mathbf{u}$ are functions of position and time:

$$N(\mathbf{x}, t) = \int M(\mathbf{v}) \, d\mathbf{v} \tag{1.3}$$

$$T(\mathbf{x}, t) = \frac{2}{3kN(\mathbf{x}, t)} \int \frac{m(\mathbf{v} - \mathbf{u})^2}{2} M(\mathbf{v}) \, d\mathbf{v} \tag{1.4}$$

$$\mathbf{u}(\mathbf{x}, t) = \frac{1}{N(\mathbf{x}, t)} \int \mathbf{v} M(\mathbf{v}) \, d\mathbf{v} \tag{1.5}$$

where

$$M(\mathbf{v}) = \frac{N(\mathbf{x}, t) \exp\{-[\mathbf{v} - \mathbf{u}(\mathbf{x}, t)]^2/[2RT(\mathbf{x}, t)]\}}{[2\pi RT(\mathbf{x}, t)]^{3/2}}$$

The equations governing the behavior of N, T, and $\mathbf{u}$ must guarantee the conservation of number of particles, the conservation of momentum, and the conservation of energy for nonreacting isolated systems. When there are several species present and transformations among the species are possible, the particle number for each species is not necessarily conserved, but the electronic charge and the "baryon" number, i.e., the number of heavy particles such as protons and neutrons, must always be conserved. (We exclude the extraordinary circumstances that might occur during gravitational collapse [2].) The conservation laws for particle number, momentum, and energy are guaranteed if the rate of change of N, T, and $\mathbf{u}$ are in the form of an appropriate divergence. The equation

$$(\partial N/\partial t) + \nabla \cdot (N\mathbf{u}) = 0 \tag{1.6}$$

expresses the conservation of particles, whereas

$$\rho(\partial \mathbf{u}/\partial t) + \rho(\mathbf{u} \cdot \nabla)\mathbf{u} = -\nabla \cdot \mathbf{P} \tag{1.7}$$

and

$$\rho(\partial T/\partial t) + \rho(\mathbf{u} \cdot \nabla)T = -(2/3k)[\nabla \cdot \mathbf{q} + \mathbf{P} : \nabla \mathbf{u}] \tag{1.8}$$

express, respectively, the conservation of momentum and energy. Two new quantities have been introduced; the pressure tensor $\mathbf{P}$ and the heat flow vector $\mathbf{q}$. They can be expressed, by means of the molecular distribution function $F^1(\mathbf{v})$, as the mean transfer of momentum and kinetic energy:

$$\mathbf{P} = m \int \mathbf{c} \mathbf{c} F^1(\mathbf{v}) \, d\mathbf{v} \tag{1.9}$$

$$\mathbf{q} = \int \frac{mc^2}{2} \mathbf{c} F^1(\mathbf{v}) \, d\mathbf{v} \tag{1.10}$$

where $\mathbf{c} = \mathbf{v} - \mathbf{u}$.

Although the conservation laws require that N, T, and $\mathbf{u}$ satisfy Eqs. (6)–(8), it is the specific task of nonequilibrium statistical mechanics to establish the precise forms of $\mathbf{P}$ and $\mathbf{q}$ *as functions* of only N, T, and $\mathbf{u}$ so that Eqs. (6)–(8) form a closed set of equations for the desired variables. The lowest-order results of nonequilibrium statistical theory in powers of the density coincide with the nonequilibrium thermodynamic results, i.e. [3],

$$\mathbf{P}_{ij} = \delta_{ij} NkT - \mu(\nabla_i u_j + \nabla_j u_i - \tfrac{2}{3}\nabla_\kappa u_\kappa) \qquad \text{(Navier-Stokes law)} \quad (1.11)$$

$$\mathbf{q} = -\kappa \nabla T \qquad \text{(Newton-Fourier law)} \qquad (1.12)$$

The statistical theory is required in addition to specify the transport coefficients of viscosity μ and of conductivity κ as functions of T for a given molecular interaction.

The foregoing results are valid for a single component gas, but analogous expansions can be given for the variables that characterize a non-reacting mixture [4]. An example of the utility of the statistical non-equilibrium theory was the prediction by Enskog of the phenomenon of thermal diffusion which led to the very useful technique of isotope separation extensively used for U^{235} separation during World War II.

2. *Kinetic.* A description of the gas which is more detailed than the one afforded by the states of local thermodynamic equilibrium (described by the fluid-mechanical equations) is needed if one wants to obtain the temperature dependence of the transport properties (μ, κ). We shall return to their density dependence shortly. From Eqs. (9) and (10), it is clear that a knowledge of the molecular distribution function (or the "one-particle" distribution) F^1 is needed. F^1 is the density of particles in the one-particle phase space (or μ-space) [5]; consequently, F^1 is a function of the position $\mathbf{x}$ and the velocity $\mathbf{v}$ of a typical particle as well as a function of the time. The states that can be fully characterized by $F^1(\mathbf{x}, \mathbf{v}, t)$ will be called states of "kinetic equilibrium." The conservation laws for states of kinetic equilibrium are satisfied if F^1 obeys the equation of continuity in μ-space:

$$(\partial F^1/\partial t) + \nabla \cdot (\mathbf{v} F^1) = -\nabla_\mathbf{v} \cdot \mathbf{J} \qquad (1.13)$$

where $(-\nabla_\gamma \cdot \mathbf{J})$ represents the net loss of particles in a region of μ — space from a cause other than the flow of particles (e.g., collisions).

The density, energy, and momentum content of a kinetic state is completely determined by F^1 through the relations

$$N = \int F^1(\mathbf{v})\, d\mathbf{v}, \qquad \mathbf{u} = \frac{1}{N} \int \mathbf{v} F^1(\mathbf{v})\, d\mathbf{v}$$

$$T = \frac{2}{3Nk} \int \frac{m(\mathbf{v} - \mathbf{u})^2}{2} F^1(\mathbf{v})\, d\mathbf{v} \qquad (1.14)$$

Equation (14) represents the appropriate generalizations to the kinetic equilibrium states of the corresponding thermodynamical variables given in Eqs. (1) and (2).

The current $\mathbf{J}$ can be written in terms of the mean acceleration $\mathbf{a}$ due to all the particles in the system acting on the typical one under consideration, i.e.,

$$\mathbf{J} = \mathbf{a}F^1 \tag{1.15}$$

The task of nonequilibrium statistical mechanics is to determine the quantity $\mathbf{a}$ (or $\mathbf{J}$) as a functional of F^1. The equation

$$(\partial F^1/\partial t) + \nabla \cdot (\mathbf{v}F^1) = -\nabla_\mathbf{v} \cdot \mathbf{J}[F^1] \tag{1.16}$$

is then a closed equation for F^1. Equation (16) is called, following Bogolubov [6], a kinetic equation.

It is shown that, in lowest order in powers of the density, the appropriate equation is the Boltzmann equation [7]:

$$\frac{\partial F^1(\mathbf{v}_1)}{\partial t} + \mathbf{v}_1 \cdot \nabla F^1(\mathbf{v}_1) = \int d\mathbf{v}_2 |\mathbf{v}_1 - \mathbf{v}_2| \sigma \, d\Omega [F^1(\mathbf{v}_1{}^*)F^1(\mathbf{v}_2{}^*)$$
$$- F^1(\mathbf{v}_1)F^1(\mathbf{v}_2)] \tag{1.17}$$

where σ is the differential collision cross section and $d\Omega$ the solid angle of scattering. The final velocities $\mathbf{v}_1{}^*$, $\mathbf{v}_2{}^*$ in the two-body scattering process are related by energy-momentum balance and the force law to the initial velocities $\mathbf{v}_1$ and $\mathbf{v}_2$.

In higher orders, the statistical theory should give not only the temperature dependence of the transport coefficients but also their density dependence. It is a general consequence of the Boltzmann equation, Eq. (17), that the transport coefficients are density independent ("Maxwell's law"). This fact is well verified experimentally for dilute gases. (The discrepancies between theory and experiments are typically less than 10% [4, 8, 9].) On the other hand, for "dense gases" the measured transport properties are dependent on the density as well as on the temperature. It is a major open problem of nonequilibrium theory to determine the density dependence of the transport properties and the value of the "bulk viscosity" (which vanishes identically if the Boltzmann equation is used). The density dependence of the transport properties and the determination of the bulk viscosity are three-body effects; that is, they represent the statistical average of interactions among three bodies in the gas.

In order to give a logical derivation of three-body effects, it is imperative that three-particle correlations be determined. Since the equation of Boltzmann corresponds to the statistical account of only two-body collisions (two-particle correlations), determining three-particle correla-

tions is tantamount to calculating the quantity $\mathbf{J}$ to higher order in the density.

For gases that contain more than a single species and for which chemical reactions are possible, the statistical theory of the three-body effects will yield the rates of chemical reactions. The practical importance of these quantities is considerable. We can say, in fact, that the problem of determining three-body effects and, therefore, three-body correlations is the major open problem of nonequilibrium statistical mechanics.

3. *Beyond Kinetic.* In the foregoing, we considered situations that are removed from thermodynamic equilibrium and that require a more detailed description of the gas than equilibrium requires. Systems that are even farther from equilibrium can be considered. For systems that are not adequately characterized by the behavior of one typical particle in the system, that is, systems for which kinetic equilibrium is not a sufficiently detailed description, one can consider "pair kinetic" equilibrium [10]. Such a description corresponds to states that can be described by the two-particle distribution function F^2, that is, states adequately characterized by the behavior of a typical pair of particles. The conservation principles prescribe again the general form of the equation satisfied by $F^2(\mathbf{x}_1, \mathbf{v}_1, \mathbf{x}_2, \mathbf{v}_2, t)$:

$$(\partial F^2/\partial t) + (\mathbf{v}_1 \cdot \nabla_1 + \mathbf{v}_2 \cdot \nabla_2)F^2 + \nabla_{12}U_{12} \cdot (\nabla_{\mathbf{v}1} - \nabla_{\mathbf{v}2})F^2$$
$$+ \nabla_{\mathbf{v}1} \cdot (\mathbf{a}_1 F^2) + \nabla_{\mathbf{v}2} \cdot (\mathbf{a}_2 F^2) = 0 \qquad (1.18)$$

where U_{12} is the two-particle interaction potential and $\mathbf{a}_i$ the mean acceleration imparted to particle i ($i = 1$ or 2) by all other particles in the system.

A more detailed description of the gas can be obtained in terms of the "master functions" $\varphi(\mathbf{p}_1 \ldots \mathbf{p}_r, \mathbf{x}_1 \ldots \mathbf{x}_s)$ which give the probability distribution for the momenta of r and the positions of s particles (r is not necessarily the same as s) [11–13]. The equation for φ, when expressed in terms of φ alone, is known as the master equation. In general, one may consider a definite subsystem of the entire ensemble and study the evolution for its probability distribution Ψ [12, 14–16].

We have seen how the basic conservation laws allow for the construction of increasingly more detailed descriptions of the system under consideration, leaving at every stage the "accelerations" of the corresponding moments as phenomenological quantities. It is the task of statistical mechanics to deduce the precise nature of these acceleration terms. Below, the theory that is the basis of the deductive process is reviewed. The only phenomenological feature that remains is the two-body potential.

It is worth emphasizing that the inductive approach leads rigorously to

the density hierarchy (BBGKY hierarchy) discussed in the next section. That is, if the particles of the system interact via the two-body potential U_{12}, it can be shown without difficulty that

$$\mathbf{a}F_1 = \frac{1}{m} \int dx_2 \, d\mathbf{v}_2 (\mathbf{\nabla}_{12} U_{12}) F_{12}, \qquad \mathbf{a}_i F_{12} = \frac{1}{m} \int dx_3 \, d\mathbf{v}_3 (\mathbf{\nabla}_{i3} U_{i3}) F_{123}$$

($i = 1$ or 2). A similar construction applies to the higher F^s functions. This result allows for the identification of the F^s functions of this section with the D^s functions of the next section.

C. The Liouville Theorem and the BBGKY Hierarchy

The starting point of the deductive theory is the Liouville theorem. (We are confining ourselves for simplicity to classical systems [17].) This theorem allows for a compact representation of the motion of N particles. It is readily shown that, for a system of particles interacting via a central two-body force, the motion in the phase space of the entire system (Γ-space) is that of an incompressible fluid. The Liouville theorem, in fact, states that

$$\frac{dD^N}{dt} = 0 = \frac{\partial D^N}{\partial t} + \sum_{i=1}^{N} \dot{\mathbf{x}}_i \cdot \frac{\partial D^N}{\partial \dot{\mathbf{x}}_i} + \sum_{i=1}^{N} \dot{\mathbf{p}}_i \cdot \frac{\partial D^N}{\partial \mathbf{p}_i} \tag{1.19}$$

where D^N is the probability distribution for N particles. A system of particles interacting via a two-body potential $U_{ij} = U(|\mathbf{x}_i - \mathbf{x}_j|)$ satisfies Newton's laws of motion,

$$\dot{\mathbf{x}}_i = \mathbf{v}_i, \qquad \dot{\mathbf{p}}_i = - \sum_{\substack{i=1 \\ j \neq i}}^{N} \nabla_i U_{ij} \tag{1.20}$$

Substituting Eq. (20) into Eq. (19), we can write the Liouville equation in the form

$$(\partial D^N / \partial t) + H^N D^N = 0 \tag{1.21}$$

where

$$H^N = K^N - I^N \tag{1.22}$$

and

$$K^s = \sum_{i=1}^{s} \mathbf{v}_i \cdot \nabla_i \tag{1.23}$$

$$I^s = \sum_{1 \leq i \leq j \leq s}^{s} I_{ij} \tag{1.24}$$

$$I_{ij} = \nabla_i U_{ij} \nabla_{\mathbf{v}i} + \nabla_j U_{ij} \cdot \nabla_{\mathbf{v}j}$$

For N finite, the Liouville equation is invariant under time reflection and time translations (or under reversal of the motion), and the characteristics associated with it exhibit finite Poincare recursion time. These two properties give rise, respectively, to the two pivotal conceptual problems of nonequilibrium statistical mechanics, Loschmidt's Umkehreimwand, and Zermelo's Wiederkehreinwand so excellently analyzed in the Begrifflichegrundlagen of Ehrenfest [5].

The modern view of D^N is that it describes a statistical ensemble of systems that are identical to each other in all dynamical aspects but differ in the initial conditions.

The probability interpretation of D^N hinges on the following three basic properties:

(1)   Symmetry: D^N is completely symmetric under the interchange of two (identical) particles.

(2)   Normalization: the normalization at $t = 0$ is preserved by the Liouville equation for all time.

(3) $D^N \geq 0$ at all points of phase space, a property that is again preserved in the course of time because of the Liouville equation.

As we emphasized at the beginning of this discussion, the two most important characteristics of a gas are its density and its temperature, i.e., kinetic energy. Although it is clear from dimensional considerations that the temperature must enter the Liouville equation (the interaction term contains the potential energy), the role of the density is considerably less clear. The mean density of the gas is given by

$$n = N/V \tag{1.25}$$

where N is the number of particles and V is the volume of the box that contains the gas.

Bogolubov [6], Born and Green [18], Kirkwood [19], and Yvon [20] made an important transformation of the Liouville equation, known as the BBGKY hierarchy, which allows us to make explicit the dependence of the distribution functions on both the density and the temperature of the gas. We introduce the "reduced" distributions

$$D^s = \int D^N \, d\Gamma_{N-s} \tag{1.26}$$

with the phase space measure

$$d\Gamma_{N-s} = \sum_{i=s+1}^{N} \frac{d\mathbf{x}_i}{V} \, dp_i$$

In virtue of the corresponding properties of D^N, the function D^s can be interpreted as the probability distribution for a cluster of s of the N particles in the box. It is, in fact, easy to prove from Eq. (26) and the properties of D^N that (1) D^s is fully symmetric under interchange of identical particles; (2) D^s is normalized to unity; (3) $D^s \geq 0$ for all times; and also (4) the important recursion relation: D^s can be deduced, by integration, from any D^t, $t > s$, i.e.,

$$D^s = \int D^t \left(\frac{d\mathbf{x}_{s+1}}{V} \, d\mathbf{p}_{s+1} \right) \left(\frac{d\mathbf{x}_{s+2}}{V} \, d\mathbf{p}_{s+2} \right) \cdots \left(\frac{dx_t}{V} \, d\mathbf{p}_t \right)$$

As a consequence of the Liouville equation for D^N, the set of functions D^s satisfies the coupled set of equations given in Eq. (27):

$$\frac{\partial D^s}{\partial t} + H^s D^s = \frac{N - s}{V} L^s D^{s+1} \tag{1.27}$$

where L_s is the linear phase mixing operator defined by

$$L^s = \sum_{i=1}^{s} L_{i,s+1} \tag{1.28}$$

$$L_{i,s+1} = \int d\mathbf{x}_{s+1} \, d\mathbf{v}_{s+1} \, \nabla_i U_{i,s+1} \cdot \nabla_{v_i}$$

We can now perform the limit (which we call the "bulk limit")

$$N \rightarrow \infty, \qquad V \rightarrow \infty, \qquad n \text{ fixed} \tag{1.29a}$$

The limit in Eq. (29a) guarantees that the Poincare recursion time tends to infinity

$$T_P \rightarrow \infty \tag{1.29b}$$

so that the dynamical system is no longer recursive. The limit in Eq. (29a) is applied to Eq. (27). The terms in Eq. (27) are then made dimensionless with respect to the following three parameters: the range r_0 of the two-body potential as the unit of length, the depth ϕ_0 of the two-body potential (which is assumed repulsive) as the unit of the interaction energy, and $v_{th} = (kT/m)^{1/2}$, the thermal velocity, as the unit of speed. In terms of these variables, we then have the BBGKY hierarchy:

$$\frac{\partial D^s}{\partial t} + K^s D^s - \left(\frac{\phi_0}{kT} \right) I^s D^s = (nr_0^3) \left(\frac{\phi_0}{kT} \right) L^s D^{s+1} \tag{1.30}$$

The form of Eq. (30) is fundamental in that it makes the density (nr_0^3) and energy (ϕ_0/kT) parameters of the theory explicit. This basic fact allows us to classify the important regimes of gas theory in terms of a two-dimensional diagram. We shall return to this point shortly.

It is of interest to see the manner in which modern kinetic theory views the Wiederkehreinwand and the Umkehreinwand. The recursion times of each representative of the ensemble is made to tend to infinity by the "bulk limit," Eq. (29). Surface effects are thereby neglected, and the coupled set of equations for D^s is formally maintained intact with $[(N - s)/V] = n$. Recursiveness is completely eliminated, since the Poincare recursion time is monotonic in N. Although the BBGKY hierarchy is not recursive, it is still invariant under reversal of the motion. Full irreversibility arises only as a consequence of a limiting process associated with the asymptotic expansion of the BBGKY hierarchy. Full irreversibility holds only for times long compared with the duration of one collision but short compared with the Poincare recursion time.

The physical meaning of the terms that appear in Eq. (30) is worth discussing. The quantity $K^s D^s$ represents the Poisson bracket of the kinetic energy of the s-particle subsystem with the distribution D^s:

$$K^s D^s = \left[\sum_{i=1}^{s} \frac{p_i^2}{2m}, D^s \right]_{PB} = \sum_{i=1}^{\infty} \mathbf{v}_i \cdot \nabla_i D^S \qquad (1.31)$$

The operator K^s can, therefore, be called the kinetic energy operator.

For a similar reason, the operator I^s can be called the interaction operator. It represents the mutual interaction of the s particles in the cluster. The relative importance of the interaction operator is given by the ratio ϕ_0/kT of the interaction energy to the mean kinetic energy per particle.

The terms on the left-hand side of the Eq. (30) constitute the Liouville equation for the cluster of particles in the system. The right-hand side of this equation is not zero as in the Liouville theorem for the system as a whole. It is, instead, proportional to both (nr_0^3) and (ϕ_0/kT). The operator L^s, the phase-mixing operator, represents the average acceleration exerted on the particles of the cluster by the other particles in the system. This effect is cumulative; it is proportional to n, in fact. It requires the distribution function D^{s+1} for one more particle than in the cluster of s particles under consideration because the interaction potential is assumed to be a two-body force. If three-body forces were present, the right-hand side would also contain a term proportional to D^{s+2}.

D. Regimes of Gas Theory

The physical meaning of the terms that appear in the BBGKY hierarchy, Eq. (30), have been briefly described. We shall now return to

the fundamentally important classification of the physical regimes for a gaseous system in terms of the two basic parameters $(nr_0{}^3)$ and (ϕ_0/kT). Consider the two-dimensional diagram of Fig. 1.

The points represented in Fig. 1 correspond to small values for either $(nr_0{}^3)$ or (ϕ_0/kT). We shall denote by ϵ a dimensionless parameter, small compared to unity, and discuss in turn the four regimes represented.

1. *Short-Range Regime.* We shall see that, with the basic parameters chosen as follows, the kinetic equation appropriate for this regime is the Boltzmann equation:

$$nr_0{}^3 = \epsilon, \qquad \phi_0/kT \sim 1 \qquad (\epsilon \ll 1) \qquad (1.32)$$

Since n is the mean number density of the particles in the gas and r_0 the radius of interaction of one of the particles, $nr_0{}^3$ is the expected number

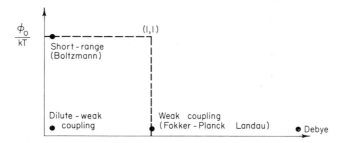

FIG. 1. Basic gaseous regimes.

of particles within a given particle's radius of influence. Equation (32) requires that this number is much less than unity. Therefore, the system of particles is "dilute" in the precise sense that the probability of finding a particle within the radius of influence of a given particle is small, i.e., $\approx \epsilon$.

The interaction potential for particles one and two has been sketched in Fig. 2 as a function of $(|\mathbf{x}_{12}|)$. (The restriction to purely repulsive potentials will be removed later on.) Figure 2 illustrates the second condition in Eq. (32),

$$kT \approx \phi_0 \qquad (1.33)$$

which requires that the mean kinetic energy per particle be of the same order of magnitude as the interparticle potential energy. The latter, therefore, can never be neglected when considering the particle collisions.

The "short-range" gas is, therefore, a very dilute system of particles with very hard interactions, i.e., the root-mean-square momentum trans-

fer at a collision is of the same order as the initial momentum. This picture corresponds clearly to a dilute gas of hard spheres of radius r_0. We expect inert gases at standard conditions to correspond to this regime. There is considerable experimental evidence that the behavior of inert gases indeed does satisfy the Boltzmann equation.

2. *Weak-Coupling Regime.* This regime was first investigated seriously by Landau for the purpose of describing a plasma. As of now. most of the experimental evidence concerning plasmas is in satisfactory

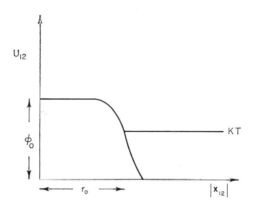

FIG. 2. Energy diagram for the short-range regime.

agreement with the Landau description [21, 22]. The choice of parameters is

$$nr_0^3 \sim 1, \qquad \phi_0/kT = \epsilon \qquad (1.34)$$

Since for this regime we have $nr_0^3 \approx 1$, the expected number of particles within a given particle's range of influence is approximately 1. That is to say, we expect at any particular time to find a particle in interaction with any given one. On the other hand, from the energy condition in Eq. (34), we have $\phi_0 = \epsilon kT$, or

$$\phi_0 \ll kT \qquad (1.35)$$

In the energy diagram of Fig. 3, we can readily see what this condition means.

In an average interaction, the colliding pair will interpenetrate completely, and there will result only a very small amount of (root-mean-square) momentum transfer. The evolution of such a system toward thermodynamical equilibrium will be dominated by the very large accumulation of small deflections. The system can be pictured as a system of soft "cotton" balls moving rapidly in a dense array (see Fig. 4).

Although the description afforded by the weak-coupling kinetic theory applies well to a plasma, we might also expect that such a description will be valid for a system of particles such as oxygen atoms at moderate temperatures where ionization does not play a major role.

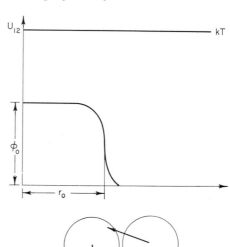

FIG. 3. Energy diagram for the weak-coupling regime.

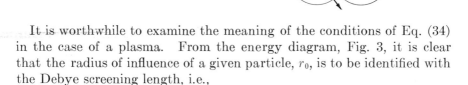

FIG. 4. Configuration space in a weakly coupled gas.

It is worthwhile to examine the meaning of the conditions of Eq. (34) in the case of a plasma. From the energy diagram, Fig. 3, it is clear that the radius of influence of a given particle, r_0, is to be identified with the Debye screening length, i.e.,

$$r = \lambda_D \tag{1.36}$$

and that the potential depth is approximately the Coulomb energy at the Debye radius,

$$\phi_0 \approx e^2/\lambda_D \tag{1.37}$$

When Eqs. (36) and (37) are employed, the parameter conditions of Eq. (34) become

$$n\lambda_D{}^3 \sim 1 \tag{1.38}$$

and

$$(e^2/\lambda_D) \cdot (1/kT) \ll 1 \qquad (1.39)$$

We can, therefore, conclude from Eq. (38) that for a weakly coupled gas the Debye shielding is of the same order as the interparticle separation, i.e.,

$$\lambda_D \sim n^{-1/3} \qquad (1.40)$$

whereas from Eq. (39) it is seen that the Debye length is much larger than the distance at which the Coulomb energy balances the mean kinetic energy:

$$\lambda_D \gg e^2/kT \qquad (1.41)$$

For laboratory plasma, we typically have

$$\lambda_D > n^{-1/3} > e^2/kT \qquad (1.42)$$

It is clear that, inasmuch as the outer inequality in Eq. (42), namely, Eq. (41), dominates the interaction, one would expect that the Landau approximation, i.e., the weak-coupling approximation, should provide a good description of plasma. In the weak-coupling description of a plasma, one must recall that the impact parameters allowed range between e^2/kT and λ_D.

3. *The Dilute Weakly Coupled Gas.* This gas is of particular importance in that it plays the role of intermediary between the short-range gas and the weakly coupled gas. That is to say, expansion of results for the short-range gas in small momentum transfer per collision will not lead directly to the weak-coupling results but rather to the dilute-weakly coupled gas. Similarly, expansion of the weakly coupled gas in powers of the dilution will lead to the dilute-weakly coupled regime. This regime is, therefore, invaluable for the cross-checking of higher-order expansions. This cross-check has become of particular interest in recent years since the discovery and proof [10, 23, 24] of the impossibility of carrying out the Bogolubov expansion consistently to higher orders.

4. *The Debye-Bogolubov Regime.* It has been remarked by Bogolubov that the choice of nr_0^3 and ϕ_0/kT corresponding to the linked relation

$$\phi_0/kT = \epsilon = 1/nr_0^3 \qquad (1.43)$$

closely resembles a laboratory plasma if we use the identification

$$\phi_0 = e^2/r_0 \qquad (1.44)$$

because both Eqs. (36) and (37) (the conditions satisfied by a laboratory plasma) follow immediately from the elimination of ϵ from Eq. (43).

From Eqs. (43) and (44), we have $(1/r_0)(e^2/kT) = 1/nr_0^3$:

$$r_0^2 = kT/ne^2 \tag{1.45}$$

It is clear from Eq. (45) that the condition in Eq. (36), $r_0 \approx \lambda_D$, is satisfied. Using Eqs. (43) and (44), we have

$$e^2/kT \ll \lambda_D \tag{1.46}$$

so that, combining Eqs. (45) and (46), we obtain

$$\lambda_D \gg n^{-1/3} \tag{1.47}$$

Finally, from Eqs. (43) and (45), we have $kT/ne^2 \gg n^{-2/3}$, so that

$$e^2/kT \ll n^{-1/3} \tag{1.48}$$

Combining Eqs. (46)–(48), we gain the full sequence of Eq. (42):

$$\lambda_D \gg n^{-1/3} \gg e^2/kT$$

Bogolubov [6] obtained for this regime a new kinetic equation that has been made explicit by Lenard [25], Guernsey [26], and Balescu [27]. The great merit of this equation is that it guarantees convergence of the collision integral for impact parameters larger than λ_D. This situation is an improvement over the corresponding situation in the weak-coupling regime of Landau where two cutoff choices are needed restricting the impact parameters to remain between e^2/kT and λ_D.

5. *The Purely Repulsive Coulomb Interaction.* By inspection of the diagram of Fig. 2 representing the (ϕ_0/kT), (nr_0^3) plane, it appears plausible that an expansion of the BBGKY should be obtainable which is uniformly valid for the entire region in the neighborhood of both axes (i.e., when there is a small parameter in the system). This possibility appears even more suggestive when one compares the kinetic equations that are valid in the four regimes just described. In the notation developed extensively in a previous paper [7], we find that in all four regimes the kinetic equation can be written in the form

$$\partial D_1{}^1(\mathbf{v})/\partial t = L_{12}\zeta^*(iO_{12})I_{12}D_1{}^1D_2{}^1 \tag{1.49}$$

where the L and I operators are defined in Eqs. (24) and (28), respectively, and are, therefore, the same in all four regimes. The linear operator $\zeta^*(iO_{12})$ is defined by

$$\zeta^*(iO_{12}) = \int_0^\infty e^{-iO_{12}\lambda} \, d\lambda \tag{1.50}$$

for any argument O_{12}. It is only O_{12} that differs from regime to regime [28].

Furthermore, if we analyze the Coulomb interaction in the three main domains of impact parameter, b, contributing to the collision integral, namely, (1) $b \sim e^2/kT$, (2) $b \sim n^{-1/3}$, and (3) $b \sim \lambda_D$, we find that the corresponding values of $(nr_0^3, \phi_0/kT)$ are as shown in the diagram of Fig. 5. It is clear that the domain in which the Coulomb interaction is important is always close to one of the two axes.

The kinetic equation corresponding to this entire region of $(nr_0^3, \phi_0/kT)$ was, in fact, obtained [28]. It coincides in the lowest order of the "local" parameter in the $(nr_0^3, \phi_0/kT)$ plane with the corresponding equations of Boltzmann, Landau, and Bogolubov. Furthermore, it can be approximated by the equations discussed by Baldwin, Hubbard, Weinstock, and Book and Frieman [29–33].

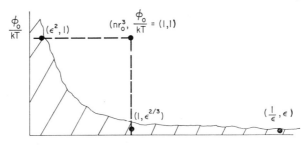

Fɪɢ. 5. Parameterization for Coulomb force.

In this section, we have shown how the description of the nonequilibrium behavior of a gas leads naturally to a microscopic theory that is fully embodied (for classical systems) in the Liouville equation. The familiar parameters of gas theory, namely, the density and the temperature, are then shown to be readily discernible in the Liouville equation if we consider the behavior of the subsystems of the entire gas formed by s particles selected at random (BBGKY hierarchy). The important regimes of gas theory (short-range gas, weakly coupled gas or Landau plasma, dilute-weakly coupled gas, Debye-Bogolubov gas) are then shown to be characterized by simple choices of these parameters. In the next section, we give a brief comparison of the three major techniques that have been developed to treat nonequilibrium statistical mechanical problems: the Synchronization Method of Bogolubov, the perturbation theory of Van Hove and Prigogine, and our method of extension, which is described in some detail.

II. THE METHODS OF MODERN KINETIC THEORY

The purpose of this section is to give a brief review of the major methods employed in the analysis of nonequilibrium statistical mechanics, an area that may be considered the youngest branch of mathematical physics.   The method of Bogolubov [6] and the method of Van Hove [34] and Prigogine [35, 36] are briefly reviewed below.   Results of these techniques are then compared with those of our method, the method of extension [10, 7], which is outlined in the present section and discussed in more detail in Section III.

We shall emphasize the role of the three-body problem for hard spheres. This problem was completely solved during 1964 for hard spheres of equal and finite radii [37, 38].   The three-body problem for hard spheres is quite interesting from the purely mechanical point of view, because its solution is not quite what one would expect on intuitive grounds.   For example, four successive binary collisions can occur among three elastic spheres. The impetus for carrying out the somewhat intricate analysis has come from the crucial open problem of calculating from first principles the behavior of three particle correlations.   Nontrivial results have been obtained recently for the N-body problem [39].

In 1946, Bogolubov [6] proposed a method for a systematic calculation of the properties of gases.   By means of his approach, he showed that Boltzmann's kinetic equation, which accounts statistically for the dynamical behavior corresponding to the two-body problem, is (in a well-defined sense) the lowest-order term in an expansion of the Liouville equation.   This method opened the way for the analysis of dense gases which requires the statistical account of the dynamics of at least three-body systems.   Given Bogolubov's assumptions, no major conceptual problems arise when one performs the required subsequent calculations. In particular, Bogolubov's method *does not* presuppose for its application a knowledge of the three-body dynamics or, for that matter, the n-body dynamics.   The straightforwardness of Bogolubov's method implies that the method can be severely tested when one proceeds to the theory of dense gases.   We show below that the basic assumptions of Bogolubov's method are rather simple but that they are, in fact, incompatible with one another for higher-order terms in the expansion of the Liouville equation.

A. Comparison of the Methods

In 1961–1962, we proposed what we believe to be a far-reaching generalization of Bogolubov's method [10].   The new method reproduces the

appropriate lowest-order kinetic equation and subsequent hydrodynamic equations. For the evaluation of the higher-order terms, our method demands the full details of three-body dynamics and, in general, of the n-body dynamics. We believe that such a demand is physically reasonable and would even suggest that Bogolubov did not calculate explicitly the higher-order terms because of his awareness that the technique he formulated was limited to lowest order. This limitation is particularly acute in the case of the master equation because of a circumstance explained in Chapter VIII of Ref. [15].

As noted previously, the aim of the statistical mechanics of systems not in equilibrium (statistical dynamics) is to determine the long-time behavior of statistical ensembles of systems whose number of degrees of freedom is infinite. In this manner, the theory exhibits the way in which statistical ensembles approach equilibrium.

There have been two major lines of development in the study of statistical mechanics of systems not in equilibrium:

(1) Ergodic Theory: This approach studies the phase space flow in completely general and abstract terms. Some names associated with this development are those of Birkhoff, Koopman, and Carleman. There are good accounts of the approach, e.g., Hopf's [40] and Halmos' [41].

(2) Kinetic Theory: The aim of this theory is to construct specific equations of motion for the stochastic variable appropriate to a given irreversible regime. This approach was initiated in the middle of the 19th century, outstandingly, by Boltzmann. His "Lectures on the Theory of Gases" of 1896 and 1898 appeared nearly 30 years after his first papers on the subject [42].

There is a certain amount of analogy between ergodic theory and general field theory, on the one hand, and between kinetic theory and model field theories, on the other. Model field theories try to calculate cross sections and decay rates for specific elementary processes. Of course, the two lines of thought, ergodic theory and kinetic theory, are, in principle, completely compatible with each other. They differ merely by emphasizing different aspects of the same problem. It is an important desideratum to bridge the gap between them.

The program that the solution of the three-body problem for hard spheres opens, if carried out successfully, would bring the two points of view very close together.

It is worthwhile to interject the following comments. The theory has been set up as a nonquantum-mechanical, nonrelativistic theory. One might therefore ask whether such a theory is completely empty and

intrinsically disjoint from experiment in contradiction with the idea that kinetic theory is a concrete approach to irreversibility.

Firstly, we do not share the opinion that the two defects mentioned can be trivially taken care of. Secondly, kinetic theory can predict, by means of a systematic expansion of the kinetic equation due to Enskog and Chapman [43], the values of such observable quantities as the thermal conductivity and the kinematic viscosity. For simple gases such as argon and helium, at standard conditions of temperature and pressure, the checks with experiment are [44, 9]

$$\frac{k_{\text{theory}} - k_{\text{exp}}}{k_{\text{theory}}} \leq 10\% \tag{2.1}$$

The nonquantum-mechanical, nonrelativistic theory can therefore cope with a large class of experiments to within a few percent.

We shall now summarize the results that we have obtained with our new method. In order to make our results appear in their proper perspective, we shall first review the three mathematical techniques that are available today for the analysis of nonequilibrium statistical mechanical problems. Each of the methods is based on three major assumptions that we shall denote by A, B, and C. We retain this labeling in all three cases to exhibit as closely as possible the parallels.

The first method is the "method of synchronization" of Bogolubov (1946) [6]. The three assumptions are as follows:

(A$_1$) For $s > 1$, the time dependence of F^s is included through F^1 only. F^s is the probability distribution for s particles.

(B$_1$) The $F^s[F^1]$ can be expanded in powers of ϵ, where ϵ is an appropriate small parameter characteristic of the system. For a neutral gas, ϵ is the dilution, and for a weakly coupled or a Coulomb gas, ϵ is the relative momentum transfer.

(C$_1$) The third assumption is a generalized molecular chaos assumption that can be written mathematically, for spatially homogeneous gases, as

$$S_{-\infty}F^s[F^1] = S_{-\infty} \prod_{i=1}^{s} F^1 \tag{2.2}$$

The method of Bogolubov has achieved success in the following two major respects:

(1) A new kinetic equation has been obtained for plasmas (the kinetic equation of Bogolubov) which has been given in explicit form simultaneously and independently by Lenard [25], Guernsey [26], and Balescu

[27]. This equation requires one less cutoff than the Boltzmann-like equation employed by Landau [45] for plasmas.

(2) The Bogolubov theory has been the first systematic technique for calculating solutions to the Liouville equation in powers of a small parameter. This technique opened the way to the theory of dense gases which was not, however, carried out by Bogolubov himself. In our opinion, Bogolubov's method is, in fact, intrinsically insufficient for the theory of dense gases.

The second method is the perturbation theory of Van Hove [34] (1955) and of Prigogine [35] (1956). The three basic assumptions of the method are usually reworded in terms of the Fourier transforms of the N-particle distribution function. They are best stated in the following slightly inverse order:

(B₂) The Fourier transforms are expandable in powers of the same parameter ϵ used in Bogolubov's theory.

(A₂) The expansion in powers of ϵ is nonuniform for large times, i.e., secularly divergent. The method of Van Hove and Prigogine for handling the secularity is that of summing all the terms that are most singular at every stage, that is, sum all terms of the form $(\epsilon t)^n$ first, next sum all the terms that are of the form $(\epsilon^2 t)^n$, and so on. This process essentially yields the solution of the problem in powers of the quantity ϵ, provided that the summations are meaningful.

(C₂) The Prigogine school has confined itself primarily to molecular chaos at $t = 0$, namely, the distribution for N bodies is a product of the one-body distribution functions.

The perturbation theory has been successful in that the results of Bogolubov have been rederived by perturbation expansions. In particular, Balescu derived, by means of perturbation theory, the same equation for the plasma which was derived in 1946 by Bogolubov. We believe it is worth noting that perturbation expansions are known to be inadequate when attractive or binding potentials occur. We believe, therefore, that a perturbation technique approach to irreversible phenomena, in which a binding potential plays an essential role, is extremely delicate at best.

The third method is the "method of extension" proposed in the Rutgers Lectures of 1961–1962 [10] and related papers [7, 46, 47]. The method is based on the following three assumptions:

(A₃) Imagine you give a set of functions $\tau_k(t)$ and you express a function F^s in terms of another $\mathbf{F}^s$ as follows:

$$F^s(t) = [\mathbf{F}^s(\tau_0, \tau_1, \ldots, \tau_n)]_{\tau_k = \tau_k(t)} \qquad (2.3)$$

Clearly, this procedure is simply a parametrization of the unknown function. It is readily verified that the time derivatives of unknown functions acquire a form similar to that yielded by assumption A_1 of Bogolubov, even though our form is considerably more general.

(B₃) We assume that the function F^s can be expressed in the form of an asymptotic expansion:

$$F^s = \sum_n g_n(\epsilon)F^s(n) \qquad \frac{g_{n+1}}{g_n} \to 0 \quad \text{as} \quad \epsilon \to 0 \qquad (2.4)$$

The functions τ_k are then chosen so as to eliminate the divergence in the asymptotic expansion with respect to ϵ. We believe that both A_3 and B_3 are much more general than the corresponding assumptions of either of the previous methods.

(C₃) We *do not use* the analog of molecular chaos as an assumption; we consider it a major achievement of our theory that, simply by imposing the requirement that a kinetic equation exist in the form

$$\partial F^1/\partial t = A[F^1] \qquad (2.5)$$

where A stands for a functional depending on F^1 only, we are able to calculate from first principles the initial distributions for which such a kinetic equation applies. In other words, we are able to give, from first principles, a mechanical explanation of what is meant by molecular chaos. In order to have a kinetic equation, one does not need molecular chaos initially. Instead, one must require that the correlations among the colliding particles have a form that will be given below.

We now summarize in some detail the important results yielded by the method of extension to date.

1. *Equivalence Theorems.* We have been able to derive the Bogolubov method from our extension technique by means of the following choices for the unknown functions $\tau_k(t) = \epsilon^k t$. Furthermore, we have been able to derive the lowest-order Kirkwood theory by means of the following definition of the fast time average:

$$\langle \mathbf{F}^s(\tau_0, \tau_1 \ldots, \tau_n)\rangle_0 = \lim_{T \to \infty} \frac{1}{2T} \int_{-T}^{T} \mathbf{F}^s(\tau_0, \tau_1, \ldots, \tau_n)\, d\tau_0 \quad (2.6)$$

These two equivalence theorems establish the previous derivations of irreversible equations as well-defined special cases of ours [10, 7].

2. *The Principle of Absence of Parallel Motions.* We have already said that the assumption C_1 of Bogolubov and Prigogine can be replaced by a definition of "kinetic equation," and we can then calculate the distributions that will allow for the existence of such an equation. The detailed

results can be found elsewhere [10, 7]. We confine ourselves here to giving the outstanding result in terms of the two-particle correlation function g, which is defined by

$$g \equiv F^2 - F^1 F^1 \tag{2.7}$$

where F^2 is the probability distribution function for two particles. In order that the kinetic equation exist, the quantity g must satisfy

$$\int_0^\infty L e^{-O\lambda} g(0) \, d\lambda < \infty \tag{2.8}$$

where L and O are linear operators defined elsewhere [7]. In the case of weak momentum transfers at each collision, the preceding condition can be expressed as

$$v^2 g(\mathbf{v}) \sim v^\eta \qquad (v \to 0) \tag{2.9}$$

where η is any positive number, $\mathbf{v}$ is the relative velocity of the two particles, and $|v|$ is its magnitude.

3. *The Transient Law.* It has been possible by means of our technique, which does not average over time intervals of the order of duration of one collision, to calculate explicitly the manner in which the distribution functions approach either the kinetic or the hydrodynamic regime. It is clear that such a calculation would be impossible with the averaging implied by the Bogolubov theory. The result is that for very long times the departures from kinetic or hydrodynamic behaviors are power laws rather than the expected exponential decay [7]. We consider this result important and susceptible to experimental test.

4. *The Coulomb Kinetic Equation.* It has been possible to derive a kinetic equation that is completely convergent [28]. This equation is very important because it allows for a rigorous calculation of the electrical conductivity and other transport properties of a plasma. Such a calculation up to now has been marred by the requirements of cutoffs for either small- or large-impact parameters or both. In particular, the effect of very high temperature has not been explored up to now because of a lack of basic theory.

5. *The Binding Theory.* At the very early stages of our work, the Bogolubov theory was cast in a form for which binding could be introduced. It has been found that such modification of Bogolubov theory requires mathematical manipulations that become extremely dubious. It is now possible to see the reasons why the original approach to binding has resulted in so much difficulty. Effectively, an average over the time scale which is measured in units of the duration of one collision is pre-

supposed by Bogolubov theory.   This means that, if there are periods in the system (such as the periods of the bound state orbits) which are of that order of magnitude, then they cannot be seen.   This clearly makes Bogolubov's theory extremely delicate in the case of attraction.   In fact, it has not been carried out up to now, and, therefore, it has not been possible to ascertain the effects of attraction on a gas.

6. *The Relaxation Equations.*   By means of our technique of expanding the Liouville equation which emphasizes the physical time scales rather than the specific parameters involved, it has been possible to devise expansions other than the conventional kinetic expansion which lead to the relaxation form of the irreversible equation, for example, the Krook model [48].   We believe that we have gained an insight by this method into the phenomenon of relaxation to thermodynamic equilibrium by giving an interpretation, in terms of the particle-particle interaction, of the relaxation time that enters the Krook equation [49].   The conditions for the validity of Krook's equation can be ascertained, unambiguously, by means of our techniques from first principles, that is to say, directly from the Liouville equation.   We expect that there are situations in which a kinetic equation of the Boltzmann type does not hold; nonetheless, a relaxation equation might hold.

The outstanding new feature of our method is a formalism that allows one to use explicitly the scales of time which are pertinent to the physics of the problem at hand.   The time scales have been emphasized to a great extent by Bogolubov, who made the discrepancy between two time scales the basis of the idea of synchronization.   Although the idea goes back to Kirkwood, George Uhlenbeck is to be credited for having brought forcefully the physics of the different time scales to the attention of the physicists in the West [50].

We shall discuss in the next section the physics of the time scales, but we can give here a simple example.   In the description of a neutral gas, such as the air in a room, our method uses two independent time variables.   One time variable (which is read on a fast clock) describes phenomena that occur during one collision, whereas the other time variable (which is read on a slow clock) describes phenomena that occur during the relaxation of a gas to thermodynamic equilibrium.   Since these two times, i.e., the duration of one collision and the relaxation time to thermodynamic equilibrium, are widely separated (by orders of magnitude for normal gases), it is clearly advantageous to have an explicit mathematical formalism where it is possible to treat them separately. The strength of this approach shows itself in the directness and simplicity with which the entire range of known results in the theory of irreversibility has been derived.

It is, therefore, very tempting with this approach to calculate higher-order effects, e.g., to investigate the density dependence of transport properties for neutral gases.

B. The Divergence Problem

We have said that synchronized solutions follow from extended solutions if times on the fast time scale become large, i.e., in the limit $\tau_0 \to \infty$. Let us therefore consider this special case first. It has been possible [24] to reformulate the Bogolubov synchronized solutions in the following terms. The two-particle distribution function g to any order ν is a function of the relative position $\mathbf{x}$ and the relative velocity $\mathbf{v}$ of the two particles. As a consequence of synchronization, g satisfies a simple differential equation and boundary condition.

For the weakly coupled gas, Bogolubov's synchronization assumptions lead immediately in any order ν of ϵ to the equation

$$\mathbf{v} \cdot \nabla g^\nu(\mathbf{x}, \mathbf{v}) = \sigma^\nu(\mathbf{x}, \mathbf{v}) \tag{2.10}$$

which is to be solved with the "boundary condition" (generalized stosszahlansatz)

$$g^\nu(\mathbf{x} - \mathbf{v}\lambda, \mathbf{v}) \xrightarrow[\lambda \to \infty]{} 0 \tag{2.11}$$

The functions σ^ν are calculated from the hierarchy of the reduced distribution functions [24], with the simple results

$$\sigma^0 = 0 \tag{2.12}$$
$$\sigma^1 = \nabla U_{12} \cdot (\mathbf{D}) F_1 F_2 \tag{2.13}$$
$$\sigma^2 = \delta_1 + \delta_2 + \delta_3 \tag{2.14}$$

The quantities δ_i are given by

$$\delta_1 \equiv (\nabla U \cdot \mathbf{D}) \int_0^\infty \nabla U (\mathbf{x} - \mathbf{v}\lambda) \, d\lambda \cdot \mathbf{D} F_1 F_2 \tag{2.15}$$

$$\delta_2 \equiv \int d\mathbf{x}_3 \, d\mathbf{v}_3 \, [\nabla_{13} U(\mathbf{x}_{13}) \cdot \nabla_{v_1}] \int_0^\infty \nabla_{23} U(\mathbf{x}_{23} - \mathbf{v}_{23}\lambda) \, d\lambda \cdot \mathbf{D}_{23} F_1 F_2 F_3 \tag{2.16}$$

$$\delta_3 \equiv \int d\mathbf{x}_3 \, d\mathbf{v}_3 \, [\nabla_{23} U(\mathbf{x}_{23}) \cdot \nabla_{v_2}] \int_0^\infty \nabla_{13} U(\mathbf{x}_{13} - \mathbf{v}_{13}\lambda) \, d\lambda \cdot \mathbf{D}_{13} F_1 F_2 F_3 \tag{2.17}$$

We have used the notation $\mathbf{D}_{ij} = \nabla_{v_i} - \nabla_{v_j}$ as well as the convention that subscripts denote particle variables. Expressions similar to Eqs. (13) and (14) can be calculated for any ν.

Clearly, Eq. (11) constitutes a consistency requirement on the behavior of σ^ν. Provided that Eqs. (11) and (12) are thus consistent, the system

has the *unique* solution

$$g^\nu(\mathbf{x}, \mathbf{v}) = \int_0^\infty \sigma^\nu(\mathbf{x} - \mathbf{v}\lambda, \mathbf{v})\, d\lambda \qquad (2.18)$$

It is now easy to verify that σ^0 and σ^1 are compatible with Eq. (11) by virtue of the finite range of U. On the other hand, σ^2 (as well as the higher σ^ν) are incompatible with Eq. (11) since the variable shifts, due to the integration in δ_2 and δ_3, give the function an infinite (spatial) range.

We mention in this context an interesting paper on the method of extension by Frank *et al.* [51] where an interesting discussion of the difficulties arising from σ^2 is described. We have not been able to verify completely their calculation.

We have seen that the assumptions of synchronization lead the theory to an impasse when we attempt to calculate the higher-order terms. The divergence difficulty discussed in Refs. [7, 10, 24] has been studied repeatedly [52–58]. In order to indicate the possible approaches that are available, we want to emphasize two important features that throw light on the physical aspects of the problem:

(i) The parameter ϕ_0/kT becomes large when the relative velocity of two particles is small. An expansion that treats ϕ_0/kT as small must break down for those particles that move very slowly relative to each other, because the effective temperature for such particles is, in fact, very small. One therefore expects the small momentum transfer regimes to represent poorly such a situation. This phenomenon is closely related to the formula for absence of parallel motions described previously.

(ii) If two particles interact in a corner of the room and one of the outgoing particles then collides with a third particle in another corner of the room, one has, as a consequence of momentum and energy balance, a three-body correlation with a correlation length much larger than a mean free path. Such successive two-body collisions, one expects, have been counted as two-body terms and should not play a role in the three-body phenomena or higher. One can, however, verify that the Bogolubov synchronized expansion does, in fact, strongly emphasize these successive two-body collisions. In the language of time scales, these collisions play the dominant role on the third time scale. On this time scale, thermodynamic equilibrium already exists because the H-theorem implied by the Boltzmann equation is derived on the *second* time scale.

We want now to summarize briefly the suggestions that have been made for exploring the situation in higher order.

1. *Closure.* This procedure was proposed by the author [10]. The lowest-order kinetic equation guarantees an H-theorem. This means that the molecular distribution function becomes Maxwellian after the slow time scale has been exhausted. The system should then be in thermodynamic equilibrium, and nothing but fluctuations should occur thereafter. We propose, therefore, that the higher time scales should play no role and, in fact, that the distribution of particles be completely independent of the higher time scales. In an unpublished work with Engelmann, it has been possible to show that closure is consistent with the Liouville equation in the weak-coupling limit and that this, consequently, implies that the rate of change of the distribution function given by Landau is the true one, in the sense of an asymptotic expansion. This is, to date, the only rigorous proof of the asymptotic nature of the kinetic expansions. Closure has been discussed again recently [59].

2. *Treating Initial Correlations Dynamically.* This idea was suggested first, to our knowledge, by Professor W. Hayes in 1962. The idea is that we cannot treat for dense gases the initial value of the two-particle correlation as a priori given, but we must instead treat them dynamically. It is clear that approaches 1 and 2 are related, because the pair kinetic equations given in approach 1 are, in fact, interpretable as equations for a dynamical treatment of the two-particle correlation. It is interesting that similar ideas had been entertained already by both Grad [60] and Uhlenbeck [61].

3. *Eliminating Supersecularities by Uniformizing Supersecular Problems.* The method of extension has not been sufficiently investigated. The number of unknown functions is so large, even if we stay close to the Bogolubov solution, that it is difficult to obtain a definite answer. In addition, the precise nature of the nonuniformity in the higher-order terms is not really known because the dynamics of three- and higher-body clusters has, until very recently, not been written down explicitly. In some sense, one must resum singular contributions. A start in this direction is contained in other works [55, 56, 62].

4. *The Projection Problem.* This is a philosophy whereby the Choh-Uhlenbeck formula is retained via the following reasoning. If we insert in the nonconvergent parts for the higher-order correlation given by the synchronized solutions the Maxwellian distribution, we find that these parts vanish identically for the kinetic equation [63]. The collision integrals have, therefore, a projection property that plays a crucial role. In fact, we can go further. We can prove that, if we substitute the divergent second-order distribution into the rate of change for the distribution function, the divergencies cancel. It is therefore suggested that we should maintain the resulting expression, even though the logical basis for its

derivation has completely disappeared. This point of view is not unrelated to the philosophy of closure.   It seems to us that the major question here, in view of the fact that the logical foundation of the theory has disappeared, is whether or not the phenomenological theory that results is in agreement with experiment.   This can be checked in principle, for example, by calculating the bulk viscosity of a dense gas.   Such calculations are not easy and are, in fact, only partially available at present.

If we want to ascertain with rigor the possibility of giving a logically compelling answer to the question raised by the divergence of the synchronized expansion, and put in proper perspective the position of the H-theorem, we must, in our opinion, introduce the three-body dynamics explicitly.   This gives rise to the program to be described in the next paragraphs.

C. The N-Body Problem for Hard Spheres

1. *The Two-Body Problem.* We shall discuss briefly the two-body problem for hard spheres to make clear what are the dynamical assumptions that enter into the calculations given below.

(1) STATE AND ITS EVOLUTIONS:

We consider a binary collision

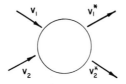

The velocities after the collision are given in terms of those before collision by means of the formulas

$$\mathbf{v}_1{}^* = \mathbf{v}_1 - \mathbf{k}\mathbf{k} \cdot (\mathbf{v}_1 - \mathbf{v}_2) = \mathbf{P} \cdot \mathbf{v}_2 + \mathbf{N} \cdot \mathbf{v}_1$$
$$\mathbf{v}_2{}^* = \mathbf{v}_2 + \mathbf{k}\mathbf{k} \cdot (\mathbf{v}_1 - \mathbf{v}_2) = \mathbf{P} \cdot \mathbf{v}_1 + \mathbf{N} \cdot \mathbf{v}_2$$

(2.19)

where we have introduced the tensors

$$\mathbf{P} = \mathbf{k}\mathbf{k}, \qquad \mathbf{N} = \mathbf{I} - \mathbf{k}\mathbf{k}$$

(2.20)

The state can be represented by means of the following table:

$$\psi(t) = \begin{Bmatrix} \mathbf{x}_1(t) & \mathbf{v}_1(t) \\ \mathbf{x}_2(t) & \mathbf{v}_2(t) \end{Bmatrix}$$

(2.21)

There are then two transformations on the state vector which must be

discussed: the momentum transfer at collision, and the free streaming between collisions.

We can choose at $t = 0^-$ (immediately prior to collision at $t = 0$):

$$\psi(0^-) = \begin{Bmatrix} \mathbf{x}_1 & \mathbf{v}_1 \\ \mathbf{x}_2 & \mathbf{v}_2 \end{Bmatrix} \tag{2.22}$$

Using the preceding formula, we can then write the state at $t = 0^+$ as

$$\psi(0^+) = \begin{Bmatrix} \mathbf{x}_1 & \mathbf{P} \cdot \mathbf{v}_2 + \mathbf{N} \cdot \mathbf{v}_1 \\ \mathbf{x}_2 & \mathbf{P} \cdot \mathbf{v}_2 + \mathbf{N} \cdot \mathbf{v}_2 \end{Bmatrix}, \qquad \mathbf{k} = \frac{\mathbf{x}_1 - \mathbf{x}_2}{|\mathbf{x}_1 - \mathbf{x}_2|} \tag{2.23}$$

This formula completely specifies the momentum transfer properties in two-body collisions. If we now want to consider the state for $t > 0$, we then have to write simply

$$\psi(t) = \begin{Bmatrix} \mathbf{x}_1 + (\mathbf{P} \cdot \mathbf{v}_2 + \mathbf{N} \cdot \mathbf{v}_1)t & \mathbf{P} \cdot \mathbf{v}_2 + \mathbf{N} \cdot \mathbf{v}_1 \\ \mathbf{x}_2 + (\mathbf{P} \cdot \mathbf{v}_1 + \mathbf{N} \cdot \mathbf{v}_2)t & \mathbf{P} \cdot \mathbf{v}_1 + \mathbf{N} \cdot \mathbf{v}_2 \end{Bmatrix}, \qquad t > 0 \tag{2.24}$$

(2) The Necessary and Sufficient Conditions for a Collision to Occur:

We shall solve explicitly the two-body problem. To solve the two-body problem means, in fact, the following: given arbitrary positions and velocities for the two bodies, the trajectories for all future time are specified unambiguously. For the simple kinematical problem given by hard-sphere collisions, the answer can be expressed in the following form. We shall be able to calculate a domain in the phase space of the two bodies for which collisions will occur in the future, that is, the domain $\Gamma_1(2)$. The subscript characterizes the number of collisions, the argument the number of particles. Let $\mathbf{x}$ be the relative position and $\mathbf{v}$ the relative velocity vectors in three-dimensional space. If a collision is to occur at the time τ, then we must have

$$|\mathbf{x} + \mathbf{v}\tau| = 1 \tag{2.25}$$

We readily see that this equation represents a quadratic for τ with solutions

$$\tau = - \frac{\mathbf{x} \cdot \mathbf{v} \pm [v^2 - (\mathbf{x} \times \mathbf{v})^2]^{1/2}}{v^2}$$

The sign must be chosen negative if one is not to allow for penetration of the spheres. The other solution corresponds to the spheres having gone through each other. From the resulting formula, namely, $(\tau > 0)$

$$\tau = - \frac{\mathbf{x} \cdot \mathbf{v} - [v^2 - (\mathbf{x} \times \mathbf{v})^2]^{1/2}}{v^2} \tag{2.26}$$

we can see that we must have τ positive and real for two collisions in the future, $\tau = 0$ for collision in the present, $\tau =$ negative and real for collision in the past, and finally τ complex for no collision.

In order to describe these conditions precisely, we introduce the following notation. Let $\mathbf{p}$ and $\mathbf{q}$ be two arbitrary vectors and R an arbitrary real number. We then call

$$C(\mathbf{p}, \mathbf{q}, R)$$

the cone of vectors whose origin is at the vector $\mathbf{o}$ and whose tip lies within the cone whose apex is at $\mathbf{p}$ and is defined by the tangents to the sphere of radius R with center at $\mathbf{q}$. We show these geometrical objects in Fig. 6. The notation appears a little complicated for the purposes of the two-body problem, but it is essential for the three-body problem. We then see that the necessary and sufficient conditions given for a collision in the future correspond to the following equation:

$$\mathbf{v} \, \epsilon \, C(\mathbf{o}, -\mathbf{x}, 1) \tag{2.27}$$

This equation defines in fact $\Gamma_1(2)$, namely, the set of $\mathbf{x}$ and $\mathbf{v}$ that satisfy the foregoing equation. In diagram form, we can see this depicted in Fig. 7. This is a slightly unfamiliar version of a well-known kinematical fact, namely, that collisions occur only within the Boltzmann cylinder that is depicted in Fig. 8. The difference between the two representations of $\Gamma_1(2)$ is due to whether one chooses $\mathbf{x}$ and then determines $\mathbf{v}$ or vice versa.

The orbits are specified by giving the state at $t = 0$. Since the momentum transfer introduces jumps in the velocities, the complete specification of the state is given piecewise in the time variable.

2. *The Three-Body Problem.* Since the results have been already described in a recent note [38] and the complete proofs are being prepared for publication, we shall confine ourselves here to brief remarks.

(1) CLASSIFICATION OF THE COLLISION CHAINS:

It is important in the N-body problem to have a systematic classification of the binary collision chains. This can be done for the three-body problem as follows: denote the spheres by the numbers 1, 2, and 3. The first collision then can occur in only one way, namely, 1 and 2 can collide. All other possible first binary collisions can be relabeled so as to be of the foregoing type. The first two collisions can occur in only one way, namely, in the sequence (1, 2)—(2, 3). The third collision, however, can occur in either of two forms, depending on whether all three of the pairs participate or only two of them do. We call the case in which only

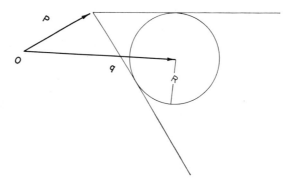

FIG. 6. The collision cone.

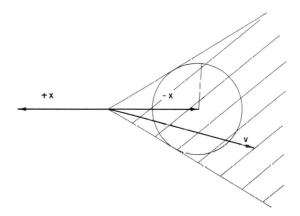

FIG. 7. Phase space for one future collision.

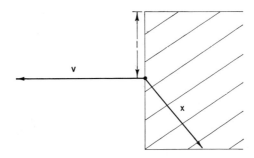

FIG. 8. The Boltzmann cylinder for $\Gamma_2(1)$.

two pairs participate r for rebound and the other case c for cyclic. These first three chains are depicted in Fig. 9.

Any chain of four collisions such as the one depicted in Fig. 9 is decomposible in terms of the r and c chains as shown in the diagram. We therefore have four distinct possibilities for the collision chains: rr, rc, cr, cc. Clearly, rc and cr are related by time reversal. Only the equivalent classes that are invariant under particle permutations and time reversal are important.

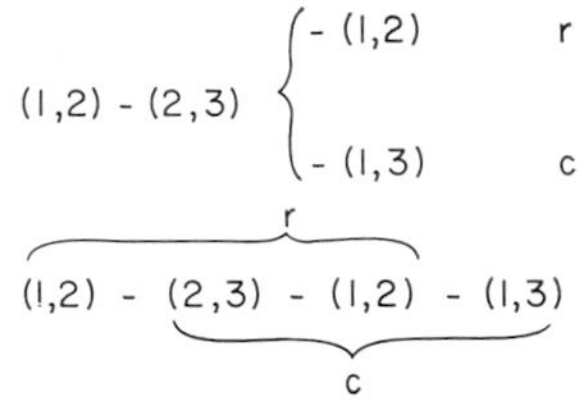

$$
(1,2) - (2,3) \begin{cases} - (1,2) & r \\[2mm] - (1,3) & c \end{cases}
$$

$$
\underbrace{(1,2) - \overbrace{(2,3) - (1,2)}^{r} - (1,3)}_{c}
$$

FIG. 9. Three-body collision chains.

For the fifth collision, we have the following eight cases

$$
\begin{array}{lll}
rrr & & \\
rrc & rcr & crr \\
rcc & crc & ccr \\
ccc & &
\end{array}
$$

of which the last column can be completely eliminated by time reversal. We are, therefore, left with six classes. Each of the classes must be analyzed by means of the necessary and sufficient conditions that are described in the previous paragraph.

(2) CHOICE OF REFERENCE FRAME:

The appropriate choice of the reference frame is the most important part of the investigation. In the wrong reference frame, one cannot proceed. We have, for the three-body problem, the state written down, in general, as follows:

$$
\psi(t) = \begin{Bmatrix} \mathbf{x}_1 & \mathbf{v}_1 \\ \mathbf{x}_2 & \mathbf{v}_2 \\ \mathbf{x}_3 & \mathbf{v}_3 \end{Bmatrix} \tag{2.28}
$$

The reference frame is chosen in such a way that for r-type collisions

$$
\psi(t_{\mathrm{II}}{}^{+}) = \begin{Bmatrix} \mathbf{x} & \mathbf{u}_1 \\ \mathbf{0} & \mathbf{0} \\ \mathbf{k} & \mathbf{u}_3 \end{Bmatrix} \tag{2.29}
$$

(3) Inequalities:

We give as an illustration the chain of inequalities that correspond to the case given in Fig. 10 which, in fact, are shown to be the only possibility for four collisions. These inequalities are written down in tabular form in Fig. 11, and the connections are shown.

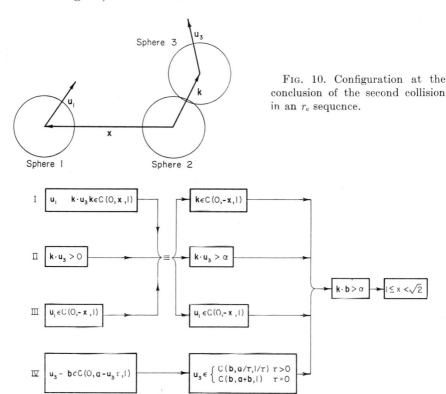

Fig. 10. Configuration at the conclusion of the second collision in an r_c sequence.

Fig. 11. Domains for the r_c collision chain.

The proof of each of the inequalities is rather straightforward once the precise inequalities desired are written down. The difficulty lies entirely in knowing which inequality to prove. The notation introduced, apart from the state variables already given, is as follows:

$$
\begin{aligned}
&\mathbf{a} = \mathbf{k}' - \mathbf{k}, && \mathbf{k}' = \mathbf{x} + \mathbf{u}_1\tau \\
&\mathbf{b} = \mathbf{u}_1 - (\mathbf{k}' \cdot \mathbf{u}_1)\mathbf{k}', && \tau = \text{time interval between II and III} \qquad (2.30)
\end{aligned}
$$

The decoupling process consists in choosing the following chain of variables: $\mathbf{x}, \mathbf{k}, \mathbf{u}_1, \mathbf{u}_3$.

The quantity α is the largest root of a quadratic equation

$$Q(\alpha) = 0$$

The polynomial Q has coefficients that depend only on $\mathbf{x}$ and $\mathbf{k}$. Therefore, it is always possible to specify $\mathbf{u}_1$ unambiguously.

The first three collisions therefore occur in the following domain:

$$|\mathbf{x}| \geq 1, \qquad \mathbf{k} \text{ and } \mathbf{u}_1 \in \mathbf{B}(\mathbf{x}) \equiv C(\mathbf{o}, -\mathbf{x}, 1) \qquad (2.31)$$

In establishing the conditions for the fourth collision, we find an important result that we can call the "square-root-two theorem." The inequalities in the table are incompatible if $|\mathbf{x}|$ is greater than the square

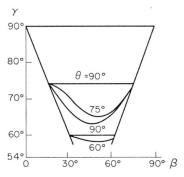

FIG. 12. Cross sections of the $(\beta, \gamma, \phi, \theta)$ space $(\phi = 0)$.

root of two, namely, in order to have four collisions, we must have the following inequality:

$$1 < |\mathbf{x}| < 2^{1/2} \qquad (2.32)$$

whose "dimensional" version is

$$(2r_0) < |\mathbf{x}| < 2^{1/2}(2r_0) \qquad (2.33)$$

This result shows that, if the radius goes to zero, we cannot have four collisions. Therefore, four successive collisions are strictly a finite radius effect.

We can now add the following simple remark. The proof is valid in any number of dimensions because only scalar quantities appear in the proofs. All the cross-products can always be transformed into dot products by means of the Lagrange identity:

$$(\mathbf{x} \times \mathbf{v})^2 = x^2 v^2 - (\mathbf{x} \cdot \mathbf{v})^2$$

In the coplanar case, there are five variables. They can be chosen in such a way that three are angles and two are velocities, namely, the $\mathbf{u}_3$ components. We then find that the domain in the angular space is of the form shown in Fig. 12. To each point in the angular domain, there

corresponds one triangle. We know, therefore, that Γ_4 is bounded. It, consequently, has zero relative measure with respect to Γ_i for i less than 4.

We have so far only discussed the collision chain rc. We can show that rr and cc are incompatible by a reasoning analogous to the one just described. It is worth noticing that there are only two special cases in which the maximum number of binary collisions is three: in colinear motion, and for point particles.

The eight possibilities for five collisions can immediately be reduced to two, namely, rcr and crc, by virtue of the preceding results. It is then possible to prove that these chains are impossible.

The solution of the three-body problem has opened the way to a very interesting program. It is within the realm of mathematical imagination that we should be able to construct the quantity $\Gamma_N(v)$, that is to say that we should be able to give an explicit solution, in the sense just described, by induction, for the N-body problem for classical hard spheres. The solution of such a problem would be of major interest. It would be the first time that a nontrivial mechanical model would be made available for nonequilibrium statistical mechanics.

Considerable progress has been recently made in the solution of the most pressing combinatorial aspects of the problem [39].

III. THE PHYSICS OF THE INDEPENDENT TIME SCALES

In this section, we shall discuss the physical foundations of the method of extension. We shall illustrate, by means of a simple example, a recent improvement that permits the construction of the rates at which our independent clocks have to march.

Consider the BBGKY hierarchy for a spatially homogeneous gas and for $s = 1$. It reads

$$\frac{\partial D^1}{\partial t} = (nr_0{}^3) \left(\frac{\phi_0}{kT}\right) L^1 D^2 \tag{3.1}$$

The most important feature of our new theory is that we have relinquished the description of interactions among particles of the gas in terms of localized, two-body collisions, a conception very well suited to hard-sphere laboratory gases only. The new emphasis is on the time scales of the processes under investigation. We shall begin the section by showing how the form of the one-body distribution, Eq. (1), does, in fact, lead to the physics of the various regimes. We must first remember that the time t that enters Eq. (1) is already dimensionless, and it is,

in fact, measured in units of

$$t_0 = r_0/v_{th} \tag{3.2}$$

Consider now a very simple model of Eq. (1):

$$\partial f/\partial t = -\epsilon f \tag{3.3}$$

where ϵ is a fixed parameter rather than a linear operator as in Eq. (1). It is clear that in Eq. (3), upon division by ϵ, we have a representation of the behavior of f in terms of the *intrinsic* time of the phenomenon which very clearly is (ϵt):

$$\partial f/\partial(\epsilon t) = -f \tag{3.4}$$

Returning now to Eq. (1), we see that the intrinsic time variable for the one-body distribution function is, in fact,

$$t_1 = t(nr_0{}^3)(\phi_0/kT) \tag{3.5}$$

We now take up, in turn, the major regimes discussed in the first section.

A. Short-Range Regime

We have seen that this regime, which is characterized by

$$nr_0{}^3 = \epsilon, \qquad \phi_0/kT \sim 1 \tag{3.6}$$

is appropriate for spheres of radius r_0 and with a hard potential in the sense that $\phi_0 \sim kT$.

For such particles, we see that the quantity $t_0 = r_0/v_{th}$ represents the expected duration of one collision. This is a very short time, one of microscopic length.

Since, on the other hand, the mean free path λ is given by

$$\lambda = 1/nr_0{}^2 \tag{3.7}$$

we have, for the expected mean free time between collisions,

$$\tau = \frac{\lambda}{v_{th}} = \left(\frac{1}{nr_0{}^2}\right)\frac{1}{v_{th}} = \left(\frac{1}{nr_0{}^3}\right)\frac{r_0}{v_{th}} = \frac{1}{\epsilon}t_0 \tag{3.8}$$

By comparison with Eq. (5), we see that the mean free time is the intrinsic time for the rate of change of the one-body distribution. The reader is urged to realize that a slow clock (relative to a standard one) beats with *very large units* of time, Eq. (8); its progress (relative to the standard clock) is *very slow*, Eq. (5).

We have focused here our attention on a spatially homogeneous system. If there are small gradients in the system, a new time scale appears:

$$\tau' = \frac{L}{v_{th}} = \frac{1}{v_{th}} \frac{1}{|\nabla \log T|} \tag{3.9}$$

where we have taken the temperature gradient to be characteristic of the inhomogeneities present.   It is on the ratio

$$\tau/\tau' = \lambda/L \tag{3.10}$$

that the "hydrodynamic" expansion is based, whereby the Navier-Stokes equations are deduced from kinetic theory [64].

In summary, for a system of particles satisfying the short-range conditions, we expect the molecular distribution to be stationary for times comparable to r_0/v_{th}, whereas we expect it to relax to its (local) thermodynamic value in times comparable to λ/v_{th}.   Finally, we expect all weak inhomogeneities to be smoothed out by viscous and conductive dissipation over times comparable to L/v_{th}.   These expectations are fully borne out by the mathematical developments.

B. The Landau (or Weakly Coupled) Gas

The conditions for weak coupling are, as we have seen,

$$nr_0{}^3 \sim 1 \tag{3.11}$$

and

$$\phi_0/kT = \epsilon \tag{3.12}$$

From Eq. (11), we see at once, as was remarked in Section I,

$$r_0 \sim n^{-1/3} \tag{3.13}$$

namely, the size of the particles is of the same order of magnitude of the expected interparticle separation.   The mean free path is given by

$$\lambda = 1/nr_0{}^2 = r_0/nr_0{}^3 \sim r_0 \tag{3.14}$$

and we have, therefore,

$$\lambda \sim n^{-1/3} \sim r_0 \tag{3.15}$$

For a weakly coupled gas, the slow evolution of the velocity distribution D^1 does not occur over times of the order of λ/v_{th} because, in fact, λ/v_{th} is of the same order of magnitude as the duration of one collision.   The slow time scale for this system is physically entirely different.   It is given by the expected "acceleration time" τ_a, namely, the time required on the average to change a molecular speed by an amount comparable to the thermal speed.   Since the acceleration, because of particle-particle inter-

action, is of the order of

$$a \sim (\phi_0/r_0)(1/m) \tag{3.16}$$

we have $v_{th} \sim a\tau_a$, or

$$\tau_a \sim \frac{v_{th}}{a} = \frac{m v_{th}^2}{\phi_0} \frac{r_0}{v_{th}} = \frac{1}{\epsilon} \frac{r_0}{v_{th}} \tag{3.17}$$

By comparison with Eq. (8), we see immediately that the acceleration time plays for the weakly coupled gas the same role played by λ/v_{th} for a short-range gas.

The slow evolution of the distribution D^1 takes place on a scale even slower than τ_a whose units are

$$\tau_a' = (1/\epsilon^2)(r_0/v_{th}) \tag{3.18}$$

because, on the average, no momentum is transferred in binary collisions. There are, in fact, equal chances for a given particle to *lose* or to *gain* momentum in a collision. It is only the root-mean-square momentum transfer $(\phi_0/kT)^2$ that does not vanish. The expected time required for a root-mean-square momentum transfer during a collision is, in fact, given by Eq. (18).

C. The Debye-Bogolubov Gas

This regime is characterized by

$$n\lambda_D{}^3 = 1/\epsilon, \qquad (e^2/\lambda_D)(1/kT) = \epsilon \tag{3.19}$$

The short-time scale for this regime is the expected time for the traversal of a Debye radius by a particle

$$t_0 = \lambda_D/v_{th} = 1/\omega_p \tag{3.20}$$

The slow variation of D^1 takes place on the scale

$$\tau = \frac{1}{\epsilon} \frac{\lambda_D}{v_{th}} = \left(\frac{kT}{\phi_0}\right) \cdot \frac{\lambda_D}{v_{th}} = \left(\frac{1}{v_{th}}\right) \frac{1}{n(e^2/kT)^2} \tag{3.21}$$

We see from Eq. (21) that we can assign to the Debye spheres an effective mean free path

$$\lambda_{\text{eff}} = [n(e^2/kT)^2]^{-1} \tag{3.22}$$

since, in fact, e^2/kT is a radius that corresponds to the expected Rutherford cross section

$$\sigma_{\text{R}} \sim (e^2/kT)^2 \tag{3.23}$$

This is well borne out by the mathematical development. It is one of the main results of Bogolubov's approach that the kinetic equation

obtained in this regime drives the system to thermodynamical equilibrium in a time comparable to λ_{eff}/v_{th}.

D. The Choice of Intrinsic Time Scales

We are now prepared to exhibit the manner in which the method of extension exploits the intrinsic time scales of a gaseous system by reference to our model, Eq. (3).

In fact, some time ago [10], we introduced a mathematical method, which is designed to exploit to the fullest the presence of a small parameter whenever one is available in a problem. The method has been discussed repeatedly [7, 46, 47, 65–68]. The point at issue is that, in many situations for which a small parameter exists (we shall denote it by ϵ with $0 < \epsilon \ll 1$), direct expansion in ϵ fails very badly in a domain of major interest. For example, expansion of the Liouville equation in powers of the strength of the two-body interaction breaks down for times of the order of the time of relaxation of the system to thermodynamic equilibrium and thus fails to give the crucial information of how a (weakly coupled) gas approaches equilibrium. This failure of the perturbation expansion is expressed mathematically by saying that there is a (strong) nonuniformity in the expansion for small ϵ in the domain in question (large times for our example). The problem that our method is to solve, then, is that of *uniformizing* the expansion in ϵ.

It has become clear through the solution of several problems that our new method (the method of "extension") is of very considerable generality and of wide applicability. Since the presentation of reference [10] is rather abstract and relies on composition of mappings, it is useful to have a more explicit account of the theory. This discussion starts with such an account and proceeds to discuss the compatibility conditions of the extended expansion and a very general uniformizing expansion formula. After a discussion of the mechanics of the expansion procedure, we shall exhibit a constructive procedure for the determination of the time scales.

Consider the function f of the time variable

$$f(t) = e^{-\epsilon(t/t^*)} \tag{3.24}$$

where t^* is a fixed constant with dimensions of time, and t is (real) and positive. We have, then, from Eq. (24),

$$1 \geq f \geq 0, \qquad \text{all } t \tag{3.25}$$

and also

$$f(t) \xrightarrow[t\to\infty]{} 0 \tag{3.26}$$

Since ϵ is very small, however, f decays to zero very slowly. Let us suppose that f represents a physically observable quantity such as the

temperature difference between two rather well-insulated bodies. An observer who measures f and who is tabulating his readings with the help of a clock whose unit of time is t will have to wait a long time (the more so the smaller ϵ is) in order to detect any change at all in f (see Fig. 13). In fact, from Eq. (24), we see that the rate of change of f

$$\frac{\partial f(t)}{\partial (t/t^*)} = -\epsilon f(t) \tag{3.27}$$

is small of order ϵ. For our observer, it would seem at first it is quite legitimate to perform a Taylor expansion of Eq. (24) and write

$$f(t) = f_0(t) + \epsilon f_1(t) + \epsilon^2 f_2(t) + \cdots \tag{3.28}$$

with

$$f_0 = 1 \tag{3.29}$$

Equation (29), which of course also follows from Eq. (27) if $f(0) = 1$, is used as the initial value for t. We then have, from Eqs. (28) and (29),

$$f \approx f_0 = 1 \tag{3.30}$$

within "small corrections." This behavior is shown in Fig. 13.

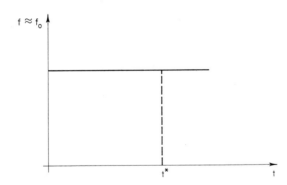

FIG. 13. Lowest approximation for a slowly decaying system.

When our observer realizes that some correction to the representation Eq. (30) is needed, that is, if he is interested in the long-time behavior of the system, he will consider a refinement to the lowest approximation given by Eq. (29)

$$f \approx f_0 + \delta f \tag{3.31}$$

and will investigate the quantity $\delta f = \epsilon f_1$, which corrects f_0. The result is

$$\epsilon f_1(t) = -\epsilon (t/t^*) \tag{3.32}$$

Clearly, δf is a small correction to f_0 provided that

$$t/t^* < 1 \tag{3.33}$$

However, $|\delta f|$ increases with t, and δf exactly *cancels* f_0 (and, therefore, it certainly ceases to be a small correction to f_0) when $1 - \epsilon(t/t^*) = 0$, or

$$t = t^*/\epsilon \tag{3.34}$$

If our observer were to insist on representing the behavior of f by means of the approximation $1 - \epsilon(t/t^*)$, he would find very large discrepancies after times of the order t^*/ϵ or longer. Thus, for $t/t^* = 1/\epsilon^2$, we have

$$(f_0 + \epsilon f_1)_{t=t^*/\epsilon^2} = 1 - (1/\epsilon) \approx -(1/\epsilon) \ll 0 \tag{3.35}$$

whereas from Eq. (24) we know that f is always nonnegative and less than or equal to one.

The discrepancy is because the quantity $\delta f \approx \epsilon f_1$ of Eq. (32) is not $O(\epsilon)$, that is,

$$\delta f \underset{\epsilon \to 0}{\nrightarrow} 0 \tag{3.36}$$

but rather it is $O(\epsilon t)$, that is,

$$\delta f \xrightarrow[\epsilon t \to 0]{} 0 \tag{3.37}$$

The "small correction" δf is not small simply when ϵ is small ($\epsilon \ll 1$ is the basic piece of information which is available) but in fact only when the combination (ϵt) is small.

It is easily verified that, for the Taylor expansion of f, if terms up to order ϵ^n are kept, the correction will be $O(\epsilon^{n+1}t^{n+1})$. The power of t which accompanies the corresponding power of ϵ simply *cannot* be dropped. This is an expression of the fact that f is an *analytic function* of the variable ϵt but not of the variable ϵ.

The direct Taylor expansion does not take full advantage of the smallness of ϵ because, for sufficiently large t, one must keep essentially all powers of t in order to have an accurate representation of f.

Another way of saying this is that $\exp[-\epsilon(t/t^*)]$ is its own asymptotic expansion for small ϵ, that is, we can write

$$f = e^{-\epsilon(t/t^*)} + O(\epsilon) \tag{3.38}$$

because, from Eq. (1), we obviously have

$$f - e^{-\epsilon(t/t^*)} \xrightarrow[\epsilon \to 0]{} 0 \tag{3.39}$$

Clearly, if instead of using the variable t and a clock whose basic unit is t^*, our observer were to use the *slow* variable $t' = \epsilon t$ (or, alternatively, an observer were endowed with a clock whose scale is measured in the *giant*

units of t^*/ϵ) the situation would be far more transparent, because Eq. (38) reads

$$f = e^{-t'/t^*} + O(\epsilon) \tag{3.40}$$

which, of course, is a very accurate representation of f. In fact, the coefficient of the $O(\epsilon)$ correction is identically zero for this extremely simple example.

The method of extension allows us, as we shall see shortly, always to perform readings on appropriate scales by employing a sufficient number of independent observers. For the simple example under discussion, the scales in question are time scales, but it will be clear that the method does not require any restrictions on the nature of the variables in the problem.

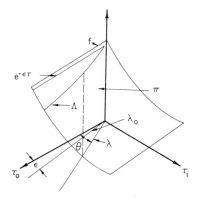

FIG. 14. Extension of a slowly decaying function.

We can now introduce our method by the following considerations. Imagine a three-dimensional space (see Fig. 14) with three orthogonal axes labeled τ_0, τ_1, and $\mathbf{f}$. For the example that we have in mind, τ_0 and τ_1 are "temporal" coordinates, and we can imagine that readings on two different clocks, the *fast* clock and the *slow* clock, correspond to the points on the τ_0 and τ_1 axes, respectively. $\mathbf{f}$ is, by definition, the following function of the two (independent) variables τ_0 and τ_1:

$$\mathbf{f}(\tau_0, \tau_1) = ce^{-\tau_1} \tag{3.41}$$

where c is a given constant. The surface that corresponds to $\mathbf{f}$ and that is depicted in Fig. 14 is a cylindrical surface that is constant in τ_0 while it decays exponentially in τ_1.

We can readily establish a connection between $\mathbf{f}(\tau_0, \tau_1)$ and $f(t)$. Introduce the dimensionless time variable

$$\tau = t/t^* \tag{3.42}$$

then, from Eq. (1), we can write f as

$$f = e^{-\epsilon\tau} = f[\tau] \tag{3.43}$$

Suppose now that a plane π through the **f** axis is introduced in the space of Fig. 14. π will intersect the (τ_0, τ_1) plane (see Fig. 14) along a line λ, which is given by the equation

$$\tau_1 = \tan\theta\tau_0 \tag{3.44}$$

where θ is the angle between the τ_0 axis and λ. π will also intersect the surface **f** along a definite line Λ.

Along Λ, **f** acquires the values f by virtue of Eq. (44) if we choose θ to be very small and τ_0 to coincide with τ, that is,

$$\tau_0 = \tau, \qquad \tan\theta = \epsilon \qquad \text{(on } \lambda_0) \tag{3.45}$$

Then we see from Eq. (41) that

$$\mathbf{f}(\tau, \epsilon\tau) = ce^{-\epsilon\tau} \tag{3.46}$$

which is identical with Eq. (43) provided that

$$c = 1 \tag{3.47}$$

With the choice Eq. (47), we therefore have

$$\mathbf{f}(\tau, \epsilon\tau) = f[\tau] \tag{3.48}$$

To make **f** coincide with f, we simply had to choose judiciously the line λ to coincide with λ_0.

Now we can see what is meant by "extension" and what is its advantage. The function **f** of Eq. (41) is completely independent of ϵ and is very much like the function Eq. (40) of t' in that its asymptotic expansion in ϵ is very simple. Furthermore, **f** coincides exactly with f along an appropriate trajectory λ_0 in the (τ_0, τ_1) plane. The function **f** is an "extension" of the function f, and the plane (τ_0, τ_1) is an "extension" of the (half-) line t. Equation (48) represents the "restriction" of the (extended) function **f** to the "standard" variables $\tau_0 = \tau$, $\tau_1 = \epsilon\tau$.

We can now set down more formally some basic definitions. Given a function $f(t)$, where t is in general an n-dimensional vector, and a function $\mathbf{f}(\tau_0, \tau_1, \ldots \tau_N)$ of the N-independent variables τ_0 to τ_N (each of which is an n-dimensional vector), we say that **f** is an extension of f if and only if there exists a set of $(N) \times (n)$ equations

$$\tau_k = \tau_k(\tau) \qquad (k = 1, 2, \ldots, N) \tag{3.49}$$

which, when inserted into **f**, give

$$\mathbf{f}[\tau_0(\tau), \tau_1(\tau), \ldots, \tau_N(\tau)] = f[\tau] \qquad (3.50)$$

We call the space of N-tuplets

$$\mathbf{\tau} = \{\tau_0, \tau_1, \ldots, \tau_N\} \qquad (3.51)$$

the extension of the domain $\{\tau\}$, and Eq. (49) the "trajectory" in the extended domain.

It is immediately clear that there are *infinitely many* extensions that correspond to a given function. This is so even when a definite trajectory has been chosen. A two-fold freedom is thereby introduced by considering the trajectory and choosing the extension itself.

The advantage of dealing with the extended functions **f** lies in the possibility of choosing an **f** with simpler and smoother dependence on the parameter ϵ than that offered by f itself. Thus, corresponding to an f that is not even analytic in ϵt^α, one can always choose an **f** that is analytic in ϵ. For example, $f = \exp(-\tau/\epsilon)$, and $\mathbf{f} = \exp(-\tau_{-1})$ with $\tau_{-1} = \tau/\epsilon$.

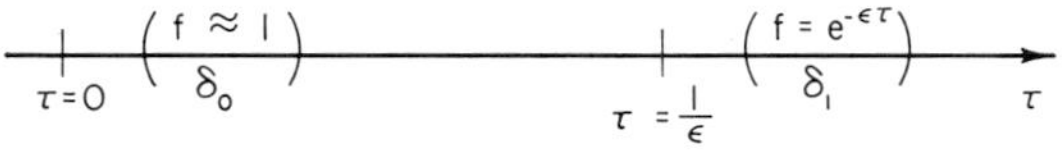

FIG. 15. Asymptotic expansion of slow decay.

The task of understanding the behavior of a quantity in a domain of interest δ_1 is thereby greatly facilitated even when this domain is far removed from the domain δ_0 in which the direct expansion in ϵ yields a valid description (see Fig. 15).

In terms of the variable τ given by Eq. (42), we readily see that the function $f = \exp(-\epsilon\tau)$ is fully defined by the differential equation

$$\frac{\partial f[\tau]}{\partial \tau} = -\epsilon f[\tau] \qquad (3.52)$$

with the initial condition

$$f[0] = 1 \qquad (3.53)$$

Since the problems of mathematical physics are very often formulated in terms of differential (or integrodifferential) equations subject to definite initial and boundary conditions, we shall illustrate the construction of the extension **f** from the point of view of Eqs. (52) and (53).

First of all, we can reproduce the Taylor Expansion of f for small ϵ by performing a *perturbation expansion* of Eqs. (52) and (53):

$$f[\tau] = f_0[\tau] + \epsilon f_1[\tau] + \epsilon^2 f_2[\tau] + \cdots \qquad (3.54)$$

and, substituting this expression into Eqs. (52) and (53), we obtain by equating powers of ϵ

$$\partial f_0/\partial \tau = 0 \tag{3.55}$$
$$\partial f_1/\partial \tau = -f_0 \tag{3.56}$$

and, in general,

$$\partial f_n/\partial \tau = -f_{n-1} \tag{3.57}$$

These equations must be integrated subject to the initial conditions obtained by substituting Eq. (54) into Eq. (53), namely,

$$f_0[0] = 1 \tag{3.58}$$
$$f_n[0] = 0, \qquad n > 0 \tag{3.59}$$

The result is clearly

$$f_n[\tau] = (-1)^n \frac{\epsilon^n \tau^n}{n!} \tag{3.60}$$

which corresponds to the Taylor expansion of Eq. (43). We have seen in the previous analysis that the higher terms cannot be considered as yielding "small corrections" to the lower ones for sufficiently long times.

We want now to show how the method of extension uniformizes the perturbation expansion, Eqs. (54) and (60).

Consider a function $\mathbf{f}(\tau_0, \tau_1)$ of the two independent variables τ_0 and τ_1 which is an extension of $f(t)$ along the "trajectory" λ_0 given by the equations

$$\lambda_0: \qquad \tau_0 = g_0(\tau), \qquad \tau_1 = \epsilon g_1(\tau) \tag{3.61}$$

where g_0 and g_1 are as yet unspecified functions of τ but not of ϵ. To simplify the discussion, we assume $g_0(0) = g_1(0) = 0$. Along the trajectories indicated in Eq. (61), we obtain, using the chain rule of differentiation, the following result:

$$\left(\frac{\partial f}{\partial \tau}\right)_{\lambda_0} = \left(g_0 \frac{\partial f}{\partial \tau_0} + \epsilon g_1 \frac{\partial f}{\partial \tau_1}\right)_{\lambda_0} \tag{3.62}$$

Now, it is clear that any $\mathbf{f}$ that satisfies the differential equation

$$\frac{d\tau_0}{d\tau} \frac{\partial \mathbf{f}(\tau_0, \tau_1)}{\partial \tau_0} + \frac{d\tau_1}{d\tau} \frac{\partial \mathbf{f}(\tau_0, \tau_1)}{\partial \tau_1} = -\epsilon \mathbf{f}(\tau_0, \tau_1) \tag{3.63}$$

where the derivatives $d\tau_i/d\tau$ are evaluated at λ_0, and

$$\mathbf{f}(0, 0) = 1 \tag{3.64}$$

is an extension of $f(t)$.

This follows from the definition of extension given by Eq. (50). In fact, if we specialize Eq. (63) to the trajectories given by Eq. (61), we can

use Eq. (62) to rewrite the left-hand side of Eq. (63), with the result

$$\frac{\partial \mathbf{f}[\tau]}{\partial \tau} = -\epsilon \mathbf{f}[\tau] \tag{3.65}$$

where we have used the notation

$$\mathbf{f}[\tau] \equiv \mathbf{f}[g_0(\tau), \epsilon g_1(\tau)] \tag{3.66}$$

for the restriction of $\mathbf{f}$ to λ_0. Also, since $g_0(0) = g_1(0) = 0$, Eq. (64) reads, with the notation of Eq. (66),

$$\mathbf{f}[0] = 1 \tag{3.67}$$

Equations (65) and (67) coincide with Eqs. (52) and (53) exactly, whereby our contention is proved.

The characteristics of the partial differential equation, Eq. (63), are given by

$$d\tau_0/\dot{\tau}_0 = d\tau_1/\dot{\tau}_1 \tag{3.68}$$

For the very simple choice of trajectories, Eq. (45),

$$d\tau_0/d\tau = 1, \qquad d\tau_1/d\tau = \epsilon \tag{3.69}$$

then Eq. (68) gives immediately

$$\tau_1 = \epsilon \tau_0 + \text{const}$$

which isolates the "standard" direction in the (τ_0, τ_1) plane.

We can now use Eqs. (63) and (64) to determine a class of extensions of $\mathbf{f}$. With the use of Eq. (69), Eq. (63) gives

$$\frac{\partial \mathbf{f}}{\partial \tau_0} + \epsilon \frac{\partial \mathbf{f}}{\partial \tau_1} = -\epsilon \mathbf{f}(\tau_0, \tau_1) \tag{3.70}$$

If we now expand the extended function $\mathbf{f}$ in powers of ϵ and demand that the expansion be asymptotic in ϵ, that is,

$$\begin{aligned} \mathbf{f} &= \mathbf{f}_0 + 0(\epsilon) \\ &= \mathbf{f}_0 + \epsilon \mathbf{f}_1 + 0(\epsilon^2) \end{aligned} \tag{3.71}$$

we find, by equating powers of ϵ,

$$\partial \mathbf{f}_0/\partial \tau_0 = 0 \tag{3.72}$$

and

$$\frac{\partial \mathbf{f}_1}{\partial \tau_0} + \frac{\partial \mathbf{f}_0}{\partial \tau_1} = -\mathbf{f}_0 \tag{3.73}$$

Equations (72) and (73) should be compared with Eqs. (55) and (56), respectively. We see two major differences between the extended pertur-

bation theory of Eqs. (72) and (73) and the direct perturbation theory of Eqs. (55) and (56):

(1) In zeroth order (apart from the variable τ being replaced by τ_0) with the extended expansion, we have a *partial* differential equation rather than an *ordinary* one. The integral of Eq. (72) is therefore an arbitrary function of τ_1

$$\mathbf{f}_0(\tau_0, \tau_1) = A(\tau_1) \tag{3.74}$$

rather than a constant.

(2) In first order, an altogether new term appears, the quantity $\partial \mathbf{f}_0/\partial \tau_1$. Such a quantity is characteristic of the new method and is responsible for our ability to achieve a uniform expansion or, more formally, to enforce the conditions Eq. (71). The solution of Eq. (73) is clearly

$$\mathbf{f}_1(\tau_0, \tau_1) = B(\tau_1) - \tau_0[A(\tau_1) + (\partial A/\partial \tau_1)] \tag{3.75}$$

We are now ready to obtain the *necessary and sufficient* conditions for uniform validity of our expansion. It is worth remarking that Eq. (71) required that the expansion of $\mathbf{f}$ be uniformly valid on the extended domain, that is, for all τ_0 and τ_1, not just along λ_0.

To prevent the growth of $\mathbf{f}_1(\tau_0, \tau_1)$ for large τ_0, it is sufficient to require

$$A + (\partial A/\partial \tau_1) = D(\tau_0) \tag{3.76}$$

where $D(\tau_0)$ decays for large τ_0 at least as $1/\tau_0$

$$D(\tau_0) \equiv O(1/\tau_0) \qquad (\text{large } \tau_0) \tag{3.77}$$

This is clear from Eq. (75). Equations (72) and (73), viewed as differential conditions on $\mathbf{f}_0$, must, however, be compatible; thus

$$\partial^2 \mathbf{f}_0/\partial \tau_0\, \partial \tau_1 = \partial^2 \mathbf{f}_0/\partial \tau_1\, \partial \tau_0 \tag{3.78}$$

But Eq. (76) will be compatible with Eq. (72) only if

$$\partial D(\tau_0)/\partial \tau_0 = 0 \tag{3.79}$$

Hence we must have

$$D = \text{const} \tag{3.80}$$

From Eq. (77), we see that the constant in Eq. (80) must be zero. Therefore, returning to Eq. (76), we find that

$$A + (\partial A/\partial \tau_1) = 0 \tag{3.81}$$

is the *necessary and sufficient* condition for the uniformity of the expansion Eq. (71).

It is worth noting that the sufficiency comes from an appropriate analysis of the singularities in the perturbation expansion, whereas the

necessity comes from the compatibility conditions of the extended perturbation equations. This feature is again a characteristic of the new method.

The solution of Eq. (81) is

$$A(\tau_1) = ce^{-\tau_1} \tag{3.82}$$

where c is a constant. By Eq. (74), we then have

$$\mathbf{f}_0(\tau_0, \tau_1) = ce^{-\tau_1} \tag{3.83}$$

This function coincides with Eq. (41).

Clearly, Eq. (64) requires $c = 1$ [to be compared with Eq. (47)], whereas use of Eq. (69) gives immediately, utilizing Eq. (65),

$$\mathbf{f}[\tau] = e^{-\epsilon\tau} = f[\tau]$$

This is the desired result. For the very simple example that we have discussed, it has been possible to obtain the exact answer with first-order theory. Of course, this is not a general feature of the method.

The very special choice of the trajectories, Eq. (69), was dictated by the nature of the nonuniformity exhibited by the perturbation series, Eq. (60). For the general problem, such a special choice is, of course, totally inadequate. We shall give, below, a general theorem that facilitates this choice in complex problems.

Other examples that can be handled with the simple extension scheme are given by the functions

$$1 - \epsilon\tau, \quad \sin \epsilon\tau, \quad \exp(+\epsilon\tau), \quad \sin \tau e^{-\epsilon\tau},$$
$$e^{-\tau} \cdot e^{-\epsilon\tau}, \quad e^{-\tau} + e^{-\epsilon\tau}$$

which correspond, respectively, to the differential equations

$$\dot{f} = -\epsilon; \quad \ddot{f} = -\epsilon^2 f; \quad \dot{f} = +\epsilon f; \quad \ddot{f} + 2\epsilon\dot{f} + (1 + \epsilon^2)f = 0;$$
$$\dot{f} = -(1 + \epsilon)f; \quad \ddot{f} + (1 + \epsilon)\dot{f} + \epsilon f = 0$$

The functions appearing in these simple examples are analytic in $\epsilon\tau$. Clearly, for functions analytic in ϵ alone, the Taylor expansion can be made to agree term by term with an asymptotic expansion, and there is no question of nonuniformity. For functions analytic in $\epsilon\tau$, the Taylor and asymptotic expansions can no longer be made to coincide term by term. Extension then facilitates the calculation of the asymptotic expansion. It must be emphasized that the extension must be so chosen that *its restriction* is the asymptotic expansion of f. This could be achieved for our simple examples by requiring Eq. (71)

$$\mathbf{f} = \mathbf{f}_0 + O(\epsilon)$$

but the *precise* condition on the extension is, in fact, the restriction to λ_0 of this condition, namely,

$$f = [\mathbf{f}_0] + O(\epsilon)$$

where we have introduced the notation

$$[\phi] \equiv \phi[\tau(\tau)] = \phi[\tau] \tag{3.84}$$

to denote, generally, the restriction of a function of τ_n to the values it acquired along the trajectories indicated in Eq. (49). For sufficiently complicated functions, the deceivingly slight difference between these last two equations can make for some difficult calculations.

The reader has certainly become aware of the possibility of summarizing the information contained in the different (time) scales τ_n into a single function $T(\tau_0, \tau_1, \ldots, \tau_N)$. Such a "superclock" is, in fact, very useful in many respects. For example, it helps in choosing, in a "canonical" manner, the extended function $\mathbf{f}(\tau_0, \tau_1, \ldots, \tau_N)$. We can easily illustrate this simple but important fact by means of our exponential function, Eq. (43). The extension of f which we have found to be useful, in view of our knowledge that ϵ is small, is given by Eq. (41) with the condition Eq. (47), i.e.,

$$\mathbf{f}(\tau_0, \tau_1) = e^{-\tau_1} \tag{3.85}$$

Consider now the superclock T defined by

$$T(\tau_0, \tau_1) = \tau_1/\epsilon \tag{3.86}$$

We then have, by use of Eq. (41), that our original f, as a function of the superclock variable [given by Eq. (86)], coincides with its extension $\mathbf{f}$ [given by Eq. (85)]. Thus,

$$f[T] = e^{-\epsilon T} = e^{-\epsilon(\tau_1/\epsilon)} = \mathbf{f}(\tau_0, \tau_1) \tag{3.87}$$

This very simple example illustrates a general truth. It is always possible to represent an extension of a given function with the function itself and an appropriate superclock [10]. Thus, roughly speaking, the superclock affects the "inversion" of the extension and focuses on the independent variable all the information contained in the separate clocks τ_n.

It is clear from the definition just given for T that the superclock must satisfy the following requirement: when the independent clocks τ_n have the values given by the trajectories of Eq. (49), then T must reduce simply to the standard time variable, i.e. [in our example the independent variable was made dimensionless by means of Eq. (42)],

$$T[\tau_0(\tau), \tau_1(\tau), \ldots, \tau_N(\tau)] = \tau \tag{3.88}$$

This equation immediately suggests that we might *expand* in powers of ϵ, not the dependent, but the independent variable. For example, we might choose the simple dependence of T on its arguments:

$$T = \tau_0 + \epsilon\tau_1 + \epsilon^2\tau_2 + \cdots \tag{3.89}$$

and proceed from here. This ansatz is, in fact, extremely useful for many purposes, and it is the basis for the method of Poincare-Lighthill [10]. To appreciate the usefulness of the expansion Eq. (89), even when the superclock is kept on λ_0, consider an equation of the form

$$\partial f[\tau]/\partial\tau = G[f, \tau] \tag{3.90}$$

which, written in terms of T, is

$$\partial f[T]/\partial T = G[f, T] \tag{3.91}$$

We have now the possibility of *assuming* the form Eq. (89) for T while leaving *open* the dependence of τ_n on τ. Suppose, in fact, that the τ_n depend on a parameter S in a form that is still to be specified. Then Eq. (91) can be written as, using once more the chain rule of differentiation,

$$\frac{dS}{dT}\frac{\partial f}{\partial S} = G[f, T] \tag{3.92}$$

or, multiplying by dT/dS,

$$\frac{\partial f}{\partial S} = G\frac{dT}{dS} \tag{3.93}$$

which, by virtue of Eq. (89), becomes

$$\frac{\partial f}{\partial S} = G\left[\frac{d\tau_0}{dS} + \epsilon\frac{d\tau_1}{dS} + \cdots\right] \tag{3.94}$$

With this procedure, one can stretch or contract the independent variable so as to follow the quirks of f smoothly through the parameter S. With the superclock restricted to λ_0, it is difficult, however, to *separate* the different components of a system which instead are easily discerned in terms of the independent τ_n. Thus, a glance at Eq. (86) shows that, for our simple exponential, the appropriate superclock is nonanalytic in ϵ and not at all of the type Eq. (89). It is easy to give an example where a "mixture" of the simple choices Eqs. (89) and (69) are to be used to obtain a uniform asymptotic expansion of the unknown function.

We now give a general form of the derivative expansion from which both Eqs. (70) [or Eq. (62)] and (94) are readily obtained by specialization.

Consider a function $f(\tau)$ that satisfies Eq. (90). Imagine now the variable τ replaced by the supervariable T, which is as yet an unspecified

function of a parameter S. We thus obtain the form of Eq. (93). Suppose now that the *new domain* $\{S\}$ is extended. Call σ_n the variables that parametrize the extension of $\{S\}$. In this extended space, we can then write, as in Eq. (51),

$$\mathbf{d} = \{\sigma_0, \sigma_1, \ldots, \sigma_n\} \tag{3.95}$$

with the requirement that, along appropriate trajectories,

$$\sigma_n = \sigma_n(S), \qquad n = 1, 2, \ldots, M$$

we must recover our f. We can now write, using the chain rule Eq. (62),

$$\dot\sigma_0 \frac{\partial \mathbf{f}}{\partial \sigma_0} + \dot\sigma_1 \frac{\partial \mathbf{f}}{\partial \sigma_1} + \cdots \dot\sigma_M \frac{\partial \mathbf{f}}{\partial \sigma_M}$$
$$= G\left[\dot\sigma_0 \frac{\partial \mathbf{T}}{\partial \sigma_0} + \dot\sigma_1 \frac{\partial \mathbf{T}}{\partial \sigma_1} + \cdots \dot\sigma_M \frac{\partial \mathbf{T}}{\partial \sigma_M} \right] \tag{3.96}$$

If we now expand $\mathbf{f}$ and $\mathbf{T}$ in ϵ and also G, whenever G is an ϵ-dependent quantity, and if we imagine that the σ_n's are ordered in ϵ, we obtain a very general form of uniformizing expansion.

Clearly, if only one σ_M is retained, Eq. (96) reduces to the Poincare-Lighthill formula, Eq. (94); whereas if S and T are made to coincide with τ, we recover the Enskog-Bogolubov formula, Eq. (62) [or Eq. (63) with appropriate right-hand side] [4, 6]. The new equation, Eq. (96), thus constitutes a strong generalization of these older theories.

We now give a constructive procedure to determine the fundamental variables required by the method of extension. The construction allows for the introduction of arbitrary scaling functions that are determined by the requirement that the expansion of the unknown function be *uniformly* valid.

We illustrate the procedure by means of the familiar example of a simple exponential decay. Consider

$$\partial f / \partial t = -\epsilon f, \qquad f(0) = 1 \tag{3.97}$$

Since the Taylor expansion of $f(t)$ in ϵ does not coincide with the asymptotic expansion of $f(t)$ in ϵ for large t, we introduce an extension of $f(t)$, $\mathbf{f}(\tau_0, \tau_1)$. The two fundamental variables τ_0 and τ_1 are to be determined as functions of t:

$$\dot\tau_0 = g(t), \qquad \dot\tau_1 = \epsilon h(t) \tag{3.98}$$

We can assume, for convenience,

$$\tau_0(t) = t \tag{3.99}$$

The extension of Eq. (97) gives, by virtue of Eq. (99),

$$\frac{\partial \mathbf{f}}{\partial \tau_0} + \epsilon h(\tau_0) \frac{\partial \mathbf{f}}{\partial \tau_1} = -\epsilon \mathbf{f}(\tau_0, \tau_1) \tag{3.100}$$

Expanding $\mathbf{f}$ as $\mathbf{f}^0 + \epsilon \delta \mathbf{f}$, we find

$$\partial \mathbf{f}^{(0)} / \partial \tau_0 = 0 \tag{3.101}$$

$$\frac{\partial \delta \mathbf{f}}{\partial \tau_0} + h(\tau_0) \frac{\partial \mathbf{f}^0}{\partial \tau_1} = -\mathbf{f}^0 \tag{3.102}$$

which are readily integrated as

$$\mathbf{f}^0 = A(\tau_1) \tag{3.103}$$

$$\delta \mathbf{f} = -\tau_0 A(\tau_1) - \frac{\partial A}{\partial \tau_1} \int_0^{\tau_0} h(\tau) \, d\tau + B(\tau_1) \tag{3.104}$$

The uniformity of the expansion requires that

$$\epsilon \delta \mathbf{f} / \mathbf{f}^0 \to 0, \qquad \epsilon \to 0 \tag{3.105}$$

or, from Eq. (104), by differentiating with respect to τ_0

$$0 = 1 + \frac{\partial \log A(\tau_1)}{\partial \tau_1} h(\tau_0) \tag{3.106}$$

Differentiating again, we find

$$h(\tau_0) = \text{const} = k$$

which, inserted into Eq. (98), yields, using Eq. (99),

$$\tau_1(t) = \epsilon k t + \tau_1(0) \tag{3.107}$$

Thus the desired result has been constructed.

Equation (67) shows that the educated "guess" that one would make for the proper time scale, $\tau_1 = \epsilon t$ [from dimensional considerations by inspection of Eq. (97)], is in fact necessary.

In view of the great variety of kinetic equations that have been derived by the method just described, we give in the next section a summary of the kinetic equations available in the various notations currently used.

IV. KINETIC EQUATIONS

In this section, we summarize the kinetic equations that are appropriate to the different gaseous regimes. In recent literature, these equations have appeared in different notations, which makes it difficult to

recognize the similarities as well as the differences. We give here the most important forms of each equation.

A. The Short-Range Regime

The kinetic equation valid in this regime is Boltzmann's. We give three alternative forms of this equation:

$$\partial F^1/\partial t = LS_{-\infty}{}^2 F^1 F^1 \qquad \text{(Bogolubov [6])} \qquad (4.1)$$

$$\partial F^1/\partial t = L\zeta^*(iH^2) F^1 F^1 \qquad \text{(Sandri [7])} \qquad (4.2)$$

The original form is

$$\frac{\partial F^1(x_1)}{\partial t} = \int d\mathbf{v}_2 \, d\Omega |\mathbf{v}_1 - \mathbf{v}_2| \sigma [F^1(\mathbf{v}_1{}^*) F^1(\mathbf{v}_2{}^*)$$
$$- F^1(\mathbf{v}_1) F^1(\mathbf{v}_2)] \qquad \text{(Boltzmann [42])} \qquad (4.3)$$

The only symbol that appears in these equations which was not defined in Section I is

$$S_{-\infty}{}^2 \equiv \lim_{\tau \to \infty} \exp \left[-H^2 \lambda \right]$$

B. Landau or Weak-Coupling Regime

We give, again, three equivalent alternatives. The most compact version of the Landau equation is

$$\partial F^1/\partial t = L\zeta^*(iK^2) I^2 F^1 F^1 \qquad \text{(Sandri [7])} \qquad (4.4)$$

A very useful form is

$$\partial F^1/\partial t = -(\partial/\partial \mathbf{v}) \cdot \mathbf{J}(\mathbf{v}) \qquad \text{(Bernstein [22])} \qquad (4.5)$$

where the velocity-space current is given by

$$\mathbf{J}(\mathbf{v}) = \int d\mathbf{v}' \, Q(\mathbf{v}, \mathbf{v}') \cdot \left\{ \frac{\partial F^1(x)}{\partial \mathbf{v}} F^1(\mathbf{v}') - \frac{\partial F^1(\mathbf{v}')}{\partial \mathbf{v}'} F^1(\mathbf{v}) \right\} \qquad (4.6)$$

and the tensor Q is given in terms of the Fourier transform $\tilde{U}(\mathbf{q})$ of the potential by

$$Q_{ij} = -\frac{1}{8\bar{u}^2} \int d\mathbf{q} \, \delta(\mathbf{q} \cdot \mathbf{v} - \mathbf{q} \cdot \mathbf{v}') q_i q_j \tilde{U}^2(\mathbf{q}) \qquad (4.7)$$

Finally, the Fokker-Planck form is

$$\frac{\partial F^1}{\partial t} = \frac{\partial}{\partial \mathbf{v}} (\mathbf{A} F^1) + \frac{\partial^2}{\partial \mathbf{v} \, \partial \mathbf{v}} : (\mathbf{B} F^1) \qquad (4.8)$$

The coefficient of "friction" in velocity space $\mathbf{A}$ is

$$\mathbf{A} = -2 \int d\mathbf{v}' \; \Gamma F^1(\mathbf{v}') \frac{\partial}{\partial \mathbf{v}} \frac{1}{|\mathbf{v} - \mathbf{v}'|} \tag{4.9}$$

and the diffusion tensor in velocity space $\mathbf{B}$ is

$$\mathbf{B}_{ij} = \frac{1}{2} \int d\mathbf{v}' \; \Gamma F^1(\mathbf{v}') \frac{\partial^2}{\partial v_i \, \partial v_j} |\mathbf{v} - \mathbf{v}'| \tag{4.10}$$

with the cutoff factor

$$\Gamma = \frac{4\pi e^4}{m^2} \log \Lambda \, , \qquad \Lambda = \frac{3(kT)^{3/2}}{e^3(4\pi n)^{1/2}} \tag{4.11}$$

C. Debye-Bogolubov Regime

There are two alternative forms:

$$\partial F^1/\partial t = L\zeta^*(iK^2 - i\Gamma^2)I^2 F^1 F^1 \qquad \text{(Sandri [7])} \tag{4.12}$$

where $(\Gamma^2\Lambda)_{12} \equiv L_{13}F_1{}^1\Lambda_{23} + L_{23}F_2{}^1\Lambda_{13}$ and the Lenard-Guernsey-Balescu form

$$\frac{\partial F^1}{\partial t} = -\frac{\partial}{\partial \mathbf{v}} \cdot \mathbf{J}(\mathbf{v}) \tag{4.13}$$

where the velocity space current is given by Eq. (6), with the tensor Q given by

$$Q_{ij} = -\frac{1}{8\pi^2} \int d\mathbf{q} \; \delta(\mathbf{q} \cdot \mathbf{v} - \mathbf{q} \cdot \mathbf{v}') \frac{q_i q_j \tilde{U}^2(\mathbf{q})}{|1 + \tilde{U}(\mathbf{q})\Psi(\mathbf{k}, \mathbf{k} \cdot \mathbf{v})|^2} \tag{4.14}$$

The function Ψ is, in turn, given by

$$\Psi(\mathbf{k}, u) = \int_{-\infty}^{+\infty} \frac{du'}{u - u' - i\epsilon} \frac{\partial f(\mathbf{k}, u)}{\partial u'} \tag{4.15}$$

with

$$f(\mathbf{K}, u) = \int d\mathbf{v} \; F^1(\mathbf{v}) \; \delta(u - \mathbf{K} \cdot \mathbf{v}) \tag{4.16}$$

D. Stable Coulomb Force

For stable plasmas, we have [28]

$$\partial F^1/\partial t = L\zeta^*(i\sigma)I^2 F^1 F^1$$
where
$$\sigma = H^2 - \Gamma^2 \tag{4.17}$$

We recover the result given by Book and Frieman [31] and Weinstock [32] by noting that

$$L\zeta^*(i\sigma)I^2 \approx L[\zeta^*(iH^2) - \zeta^*(iK^2) + \zeta^*(iK^2 - i\Gamma^2)]I^2 \tag{4.18}$$

The basic reason why the linear combination of the collision integrals in Eq. (18) leads to a convergent result is that both Landau cutoffs are logarithmic, as shown by Eq. (11).

E. The Relaxation Equation

Krook and collaborators [49] have given on phenomenological grounds a formalization of Jeans' relaxation equation [68] by setting

$$\partial F^1/\partial t = (M - F^1)/\tau \tag{4.19}$$

By introducing the relative departure of the molecular distribution function from thermodynamical equilibrium Δ (M is the Maxwellian distribution),

$$M\Delta \equiv F^1 - M \tag{4.20}$$

we have the simple relaxation law of Jeans

$$\Delta = -(1/\tau)\Delta \tag{4.21}$$

which clearly drives the molecular distribution to thermal equilibrium. We have seen that the kinetic equation valid in the four previously described regimes can be written in the form

$$\partial F^1/\partial t = L\zeta^* I^2 F^1 F^1 \tag{4.22}$$

Inserting Eq. (20) in the form $F^1 = M(1 + \Delta)$, we have, since $\partial M/\partial t = 0$,

$$\partial \Delta/\partial t = -(1/\tau)\Delta \tag{4.23}$$

where $1/\tau$ is the linear operator (subscripts denote particle indices)

$$\left(-\frac{1}{\tau}\Delta\right)_1 \equiv M_1^{-1}L_{12}(\zeta^*I)_{12}M_1M_2(\Delta_1 + \Delta_2) \tag{4.24}$$

The condition for the validity of Jeans' relaxation law is then that the spectrum of the linear operator $1/\tau$ should have a well-separated dominant eigenvalue. Since the H-theorem is valid for Eq. (22), it is easy to show that the spectrum of $1/\tau$ is positive definite, and real. In Fig. 16, a spectrum is shown for which the simple relaxation law will hold.

This circumstance is ideally suited for the point of view advocated in the third section. We have placed the foundations of our theory of irreversibility on the notion of well-separated time scales in sharp contrast with the view held classically (Boltzmann) of sharply localized particle-particle collisions. We can place well-defined conditions directly on the Liouville equation in order to secure Jeans' relaxation equation.

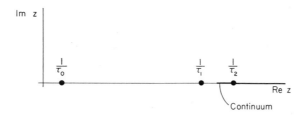

FIG. 16. The relaxation spectrum.

By direct integration of the Liouville equation (for a spatially homogeneous gas), we find, in fact $(F^1 \equiv D^1)$,

$$\partial D'/\partial t = -\int d\Gamma_{N-1} H^N D^N \qquad (4.25)$$

If we now set, initially,

$$D^N = \prod_{i=1}^{N} M_i(1 + \epsilon\Delta_i) + G^N = \left(\prod_{i=1}^{N} M_i\right)\left(1 + \epsilon \sum_{i=1}^{N} \Delta_i\right) + G^N \qquad (4.26)$$

where we have assumed ϵ to be small, we find readily (the proof is given in Ref. [48]) the form Eq. (23) with the linear operator

$$-\frac{1}{\tau}\Delta = M^{-1} \int dP_{N-1} L_0 \zeta_0 * I^N \prod_{i=1}^{N} M_i \sum_{j=1}^{N} \Delta_j \qquad (4.27)$$

The precise and completely general conditions for the validity of Jeans' relaxation equation can, therefore, be given. They are as follows:

(J1) The statistical correlation G^N must phase mix over a time scale t_0 that is much shorter than the scale on which D^1 changes.

(J2) The spectrum of the linear operator $1/\tau$ given in Eq. (27) must have a dominant eigenvalue.

These two conditions are somewhat implicit because of the complexity of Eq. (27). Their importance lies in the fact that they are clear-cut and derivable directly from first principles. As our understanding of the spectrum of the operator $1/\tau$ increases, the "Jeans" conditions, J1 and J2, will become increasingly more useful. It is worth contrasting the physical meaning of $1/\tau$ of Eq. (27), which is, in fact, the "collision integral" for the relaxation form of kinetic theory, with the Boltzmann collision integral. This latter corresponds to a single collision of the particle chosen as typical with each of the others that cross its path; the former includes *all* collisions of our chosen particle with each of the others in the gas. The distinction is best seen if we recall

the r-type collisions of Section II. Even confining ourselves to a sub-system of three particles, we need take into account such sequences as (1, 2)—(2, 3)—(1, 2) in which particle 1 undergoes several collisions.

Relaxation equations are considerably more readily treated than the kinetic equations of Boltzmann's type. They can be, therefore, of great use in analyzing complex situations. In a recent series of studies, we have initiated a phenomenological analysis of the transport properties of real gases [9] which is based on this remark.

ACKNOWLEDGMENT

This work was supported by the Office of Aerospace Research. The author is particularly indebted to Dr. A. Kritz for a critical reading of the manuscript and many pertinent suggestions.

REFERENCES

1. Gibbs, W., "Elementary Principles in Statistical Mechanics." Dover, New York, 1960.
2. Harrison, B. K., Thorne, K. S., Wakano, M., and Wheeler, J. A. "Gravitation Theory and Gravitational Collapse." Univ. of Chicago Press, Chicago, Illinois, 1965.
3. Fitts, D. D., "Nonequilibrium Thermodynamics." McGraw-Hill, New York, 1962.
4. Chapman, S. and Cowling, T. G., "The Mathematical Theory of Non-uniform Gases." Cambridge Univ. Press, London and New York, 1960.
5. Ehrenfest, P. and Ehrenfest, T., "The Conceptual Foundations of the Statistical Approach in Mechanics." Cornell Univ. Press, Ithaca, New York, 1959.
6. Bogolubov, N. N., Problems of a Dynamical Theory in Statistical Physics, in "Studies in Statistical Mechanics I." North-Holland Publ., Amsterdam, 1962.
7. Sandri, G., *Ann. Phys. NY* **24**, 332, 380 (1963).
8. Hirschfelder, J. O., Curtiss, C. F., and Bird, R. B., "Molecular Theory of Gases and Liquids." Wiley, New York, 1964.
9. Sandri, G., Kritz, A., and Schatzman, F., Kinetic Thermodynamics. ARAP Rept. (1966).
10. Sandri, G., The New Foundations of Statistical Dynamics. Rutgers Lectures (1961–62).
11. Pauli, W., "Probleme der Modernen Physik," p. 30. Hirzel, Leipzig, 1928.
12. Sandri, G., *Nuovo Cimento* **32**, 985 (1964).
13. Sandri, G., *Nuovo Cimento* **36**, 300 (1965).
14. Sandri, G., General Theory of Irreversibility. *Bull. Am. Phys. Soc.* **9**, 227 (1964).
15. Sandri, G., Sullivan, R., Kritz, A., and Schatzman, F., Statistical Mechanical Theory of Dense Plasmas. ARAP Rept. (1964).
16. Zwanzig, R., *Physica* **30**, 1109 (1964).
17. Tolman, R. C., "The Principles of Statistical Mechanics." Oxford Univ. Press (Clarendon), London and New York, 1938.
18. Born, M., and Green, H. S., A General Kinetic Theory of Liquids, I. *Proc. Roy. Soc.* (*London*) **A188**, 10 (1949).
19. Kirkwood, J. G., *J. Chem. Phys.* **14**, 180 (1946).

20. Yvon, J., *Acta Sci. Ind.* **203** (1935).
21. Kritz, A. and Sandri, G., *Bull. Am. Phys. Soc.* **10**, 604 (1965).
22. Bernstein, I. B. and Robinson, B., A Variational Calculation of Plasma Transport Properties. Matterhorn Rept. (1959).
23. Sandri, G., Higher Order Kinetic Equations. *Bull. Am. Phys. Soc.* **8**, 152 (1963).
24. Sandri, G., *Nuovo Cimento* **31**, 1131 (1964).
25. Lenard, A., *Ann. Phys. NY* **10**, 3 (1960).
26. Guernsey, R. L., The Kinetic Theory of Fully Ionized Gases. Univ. of Michigan Rept., UMRI Project 03114 (1960).
27. Balescu, R., *Phys. Fluids* **3**, 62 (1960).
28. Sandri, G., *Phys. Rev. Letters* **11**, 178 (1963).
29. Baldwin, D., *Phys. Fluids* **5**, 1523 (1962).
30. Hubbard, J., *Proc. Roy. Soc. (London)* **A261**, 371 (1961).
31. Book, D. and Frieman, E., *Phys. Fluids* **6**, 1700 (1963).
32. Weinstock, J., *Phys. Rev.* **133**, A673 (1964).
33. Frieman, E., *Phys. Today* **15**, 28 (1962).
34. Van Hove, L., Hugenholtz, N. M., and Howland, L. P., "Quantum Theory of Many-particle Systems." Benjamin, New York, 1961.
35. Prigogine, I., "Nonequilibrium Statistical Mechanics." Wiley (Interscience), New York, 1962.
36. Prigogine, I and Balescu, R., *Physica* **25**, 281, 302 (1959); **26**, 145 (1960).
37. Thurston, W. and Sandri, G., *Bull. Am. Phys. Soc.* **9**, 386 (1964). In this paper, the first known example of four successive collisions was given. A similar result was obtained by J. Foch. I am particularly indebted to G. Uhlenbeck for pointing this out to me.
38. Sandri, G., Sullivan, R., and Norem, P., *Phys. Rev. Letters* **13**, 743 (1964).
39. Woodrow, P., Sullivan, R., and Sandri, G., Ann. SIAM Meeting (1965).
40. Hopf, E., "Ergodentheorie." Chelsea, New York, 1948.
41. Halmos, P. R., "Ergodic Theory." Chelsea, New York, 1956.
42. Boltzmann, L., "Lectures on Gas Theory." University of California Press, Berkeley, California, 1964.
43. Chapman, S. and Cowling, T. G., "The Mathematical Theory of Non-uniform Gases." Cambridge Univ. Press, London and New York, 1960.
44. Hirschfelder, J. O., Curtiss, C. F., and Bird, R. B., "Molecular Theory of Gases and Liquids." Wiley, New York, 1964.
45. Landau, L. D., *Physik. Zats. Sowjetunion* **10**, 154 (1960).
46. Sandri, G., *Nuovo Cimento* **36**, 67 (1965).
47. Sandri, G. and Sullivan, R., *Nuovo Cimento* **37**, 1799 (1965).
48. Sandri, G., On the Relationship Between the Single-relaxation-time Equation and Liouville's Theorem. ARAP Rept. (1966); also to be published.
49. Bhatnagar, P. L., Gross, E. P., and Krook, M., *Phys. Rev.* **94**, 511 (1954).
50. Uhlenbeck, G. E., *Phys. Today* **13**, 16 (1960).
51. Frank, D., Pfirsch, D., and Priess, S., *Z. Naturforsch.* **20**, 147 (1965).
52. Weinstock, J., *Phys. Rev.* **132**, 454 (1963).
53. Cohen, E. G. D. and Dorfman, R., *Phys. Letters* **16**, 124 (1965).
54. Sengers, J. V., *Phys. Rev. Letters* **15**, 515 (1965).
55. Kawasaki, K. and Oppenheim, I., *Phys. Rev.* **139A**, 1763 (1965).
56. van Leeuwen, J. M. J. and Weijland, A., *Phys. Letters* (to be published).
57. Dorfman, R., Transport Coefficients for Dense Gases, this book, Section III, pp. 199–212.

58. Montgomery, D., Connection between the Bogolubov and the Frieman and Sandri Methods. Utrecht Preprint (to be published).
59. Frieman, E. and Goldmann, R., to be published.
60. Private communication (1963).
61. Private communication (1963).
62. Fibich, M. and Sandri, G., Statistical Mechanics of Charged Particles in the Presence of Magnetic Irregularities. ARAP Rept. 82.
63. Choh, S. T. and Uhlenbeck, G. E., The Kinetic Theory of Phenomena in Dense Gases. Navy Theoret. Phys. Contract Rept. No. NONR 1224(15) (1958).
64. McCune, J., Morse, T., and Sandri, G., On the Relaxation of Gases Toward Continuum Flow, *in* "Rarefied Gas Dynamics," Vol. I, p. 115. Academic Press, New York, 1963.
65. Frieman, E., *J. Math. Phys.* **4**, 410 (1963).
66. Montgomery, D. and Tidman, D., *Phys. Fluids* **2**, 242 (1964).
67. van Dyke, M., "Perturbation Methods in Fluid Dynamics." Academic Press, New York, 1964. Related forms of the method are discussed here.
68. Jeans, J., "Kinetic Theory of Gases." Cambridge Univ. Press, London and New York, 1946.

Enhanced Fluctuations in Plasmas

D. A. TIDMAN

INSTITUTE FOR FLUID DYNAMICS
AND APPLIED MATHEMATICS
UNIVERSITY OF MARYLAND
COLLEGE PARK, MARYLAND

Some of the consequences of enhanced plasma fluctuations for the emission or scattering of electromagnetic waves by a plasma are discussed.

I. INTRODUCTION

Most plasmas, whether they are produced in the laboratory or naturally occurring, are far from thermal equilibrium. One consequence of this is that they are very "noisy," i.e., various modes of the plasma are highly excited to more than the energy of $KT/2$ per propagating mode appropriate to thermal equilibrium. This excited wave spectrum may take the form of macroscopic turbulence excited externally or by instabilities, or at a lower amplitude level it is continually present in the form of the natural fluctuations of a many-body system. Such turbulent motion plays an important role in the processes of scattering and emission of electromagnetic radiation by a plasma, and also contributes to transport processes such as the rapid diffusion of plasma across a magnetic field through wave-particle scattering.

The chart illustrates the domains of theoretical activity applicable to several amplitude levels of disordered plasma motion. The conventional

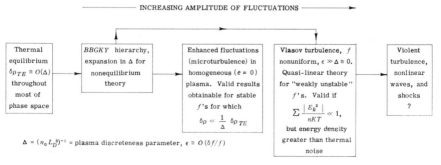

INCREASING AMPLITUDE OF FLUCTUATIONS →

Thermal equilibrium $\delta \rho_{TE} \cong O(\Delta)$ throughout most of phase space	*BBGKY* hierarchy, expansion in Δ for nonequilibrium theory	Enhanced fluctuations (microturbulence) in homogeneous $(e=0)$ plasma. Valid results obtainable for stable f's for which $\delta \rho \ll \frac{1}{\Delta} \delta \rho_{TE}$	Vlasov turbulence, f nonuniform, $\epsilon \gg \Delta \cong 0$. Quasi-linear theory for "weakly unstable" f's. Valid if $\sum \frac{|E_k^2|}{nKT} \ll 1$, but energy density greater than thermal noise	Violent turbulence, nonlinear waves, and shocks ?

$\Delta = (n_0 L_D^3)^{-1}$ = plasma discreteness parameter, $\epsilon \cong O(\delta f/f)$

399

BBGKY [1] theory is in the second box.   It is useful for plasmas in which $\Delta^{-1} \equiv n_0 L_D{}^3 \gg 1$, where n_0 is the average electron density and L_D the Debye length, but it has only been practical to calculate the fluctuation spectrum to $O(n_0 L_D{}^3)^{-1}$ for cases in which the one particle distribution, f, is nearly spatially homogeneous and stable.   Plasmas that are "weakly unstable" and for which effects of $O(n_0 L_D{}^3)^{-1}$ can be neglected fall in box 4, i.e., the domain of weakly turbulent Vlasov plasmas to which perturbation techniques (e.g., the quasi-linear theory) of one sort or another can be applied.

In this paper, we confine our discussion to the domain of box 3, i.e., to some simple comments on enhanced fluctuations excited by non-Maxwellian but stable plasmas.

II. ELECTRIC FIELD FLUCTUATIONS OF A NONTHERMAL PLASMA

Consider the electric field fluctuations in a Coulomb gas of particles free of magnetic field.   We define the autocorrelation function C and spectral density S for these fluctuations by

$$C(\mathbf{x}, t) = \langle \mathbf{E}(\mathbf{X}, T)\mathbf{E}(\mathbf{X} + \mathbf{x}, T + t) \rangle, \tag{1}$$

$$S(\mathbf{k}, \omega) = \int_{-\infty}^{\infty} d\mathbf{x}\, dt\, e^{-i(\mathbf{k}\cdot\mathbf{x}+\omega t)}\, C(\mathbf{x}, t). \tag{2}$$

C measures the relatedness at different points of a fluctuating quantity, and S gives the Fourier spectrum of the fluctuations $[C(|x| \to \infty$ or $t \to \infty) \to 0]$.   Formulas for bremsstrahlung, or radiation scattering cross sections, etc., can be expressed in terms of various spectral densities like S.

Now it has been shown by Rostoker [2] and simplified more recently by Dawson and Nakagawa [3] that many results of kinetic theory can be obtained by a consideration of test-particle results.   In particular, it is simple to calculate the spectral density S by using the result that to first order in Δ the plasma can be regarded as an uncorrelated gas of dressed test particles.   By a dressed test particle, we mean a particle plus its attendant disturbance of the surrounding medium, i.e., polarization cloud and Cerenkov wake.   Thus the electric field at $\mathbf{x}$ due to a test particle of charge e_t, velocity $\mathbf{v}_1$, located at $\mathbf{x}_1$ at time t, is

$$\mathbf{E}(\mathbf{x}\,;\mathbf{x}_1,\mathbf{v}_1,t) = -\frac{e_t}{2\pi^2} \int \frac{d\mathbf{k}\; i\mathbf{k} e^{i\mathbf{k}\cdot(\mathbf{x}-\mathbf{x}_1)}}{k^2 D(\mathbf{k},\,-i\mathbf{k}\cdot\mathbf{v}_1)} \tag{3}$$

where $D(\mathbf{k}, i\omega)$ is the plasma dielectric constant,

$$D(\mathbf{k}, i\omega) = 1 - \sum \frac{\omega_j^2}{k^2} \int \frac{d\mathbf{v} \, \mathbf{k} \cdot \partial f_j/\partial \mathbf{v}}{(\omega + \mathbf{k} \cdot \mathbf{v})}, \; \text{Im}(\omega) < 0, \tag{4}$$

and $\omega_j = (4\pi n_{0j} e_j^2/m_j)^{1/2}$, the plasma frequency on the jth species of particle in the plasma.

We next calculate C as follows:

$$\langle \mathbf{E}(\mathbf{x}, t)\mathbf{E}(\mathbf{x}', t') \rangle = \sum \frac{n_{0j}}{V} \int \mathbf{E}(\mathbf{x} ; \mathbf{x}_1, \mathbf{v}_1, t)\mathbf{E}(\mathbf{x}' ; \mathbf{x}_1', \mathbf{v}_1', t')$$
$$\times W(\mathbf{x}_1, \mathbf{v}_1, t ; \mathbf{x}_1', \mathbf{v}_1', t') \, d\mathbf{x}_1 \, d\mathbf{v}_1 \, d\mathbf{x}_1' \, d\mathbf{v}_1'$$

where W is the joint probability of finding a particle in $d\mathbf{x}_1 \, d\mathbf{v}_1$ at t and the same particle in $d\mathbf{x}_1' \, d\mathbf{v}_1'$ at t'. There are n_{0j} such contributions to

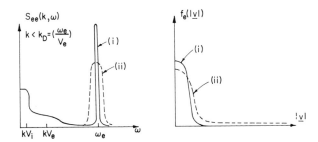

FIG. 1. Plot of spectral density for a Maxwellian distribution (case i) and a distribution with a non-Maxwellian tail (case ii).

$\langle \; \rangle$ from the jth species. V is a volume in which the plasma is enclosed and over which the space integrations go, and we take $V \to \infty$ later.

Now if the test particles are assumed to be uncorrelated,

$$W = Vf(\mathbf{v}_1) \, \delta[\mathbf{x}_1' - \mathbf{x}_1 + \mathbf{v}_1(t' - t)] \, \delta(\mathbf{v}_1' - \mathbf{v}_1),$$

which leads immediately to

$$S(\mathbf{k}, \omega) = (4\pi e)^2 \frac{\mathbf{k}\mathbf{k}}{k^4} \frac{2\pi}{k} \frac{\Sigma n_{0j} F_j(\omega/k)}{|D(\mathbf{k}, i\omega)|^2}, \tag{5}$$

$$F_j(u) = \int d\mathbf{v} \, \delta\left(u - \frac{\mathbf{k} \cdot \mathbf{v}}{k}\right) f_j(\mathbf{v}). \tag{6}$$

In Fig. 1, we have drawn the function $S = Tr(\mathbf{S})$ as a function of ω for a fixed wavenumber $k < k_D$ and for the case of thermal equilibrium, i.e., a Maxwellian f. The spectral density S has two shelves at $0 < \omega \gtrsim O(kV_i)$ and for $\omega \gtrsim O(kV_e)$. These correspond to Fourier components

that drift with phase velocities of the order of the thermal velocities V_i and V_e of the ions and electrons, respectively. There is also a sharp resonance at $\omega \cong \omega_e$ and width $\gamma_L(\omega_e/k)$ which is the Landau damping decrement for longitudinal plasma oscillations of phase velocity ω_e/k. This resonance becomes wider and has more area under it for electron distributions that have non-Maxwellian tails, as illustrated by distribution (ii) in Fig. 1. It has its origin in the emission of Cerenkov electron plasma waves by the high-energy electrons in the tail of the distribution and their subsequent reabsorption through Landau damping.

The energy density in the propagating ($k < k_D$) spectrum of enhanced plasma oscillations represented by the resonance in S at $\omega \cong \omega_e$ can be calculated from (5) as

$$\frac{\langle E^2 \rangle}{8\pi}\bigg|_{k<k_D} \cong \frac{8n_0 e^2}{\omega_e} \int_0^{k_D} k \, dk \, \frac{F_e(\omega_e/k)}{|F_e{}'(\omega_e/k)|} \tag{7}$$

for an electron ion plasma with $n_{0e} = n_{0i} = n_0$. Consider as an example of a distribution of electrons with a high-energy tail the function

$$f_e = \frac{\beta}{(2\pi)^{3/2} V_e{}^3} \exp\left(-\frac{v^2}{2V_e{}^2}\right) + \frac{(1-\beta)}{(2\pi)^{3/2} V_E{}^3} \exp\left(-\frac{v^2}{2V_E{}^2}\right), \tag{8}$$

where $1 \gg (1-\beta) \geq 0$, and $V_E{}^2 \gg V_e{}^2$. The case $\beta = 1$ recovers thermal equilibrium. One can then readily show that

$$\frac{\langle E^2 \rangle}{\langle E^2 \rangle_{\text{thermal equilib}}} \cong \frac{V_E{}^2/V_e{}^2}{\{2 \ln[V_E/V_e(1-\beta)]\}^{1/2}} \tag{9}$$

Thus, for example, if $V_E \cong 20 V_e$, $(1-\beta) \cong 0.1$, we have an enhancement factor of 100 in the energy density of these fluctuations compared to thermal equilibrium.

III. EMISSION AND SCATTERING OF RADIATION

Such enhanced fluctuations naturally lead to enhanced emission [4] or scattering [5] of electromagnetic radiation by a plasma. For an optically thin slab of Maxwellian plasma, the bremsstrahlung emission is largely continuous with two sharp peaks with negligible area under them near frequencies ω_e and $2\omega_e$ (see Fig. 2, case i). These peaks have their origin in the emission that takes place in the combination scattering of ion plasma oscillations (*ipo*) by electron plasma oscillations (*epo*), and the latter waves by themselves. Thus,

$$\begin{aligned} (epo) + (ipo) &\to \text{radiation at } \omega_e, \\ (epo) + (epo) &\to \text{radiation at } 2\omega_e. \end{aligned} \tag{10}$$

The emission at these two frequencies is superposed on the background continuous spectrum and is given by [4]

$$I_{\omega_e} \cong \frac{e^2\omega_e{}^2 3^{1/2} V_e}{3\pi^2 c^3} \int_0^{k_D} k^2 \, dk \, \frac{F_e(\omega_e/k)}{|F_e{}'(\omega_e/k)|},$$

$$I_{2\omega_e} \cong \frac{\omega_e{}^4 3^{1/2} e^2}{5\pi^2 c^5} \int_0^{k_D} dk \, \frac{F_e{}^2(\omega_e/k)}{|F_e{}'(\omega_e/k)|^2} \quad \text{ergs/sec/cm}^3. \tag{11}$$

For the distribution (8), these become

$$I_{\omega_e} \cong 6.10^{-25} n_0^{5/2} T^{-3/2} (V_E/c)^2 \alpha^{-4}$$

$$I_{2\omega_e} \cong 5.10^{-25} n_0^{5/2} T^{-3/2} (V_E/c)^4 \alpha^{-3} \quad \text{ergs/sec/cm}^3 \tag{12}$$

with $\alpha^2 = 2 \ln [V_E/V_e(1 - \beta)]$. We recover the thermal equilibrium result by setting $\alpha = 1$, $V_E = V_e$ in the foregoing expressions. Similar formulas for enhanced scattering cross sections of radiation also exist.

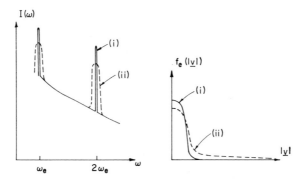

Fig. 2. Schematic plot of emission intensity of radiation for the Maxwellian and non-Maxwellian distributions (i and ii).

In conclusion, it is interesting to point out that enhanced fluctuations produced by suprathermal electrons play an important role in a number of astrophysical plasma phenomena; types II and III radio bursts from the sun have a two-harmonic structure at the plasma frequency ω_e and $2\omega_e$ of the coronal plasma and can be satisfactorily understood [6] in terms of the enhanced emission of the type we have discussed. Another example is the high-energy tail of photoelectrons for the ionospheric plasma. This gives rise to an enhanced cross section for backscatter of an incident radio wave of frequency Ω at frequencies $\Omega \pm \omega_e$. This has recently been observed by Perkins et al. [5] using the Arecibo radio dish.

ACKNOWLEDGMENT

This work was supported in part by National Aeronautics and Space Administration Grant NSG 220-62.

REFERENCES

1. Montgomery, D. C. and Tidman, D. A., "Plasma Kinetic Theory," McGraw-Hill, New York, 1964.
2. Rostoker, N., *Nucl. Fusion* **1**, 101 (1961); also *Phys. Fluids* **7**, 479 (1964); *ibid.* **7**, 491 (1964).
3. Dawson, J. M. and Nakayama, T., *Phys. Fluids* **9**, 252 (1966).
4. Tidman, D. A. and Dupree, T. H., *Phys. Fluids* **8**, 1860 (1965).
5. Perkins, F. W., Salpeter, E. E., and Yngvesson, K. O., *Phys. Rev. Lett.* **14**, 579 (1965); also Perkins, F. W. and Salpeter, E. E., *Phys. Rev.* **139**, A55 (1965).
6. Tidman, D. A., *Planetary Space Sci.* **13**, 781 (1965).

Dynamics of a Gyroviscous Plasma

WILLIAM A. NEWCOMB

LAWRENCE RADIATION LABORATORY
UNIVERSITY OF CALIFORNIA, LIVERMORE, CALIFORNIA

A collisionless plasma in a strong magnetic field is well known to exhibit a reactive type of viscosity (as opposed to a resistive type), which will be referred to here as the gyroviscosity. It is the purpose of this paper to develop a systematic dynamical theory of the gyroviscous plasma. The main applications of the theory are in the field of linear stability analysis, since the gyroviscosity is a strongly stabilizing effect. Nonetheless, the attempt is made here to avoid any exclusive preoccupation with stability problems.

For continuous fluids in general, and for plasmas in particular, there are two natural ways of defining the fluid velocity. There is first the observed velocity of a test particle, say a radioactive tracer ion, which presumably is carried along with the fluid, and there is also the momentum per unit mass, with electromagnetic corrections if necessary. In the case of the gyroviscous plasma, these two velocities are not the same, but they are related to each other in a symmetrical way. There is, in short, a duality theorem according to which the dynamical equations are invariant under the exchange of the two velocities, if at the same time the direction of the magnetic field is reversed. From this, one can derive a number of interesting consequences: (1) There are two types of localized perturbations that are carried along with the moving plasma. One type goes with the one velocity and the other type with the other. Both velocities, therefore, can in principle be observed and measured directly. (2) There are two independent energy integrals. (3) It is a sufficient condition for the stability of a plane parallel flow that the two velocities, in some suitably chosen reference frame, be everywhere opposite in direction.

There is a third natural velocity midway between the other two. If the dynamical equations are written in terms of this third velocity, then the gyroviscous force is derivable from a potential-energy function. In this formulation, the equations are the same as those of a nongyroviscous plasma with an extra stabilizing **B** field.

I. INTRODUCTION

In this paper we wish to discuss the general behavior of a rarefied collisionless plasma in a strong magnetic field. The salient feature of such

a plasma that we wish to emphasize is its gyroviscosity, a nondissipative type of viscosity in which the mean gyration radius takes the place of the collision mean free path. It bears the same relation to an ordinary viscosity as a reactance does to a resistance.

The existence of the gyroviscosity has been known for a long time, and there are numerous calculations in the literature of the gyroviscosity coefficient [1–4]. Let ω_c be the cyclotron frequency, and let τ be the mean time between collisions. Some of these calculations treat the general case of a finite $\tau\omega_c$, and others consider only the collisionless limit, $\tau\omega_c \rightarrow \infty$. In the general case, there are two coefficients (for plane motions transverse to the field), namely, the ordinary viscosity and the gyroviscosity, but the collisionless limit is the only case that we are going to consider here. In this case, there is only the gyroviscosity.

In most of the early work on collisionless plasma dynamics, for example that of Chew *et al.* [5] (or CGL from now on), it was assumed that the gyroviscosity is a negligibly small effect. This was the result of a general scaling law under which the equivalent Reynolds number goes to infinity in the limit of a large-scale system. It was first shown by Rosenbluth and co-workers [6], however, that there is another type of scaling with a different result, a type of scaling in which the time goes up as the square of the linear dimensions. The CGL scaling is the right one to use (and in fact the only possible one) in a general three-dimensional geometry, but the Rosenbluth scaling is good for various important special geometries, mostly two-dimensional. Within the limits of the two-dimensional geometry, the Rosenbluth type of scaling is the general type. Rosenbluth concentrated on the case of plane motion transverse to a uniform magnetic field, and we shall do the same here. Elsewhere, however, we shall treat the more realistic case of an axisymmetric system with a large aspect ratio [7]. This too is "essentially" a two-dimensional geometry, and under appropriate identifications the axisymmetric equations are precisely the same as the plane-motion equations.

In our language, Rosenbluth scaling means a finite Reynolds number and a nonnegligible gyroviscosity. In Rosenbluth's language, on the other hand, the emphasis is on other things such as higher-order drifts of guiding centers, and the gyroviscosity as such does not appear at all. But the effect is the same in either case, however one wishes to explain it, namely a very powerful stabilization of what would otherwise be a clearly unstable system. That the stabilization effect *could* be explained in terms of the gyroviscosity was the discovery of Roberts and Taylor [8], and it is our intention here to develop the implications of this viewpoint in a systematic way. The subject has also been treated extensively in a recent paper by Rosenbluth and Simon [9].

There is some question concerning the proper definition of the plasma velocity, even a controversy of sorts [9]. Suppose we define it oper-

ationally as that velocity which one would measure by a radioactive tracer experiment. It would then be the guiding-center drift velocity, approximately

$$v = (E \times B)/B^2, \tag{1.1}$$

since the guiding centers of tracer ions would have the same drift velocity as any others. From another viewpoint, however, one can take it to be the momentum per unit mass, call it u, which (under Rosenbluth scaling) is not the same thing. Now either of these may be taken as the basic velocity, and indeed, according to a certain duality theorem, to be given in due course, the relation between them is quite symmetrical. Later on, we shall make this our central theme.[1] At first, however, we shall concentrate on the drift velocity v, making it our initial object to derive the lowest-order equations for the flow of guiding centers.

For the two-dimensional case of interest here, it is convenient to have a special notation for cross products. Let A be any vector in the plane of motion, and let b be the unit normal to that plane (or the unit vector along B in our case). We shall always write A^* for $A \times b$,

$$A^* = A \times b, \tag{1.2}$$

so that (1.1), for example, will be written as

$$v = E^*/B. \tag{1.3}$$

Taking the z axis along b, we assume that everything is independent of z. The unit vectors in the transverse plane will be written as e_x, e_y, and the unit dyadic will be written as I,

$$I = e_x e_x + e_y e_y. \tag{1.4}$$

Some obvious identities are

$$A \cdot I = I \cdot A = A, \tag{1.5}$$

$$A^{**} = -A, \tag{1.6}$$

$$A^* \cdot A = A \cdot A^* = 0, \tag{1.7}$$

$$A^* \cdot F^* = A \cdot F, \tag{1.8}$$

$$A^* \cdot F + A \cdot F^* = 0, \tag{1.9}$$

$$AF + F^*A^* = IA \cdot F. \tag{1.10}$$

---

[1] I do not agree with the statement of Rosenbluth and Simon that the u formulation requires a uniform temperature.

We shall write sym(A) for the symmetric part of a dyadic A. Thus,

$$[\mathrm{sym}(A)]_{ij} = \tfrac{1}{2}(A_{ij} + A_{ji}), \tag{1.11}$$

$$\begin{aligned} \mathbf{F} \cdot [\mathrm{sym}(A)] &= [\mathrm{sym}(A)] \cdot \mathbf{F} \\ &= \tfrac{1}{2}(\mathbf{F} \cdot A + A \cdot \mathbf{F}). \end{aligned} \tag{1.12}$$

The gradient operator ∇ satisfies the same identities as any other vector. Thus,

$$\mathbf{b} \cdot \nabla \times \mathbf{A} = \nabla \cdot \mathbf{A}^* = -\nabla^* \cdot \mathbf{A}, \tag{1.13}$$

$$\nabla^* \cdot \mathbf{A}^* = \nabla \cdot \mathbf{A}, \tag{1.14}$$

$$\nabla^* \cdot \nabla = \nabla \cdot \nabla^* = 0, \tag{1.15}$$

$$(\mathbf{A} \cdot \nabla\mathbf{F})^* = \mathbf{A} \cdot \nabla\mathbf{F}^*, \tag{1.16}$$

$$\mathbf{A} \cdot \nabla^*\mathbf{F}^* = A\nabla \cdot \mathbf{F} - \nabla\mathbf{F} \cdot \mathbf{A}, \quad \text{etc.} \tag{1.17}$$

One last identity, which is not quite so obvious, is

$$\nabla \cdot (A\nabla \cdot \mathbf{A}^*) = \nabla \cdot (\mathbf{A} \cdot \nabla\mathbf{A}^*). \tag{1.18}$$

It is perhaps most easily verified by writing out the components.

II. EQUATIONS OF THE GUIDING-CENTER FLOW

Naturally our treatment will be nonrelativistic, which, as always, implies lowest order in v^2/c^2. There is, however, at least one characteristic phase velocity that can be either a small velocity of order v or a large velocity of order c. That is the Alfvén speed c_A,

$$c_A{}^2 = \frac{B^2}{\mu_0(\rho + \epsilon_0 B^2)} = \frac{c^2\epsilon_0 B^2}{\rho + \epsilon_0 B^2}, \tag{2.1}$$

where B is the magnetic field in rationalized units and ρ is the mass density. Now, for any ordinary conducting fluid such as a liquid metal, and for any attainable field strengths, it will always be the case that $\rho \gg \epsilon_0 B^2$, giving a c_A very much less than c. What we are dealing with here, however, is not an ordinary fluid but a highly rarefied laboratory plasma, and in a very strong field. In this case, under actual conditions, one can very well have a ρ of order $\epsilon_0 B^2$ or even less. The appropriate assumption here, therefore, is c_A of order c.

Comparing (2.1) with the standard formula for c,

$$c^2 = (\epsilon_0\mu_0)^{-1}, \tag{2.2}$$

we note that both c and c_A will go to infinity (as we want them to) if we take $\mu_0 \to 0$. Similarly in the other case (c_A of order v) we could take $\epsilon_0 \to 0$ and get $c \to \infty$, with c_A finite. That would give the usual type of

magnetohydrodynamics with no displacement currents and no electro-static forces. In either case, there is a complete system of lowest-order dynamical equations with the essential nonrelativistic property of Galilean invariance. (That is what the principle of relativity requires under so-called "nonrelativistic" conditions.) What we wish to emphasize, how-ever, is the existence of two distinct systems, depending on whether the small parameter is taken to be μ_0 or ϵ_0. Here it is taken to be μ_0.

The magnetic pressure, $B^2/2\mu_0$, goes to infinity. The dimensionless parameter β, the ratio of plasma pressure to magnetic pressure, is accord-ingly taken to be a small parameter of relativistic order. What we have, however, is not quite the same as the usual low-β limit, since we are not neglecting terms of order ϵ_0.

Setting $\mu_0 = 0$ in the $\nabla \times B$ relation, we have simply

$$\nabla \times B = 0, \tag{2.3}$$

a vacuum field. The field is essentially unperturbed by any currents flowing in the plasma. Or, to put it another way, the self-field of the plasma currents is only a relativity correction. We have already taken the field to be uniform, and we see now that this is consistent with the existence of a finite plasma current. Assume also that the field is a constant in time. Then the E field will satisfy $\nabla \times E = 0$, or in our notation,

$$\nabla^* \cdot E = 0. \tag{2.4}$$

The E field is derivable from a scalar potential.

Relations involving η and J, the charge and current densities, are

$$\eta = \epsilon_0 \nabla \cdot E, \tag{2.5}$$

$$\nabla \cdot (J + \epsilon_0 \, \partial E/\partial t) = 0. \tag{2.6}$$

These are the only such relations we have, in the lowest order, and they determine only the divergence of J, and not J itself. We shall find, however, that they suffice nonetheless to give a closed system of equations. Note that the displacement current is not neglected in (2.6). This can also be written as

$$\nabla \cdot J + \partial \eta/\partial t = 0, \tag{2.7}$$

which is the equation of charge conservation.

Aside from v^2/c^2, we have also the expansion parameters of the guiding-center drift approximation,

$$\delta = a/L, \tag{2.8}$$

and

$$\lambda = (\omega_c T)^{-1}. \tag{2.9}$$

Here a is the gyration radius, ω_c is the cyclotron frequency, L is some characteristic macroscopic length, and T is some characteristic time. Both δ and λ must be small, but not necessarily of the same order. We accordingly set $\lambda = \delta^x$, where x is to be so determined as to give maximum information. That will mean $x = 2$ (Rosenbluth scaling), not $x = 1$ (CGL scaling).

To lowest order in the expansion parameters, the guiding-center drift velocity is that given before, namely,

$$\mathbf{v} = \mathbf{E}^*/B. \tag{2.10}$$

There are also various higher-order corrections which, however, give a finite plasma current. The main component of the drift is independent of the charge and accordingly gives only a contribution $\eta\mathbf{v}$ to the total current. The rest of it is due to the higher-order drifts and to a dia-magnetic effect. Now, for this reason, the higher-order drifts occupy a very prominent place in various physical explanations given by Rosen-bluth and others [6, 10]. The approach we are using here, however, is one in which it is unnecessary to account for the currents in microscopic terms. Hence the reader should not be surprised if these higher-order drifts receive no further attention. They are very much smaller than the $\mathbf{v}$ of (2.10), so that for our purposes it is only the latter that has any significance.

From (2.4) and (2.10), we have simply

$$\boldsymbol{\nabla} \cdot \mathbf{v} = 0. \tag{2.11}$$

The lowest-order motion of the guiding centers is incompressible.

We can write the exact equation of motion in general form as

$$\partial \mathbf{S}/\partial t + \boldsymbol{\nabla} \cdot \boldsymbol{T} - \eta \mathbf{E} - \mathbf{J}^*B + \rho \boldsymbol{\nabla}\phi = 0, \tag{2.12}$$

where $\mathbf{S}$ is the momentum density and $\boldsymbol{T}$ is the stress tensor. A gravitational term has also been included for generality, although we are not going to do very much with it. Its potential ϕ is a fixed function of position.

Using a subscript α to distinguish between the various particle species present in the plasma, we write $f_\alpha(\mathbf{x}, \mathbf{c}, t)$ for the particle density in phase space. The letter c is no longer needed for the speed of light (which has gone to infinity), and so we use it from now on for the particle velocity. We have, for $\mathbf{S}$ and $\boldsymbol{T}$,

$$\mathbf{S} = \sum_\alpha m_\alpha \int \mathbf{c}f_\alpha \, dc_x \, dc_y, \tag{2.13}$$

$$\boldsymbol{T} = \sum_\alpha m_\alpha \int \mathbf{c}\mathbf{c}f_\alpha \, dc_x \, dc_y, \tag{2.14}$$

where m is the mass. It is understood that f_α has already been integrated over c_z.

We wish to put everything in terms of $\mathbf{v}$. Let $\mathbf{S}_0$ and $\boldsymbol{T}_0$, then, be the $\mathbf{S}$ and $\boldsymbol{T}$ as measured in the local rest frame of the guiding centers:

$$\mathbf{S}_0 = \sum_\alpha m_\alpha \int (\mathbf{c} - \mathbf{v}) f_\alpha \, dc_x \, dc_y \,, \tag{2.15}$$

$$\boldsymbol{T}_0 = \sum_\alpha m_\alpha \int (\mathbf{c} - \mathbf{v})(\mathbf{c} - \mathbf{v}) f_\alpha \, dc_x \, dc_y \,. \tag{2.16}$$

We have, then,

$$\mathbf{S} = \mathbf{S}_0 + \rho \mathbf{v} \,, \tag{2.17}$$

$$\boldsymbol{T} = \boldsymbol{T}_0 + \mathbf{v}\mathbf{S}_0 + \mathbf{S}_0\mathbf{v} + \rho\mathbf{v}\mathbf{v} \,, \tag{2.18}$$

with

$$\rho = \sum_\alpha m_\alpha \int f_\alpha \, dc_x \, dc_y \,. \tag{2.19}$$

We can also split off the traceless part of $\boldsymbol{T}_0$ as follows:

$$\boldsymbol{T}_0 = P\boldsymbol{I} + \boldsymbol{\pi} \,, \tag{2.20}$$

where

$$P = \frac{1}{2} \sum_\alpha m_\alpha \int (\mathbf{c} - \mathbf{v})^2 f_\alpha \, dc_x \, dc_y \,, \tag{2.21}$$

$$\pi_{11} + \pi_{22} = 0 \,. \tag{2.22}$$

The scalar part P is what we shall call the plasma pressure, although this may not be quite the same as the usual definition.

Observe now that the equation of motion is partially redundant, since we have also the incompressibility condition (2.11). Only its curl is actually needed, which we now write as

$$\nabla^* \cdot (\mathbf{F}_1 + \mathbf{F}_2 + \mathbf{F}_3 + \mathbf{F}_4) = 0 \,, \tag{2.23}$$

where

$$\mathbf{F}_1 = \partial/\partial t \, (\rho\mathbf{v}) + \nabla \cdot (\rho\mathbf{v}\mathbf{v}) \,, \tag{2.24}$$

$$\mathbf{F}_2 = -\eta\mathbf{E} - B\mathbf{J}^* \,, \tag{2.25}$$

$$\mathbf{F}_3 = \rho\nabla\phi \,, \tag{2.26}$$

$$\mathbf{F}_4 = \partial\mathbf{S}_0/\partial t + \nabla \cdot (\mathbf{S}_0\mathbf{v}) + \nabla \cdot (\mathbf{v}\mathbf{S}_0) + \nabla \cdot \boldsymbol{\pi} \,. \tag{2.27}$$

The $\boldsymbol{\pi}$ term is the gyroviscosity. As we shall find, however, it is somewhat artificial to distinguish it so sharply from the $\mathbf{S}_0$ terms. I have accordingly put them all together in the $\mathbf{F}_4$.

Let $f_\alpha^{(0)}$ be the lowest-order term of an asymptotic expansion in powers of δ and λ. It may be written as

$$f_\alpha^{(0)} = f_\alpha^{(0)}(\mathbf{x}, |\mathbf{c} - \mathbf{v}|, t) \,, \tag{2.28}$$

since the azimuthal dependence is all in the higher-order terms. It satisfies the lowest-order relation

$$\partial f_\alpha^{(0)}/\partial t + \mathbf{v} \cdot \boldsymbol{\nabla} f_\alpha^{(0)} = 0, \qquad (2.29)$$

as one can show by a rather laborious expansion of the exact kinetic equation [7]. There is no special need to go through it here, however, since it is a physically obvious result in any case.[2] We have next, also as lowest-order relations,

$$\partial \rho/\partial t + \mathbf{v} \cdot \boldsymbol{\nabla} \rho = 0, \qquad (2.30)$$

$$\partial P/\partial t + \mathbf{v} \cdot \boldsymbol{\nabla} P = 0, \qquad (2.31)$$

although actually (2.30) is the only one we will need. Note, by the way, that (2.30) is not quite the same as the exact continuity equation. The latter is

$$\frac{\partial \rho}{\partial t} + \boldsymbol{\nabla} \cdot \mathbf{S} = \frac{\partial \rho}{\partial t} + \mathbf{v} \cdot \boldsymbol{\nabla} \rho + \boldsymbol{\nabla} \cdot \mathbf{S}_0 = 0, \qquad (2.32)$$

so that what we have actually shown is $\boldsymbol{\nabla} \cdot \mathbf{S}_0 = 0$. Using (2.30), we can write

$$\mathbf{F}_1 = \rho(\partial \mathbf{v}/\partial t + \mathbf{v} \cdot \boldsymbol{\nabla} \mathbf{v}), \qquad (2.33)$$

which brings us closer to a conventional hydrodynamic description.

Considering now the electromagnetic term, we have

$$\boldsymbol{\nabla}^* \cdot \mathbf{F}_2 = -\boldsymbol{\nabla}^* \cdot (\eta \mathbf{E}) - B\,\boldsymbol{\nabla} \cdot \mathbf{J}. \qquad (2.34)$$

This shows why it was desirable to take the curl, for we can now eliminate $\mathbf{J}$ by using the charge-conservation law. (It also got rid of the $\boldsymbol{\nabla} P$ term.) Proceeding in this way, we use (2.5) to eliminate η and (2.10) to eliminate $\mathbf{E}$. The result is

$$\boldsymbol{\nabla}^* \cdot \mathbf{F}_2 = \epsilon_0 B^2 \, \boldsymbol{\nabla}^* \cdot (\partial \mathbf{v}/\partial t + \mathbf{v} \cdot \boldsymbol{\nabla} \mathbf{v}), \qquad (2.35)$$

in which the identity (1.18) has been used. Combining $\mathbf{F}_1$ and $\mathbf{F}_2$, we have

$$\boldsymbol{\nabla}^* \cdot (\mathbf{F}_1 + \mathbf{F}_2) = \boldsymbol{\nabla}^* \cdot [\sigma(\partial \mathbf{v}/\partial t + \mathbf{v} \cdot \boldsymbol{\nabla} \mathbf{v})], \qquad (2.36)$$

where

$$\sigma = \rho + \epsilon_0 B^2. \qquad (2.37)$$

The field, as we see, adds a contribution $\epsilon_0 B^2$ to the effective mass density σ. (This was first shown by Northrup [11].) The added contribution, as I have mentioned, may under actual conditions be as large as ρ or larger.

---

[2] *Note added in proof:* The time derivative acts on the explicit t argument only, not the $|\mathbf{c} - \mathbf{v}|$.

It is noteworthy that the magnetic correction term is twice the actual magnetic mass as given by $E = mc^2$. This is connected with the infinite magnetic pressure, and indeed a material fluid would behave in the same way if it were under a comparable pressure. Because one part of the fluid does work on another, there is a contribution $P\mathbf{v}$ to the energy flow vector. This corresponds to an additional momentum density, $\mathbf{S} = P\mathbf{v}/c^2$, hence an additional effective mass of P/c^2. Here the pressure is $B^2/2\mu_0$, and this accounts for the difference. Using a subscript f for the field, we have from Poynting's theorem

$$\mathbf{S}_f = \epsilon_0 \mathbf{E}^* B = \epsilon_0 B^2 \mathbf{v} = [\rho_f + c^{-2} P_f]\mathbf{v}, \tag{2.38}$$

in agreement with the foregoing. We have also

$$\tfrac{1}{2}\epsilon_0 E^2 = \tfrac{1}{2}\epsilon_0 B^2 v^2, \tag{2.39}$$

showing that the electrostatic energy functions here in the role of a kinetic energy.

Using the fact that $\epsilon_0 B^2$ is a constant, we can substitute σ for ρ throughout, so that there will only be one mass density in the problem. We have, for example,

$$\partial\sigma/\partial t + \mathbf{v} \cdot \nabla\sigma = 0, \tag{2.40}$$

and also

$$\nabla^* \cdot \mathbf{F}_3 = \nabla^* \cdot (\rho\nabla\phi) = \nabla^* \cdot (\sigma\nabla\phi), \tag{2.41}$$

since $\nabla^* \cdot \nabla\phi = 0$. The addition of a constant to the gravitational mass density makes no difference. (It would be very surprising, in fact, if it did, for in that case the principle of equivalence would be violated.)

We now come to the gyroviscosity. Consider first the effect of a gradient in the $\mathbf{E}$ field, or, what comes to the same thing, of a gradient in $\mathbf{v}$ [see Fig. 1, parts (a) and (b)]. It gives rise to an ellipticity in the gyration orbits, as is shown in part (c) of Fig. 1. (The guiding center is assumed to be on the line of vanishing $\mathbf{E}$.) This in turn gives rise to an anisotropy in the gyration velocities (or the thermal velocities), hence an anisotropy in the stress tensor.[3] It is this term that we refer to as the gyroviscosity. Let us compare it with an ordinary Newtonian viscosity, which is as indicated in Fig. 2 for the same velocity field. The stress pattern is rotated through a 45° angle in the one case as compared with

---

[3] *Note added in proof:* The reader is warned that this is a seriously incomplete explanation, and that the diagrams should therefore not be taken too literally. Picture the rosette of gyration orbits passing through a given point. Even if the orbits were strictly circular, the gradient in the drift would still give a $\cos 2\theta$ anisotropy, and the net result of this is a reversal in the sign. The formulas given below are correct as they stand, however, the explanation having been made up after the fact.

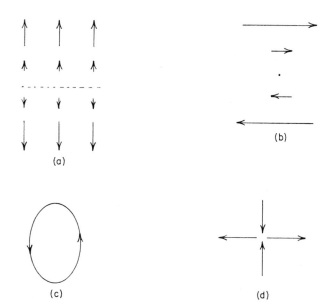

Fig. 1. The gyroviscosity: (a) the **E** field; (b) the **v** field; (c) a gyration orbit; (d) the stress tensor.

Fig. 2. A Newtonian viscosity.   The velocity field is the same as in Fig. 1: (a) the shearing stress; (b) reduction to principal axes.

the other.   It is essentially for this reason that the gyroviscosity is a nondissipative effect.

The exact formula for the gyroviscosity is[4]

$$\boldsymbol{\pi} = -\tfrac{1}{2}\mu\, \mathrm{sym}(\boldsymbol{\nabla}^*\mathbf{v} + \boldsymbol{\nabla}\mathbf{v}^*)\,, \tag{2.42}$$

with the symmetrizer as defined by (1.11), and with the coefficient μ given by[5]

$$\mu = \sum_\alpha \frac{m_\alpha^2}{2e_\alpha B} \int f_\alpha^{(0)} |\mathbf{c} - \mathbf{v}|^2 \, dc_x \, dc_y = \sum_\alpha \frac{m_\alpha P_\alpha}{e_\alpha B}\,. \tag{2.43}$$

[4] There is also a rather complicated term depending on second gradients in the $f_\alpha^{(0)}$, which, however, contributes nothing to the final result.

[5] *Note added in proof:* Apart from a numerical factor, the coefficient μ may be identified as the total angular momentum of gyration per unit volume.

The derivation may be found in any of Refs. [1–4], and it need not be repeated here. After some algebra, we end up with

$$\nabla^* \cdot \boldsymbol{\pi} = -\tfrac{1}{2}[\nabla \cdot (\mu \nabla \mathbf{v}) + \nabla \mathbf{v} \cdot \nabla \mu],\tag{2.44}$$

$$\nabla^* \cdot (\nabla \cdot \boldsymbol{\pi}) = \nabla \cdot (\nabla^* \cdot \boldsymbol{\pi}) = -\nabla \cdot (\nabla \mathbf{v} \cdot \nabla \mu).\tag{2.45}$$

One further relation that we will need is

$$\partial \mu / \partial t + \mathbf{v} \cdot \nabla \mu = 0,\tag{2.46}$$

an obvious consequence of (2.29). Note that (2.45) would vanish if there were no gradient in μ. There is no gyroviscous force in a *uniform* plasma.

For the equivalent Reynolds number R, we have

$$R = \sigma v L / \mu,\tag{2.47}$$

where L is the same as in (2.8). Now the parameter measuring the relative importance of the gyroviscosity is R^{-1}, which, therefore, we should take to be of order unity. In terms of the gyration radius a, we have essentially

$$\mu \sim na^2 eB, \qquad \sigma \sim \rho \sim nm, \qquad v \sim \mu R/\sigma L \sim R\delta(a/\omega_c),\tag{2.48}$$

where n is the particle density. If R is of order unity, therefore, we see that $\mathbf{v}$ is of relative order δ as compared with the gyration velocities. This gives also

$$\lambda \sim (\omega_c T)^{-1} \sim L/v\omega_c \sim \delta^2,\tag{2.49}$$

i.e., Rosenbluth scaling, as was stated earlier. The CGL scaling would give $R \sim \delta^{-1}$, hence only a negligible gyroviscosity. We see now that what we are considering is the case of slow drifts and weak forces. As long as we are dealing with two-dimensional motions, however, it is not a special case but the general case, since there is more physics in it. It is also the more realistic case in many of the applications.

Note that the π term is very much smaller than the plasma pressure P (which in turn is very much smaller than the magnetic pressure). We have, in short,

$$\pi, \sigma v^2 \sim \delta^2 P \sim \beta \delta^2 P_f,\tag{2.50}$$

where both β and δ are small parameters. The ∇P term in the equation of motion would be very much more important than the $\nabla \cdot \pi$ were it not for the fact that it vanishes when we take the curl.

The last term that we need is the $\mathbf{S}_0$. This is essentially a diamagnetic effect, as is indicated in Figs. 3 and 4. Even if all the guiding centers are at rest, so that none of the particles are really going anywhere, there

is still a nonvanishing mass flow if there are gradients in either the particle density or the mean gyration radius. A simple calculation gives

$$S_0 = -\nabla^*\mu , \tag{2.51}$$

where μ is the same as in the gyroviscosity.[6] If the drifts are not zero, then the calculation gives this same S_0 as an additional correction to the

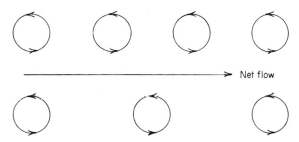

FIG. 3. Diamagnetic mass flow arising from a density gradient. The drift velocity is zero.

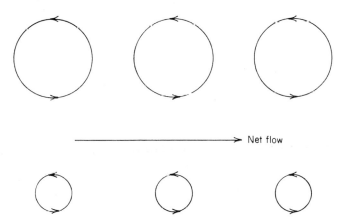

FIG. 4. Diamagnetic mass flow arising from a gradient in the mean gyration radius. Again the drift velocity is zero.

drift contribution ρv. Note that S_0 satisfies $\nabla \cdot S_0 = 0$, in agreement with what was said earlier. Using (2.46), we readily obtain

$$\nabla^* \cdot (\partial S_0/\partial t + v \cdot \nabla S_0 + S_0 \cdot \nabla v) = 2\nabla \cdot (\nabla v \cdot \nabla \mu) . \tag{2.52}$$

This is twice the contribution of the π term but with the opposite sign.[7]

[6] See, for example, Spitzer [12].

[7] *Note added in proof:* The net result, in other words, is to cancel the rosette effect mentioned in an earlier note, leaving only the direct contribution of the ellipticity.

To lowest order in δ, the gyration velocities average out to zero, since there is no azimuthal dependence in $f_\alpha^{(0)}$. This explains why the $\mathbf{S}_0$ is absent under the CGL scaling. Here, however, the gyration velocities are larger than $\mathbf{v}$ to begin with, by one order in δ, so that the mean gyration velocity is of the *same* order in δ as $\mathbf{v}$.[8]

There is also a diamagnetic current $\mathbf{J}_0$, arising in the same way as the $\mathbf{S}_0$:

$$\mathbf{J}_0 = -B^{-1}\boldsymbol{\nabla}^*P. \tag{2.53}$$

Note then that the large $\boldsymbol{\nabla}P$ force in the equation of motion is balanced by the magnetic force $\mathbf{J}_0{}^*B$. But that has very little to do with the dynamics. The dynamical behavior is entirely determined, in fact, by the interplay of the small forces that remain after the application of the curl operator. This is an elementary example of Kruskal's *principle of annihilation* [13].

We have obviously $\boldsymbol{\nabla} \cdot \mathbf{J}_0 = 0$, and in fact the $\boldsymbol{\nabla} \cdot \mathbf{J}$ of Eq. (2.34) arises entirely from higher-order effects. These include both higher-order drifts and higher-order corrections to the diamagnetic current. As has already been indicated, however, it is unnecessary to go into these things.

Putting all the pieces together, we get the following as the complete system of differential equations:

$$\boldsymbol{\nabla}^* \cdot \left[\sigma\!\left(\frac{\partial \mathbf{v}}{\partial t} + \mathbf{v} \cdot \boldsymbol{\nabla}\mathbf{v} + \boldsymbol{\nabla}\phi \right) \right] + \boldsymbol{\nabla} \cdot (\boldsymbol{\nabla}\mathbf{v} \cdot \boldsymbol{\nabla}\mu) = 0, \tag{2.54}$$

$$\boldsymbol{\nabla} \cdot \mathbf{v} = 0, \tag{2.55}$$

$$\frac{\partial \sigma}{\partial t} + \mathbf{v} \cdot \boldsymbol{\nabla}\sigma = 0, \tag{2.56}$$

$$\frac{\partial \mu}{\partial t} + \mathbf{v} \cdot \boldsymbol{\nabla}\mu = 0. \tag{2.57}$$

We also need boundary conditions. Assume, then, that the plasma region is bounded by a perfectly conducting solid wall. Then the boundary condition is $E_{\text{tang}} = 0$, or

$$\mathbf{n} \cdot \mathbf{v} = 0, \tag{2.58}$$

where $\mathbf{n}$ is the unit normal. Assume also that the region is simply connected, in which case the boundary is all in one piece. (Otherwise we have to impose extra line-integral conditions pertaining to the external

---

[8] *Note added in proof:* This pertains to the ensemble of particles passing instantaneously through a given point, for on any one orbit the distribution is taken to be uniform.

currents and voltages.)   Assume finally, as an extra initial condition, that the contour lines of constant σ and μ are the same, and that the boundary line is one of them.   Thus,

$$\nabla\sigma \cdot \nabla^*\mu = 0, \tag{2.59}$$

$$\mathbf{n}^* \cdot \nabla\sigma = 0, \tag{2.60}$$

$$\mathbf{n}^* \cdot \nabla\mu = 0. \tag{2.61}$$

It suffices to impose these extra conditions initially, since it then follows from Eqs. (2.56) and (2.57) that they will continue to hold for all t.

The scaling law under which the equations are invariant is as follows:

$$\begin{aligned}
\mathbf{x} &\rightarrow \Lambda\mathbf{x}, & \phi &\rightarrow \Lambda^{-2}\phi, \\
t &\rightarrow \Lambda^2 t, & \sigma &\rightarrow \sigma, \\
\mathbf{v} &\rightarrow \Lambda^{-1}\mathbf{v}, & \mu &\rightarrow \mu,
\end{aligned} \tag{2.62}$$

where Λ is an arbitrary parameter.   This, of course, is precisely the Rosenbluth scaling law, and its function is to define the ordering rules in the asymptotic expansion.   Relative order δ^n in the expansion means relative order Λ^{-n} under scaling.   The charge density is obviously scaled by a factor Λ^{-2}, for example, giving a quasi-neutrality condition good to two orders in δ.

III. CONSTANTS OF THE MOTION

For the energy integral of the system we obtain

$$H = \int\sigma(\tfrac{1}{2}v^2 + \phi)\, dx\, dy, \tag{3.1}$$

in which the μ term does not appear.   We see, then, that the gyroviscous force does no work.   It is like the magnetic force on a single particle. This is not the whole story, however, for we shall presently find that there is also a second energy integral.

To prove the constancy of H, we first write the equation of motion, Eq. (2.54), as

$$\sigma\left(\frac{\partial\mathbf{v}}{\partial t} + \mathbf{v}\cdot\nabla\mathbf{v} + \nabla\phi\right) + \nabla^*\mathbf{v}\cdot\nabla\mu + \nabla\lambda = 0, \tag{3.2}$$

where λ is some scalar function of position.   This scalar λ has essentially the same role in the theory as the hydrostatic pressure in ordinary incompressible hydrodynamics.   In fact the equations would be exactly the same if it were not for the μ term.

Let us write

$$\frac{d\mathbf{v}}{dt} = \frac{\partial \mathbf{v}}{\partial t} + \mathbf{v} \cdot \nabla \mathbf{v}, \tag{3.3}$$

$$\frac{d\sigma}{dt} = \frac{\partial \sigma}{\partial t} + \mathbf{v} \cdot \nabla \sigma = 0, \tag{3.4}$$

$$\frac{d\mu}{dt} = \frac{\partial \mu}{\partial t} + \mathbf{v} \cdot \nabla \mu = 0, \tag{3.5}$$

$$\frac{d}{dt} (dx\,dy) = 0, \tag{3.6}$$

so that d/dt, in general, is the time derivative following the guiding centers. We have

$$\begin{aligned}
\frac{dH}{dt} &= \int \sigma \mathbf{v} \cdot \left(\frac{d\mathbf{v}}{dt} + \nabla \phi \right) dx\,dy \\
&= - \int \mathbf{v} \cdot (\nabla^* \mathbf{v} \cdot \nabla \mu + \nabla \lambda)\,dx\,dy \\
&= \int [\mu \nabla \cdot (\mathbf{v} \cdot \nabla^* \mathbf{v}) + \lambda \nabla \cdot \mathbf{v}]\,dx\,dy = 0.
\end{aligned} \tag{3.7}$$

We have used here the incompressibility condition, $\nabla \cdot \mathbf{v} = 0$, and also the identity $\nabla \mathbf{v} \colon \nabla^* \mathbf{v} = 0$, which is a special case of (1.7).

Our derivation of $dH/dt = 0$ would not be valid, in general, in a multiply connected region, even though the differential equations and boundary conditions are the same. This is evident from the example of the rotating-plasma condenser. In that type of situation, one can have a multivalued λ, and that is what accounts for the failure of (3.7). This is one essential respect in which the present theory differs from ordinary hydrodynamics. The equations are the same (apart from the μ term), but the line-integral conditions in a multiply connected region are not the same.

Another important constant is the circulation invariant,

$$C(\mu_0) = \oint_{\mu = \mu_0} [\mathbf{v} - (1/2\sigma)\,\nabla^* \mu] \cdot d\mathbf{l}, \tag{3.8}$$

where the path of integration, as is indicated, is the contour line $\mu = \mu_0$. For any value of μ_0, we have

$$d/dt\,C(\mu_0) = 0. \tag{3.9}$$

The direct verification of this from (3.2) is straightforward but slightly tedious.

Like most constants of the motion, the circulation C arises from a symmetry operation, in this case the exchange of identical fluid elements. Identical elements are understood here to mean those having the same σ

and the same μ, and the purpose of our extra condition (2.59) was to ensure that such elements would exist.

If the system has either translational or rotational symmetry, then there is also a canonical momentum invariant. Taking all these constants into account, one can derive the stability conditions in a simple and natural way [7]. In this the commanding position is occupied by the circulation invariant, since it is the one that depends on the μ term.[9]

IV. THE DUALITY THEOREM

Let S_t be the total momentum density, including the electromagnetic momentum:

$$\mathbf{S}_t = \rho\mathbf{v} + \mathbf{S}_0 + \epsilon_0\mathbf{E}*B$$
$$= \sigma\mathbf{v} - \boldsymbol{\nabla}*\mu, \tag{4.1}$$

and let $\mathbf{u}$ be the equivalent mass-flow velocity:

$$\mathbf{S}_t = \sigma\mathbf{u}, \tag{4.2}$$
$$\mathbf{u} = \mathbf{v} - (1/\sigma)\boldsymbol{\nabla}*\mu. \tag{4.3}$$

Comparing this with (3.8), we see that the circulation invariant can be written as

$$C(\mu_0) = \tfrac{1}{2} \oint_{\mu=\mu_0} (\mathbf{u} + \mathbf{v}) \cdot \mathbf{dl}. \tag{4.4}$$

The dependence on $\mathbf{u}$ and $\mathbf{v}$ is symmetrical.

Now, using the extra conditions (2.59)–(2.61), let us change variables from $\mathbf{v}$ to $\mathbf{u}$ throughout. What we get is

$$\boldsymbol{\nabla}* \cdot \{\sigma[\partial\mathbf{u}/\partial t + \mathbf{u} \cdot \boldsymbol{\nabla}\mathbf{u} + \boldsymbol{\nabla}\phi]\} - \boldsymbol{\nabla} \cdot (\boldsymbol{\nabla}\mathbf{u} \cdot \boldsymbol{\nabla}\mu) - 0, \tag{4.5}$$
$$\boldsymbol{\nabla} \cdot \mathbf{u} = 0, \tag{4.6}$$
$$\partial\sigma/\partial t + \mathbf{u} \cdot \boldsymbol{\nabla}\sigma = 0, \tag{4.7}$$
$$\partial\mu/\partial t + \mathbf{u} \cdot \boldsymbol{\nabla}\mu = 0, \tag{4.8}$$
$$\mathbf{n} \cdot \mathbf{u} = 0. \tag{4.9}$$

This is the same system of equations as before, except for a change in the sign of the μ term. A change in the sign of μ is the same as a reversal in the direction of $\mathbf{B}$. We see, then, that the equations are invariant under the transformation

$$\mathbf{u} \to \mathbf{v}, \qquad \mathbf{v} \to \mathbf{u}, \qquad \mathbf{B} \to -\mathbf{B}. \tag{4.10}$$

This is the duality theorem referred to earlier.

It is worth mentioning that the two situations related by the duality theorem are physically distinct. Consider, as a simple illustration, a

---

[9] Actually, the momentum invariant does too, but only in a trivial way.

rotating plasma column. Its structure is defined by three independent functions of r, let us say

$$\sigma = f(r), \qquad \mu B = g(r), \qquad E_r = h(r). \tag{4.11}$$

Alternatively, we could take σ, v_θ, and u_θ. Now the dual situation has the same σ and the same μB, but

$$E_r = -h + g'/f, \tag{4.12}$$

which is physically another case. Nonetheless, the two cases are related in a symmetrical way. It would be impossible, for example, to have one of them stable and the other unstable.

An immediate corollary of the duality theorem is the existence of a second energy integral,

$$H_u = \int \sigma(\tfrac{1}{2}u^2 + \phi) \, dx \, dy. \tag{4.13}$$

Let Δ be the difference between the two energy integrals. We have

$$\begin{aligned}
\Delta &= H_v - H_u \\
&= \tfrac{1}{2} \int \sigma(\mathbf{v} - \mathbf{u}) \cdot (\mathbf{v} + \mathbf{u}) \, dx \, dy \\
&= \tfrac{1}{2} \int (\mathbf{v} + \mathbf{u}) \cdot \nabla^* \mu \, dx \, dy \\
&= \int_{\mu\min}^{\mu\max} C(\mu) \, d\mu.
\end{aligned} \tag{4.14}$$

Thus the two energy integrals differ by an integrated circulation invariant.

We now ask what happens when the plasma is subjected to a small localized perturbation. The answer, as we shall find, is contained in the duality theorem. Consider first the closely related problem of the propagation of a discontinuity. There is a certain curve in the x, y plane, moving with a certain velocity $\mathbf{V}$, and with finite jumps in various derivatives from one side of the curve to the other. (Of course, it is only a discontinuity on the scale of the macroscopic motion. In reality, it is a transition layer with a finite thickness of at least several gyration radii.) Let the discontinuity curve intersect the σ, μ contours at an arbitrary angle. Then, in order that the differential equations be integrable through the transition layer, it is necessary that the discontinuities only appear in the first derivatives of $\mathbf{u}$ and $\mathbf{v}$ and in the second derivatives of σ and μ. We have to assume, in other words,

$$\Delta \mathbf{u} = \Delta \mathbf{v} = 0, \tag{4.15}$$

$$\Delta \sigma = 0, \qquad \Delta \mu = 0, \tag{4.16}$$

$$\Delta(\nabla \sigma) = 0, \qquad \Delta(\nabla \mu) = 0, \tag{4.17}$$

$$\Delta(\partial \sigma/\partial t) = 0, \qquad \Delta(\partial \mu/\partial t) = 0, \tag{4.18}$$

where Δ stands for the jump across the discontinuity curve. Further conditions are obtained by taking directional derivatives along the curve,

and also the time derivatives following its motion.   Let $\mathbf{N}$ be the unit normal.   The directional derivatives give

$$\Delta(\mathbf{N}^* \cdot \nabla\mathbf{u}) = \Delta(\mathbf{N}^* \cdot \nabla\mathbf{v}) = 0, \tag{4.19}$$

$$\Delta(\mathbf{N}^* \cdot \nabla \nabla\mu) = 0, \quad \text{etc.} \tag{4.20}$$

and the time derivatives give

$$\Delta(\partial\mathbf{v}/\partial t + \mathbf{V} \cdot \nabla\mathbf{v}) = 0, \tag{4.21}$$

$$\Delta(\partial\sigma/\partial t + \mathbf{V} \cdot \nabla\sigma) = 0, \quad \text{etc.} \tag{4.22}$$

Next, by integration of (3.2) across the discontinuity, we have

$$\Delta\lambda = 0, \tag{4.23}$$

and by differentiation,

$$(\mathbf{N}^* \cdot \nabla\lambda) = 0. \tag{4.24}$$

Using next the fact that (3.2) is satisfied on each side of the discontinuity, and taking its tangential component, we have

$$\sigma\Delta(\mathbf{N}^* \cdot \partial\mathbf{v}/\partial t) + \sigma\mathbf{v} \cdot \Delta(\nabla\mathbf{v} \cdot \mathbf{N}^*) + \Delta(\mathbf{N}^* \cdot \nabla^*\mathbf{v}) \cdot \nabla\mu = 0, \tag{4.25}$$

or

$$\sigma(\mathbf{v} - \mathbf{V}) \cdot \Delta(\nabla\mathbf{v} \cdot \mathbf{N}^*) + \Delta(\mathbf{N} \cdot \nabla\mathbf{v}) \cdot \nabla\mu = 0, \tag{4.26}$$

in which (4.21) has been used.   This can be simplified as follows.   Using (4.19), the identities (1.9) and (1.10), and the further identity

$$I = \mathbf{NN} + \mathbf{N}^*\mathbf{N}^*, \tag{4.27}$$

we obtain

$$\begin{aligned}
\Delta(\nabla\mathbf{v} \cdot \mathbf{N}^*) &= \Delta[(\mathbf{NN} + \mathbf{N}^*\mathbf{N}^*) \cdot \nabla\mathbf{v} \cdot \mathbf{N}^*] \\
&= -\mathbf{N}\Delta(\mathbf{N} \cdot \nabla\mathbf{v}^* \cdot \mathbf{N}) \\
&= -\mathbf{N}\Delta(\mathbf{N} \cdot \nabla^*\mathbf{v} \cdot \mathbf{N} + \nabla \cdot \mathbf{v}^*) \\
&= \mathbf{N}\Delta(\mathbf{N}^* \cdot \nabla\mathbf{v} \cdot \mathbf{N} + \nabla^* \cdot \mathbf{v}) \\
&= \mathbf{N}\Delta(\nabla^* \cdot \mathbf{v}).
\end{aligned} \tag{4.28}$$

Similarly,

$$\Delta(\mathbf{N} \cdot \nabla\mathbf{v}) = \mathbf{N}^*\Delta(\nabla^* \cdot \mathbf{v}). \tag{4.29}$$

We have finally, therefore,

$$[\sigma\mathbf{N} \cdot (\mathbf{v} - \mathbf{V}) + \mathbf{N}^* \cdot \nabla\mu]\,\Delta(\nabla^* \cdot \mathbf{v}) = 0, \tag{4.30}$$

or

$$\sigma\mathbf{N} \cdot (\mathbf{u} - \mathbf{V})\,\Delta(\nabla^* \cdot \mathbf{v}) = 0. \tag{4.31}$$

Proceeding along the same lines, we could get another independent jump condition, namely

$$\sigma\mathbf{N} \cdot (\mathbf{v} - \mathbf{V})\,\Delta[\nabla \cdot (1/\sigma\,\nabla\mu)] + \mathbf{N}^* \cdot \nabla\mu\,\Delta(\nabla^* \cdot \mathbf{v}) = 0. \tag{4.32}$$

It is easier and more instructive, however, if we use only (4.31) with the duality theorem.

Observe first that any discontinuity in $\nabla^* \cdot \mathbf{v}$ implies $\mathbf{N} \cdot (\mathbf{V} - \mathbf{u}) = 0$. (This is a discontinuity in the charge density, by the way, since obviously $\nabla^* \cdot \mathbf{v}$ is proportional to $\nabla \cdot \mathbf{E}$.) Now consider two such discontinuity curves intersecting in a point P. Both curves satisfy $\mathbf{N} \cdot (\mathbf{V} - \mathbf{u}) = 0$, and the point P must accordingly be moving with the velocity $\mathbf{u}$. This, then, is the velocity that we assign to a localized perturbation in the charge density. (Any perturbation may be approximated by a network of discontinuity lines, and the points of intersection will have the assigned velocity.) Appealing now to the duality theorem, we assert that there will also be discontinuities carried along with the velocity $\mathbf{v}$, the guiding-center velocity. (Obviously the reversal in $\mathbf{B}$ makes no difference here.) These too will have to satisfy the jump condition (4.31), which now implies $\Delta(\nabla^* \cdot \mathbf{v}) = 0$. The dual condition to this is $\Delta(\nabla^* \cdot \mathbf{u}) = 0$, which accordingly must be satisfied by the discontinuities of the first type, those with the velocity $\mathbf{u}$. To summarize, then, we have found two distinct types of discontinuity, let us say type I, satisfying

$$\mathbf{V} = \mathbf{u}, \qquad \Delta(\nabla^* \cdot \mathbf{u}) = 0, \qquad (4.33)$$

and type II, satisfying

$$\mathbf{V} = \mathbf{v}, \qquad \Delta(\nabla^* \cdot \mathbf{v}) = 0. \qquad (4.34)$$

Similarly, there are two types of localized perturbations. A general perturbation may be analyzed into a perturbation in $\nabla^* \cdot \mathbf{v}$ and a perturbation in $\nabla^* \cdot \mathbf{u}$. The former will be carried along with the velocity $\mathbf{u}$ and the latter with the velocity $\mathbf{v}$. Both velocities, then, are directly observable, at least in principle. Each has a direct operational significance.

It is worth noting that the duality theorem and its consequences depend strongly on the inclusion of the electromagnetic correction terms in the definition of $\mathbf{u}$, both the electromagnetic momentum and the electromagnetic mass. We could have defined a mass-flow velocity $\mathbf{u}_p$ for the plasma alone, writing $\mathbf{S} = \rho\mathbf{u}_p$, without the electromagnetic corrections. But that velocity $\mathbf{u}_p$ would be entirely devoid of any physical significance (except, of course, in the limiting case $\epsilon_0 B^2/\rho \to 0$, where $\mathbf{u}$ and $\mathbf{u}_p$ are the same). For it is $\mathbf{u}$, and not $\mathbf{u}_p$, that has all the desirable properties.

V. THE SYMMETRICAL FORMULATION

Let us now introduce a third basic velocity $\mathbf{w}$,

$$\mathbf{w} = \tfrac{1}{2}(\mathbf{u} + \mathbf{v}). \qquad (5.1)$$

This third velocity does not have the same direct operational significance as the other two, since there is nothing actually moving with this velocity,

nothing like the type I or type II perturbations. It is nonetheless a highly useful velocity, as will presently appear.

In terms of **w**, the equation of motion is

$$\mathbf{\nabla}^* \cdot [\sigma(\partial \mathbf{w}/\partial t + \mathbf{w} \cdot \mathbf{\nabla} \mathbf{w} + \mathbf{\nabla}\phi)] + \tfrac{1}{4}\mathbf{\nabla}\mathbf{\nabla}^*: \quad [(1/\sigma)\,\mathbf{\nabla}\mu\,\mathbf{\nabla}\mu] = 0, \quad (5.2)$$

or alternatively,

$$\sigma(\partial \mathbf{w}/\partial t + \mathbf{w} \cdot \mathbf{\nabla} \mathbf{w} + \mathbf{\nabla}\phi) + \tfrac{1}{4}\mathbf{\nabla} \cdot [(1/\sigma)\,\mathbf{\nabla}\mu\,\mathbf{\nabla}\mu] + \mathbf{\nabla}\lambda = 0, \quad (5.3)$$

where λ is again an uninterpreted scalar. The important feature is the absence of the velocity from the μ term. It means that the gyroviscous force is now derivable from a potential-energy function. The remaining equations are the same as before, namely,

$$\mathbf{\nabla} \cdot \mathbf{w} = 0, \tag{5.4}$$

$$\partial\sigma/\partial t + \mathbf{w} \cdot \mathbf{\nabla}\sigma = 0, \tag{5.5}$$

$$\partial\mu/\partial t + \mathbf{w} \cdot \mathbf{\nabla}\mu = 0, \tag{5.6}$$

$$\mathbf{n} \cdot \mathbf{w} = 0, \tag{5.7}$$

and the energy integral is

$$H_w = \int [\sigma(\tfrac{1}{2}w^2 + \phi) + (1/8\sigma)(\mathbf{\nabla}\mu)^2]\, dx\, dy. \tag{5.8}$$

As was stated above, the gyroviscosity is now a potential-energy term.

Our problem, call it Problem A, is to investigate the gyroviscous equations. Let a new problem, Problem B, be defined as follows:

(1) It is still a plane-motion problem in the x, y plane, with an incompressible fluid.

(2) The magnetic field is now *in* the plane of motion, and with an arbitrary dependence on x and y. The vector potential is $\mathbf{A} = A\mathbf{e}_z$, and we now have

$$\mathbf{B} = \mathbf{\nabla}^* A. \tag{5.9}$$

(3) There is no gyroviscosity. This will consequently be a standard hydromagnetic problem of the pre-Rosenbluth type. There is only one fluid velocity, which we write as **w**.

(4) The Alfvén speed c_A will now be a small velocity of order **v** (see Section II). Hence we shall now be taking $\epsilon_0 \to 0$ rather than $\mu_0 \to 0$ as the n.r. limit. The current density is $\mathbf{J} = J\mathbf{e}_z$, and we now have

$$J = (1/\mu_0)\mathbf{\nabla} \cdot \mathbf{B}^*, \tag{5.10}$$

with no displacement current in the limit as $\epsilon_0 \to 0$. The magnetic force per unit volume is

$$-J\mathbf{B}^* = (1/\mu_0)\mathbf{\nabla} \cdot (\mathbf{B}^*\mathbf{B}^*) = (1/\mu_0)\mathbf{\nabla} \cdot (\mathbf{\nabla}A\mathbf{\nabla}A), \tag{5.11}$$

as can easily be verified. We have also $\eta = \epsilon_0 \nabla \cdot \mathbf{E} \to 0$, hence no electrostatic force. The complete equation of motion is

$$\sigma \left(\frac{\partial \mathbf{w}}{\partial t} + \mathbf{w} \cdot \nabla \mathbf{w} + \nabla \phi \right) + \frac{1}{\mu_0} \nabla \cdot (\nabla A \, \nabla A) + \nabla P = 0, \quad (5.12)$$

where σ is now the same as ρ.

(5) The electrical conductivity is infinite, which, as always, has the implication that the flux lines are carried along by the moving fluid. This gives

$$\partial A / \partial t + \mathbf{w} \cdot \nabla A = 0, \quad (5.13)$$

(6) The mass density σ (or ρ) is constant along the flux lines, just as it is along the μ contours in Problem A.

We see now that there is a perfect correspondence between Problems A and B if we make the identification

$$\frac{1}{2} \int \frac{d\mu}{\sigma^{1/2}} \to \frac{A}{\mu_0^{1/2}}. \quad (5.14)$$

The integral on the left is meaningful, since σ is by assumption a function of μ alone. The equations are the same in each case, and everything in Problem A is identified with something familiar in Problem B. The type I and type II perturbations, for example, are identified with the two Alfvén waves propagating in opposite directions along the flux lines. We have, in fact,

$$(\mathbf{u} , \mathbf{v}) = \mathbf{w} \mp \frac{1}{2\sigma} \nabla^* \mu \to \mathbf{w} \mp \frac{1}{\sigma^{1/2}} \mathbf{B}. \quad (5.15)$$

The two waves are Doppler-shifted in the obvious way.

In Problem B, the velocity $\mathbf{w}$ is the actual velocity of a material fluid. In Problem A, it has no such significance. Still, if we can understand Problem B in terms of material fluid elements moving with velocity $\mathbf{w}$, then we can also understand Problem A in terms of immaterial fluid elements moving with that same velocity. Call them $\mathbf{w}$ elements. They satisfy the differential equation

$$d\mathbf{x} / dt = \mathbf{w}(\mathbf{x} , t). \quad (5.16)$$

Similarly, we could define $\mathbf{u}$ elements and $\mathbf{v}$ elements, and they would have a more material existence. Any of these elements, however, can serve equally well to represent the physical motion. The σ, μ contours, in the course of their motion, pass always through the same $\mathbf{u}$ elements, the same $\mathbf{v}$ elements, and the same $\mathbf{w}$ elements.

VI. STABILITY CONDITIONS

As was mentioned earlier, the gyroviscosity is a strongly stabilizing effect, and we can now see why, in terms of the B language. The σ, μ contours in Problem A have precisely the same type of rigidity as the flux lines in Problem B. We can also carry over to Problem A all the standard results on hydromagnetic stability that have been worked out for Problem B. Suppose $\mathbf{w}$ vanishes identically. Then, in Problem B, we have a static equilibrium, and we have also the standard hydromagnetic energy principle as its necessary and sufficient condition for stability [14]. If $\mathbf{w}$ does not vanish identically, then the equilibrium is merely stationary, and we do not have quite such a good result. We do, however, have the Frieman-Rotenberg energy principle, which gives a general *sufficient* condition [15].

We might also wish to go in the opposite direction. Consider, in Problem B, a stationary flow with a constant σ. The stationary-flow condition is

$$\nabla^* \cdot (\sigma \mathbf{w} \cdot \nabla \mathbf{w} - \mathbf{B} \cdot \nabla \mathbf{B}) = 0 , \tag{6.1}$$

which is obviously satisfied, for an arbitrary $\mathbf{B}$, by a flow velocity

$$\mathbf{w} = \pm \frac{1}{\sigma^{1/2}} \mathbf{B} . \tag{6.2}$$

Is this a stable situation? Translating into the A language, we have either $\mathbf{u}$ or $\mathbf{v} = 0$. The energy integral, H_u or H_v, is an absolute minimum, and the flow is necessarily stable. In the B language, of course, this would be a simple example of the Frieman-Rotenberg condition. We might add that the same result is obtained for an arbitrary three-dimensional $\mathbf{B}$. It depends only on $\sigma = $ const, the incompressibility condition, and $\mathbf{w} = \pm \mathbf{B}\sigma^{-1/2}$. This example is due originally to Chandrasekhar [16].

To illustrate further, we consider an arbitrary plane parallel flow, let us say

$$\mathbf{w}_0 = w_0(y)\mathbf{e}_x , \tag{6.3}$$

with $0 < y < h$. The flow takes place between parallel planes, $y = 0$ and $y = h$, and in the x direction it extends from $-\infty$ to $+\infty$. Using the A language, we have also

$$\mu_0 = \mu_0(y) , \tag{6.4}$$

$$\sigma_0 = \sigma_0(y) , \tag{6.5}$$

$$u_0 = u_0(y) = w_0 - \frac{1}{2\sigma_0} \frac{d\mu_0}{dy} , \tag{6.6}$$

$$v_0 = v_0(y) = w_0 + \frac{1}{2\sigma_0} \frac{d\mu_0}{dy} . \tag{6.7}$$

We wish to consider small-amplitude linear perturbations δw, $\delta \sigma$, $\delta \mu$, etc. Integrals will be understood in the sense of mean values along the x direction. Thus,

$$\int dx\, dy = \lim_{L \to \infty} \left[\frac{1}{2L} \int_{-L}^{+L} dx \int_{0}^{h} dy \right]. \tag{6.8}$$

Let the perturbations be bounded along the x axis. Then the integral of an x derivative can always be set equal to zero.

The essence of the Frieman-Rotenberg method is to introduce an infinitesimal displacement vector $\boldsymbol{\xi}$ such that

$$\partial \boldsymbol{\xi}/\partial t + \mathbf{w}_0 \cdot \boldsymbol{\nabla} \boldsymbol{\xi} = \delta \mathbf{w} + \boldsymbol{\xi} \cdot \boldsymbol{\nabla} \mathbf{w}_0, \tag{6.9}$$

and to use $\boldsymbol{\xi}$ rather than $\delta \mathbf{w}$ as the basic dependent variable. The idea is that $\mathbf{x} + \boldsymbol{\xi}(\mathbf{x}, t)$ should represent the perturbed position, at time t, of the $\mathbf{w}$ element whose unperturbed position at that time would have been $\mathbf{x}$. In that case (6.9) follows by linearization of (5.16). Note that $\boldsymbol{\xi}$ is only defined to within an additive term $f(y)\mathbf{e}_x$, where f is an arbitrary function, since there is that much arbitrariness in the definition of what we mean by the *same* $\mathbf{w}$-element in two situations. (This is a symmetry property, by the way, the same as the one that was mentioned in Section III.) Note also that there is nothing arbitrary in the component ξ_y, which represents unambiguously the vertical displacement of a σ, μ contour.

Writing ξ and η for ξ_x and ξ_y, we have

$$\frac{\partial \xi}{\partial t} + w_0 \frac{\partial \xi}{\partial x} = \delta w_x + \frac{dw_0}{dy}\eta, \tag{6.10}$$

$$\frac{\partial \eta}{\partial t} + w_0 \frac{\partial \eta}{\partial x} = \delta w_y. \tag{6.11}$$

The incompressibility condition gives

$$\frac{\partial \xi}{\partial x} + \frac{\partial \eta}{\partial y} = 0, \tag{6.12}$$

and the linearized equations for σ and μ give

$$\delta \sigma + \eta \frac{d\sigma_0}{dy} = 0, \tag{6.13}$$

$$\delta \mu + \eta \frac{d\mu_0}{dy} = 0. \tag{6.14}$$

Next, for the equation of motion, we have

$$\sigma_0 \left(\frac{\partial}{\partial t} + v_0 \frac{\partial}{\partial x} \right) \left(\frac{\partial}{\partial t} + u_0 \frac{\partial}{\partial x} \right) \xi + \frac{\partial \lambda}{\partial x} = 0, \tag{6.15a}$$

$$\sigma_0 \left(\frac{\partial}{\partial t} + v_0 \frac{\partial}{\partial x} \right) \left(\frac{\partial}{\partial t} + u_0 \frac{\partial}{\partial x} \right) \eta + \frac{\partial \lambda}{\partial y} = 0, \tag{6.15b}$$

from which the gravitational term has been dropped in the interests of simplicity. The boundary condition is simply

$$\eta(x, 0, t) = \eta(x, h, t) = 0. \tag{6.16}$$

Note the symmetrical dependence of the equations on u_0 and v_0, in accordance with the duality theorem. If we set $u_0 \equiv v_0$, then we get the classical hydrodynamic equations as a special case.

Proceeding in the usual way, we multiply (6.15a) by $\partial \xi / \partial t$ and (6.15b) by $\partial \eta / \partial t$, we add them together, and we take the integral over $dx \, dy$ in the sense of (6.8). Integrating by parts, and using (6.12) and (6.16), we end up with

$$dH/dt = 0, \tag{6.17}$$

where

$$H = T + W, \tag{6.18}$$

$$T = \frac{1}{2} \int \sigma_0 \left[\left(\frac{\partial \xi}{\partial t} \right)^2 + \left(\frac{\partial \eta}{\partial t} \right)^2 \right] dx \, dy, \tag{6.19}$$

$$W = -\frac{1}{2} \int \sigma_0 u_0 v_0 \left[\left(\frac{\partial \eta}{\partial x} \right)^2 + \left(\frac{\partial \eta}{\partial y} \right)^2 \right] dx \, dy. \tag{6.20}$$

This, of course, is the Frieman-Rotenberg energy integral. It reduces to H_u when u_0 vanishes identically, to H_v when v_0 vanishes identically, and so forth.

We have immediately a simple sufficient condition for stability,

$$u_0 v_0 < 0, \qquad \text{for all } y. \tag{6.21}$$

The flow is stable, in other words, if the two characteristic velocities are everywhere opposite in direction. For in that case both T and W are positive-definite, and they are both bounded above for all time by the constant H. It should of course be understood that "for all time" means for all time on the time scale built into the theory. This would not exclude the possibility of an unstable mode with a growth rate, say, of order $\delta^3 \omega_c$.

Obviously, the stability of a flow does not depend on the choice of a reference frame. Another way of stating our condition, then, is that some constant V should exist such that we have either

$$u_0(y) < V < v_0(y), \tag{6.22a}$$

for all y, or

$$v_0(y) < V < u_0(y), \tag{6.22b}$$

again for all y. For in that case we can satisfy (6.21) by transformation to the moving frame whose velocity is V. Translating into the B lan-

guage, we can say that the flow is stable if a reference frame exists in which $|w_0| < c_A$ is satisfied everywhere.

ACKNOWLEDGMENT

This work was done under the auspices of the United States Atomic Energy Commission.

REFERENCES

1. Chapman, S. and Cowling, T. G., "The Mathematical Theory of Non-Uniform Gases." Cambridge Univ. Press, London and New York, 1953.
2. Kaufman, A. N., Plasma Transport Theory, *in* "La Théorie des Gaz Neutres et Ionisés" (C. DeWitt and J. F. Detoeuf, eds.), p. 293.
3. Kaufman, A. N., *Phys. Fluids* **3,** 610 (1960).
4. Thompson, W. B., "Reports on Progress in Physics," Vol. 24, p. 363. Physical Society, London, 1961.
5. Chew, G. F., Goldberger, M. L., and Low, F. E., *Proc. Roy. Soc. (London),* **A236,** 112 (1956).
6. Rosenbluth, M. N., Krall, N. A., and Rostoker, N., *Nucl. Fusion* Suppl., Part 1, 143 (1962).
7. Newcomb, W. A., *Phys. Fluids* (to be published). This paper may be broken up into a series.
8. Roberts, K. V. and Taylor, J. B., *Phys. Rev. Lett.* **8,** 197 (1962).
9. Rosenbluth, M. N. and Simon, A., *Phys. Fluids* **8,** 1300 (1965).
10. Rosenbluth, M. N. and Longmire, C., *Ann. Phys.* **1,** 120 (1957).
11. Northrup, T. G., *Phys. Rev.* **103,** 1150 (1956).
12. Spitzer, L., "Physics of Fully Ionized Gases," 2nd ed. Wiley (Interscience), New York, 1962.
13. Kruskal, M. D., Asymptotology, *in* "Mathematical Models in Physical Sciences." Prentice-Hall, Englewood Cliffs, New Jersey 1963.
14. Bernstein, I. B., Frieman, E. A., Kruskal, M. D., and Kulsrud, R. M., *Proc. Roy Soc. (London)* **A244,** 17 (1958).
15. Frieman, E. and Rotenberg, M., *Rev. Mod. Phys.* **32,** 898 (1960).
16. Chandrasekhar, S., *Proc. Natl. Acad. Sci.* **42,** 273 (1956).

SECTION VI

Experimental Plasma Physics

edited by

T. D. WILKERSON

Solar System Magnetic Fields and Plasmas

JOHN M. WILCOX

SPACE SCIENCES LABORATORY, UNIVERSITY OF CALIFORNIA
BERKELEY, CALIFORNIA

Observations of the solar magnetic field in the photosphere with the solar magnetograph, and at a distance from the sun of one astronomical unit with spacecraft magnetometers, are discussed with relation to a physical picture in which the expanding solar wind plasma stretches lines of magnetic force from the photosphere out into the interplanetary medium beyond the earth. The evolution of solar magnetic fields is described beginning with their first appearance in sunspots and bipolar magnetic regions, which then form unipolar magnetic regions and the fields in the polar regions of the sun. A relationship is established between the direction of the photospheric magnetic field at low solar latitudes and the direction of the interplanetary field as observed by spacecraft near the earth. A large-scale longitudinal structure in the interplanetary medium is discussed in which the magnetic field is directed away from the sun for several days and then toward the sun for several days. Finally, the simulation in laboratory experiments of the interaction between the streaming magnetized solar plasma and the dipole-like magnetic field of the earth is described.

This discussion will begin with the magnetic fields observed on the surface of the sun, move out to interplanetary fields and plasmas and their relation to these solar magnetic fields, and finally come to earth in a plasma physics laboratory. Against this background, we discuss some recent results obtained in collaboration with N. F. Ness with the magnetometer experiment on the IMP-1 satellite as supplemented with observations obtained in collaboration with R. Howard with the Mount Wilson Observatory solar magnetograph. In particular, two research problems of current interest are identified and discussed.

I. SOLAR MAGNETIC FIELDS

The strong magnetic fields associated with sunspots are perhaps the most familiar feature of the sun's magnetic field. Spots often appear on the surface of the sun in pairs, as shown in Fig. 1. The preceding spot

(in the sense of the solar rotation) is usually somewhat nearer the equator than is the following spot. A process that has been called magnetic bouyancy by Parker [1] may be involved in the appearance of sunspots. If we consider the pressure balance in a tube of magnetic flux below the surface of the sun, the pressure outside of the tube is supplied only by

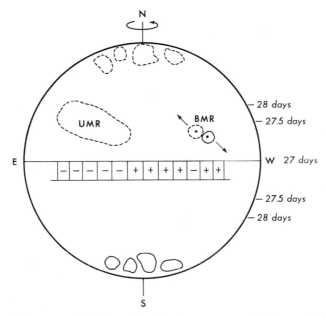

Fig. 1. Solar magnetic field regions for the sunspot cycle that ended in 1964. A pair of sunspots is surrounded by a bipolar magnetic region (BMR). Solid contours indicate magnetic field out of the sun, and dashed contours indicate magnetic field into the sun. The large region with field into the sun is a unipolar magnetic region (UMR). Field polarities in the southern hemisphere are opposite those in the northern hemisphere. When the sun is observed with fine-scale resolution, the indicated contours usually contain small areas of oppositely directed field. The synodic rotation periods at various latitudes are indicated. For quantitative analysis, a strip at a given latitude is divided into small areas as shown here and discussed in the text.

the plasma, whereas inside the tube there are two terms: the magnetic field pressure $B^2/8\pi$, plus the pressure of the plasma within the flux tube. If the temperature is approximately constant, then the mass density within the flux tube will be less than in the surrounding material, and the flux tube will begin to rise. Analysis indicates that the process is self-reinforcing, so that the tube will continue to rise until it reaches the surface of the photosphere.

Although the details about the formation of sunspots are not well known, it is an observational fact that spots do appear, as shown in Fig. 1. The magnetic field within the spot itself is several hundred gauss. Each spot is surrounded by a larger region having the same sense of field as the spot itself. A large spot will increase in size and field strength for several days, after which it will begin its decline. Usually after one solar rotation the spots have disappeared, but the surrounding bipolar magnetic region (commonly abbreviated BMR) can still be observed. In the course of several solar rotations, this region becomes weak and diffuse. There is a tendency for the following portion of a BMR to move poleward and for the preceding portion to move toward the equator. It appears that the observed dipole-like field in the polar regions of the sun is primarily a surface effect and is formed by the following portions of many BMR's that have drifted poleward. In a given solar hemisphere during a given 11-yr sunspot cycle, the preceding spot will have one sense and the following spot will have the opposite sense of magnetic field. In the opposite hemisphere, at the same time, the polarity conditions are just reversed. The preceding portions of bipolar regions drift toward the equator and appear to merge together and disappear. The following portions of several bipolar regions may combine to form a large area having predominantly one polarity of field, and this has been called by Babcock and Babcock [2] a unipolar magnetic region (UMR). An example is shown in Fig. 1. Thus we have a picture [3] of fields that are continually moving on the surface of the sun with appreciable changes occurring in a few days in the case of sunspots and in a few solar rotations in the case of the large-scale fields.

The time for magnetic field lines to diffuse into the solar plasma is extremely long. The magnetic field can be said to be frozen into the solar plasma. In the case of field lines running through the interior of the sun, the magnetic diffusion time would be comparable to the age of the sun, so that in shorter times one would not expect to find appreciable motions of the field. Thus, the observed rapid motions of the field would seem to be associated with plasma motions in the photosphere which drag the field lines about. Leighton [4] has suggested a random walk process whereby tubes of magnetic flux may move on the sun. Alfvén [5] has suggested that, in addition to the observed surface fields, there should be a general (i.e., deep-lying) solar magnetic field that would not change its sense in any measurable time. Such a field has not yet been observed.

In order to give a more quantitative discussion of the large-scale solar magnetic field directions, the following technique is employed. A heliographic latitude is selected, and a thin strip centered at the given latitude

is considered. This strip is then divided in longitude by an amount corresponding to the rotation of the sun in 12 hr. Each such area is assigned a plus sign if the field within is predominantly out of the sun and is assigned a negative sign if the field within is predominantly into the sun. Occasional ambigious cases are omitted. An example centered at 5° south of the solar equator is shown in Fig. 1. The process, of course, can be repeated at other heliographic latitudes. We then have produced a time series describing the large-scale sense of the solar magnetic field at a given latitude.

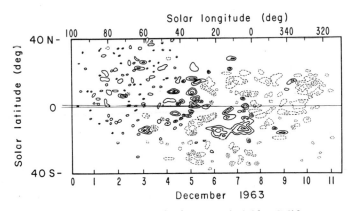

Fig. 2. Synoptic chart of the photospheric magnetic field. Solid contours represent field directed out of the sun, and dashed contours represent field directed into the sun. Contour levels are 2, 4, 8, 12, and 25 G.

The foregoing discussion is based on observations made with the solar magnetograph [6] at Mount Wilson Observatory. This instrument utilizes the longitudinal Zeeman effect so that the line-of-sight component of the photospheric magnetic field is measured. The sensitivity is about 1 G, and the angular resolution is about 23 sec of arc, which is $\frac{1}{80}$ of the solar diameter. The sun is scanned from one pole to the other in a raster pattern, the entire process taking about 1 hr. Such a solar magnetogram is obtained every day at Mount Wilson, weather permitting, and from these daily magnetograms it is possible to prepare a synoptic chart. A portion of such a synoptic chart of the photospheric magnetic field is shown in Fig. 2. The solid contours represent field directed out of the sun, and the dashed contours represent field into the sun. On the left-hand side of Fig. 2 there is a large region with field directed out of the sun which extends considerably on each side of the equator. On the right-hand side of Fig. 2 is a similar region extending on both sides of the equator with field directed into the sun. Thus we can note that the

large-scale weak fields on the sun which are the final result of the processes just discussed can extend across the equator without noticeable changes. On the other hand, the sunspots are very much related to the equator. If a spot group forms only 2° or 3° north of the equator, it will almost invariably have the polarity relations appropriate to the northern hemisphere at that time, and similarly for the southern hemisphere. It seems that the sense of the magnetic field which appears in sunspots is rather strictly related to the position with regard to the solar equator, whereas the plasma motions that eventually diffuse the flux can readily move it across the solar equator.

II. INTERPLANETARY PLASMAS AND FIELDS

We now move out into the interplanetary medium near the earth and consider observations obtained with the magnetometer experiment of Ness *et al.* [7] on the IMP-1 satellite. This satellite was launched into a highly elliptic orbit on November 27, 1963 and observed the interplanetary medium for three solar rotations thereafter. Apogee was at about 31 earth radii, which is well beyond the influence of the geomagnetic field on the sunward hemisphere. Vector measurements of the interplanetary field were obtained with fluxgate magnetometers every 20 sec with an uncertainty of $\pm \frac{1}{4}\gamma$ ($1\gamma = 10^{-5}$ G).

What might we expect to find with these observations? In a series of papers published in the late 1950's, Parker [8] has discussed the hydrodynamic expansion of the solar corona which results in what he calls the solar wind. Neugebauer and Snyder [9], with an experiment on the Mariner 2 spacecraft, have confirmed that the solar wind plasma is always flowing in a direction approximately radially away from the sun with a density of 5 protons/cm³ and a velocity of several hundred kilometers per second. The temperature is estimated in the range of 10^5 deg. A magnetic field with an average magnitude of about 5γ is frozen into the solar wind plasma. This field on the average is in the form of an Archimedes spiral [10] that is caused by the combination of the radial flow of the solar wind plasma and the solar rotation. Near the earth, the angle between the spiral magnetic field and the earth-sun line is approximately 45°, because the radial velocity of the solar wind is approximately equal to that tangential velocity which is the product of the sun's angular velocity and the sun-earth radius arm.

The left-hand portion of Fig. 3 shows the observed [10] distribution of directions of the interplanetary magnetic field component parallel to

the ecliptic. The distribution is considerably peaked in directions approximately 45° away from the earth-sun line, as predicted by the spiral theory. The right-hand portion of Fig. 3 shows the distribution of directions perpendicular to the ecliptic plane. The most important point to note is that the field is predominantly parallel to the ecliptic and not transverse to it.

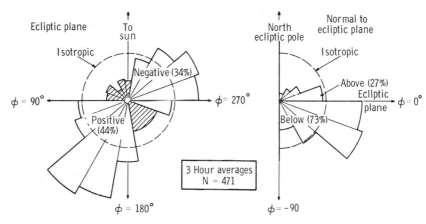

FIG. 3. Distribution of the interplanetary magnetic field directions parallel and normal to the ecliptic averaged over 3-hr intervals, as measured with the IMP-1 satellite. Both histograms show the field angular distribution per unit solid angle; the dashed circles would correspond to an isotropic distribution of the same number of vectors. The distribution is peaked in directions corresponding to the spiral stream- ing angle. The angular intervals in which the field is predominantly away from the sun and predominantly toward the sun are labeled positive and negative in this figure and represented by plus and minus signs in Fig. 6. The distribution normal to the ecliptic shows that the interplanetary field is predominantly parallel to the ecliptic rather than perpendicular to it.

Similar observations [11] have been obtained with the Mariner 4 spacecraft during the interplanetary portion of its journey to Mars.

III. EXTENSION OF THE PHOTOSPHERIC MAGNETIC FIELD INTO INTERPLANETARY SPACE

We now wish to develop a description of the sense of the interplanetary field as a function of time for comparison with the description of the sense of the photospheric magnetic field discussed previously and illus- trated in Fig. 1. For this purpose, the range in angles labeled "positive" in Fig. 3 is considered to represent an interplanetary field directed pre-

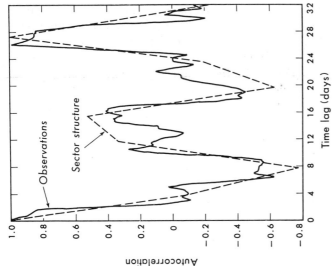

Fig. 5. Autocorrelation of the sense of the nearby interplanetary magnetic field observed with the IMP-1 satellite. The prominent positive peak at about 27 days is consistent with the corotation of the interplanetary magnetic field with the sun. The dashed line is related to the sector structure shown in Fig. 6.

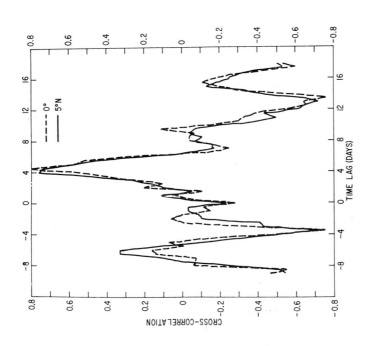

Fig. 4. Cross-correlation as a function of time lag of the sense of the nearby interplanetary magnetic field and the sense of the photospheric magnetic field for solar latitudes at the center of the visible disk and at 5°N thereof.

dominantly away from the sun, and the range of angles labeled "negative" is considered to represent an interplanetary field directed predominantly toward the sun. During most of the 12-hr periods, the interplanetary field is entirely confined to one of these two conditions. Thus, a time series describing the sense of the interplanetary field in 12-hr periods is produced. A cross-correlation of this series with the description of the sense of the photospheric magnetic field is then computed. Figure 4 shows this cross-correlation as a function of the lag between the two variables. A prominent positive correlation is observed at a lag of approximately $4\frac{1}{2}$ days. How are we to interpret this $4\frac{1}{2}$-day lag? If we assume that the velocity of the solar wind is constant and radial from the sun to the earth and use the solar wind velocity observed by plasma detectors on the IMP-1 satellite, we obtain a transit time for the solar wind from the sun to the earth which is consistent with the lag of the positive peak shown in Fig. 4. These results indicate that some of the photospheric magnetic field lines are dragged out by the solar wind to form a portion of the interplanetary magnetic field.

Since the interplanetary magnetic field lines have been shown to be rooted in the photosphere, we would expect the interplanetary magnetic field to corotate with the sun. If we compute an autocorrelation of the function just described which describes the sense of the interplanetary magnetic field, we would expect to find a large positive peak at approximately 27 days, i.e., the period of rotation of the low-latitude regions on the sun as seen from the earth. The result of this autocorrelation is displayed in Fig. 5. The large positive peak at about 27 days is consistent with the foregoing discussion. Since the peak is centered at about 27 days (and not at 28 or 29 days), the latitude of the solar source of the interplanetary field appears to be near the equator [10], as can be ascertained by comparison of the rotation periods at various latitudes given in Fig. 1.

IV. A QUASI-STATIONARY COROTATING SECTOR STRUCTURE IN THE INTERPLANETARY MAGNETIC FIELD

A longitudinal sector structure observed [12] in the interplanetary magnetic field during three solar rotations is shown in Fig. 6. For approximately $\frac{2}{7}$ of the total circumference the interplanetary field is almost entirely directed away from the sun, and then for $\frac{2}{7}$ of the circumference toward the sun, $\frac{2}{7}$ away, and finally $\frac{1}{7}$ toward the sun. This pattern

corotates with the sun as discussed previously so that it rotates once past the earth every 27 days. Satellite observations of the sense of the interplanetary magnetic field are indicated with plus and minus signs at the perimeter of Fig. 6. The first orbit is labeled, and the next orbits follow in a clockwise direction. It can be noted that the sector description at the center of the figure is a very good approximation; i.e., a sector with

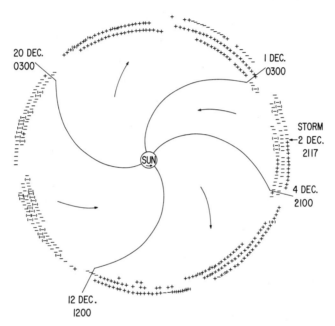

Fig. 6. The plus (away from the sun) and minus (toward the sun) signs at the circumference of the figure indicate the direction of the measured interplanetary magnetic field during successive 3-hr intervals. Parentheses around a plus or minus indicate a time during which the field direction has moved beyond the "allowed regions" shown in Fig. 3 for a few hours in a smooth and continuous manner. The inner portion of the figure is a schematic representation of a sector structure of the interplanetary magnetic field that is suggested by these observations. The deviations about the average streaming angle which are actually present are not shown in this figure.

the field labeled away from the sun is almost entirely occupied by plus signs, and, similarly, a sector with an arrow indicating field toward the sun is almost entirely occupied by minus signs. The second orbit appears to contain an exception in having several plus signs in a sector with field directed toward the sun, but this can be understood in terms of the solar wind velocity. At this time, the solar wind velocity was considerably higher than average, which means that the sector boundary was trans-

ported to the earth too soon. During most of the observations, the transit time of the solar wind from the sun to the earth was about $4\frac{1}{2}$ days. At this particular time in orbit 2, the transit time was only 3 days, and this difference of $1\frac{1}{2}$ days corresponds to the number of plus signs at the end of orbit 2. Since the sector structure corotates with the sun, an influence at the earth caused by this structure is not due to the advance of a spherical front but rather to the rotational motion of the pattern past the earth.

We can now identify and discuss the first research problem of current interest, which is simply to understand the basic cause of the sectors. Although the pattern shown in Fig. 6 was observed during only three solar rotations, an analysis of geomagnetic effects associated with the sector structure indicates that at least several parts of this pattern existed for 1 or 2 years or longer. As shown by the satellite observations at the perimeter of Fig. 6, the pattern is not a random and disordered effect but, on the contrary, a very regular one. We have known for several years that there can be certain longitudes on the sun which are active for the production of sunspots and flares over a period of 1 or 2 years, but the pattern discussed here is a large-scale regular effect occupying the entire longitudinal range on the sun. If such a sector pattern were to be quasi-stationary in equatorial latitudes, then the differential rotation at higher latitudes would twist the pattern up very thoroughly after a few solar rotations. If the twisting becomes too great, the magnetic fields might tend to merge together and wash out the sector pattern. Such a relaxation effect might appear as a change with time in the solar differential rotation. An investigation of this possibility is now in progress.

We can perhaps distinguish three characteristic scale lengths on the surface of the sun. The smallest that has been observed is related to the granulation pattern, which has a characteristic length of perhaps 700 km. The supergranulation pattern or chromospheric network observed by Simon and Leighton [13] has a characteristic length typically of 30,000 km. The sector structure discussed here would have a characteristic length of the order of the solar radius (700,000 km). The first two patterns are thought to be related to plasma motions on and near the surface of the sun. An explanation for the sector structure has not yet been proposed.

We proceed now to an analysis of the relation of the sector structure to the interplanetary magnetic field magnitude, the solar wind velocity and density, and geomagnetic effects. The magnitude of the interplanetary magnetic field is analyzed in Fig. 7. The abscissa represents the $7\frac{3}{4}$ days required for a $\frac{2}{7}$ sector to rotate past the earth. The ordinate represents the average magnitude of the interplanetary field at the same relative

position within a number of sectors.   Sectors with field directed away from the sun and with field directed toward the sun are shown separately. The magnetic field reaches a peak early in the sector of greater than 6γ and then declines in the trailing portion of the sector to less than 4γ.

The discussion so far has been entirely in terms of observations of the magnetic field.   It is clearly important to know whether the solar wind

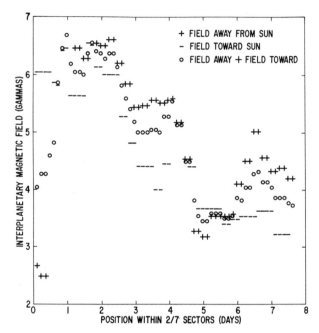

FIG. 7. Superposed epoch analysis of the magnitude of the interplanetary magnetic field as a function of position within the $\frac{2}{7}$ sectors shown in Fig. 6. The abscissa represents position within the sector, measured in days as the sector sweeps past the earth.   The ordinate is the average magnitude at the same relative position within the sectors.   The results are shown separately for the sectors with field away from the sun, the sectors with field toward the sun, and for all sectors.

plasma also is organized by the sector structure.   The observations of the solar wind by the MIT Faraday cup experiment [14] on IMP-1 have been analyzed for this purpose.   The solar wind velocity is shown in Fig. 8 in a format similar to that used in Fig. 7.   The velocity reaches a peak near the second day of the sector and then declines in the trailing portions of the sectors.   A large quantitative effect is observed in a similar analysis of the solar wind density shown in Fig. 9.   The density reaches a peak greater than 14 protons/cm³ at about the first day of the sector and then

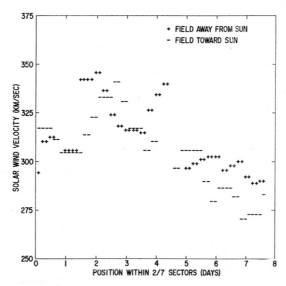

Fig. 8. Superposed epoch analysis of the solar wind velocity as a function of position within the $\frac{2}{7}$ sectors.

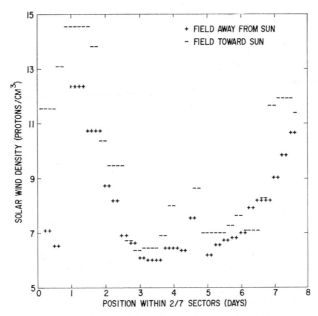

Fig. 9. Superposed epoch analysis of the solar wind density as a function of position within the $\frac{2}{7}$ sectors.

declines precipitously to less than 7 protons/cm^3 in the middle portion of the sector, and then increases again in the trailing portions of the sector.   Thus, the density reaches a peak about one day before the peak of the velocity, and in the trailing portions of the sector the density is increasing while the velocity continues to decline.   Since the solar wind plasma also participates in the sector structure, the structure is an important property of the interplanetary medium and, for that matter, of the inner solar system.

We can now identify and discuss the second research problem of current interest, which is an explanation of how the characteristic shapes of interplanetary field magnitude and solar wind velocity and density shown in Figs. 7–9 are produced.   Some quasi-stationary structure in the outer layers of the sun having a longitudinal organization similar to that shown in Fig. 6 would seem to be involved.   What is the configuration in the photosphere, chromosphere, and lower corona which produces the particular distributions that have been observed in Figs. 7–9?   Is the spiked-helmet structure sometimes observed in the lower corona of importance in this regard?   Which of the three quantities, if any, is the most fundamental?   Does a rapid increase in velocity produce a shock wave that increases the density, or is the change in density by a factor of 2 a direct reflection of conditions on the sun?   Perhaps the sector structure should be invoked in discussions of magnetic variable stars and of acceleration processes in astrophysical contexts.

V. INTERACTION WITH THE GEOMAGNETIC FIELD

Does geomagnetic activity respond as the sector structure rotates past the earth?   The answer to this question is shown in Fig. 10, which shows the same analysis applied to an index of geomagnetic activity, the 24-hr sum of Kp.   Geomagnetic activity reaches a peak of greater than 25 at approximately the second day of the sector and then declines to less than 10 in the trailing portions of the sector.   The results for sectors with field directed away from the sun and with field directed toward the sun are shown separately in Fig. 10.   The degree to which the two curves have the same shape gives one a measure of the statistical reliability of the result.   The large influence of the sectors on geomagnetic activity suggests the possibility that other details of the radiation belts may be strongly influenced by the sector pattern.   Williams [15] has found that electrons of energy greater than 270 keV at a few earth radii are considerably influenced by the sector pattern.

We may consider briefly the interaction to be expected when the streaming magnetized solar wind encounters an obstacle such as the geomagnetic
field.   The solar wind plasma is supersonic, i.e., the flow velocity is much
larger than the wave velocity within the plasma.   Thus, a collisionless
shock forms which slows down the plasma so that it can then flow around
the obstacle.   The plasma is collisionless because the mean free path for
Coulomb collisions is of the order of 1 a.u.   Nevertheless, the presence of
the weak interplanetary magnetic field couples the particles together and

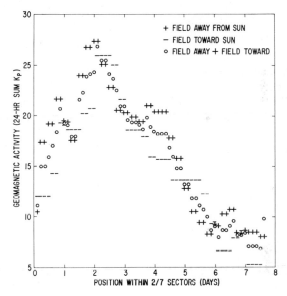

Fig. 10. Superposed epoch analysis of the geomagnetic activity index 24-hr sum
Kp as a function of position within the $\frac{2}{7}$ sectors.

produces a fluid-like motion on a distance scale greater than the proton
gyroradius, which is measured in hundreds of kilometers.   Inside the
collisionless shock surface is another surface at which pressure balance
occurs between the oncoming solar wind and the magnetic pressure of the
compressed geomagnetic field.   This latter surface is called the magneto-
pause.   Geomagnetic lines at high latitudes are pulled by the solar wind
into a long tail stretching in the antisolar direction.   This region is
bisected by a neutral sheet, which is approximately an extension of the
plane of the geomagnetic equator.   Ness [16] has discovered and eluci-
dated many of these phenomena and discusses them in a companion
paper in this volume.

VI. TERRESTRIAL PLASMAS

We may now descend to earth and land in a plasma laboratory, such as that of H. Alfvén in Stockholm, which the author has recently visited.

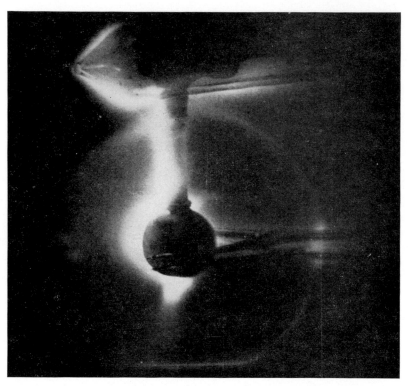

FIG. 11. Laboratory simulation [20] of the interaction between the solar wind and the geomagnetic field. The sphere in the center of the figure represents the earth and has a magnetic dipole in the vertical direction. A streaming plasma approaches from the left with a frozen-in field parallel to the dipole field that it encounters. A sphere of interaction can be distinguished.

Several laboratories in various parts of the world are attempting to simulate the interaction between the geomagnetic field and the solar wind with laboratory plasma experiments [17–19]. The experiment of Danielsson and Lindberg [20] in Stockholm is representative of these efforts. Plasma is accelerated in a coaxial gun and approaches a terrella, the latter being a small sphere with a dipole field that represents the earth. In the case

shown in Fig. 11, the magnetic field frozen into the streaming plasma is parallel to the external field of the terrella in equatorial regions. The plasma flow is from left to right, and the axis of the terrella is in the vertical direction. A spherical front can be distinguished at the boundary between the streaming plasma and the terrella field. Figure 12 shows

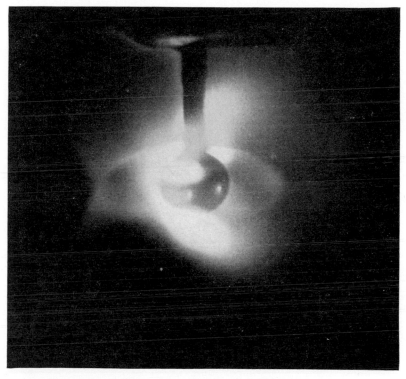

FIG. 12. Same as Fig. 11, except that the frozen-in field in the streaming plasma is antiparallel to the dipole field. The interaction surface now appears to be similar to the X-type singularity predicted by Dungey [21].

the same situation except that the terrella field is reversed, such that it is now antiparallel to the field frozen into the streaming plasma. This case has been discussed by Dungey [21], who predicts that a X-type singularity will be formed. Such a singularity can be distinguished in Fig. 12. Probe measurements indicate that the flow of the plasma is toward the X on both sides of it, as predicted by Dungey. As yet, the laboratory experiments do not show the collisionless shock or the neutral sheet discussed previously which are found in the geophysical case. One reason

for this is the difficulty of preparing a suitably hot and tenuous streaming plasma. This difficulty also exists in the laboratory experiments attempting to produce controlled thermonuclear fusion.

There has been a considerable interaction between astrophysics and the efforts toward controlled thermonuclear reactions. The early ideas of Alfvén [22] on hydromagnetic waves and on the first adiabatic invariant that came from his investigations in astrophysics have been basic to the attempts toward controlled thermonuclear reactions. On the other hand, numerous instabilities observed in the laboratory experiments have been invoked in astrophysics. One sticky problem in discussions of the sun is that of time scales. The changes in the photospheric field discussed previously occurring in times of a few days or a few solar rotations would not be allowed by simple diffusion of magnetic lines through the plasma. The solar magnetic field is an attractive energy source for solar flares, but the release of the energy within a few minutes poses a difficult theoretical problem. A number of the instabilities observed in the laboratory have been invoked at various times in attempts to explain the fast time scales observed on the sun. At the International Astronomical Union Symposium on Solar and Stellar Magnetic Fields in 1963, Cowling [23] had the following comment on these efforts: "We find ourselves in these days tempted regularly to invoke motions across the lines of force. Well, such motions are met with in certain circumstances, and we have to reckon with them. But I think one should regard it as the last confession of weakness rather than the first straw to be clutched at."

Acknowledgments

It was a privilege and pleasure to participate in this Symposium in honor of Professor Burgers. This work was supported in part by the Office of Naval Research under Contract Nonr-3656(26) and by NASA under Grant NsG 243-62.

References

1. Parker, E. N., The Formation of Sunspots from the Solar Toroidal Field. *Astrophys. J.* **121**, 491 (1955).
2. Babcock, H. W. and Babcock, H. D., The Sun's Magnetic Field, 1952–1954. *Astrophys. J.* **121**, 349 (1955).
3. Bumba, V. and Howard, R., Large-Scale Distribution of Solar Magnetic Fields. *Astrophys. J.* **141**, 1502 (1965).
4. Leighton, R. B., Transport of Magnetic Fields on the Sun. *Astrophys. J.* **140**, 1547 (1964).
5. Alfvén, H., On Sunspots and the Solar Cycle. *Arkiv. Mat. Astron. Fysik* **25B**, no. 29 (1943).
6. Babcock, H. W., The Solar Magnetograph. *Astrophys. J.* **118**, 387 (1953).
7. Ness, N. F., Scearce, C. S., and Seek, J. B., Initial Results of the IMP 1 Magnetic Field Experiment. *J. Geophys. Res.* **69**, 3531 (1964).

8. Parker, E. N., "Interplanetary Dynamical Processes." Wiley (Interscience), New York, 1963.
9. Neugebauer, M. and Snyder, C. W., The Mission of Mariner II: Preliminary Observations, Solar Plasma Experiment. *Science* **138,** 1095 (1962).
10. Ness, N. F. and Wilcox, J. M., Solar Origin of the Interplanetary Magnetic Field. *Phys. Rev. Letters* **13,** 461 (1964).
11. Coleman, P. J., Jr., Davis, L., Jr., Jones, D. E., and Smith, E. J., Preliminary Results of the Mariner 4 Magnetometer Experiment. *Trans. Am. Geophys. Union* **46,** 533 (1965).
12. Ness, N. F. and Wilcox, J. M., Sector Structure of the Quiet Interplanetary Magnetic Field. *Science* **148,** 1592 (1965).
13. Simon, G. W. and Leighton, R. B., Velocity Fields in the Solar Atmosphere. III. Large-Scale Motions, the Chromospheric Network, and Magnetic Fields. *Astrophys. J.* **140,** 1120 (1964).
14. Bridge, H. and Lyon, E., private communication (1964).
15. Williams, D. J., A 27-Day Periodicity in Outer Zone Trapped Electron Intensities. *J. Geophys. Res.* **71,** 1815 (1966).
16. Ness, N. F., paper in this volume.
17. Cladis, J. B., Miller, T. D., and Baskett, J. R., Interaction of a Supersonic Plasma Stream with a Dipole Magnetic Field. *J. Geophys. Res.* **69,** 2257 (1964).
18. Kawashima, N. and Mori, S., Experiment on the Intrusion of Plasma into a Simulated Magnetic Cavity, *Phys. Fluids* **8,** 378 (1965).
19. Osborne, F. J. F., Bachynski, M. P., and Gore, J. V., Laboratory Studies of the Variation of the Magnetosphere with Solar Wind Properties. *J. Geophys. Res.* **69,** 4441 (1964).
20. Danielsson, L. and Lindberg, L., Plasma Flow Through a Magnetic Dipole Field. *Phys. Fluids* **7,** 1878 (1964).
21. Dungey, J. W., Interplanetary Magnetic Field and the Auroral Zones. *Phys. Rev. Letters* **6,** 47 (1961).
22. Alfvén, H. and Fälthammar, C. G., "Cosmical Electrodynamics," 2nd ed. Oxford Univ. Press, London and New York, 1963.
23. Cowling, T. G., "Stellar and Solar Magnetic Fields," p. 229. North-Holland, Amsterdam, 1965.

Satellite Measurements of Magnetic Fields in Space

NORMAN F. NESS

LABORATORY FOR SPACE SCIENCES
GODDARD SPACE FLIGHT CENTER
GREENBELT, MARYLAND

The advent of the satellite and space probe era eight years ago introduced into the realm of extraterrestrial physics the possibility of directly measuring the properties of interplanetary space and the distant geomagnetic field. Since 1957, an impressive sequence of such in situ experiments has led not only to renewed investigations of well-known solar-terrestrial physical problems, but also has initiated studies investigating completely new phenomena not previously anticipated. These are represented by the Van Allen radiation belt and the phenomenon of the solar wind and its effect upon the terrestrial magnetic field. Subsequent to early suggestions by Biermann in 1951 for a continuous and substantial solar corpuscular flux to explain the observed characteristics of type I comet tails, Parker in the late 1950's developed the theory of the "solar wind" or hydrodynamic expansion of the solar corona into interplanetary space. Direct measurements by satellites have confirmed the existence of the solar wind and the continual confinement of the geomagnetic field as well as the development of an extended magnetic tail of the earth. On the sunlit side of the earth, the regular geomagnetic field terminates at approximately 85,000 km, whereas on the night side of the earth the terrestrial field is observed to trail out in a highly distorted fashion at least halfway to the distance to the moon. Standing off from the regular geomagnetic field a boundary has been observed between a turbulent boundary layer and the undisturbed interplanetary medium which is tentatively identified as a collisionless magnetohydrodynamic shock wave. The use of a continuum fluid-dynamic analogy applied to the solar wind permits an estimate of the standoff distance for a spherical object which approximates the confined geomagnetic field. Direct comparison with observations is reasonably good and suggests that the phenomenon investigated is indeed a collisionless shock. This paper will discuss the gross characteristics of the distorted geomagnetic field, its boundary layer, and the detached bow shock wave as observed recently by satellite experiments.

I. INTRODUCTION

Direct measurements of the physical properties of cislunar space have been possible only through the recent introduction of a unique type of

portable laboratory bench, namely, satellite and space probes. These devices, carrying instruments to measure magnetic fields, energetic particle, and plasma fluxes, are becoming an increasingly important tool in the study of the large-scale physics of the planets and interplanetary space.

It is now known that interplanetary space is not a void nor vacuum but rather is filled with a tenuous ionized gas moving radially from the sun at all times. This solar plasma flux, called the solar wind by Parker (1958), dominates the characteristics of the interplanetary medium from the surface of the sun to at least 2.5 a.u. and most certainly further beyond.

This paper is concerned with a discussion of satellite measurements of magnetic fields surrounding the earth in cislunar space and their interpretation. As such, this paper continues the previous discussion by Wilcox (1966) on solar system magnetic fields and plasmas to our immediate environment. Within this region of space, a number of regimes exist as defined in the context of plasma physics by β, the ratio of energy density of the plasma to the magnetic field.

For the interplanetary medium, it is clear that, in a frame of reference fixed to the earth, the solar wind forms a very high β plasma. Shown in Fig. 1 is a brief summary of the characteristics of the interplanetary medium from a field and plasma viewpoint. The average velocity of the solar wind proton, with an energy of approximately 1 keV, averaged over 1 a.u., is 385 km/sec.

Within the terrestrial magnetic field, the phenomenon of the trapped particles forming the Van Allen radiation belts represents a classical low β plasma familiar to those studying fusion devices. In addition, there is a third region of space associated with the geomagnetic field in which it appears that β is very close to unity and the field and plasma are in metastable equilibrium. This arises in the newly discovered phenomenon of the earth's magnetic tail and its imbedded, magnetically neutral sheet. This will be discussed briefly at the end of this paper.

The interaction of a solar plasma with the geomagnetic field is a subject that has been studied for more than 30 years (Chapman, 1963). Originally considered to be a transient phenomenon, the plasma was deduced to be associated with solar flares that subsequently would lead to terrestrial disturbances in the magnetic field producing auroras and associated geophysical phenomena. The two- to four-day propagation time between the assumed solar flare origin of the plasma and geophysical effects suggested the sun to be a temporary emitter of a large volume of ionized coronal gases. The interaction of this plasma with the geomagnetic field, as shown naively in Fig. 2, would compress the geomagnetic

field because of the diamagnetic properties of the plasma. From an alternate point of view, the geomagnetic field would form, within the plasma flow, a void in which the solar plasma was excluded. This volume of space was referred to initially as the Chapman-Ferraro geomagnetic cavity.

Subsequent to the studies by Biermann (1951) on the properties of ionized gas tails of comets, referred to as type I tails, a continual flux of

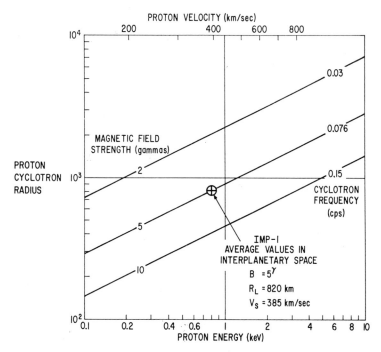

FIG. 1. Representative values of the interplanetary medium as observed during the quiet sun by the IMP-I satellite at the end of 1963. The velocity of the solar wind, V_s, is derived from directional considerations and cross correlation with the solar photospheric magnetic field and the interplanetary field as observed at 1.0 a.u. (see Wilcox, this volume). The average interplanetary magnetic field magnitude of 5.0 γ and proton energy lead to a characteristic cyclotron radius of 820 km.

plasma was invoked and subsequently studied theoretically by Chamberlain (1960) and Parker (1958). Hydrodynamic solutions were obtained for the flow of the solar wind by both of these authors. The solution by Parker, leading to a supersonic flow of the solar wind, has been shown by direct experiments (Snyder and Neugebauer, 1964) to be the proper solution, so that interplanetary space is now known to contain this con-

tinuous and substantial solar corpuscular flux of approximately 3×10^8 protons/cm²-sec moving radially away from the sun.

In our interpretation of data associated with the terrestrial magnetic field in cislunar space, the entire character of the distant geomagnetic field is determined principally by the solar wind flow. Thus, in an analysis of data obtained from satellites orbiting the earth, it is appropriate to introduce a geocentric solar ecliptic coordinate system, illustrated

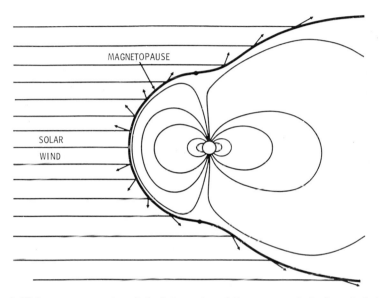

FIG. 2. Naive representation of the interaction of the very rarefied solar wind plasma with the geomagnetic field. Direct impact of the plasma with the magnetic field is represented by individual particles being specularly reflected from the boundary of the geomagnetic field. The resulting current system on the boundary provides secondary magnetic fields that distort the geomagnetic field interior to the geomagnetic cavity in the plasma stream.

in Fig. 3. Direct measurements of the solar wind flow show it to come from the solar direction within a few degrees. The earth moves through interplanetary space at a heliocentric orbital velocity of approximately 30 km/sec. Hence, the aberration effect on the solar wind flow will be less than 5°. Thus, a coordinate system with the X axis directed from the earth to the sun will always point approximately toward the solar wind flow. Within this reference frame, the two angles θ and ϕ define the latitude and longitude with respect to the plane of the ecliptic and the earth-sun line, respectively.

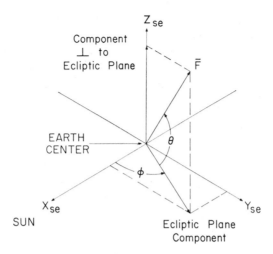

FIG. 3. Definition of the right-handed geocentric solar ecliptic coordinate system used to study the interaction of the solar plasma with the geomagnetic field. The X axis is directed from the earth to the sun at all times, and the Z axis is normal to the ecliptic plane. In this coordinate frame, the angle θ represents the latitude and ϕ the longitude as measured east of the sun.

II. MAGNETOSPHERE AND COLLISIONLESS MHD SHOCKWAVE

The entire region of space surrounding the earth originally referred to as the Chapman-Ferraro geomagnetic cavity is now referred to as the magnetosphere, representing a region of space in which the motion of charged particles is dominated by the geomagnetic field. At the time this term was proposed, neither the extent nor the characteristics of the magnetosphere were known directly, although with the concept of the continuous solar wind flow, it was clear that such a region would develop. Direct measurements by satellites since 1958 have clearly established the permanent existence of the magnetosphere and its boundary layer.

This discussion is concerned principally with the distant geomagnetic field, the termination of the regular geomagnetic field as distorted by the solar wind, and the boundary layer. Measurements of the magnetic field in space near the subsolar point of the magnetosphere have been performed by several satellites. Data from the magnetic field measurements onboard the IMP-1 satellite are shown in Fig. 4 on the inbound portion of orbit 1. It is seen that the measured geomagnetic field interior to 10.8 R_E is considerably larger than that predicted. Note that the

scale for magnitude is logarithmic, so that the magnitude distortion is emphasized for small magnetic field strengths. The abrupt decrease in magnitude of the field can only be interpreted in terms of the existence of an appreciable flow of current through which the probe has penetrated. This flow of current develops on the boundary of the geomagnetic field and generates secondary magnetic fields interior to the boundary which

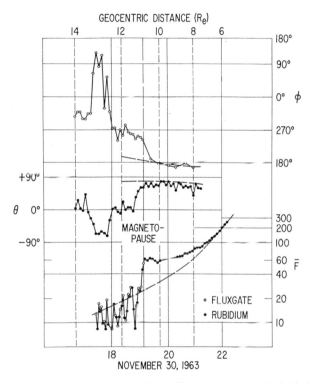

FIG. 4. Magnetic field measurements of the distant geomagnetic field obtained from the IMP-I satellite on inbound orbit 1, November 30, 1963. The abrupt discontinuity in magnitude and direction of the field at $10.8R_E$ is identified with the magnetosphere boundary. Theoretical values for F, ϕ, θ are shown as dashed curves.

distort the original geomagnetic field. Note that external to this current sheet flow there exist appreciable fluctuations in the magnetic field with no discernible wave or periodic motions. Similar observations of the geomagnetic field boundary have been obtained from the Explorer 12 satellite in 1961 (Cahill and Amazeen, 1963). Measurements of the magnetosphere boundary by both Explorer 12 and 14, as well as the IMP-1, satellites have shown that the regular geomagnetic field is

terminated on the solar side of the earth at a distance corresponding to approximately $10R_E$ (earth radii).

From these data, it is possible to infer the characteristics of the solar wind and compare them to the direct measurements. Shown in Fig. 5 is a family of theoretical curves presenting the distance of termination of the regular geomagnetic field as a function of solar wind density and velocity (or, equivalently, energy). The elementary theoretical model that is

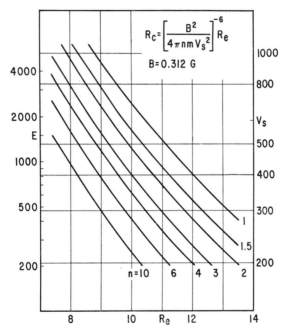

FIG. 5. Theoretical size of the magnetosphere as measured by the geocentric distance to the subsolar point, assuming normal impact of the solar plasma on a dipolar geomagnetic field.

employed is to balance the directed solar wind plasma momentum flux with the magnetic pressure transverse to the field lines in the equatorial plane of a dipole. Since the earth's rotational axis is inclined by $23.4°$ to the plane of the ecliptic and the dipole axis by $11.7°$ to the rotational axis, the maximum excursion of the geomagnetic dipole from being normal to the solar wind flow is less than $35°$. For the approximate theory, the present model employed here is sufficient. Furthermore, the fluctuations of the solar plasma flow, as measured both by flux or density and velocity separately, indicate that the characteristic distance varies with solar

activity.   Let

B_0 = equatorial geomagnetic field strength (0.312 G)
B_b = total field at boundary R_b
R_b = distance to magnetosphere boundary at subsolar point
n = solar wind density (protons/cm)
m = proton mass (gm)
V_s = solar wind velocity (cm/sec)

Then plasma and field balance requires

$$2mnV_s{}^2 = B_b{}^2/8\pi \tag{2.1}$$

But

$$B_b = 2B_0(R_E/R_b)^3 \tag{2.2}$$

thus

$$R_b = R_E[B_0{}^2/4\pi mnV_s{}^2]^{1/6} \tag{2.3}$$

Utilizing this formulation and substituting a value for the solar wind velocity of 400 km/sec yields inferred plasma densities of approximately 2 protons/cm^3.   Although this estimate is rough, it is in generally good agreement with the direct measurements of the solar wind properties and indicates that our general model of the solar wind interaction is reasonable.

A second point important in this elementary study of the termination of the regular geomagnetic field is the distance to the boundary as a function of solar plasma flow.   Note that the one-sixth power in the exponent of the coefficient multiplying the term R_E in Eq. (2.3) will reduce the effect of any solar plasma flow.   This can be quantitatively investigated by taking the logarithm of both sides and forming the fractional differential change in the termination distance, as shown in the equation below, depending upon solar plasma velocity and density:

$$\frac{\Delta R_b}{R_b} = -\frac{1}{3}\frac{\Delta V_s}{V_s} - \frac{1}{6}\frac{\Delta n}{n} \tag{2.4}$$

It is seen that the solar plasma flow must change by a factor of 2 before the size of the geomagnetic cavity is decreased by 20%.   This insensitivity to solar wind flow is directly related to the $1/R^3$ dependence of the magnitude of the dipolar geomagnetic field.   Thus, during times of solar disturbance and throughout the solar cycle, differences in the distance to the regular geomagnetic boundary should be detected.   However, they are expected to be small perturbations on the average distance of approximately $10R_E$ thus far measured.

With reference to the previous paper by Wilcox, in which the interplanetary field is shown to be approximately 5γ and reasonably steady in direction, it is clear that the magnetic fields observed exterior to the

regular geomagnetic field must be contained within a limited boundary layer, since they are not representative of the interplanetary medium. These characteristics are illustrated in the IMP-1 orbit 1 outbound path

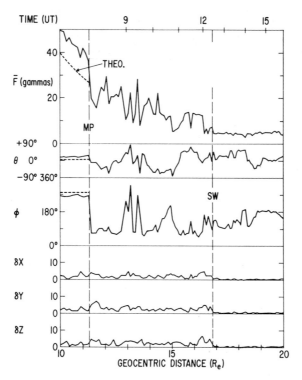

FIG. 6. Observed magnetic field obtained on outbound orbit 1 by the IMP-I satellite November 27, 1963. Clearly evident are the magnetosphere boundary at $11.3R_E$ and the collisionless MHD bow shock wave at $16.8R_E$. For a definition of these boundaries, see text.

shown in Fig. 6.   Here it is seen that the limits of the boundary layer are well defined in terms of the following:

(1) The magnitude decrease in the field at the termination of the regular geomagnetic field, associated with the current flow.

(2) The disappearance of rapid fluctuations of the magnetic field as measured by the rms deviations δX, δY, and δZ at a boundary that we identify as a collisionless magnetohydrodynamic shock wave (Kellogg, 1962; Axford, 1962).

This bow shock wave is detached from the geomagnetosphere much in the fashion of shocks detached from various blunt objects studied in the

field of hypersonic gasdynamics. We shall discuss the analogy in more detail in the following section.

It is important to recognize the observed thinness of both the magnetosphere boundary and the shock wave. The assumption that the boundary of the geomagnetic field and the shock wave is stationary during a traversal by the satellite yields a thickness of only 100 km. An example of this thinness is shown in Fig. 7 for the three solar ecliptic components of the field as the satellite crosses the shock wave. It is important to

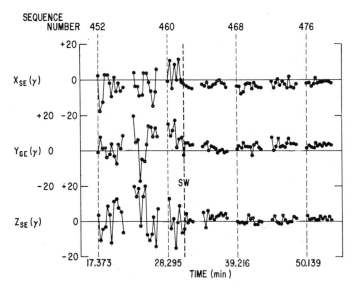

FIG. 7. Detailed variation of the three orthogonal components of the magnetic field observed during the first outbound traversal of the shock wave by IMP-I (see Fig. 6). These data expand the time scale shown on the previous figure to a distance scale corresponding to satellite motion of approximately 40 km between successive sample points. The gaps in the data correspond to continuous transmission of rubidium vapor magnetometer information in the telemetry sequence.

realize in this context that the fluctuating magnetic fields that show no regular periodic wave motion suffer from a severe aliasing problem because the individual samples are obtained at intervals of 20.5 sec. Characteristic frequencies of the plasma within the transition region correspond to cyclotron frequencies on the order of a fraction of a cycle per second and plasma frequencies on the order of 5 kc. Thus, high-frequency fluctuations are not accurately measured in this particular experiment. Indeed, this forms one of the more challenging experimental measurements of future satellites: to deduce definitively and

accurately the characteristics of the magnetic field and plasma at the shock-wave boundary.

Additional measurements carried onboard the same IMP-1 satellite (Bridge *et al.*, 1965) have shown that the plasma flow from the sun, when passing through the shock wave, is thermalized in spectrum and randomized in direction, the classical result of passing through a shock wave.

Positions of the magnetosphere boundary and shock wave, as deduced from the magnetic field experiment, are summarized in the solar ecliptic

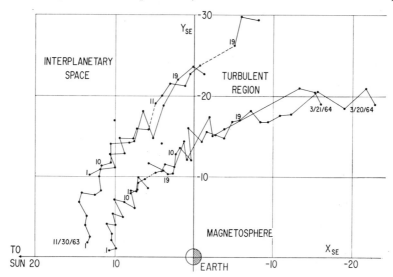

Fig. 8. Summary of the magnetosphere boundary and shock-wave positions as observed by the IMP-I satellite from November 27, 1963 through March 20, 1964. Individual observations of these boundaries have been rotated in a solar ecliptic meridian plane into the ecliptic plane. Successive traversals of the boundaries are connected by straight lines if no gaps exist in the data. The three regions of space distinguished by these two boundaries are the interplanetary medium, the turbulent transition or magnetosheath region, and the magnetosphere or distorted geomagnetic field region.

coordinate system and shown projected in the plane of the ecliptic in Fig. 8. It is seen that the shape of the magnetosphere boundary is roughly spherical on the sunlit hemisphere but that it extends out to form a rough blunt-body approximation. The detached shock wave possesses an approximately parabolic shape that is familiar from hypersonic gasdynamics. These positions correspond remarkably well with the observed boundaries, defining changes in the characteristics of the solar plasma flow as measured by plasma probes onboard the same satellite. Within the magnetosphere, no detectable flow of solar plasma

is observed, but within the transition region (or the boundary layer), a turbulent flow has been detected. Beyond the shock wave, a directed flow of solar plasma from the sun is always observed.

III. INTERPRETATION OF RESULTS

Interpretation of the observed magnetosphere boundary and collision-less shock-wave positions depends at present upon an analogy with hyper-sonic gasdynamics. Shown for reference in Fig. 9 is a shadowgraph of a

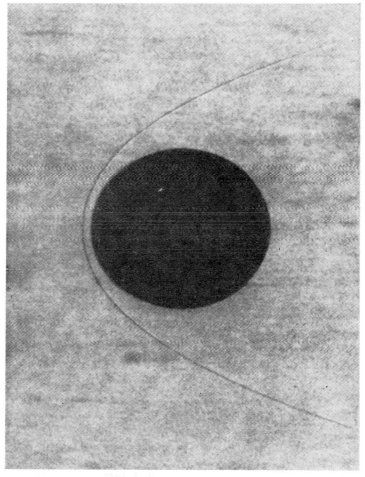

Fig. 9. Rotating mirror shadowgraph of high-speed aerodynamic flow and the detached bow shock wave surrounding a sphere at Mach 14.

sphere in hypersonic flow at Mach 14. A detached shock wave is clearly observed, roughly parabolic, surrounding the spherical object. It is important to note that in the use of this analogy it is the distorted geomagnetic field that represents the spherical object in the hypersonic flow of the solar wind. That the solar wind flow is hypersonic is clearly established by considering the characteristic phase velocities of propagation within the interplanetary medium.

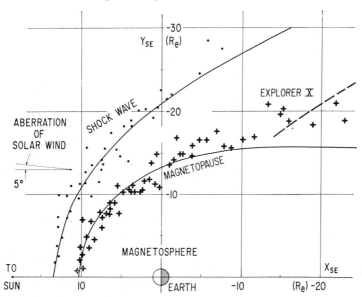

FIG. 10. Comparison of the IMP-I rectified boundary crossings with the high-speed gasdynamic shock model of Spreiter and Jones (1962). The standoff ratio has been adjusted slightly to match the observed positions. The predicted shape of the shock is seen to be rather closely matched by the observations.

With the direct measurements of the interplanetary magnetic field strength of 5γ and particle density on the order of a few per cubic centimeters, the Alfvén wave velocity is approximately 50 km/sec. The acoustical velocity within this rarefied gas is also approximately 30 to 50 km/sec, so that the three characteristic modes of propagation are all less than approximately 70 km/sec. Since the observed flow velocity is greater than 300 km/sec, this corresponds to an equivalent Mach flow, in an Alfvén (MHD) sense, of approximately 4 or greater.

Utilizing the analogy with hypersonic gas flow, Spreiter and Jones (1962) have computed the shape and position of the detached shock wave assuming a gas with a specific heat ratio of $\frac{5}{3}$. A direct comparison of the theoretical results with observations is shown in Fig. 10.

The theoretical results have been slightly adjusted with respect to moving the position of the shock wave further from the magnetosphere, which corresponds to raising the specific heat ratio to approximately 2. A best fit by least squares of a spherical object to the observed magnetosphere boundary positions has been made on the sunlit hemisphere portion. The deduced radius corresponds to $13.9R_E$, and the distance from the center of the spherical object, located at $X_{se} = -3.5R_E$, is $17.4R_E$. This leads to a standoff ratio of 1.25, in remarkable agreement with the theoretical results obtained by Hida (1953) and others for the detached bow shock wave surrounding a sphere at high Mach numbers. An excellent review of the arguments for the fluid-dynamic analogy has been given by Levy et al. (1964).

IV. THE GEOMAGNETIC TAIL

An important result of the continual confinement of the geomagnetic field by the solar wind is the existence of secondary magnetic fields generated by currents flowing on the magnetosphere boundary. Interior to the geomagnetic field, these have important effects on the motion of charged particles trapped within the geomagnetic field, as represented by the classical Van Allen radiation belts. An attempt has been made to study the internal field topology of the magnetosphere by Mead (1964), as shown in Fig. 11. The magnetosphere boundary is omitted, and the geometry of the magnetic field is shown in the noon midnight meridian plane. Clearly, a compression of the geomagnetic field in the magnetosphere is observed. Direct measurements by satellites, when compared with these theoretical models, show that on the sunlit hemisphere portion the theoretical model compares favorably with observations. However, on the night side of the earth, a significant distortion of the magnetic field, not shown in this theoretical model, has been found to exist.

Direct measurements of the terrestrial magnetic field on the night side of the earth have been performed by both the IMP-1 satellite (Ness, 1965) and Explorer 14 (Cahill, 1964). The results obtained on the 41st orbit, closest to the midnight meridian plane, are shown in Fig. 12. These magnetic field measurements were obtained during a reasonably quiet time, as measured by solar and terrestrial disturbances. The magnetic field is observed to be directed parallel to the earth-sun line. On the outbound portion of the orbit, the field is seen to be pointed away from the sun at all times with a magnitude many times greater than that theoretically predicted. On the inbound leg of the orbit it is

seen that the direction of the field abruptly changes at a radial distance of $16R_E$ from being directed away from the sun to being directed toward the sun. This abrupt change in direction of the field reflects the existence of an appreciable current flow within the earth's magnetic field on the night side of the earth. Repeated measurement of this phenomenon has shown that this current flow is approximately a planar feature roughly

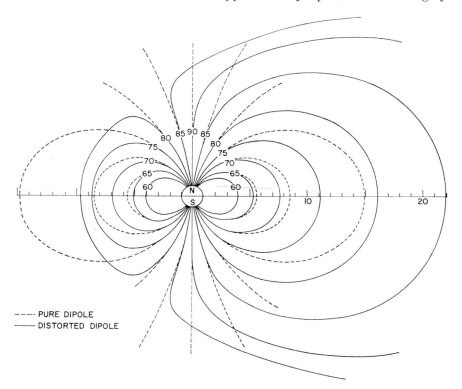

Fig. 11. Geomagnetic field line configurations in the noon midnight meridian plane. The total field is entirely the result of an internal dipole representing the earth's magnetic field and an external field due to currents on the boundary of the magnetosphere (after Mead, 1964).

paralleling the geomagnetic equatorial plane as modified by the solar wind flow. This is identified as a magnetic neutral sheet in the earth's tail (Axford *et al.*, 1965).

Shown in Fig. 13 is a summary of all measurements obtained within the magnetosphere by the IMP-1 satellite during a six-month period in 1964. These data present the *X-Y* component of the magnetic field projected on the plane of the ecliptic. The figure is separated into two

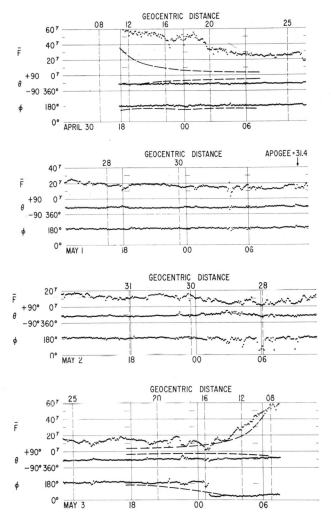

Fɪɢ. 12. Magnetic field measurements of the earth's magnetic tail near the midnight meridian plane by IMP-I on orbit 41 during April 30 through May 4, 1964. The direction of the field is observed to parallel the earth-sun line closely with a rapid change from antisolar to solar-directed sense on the inbound path at a radial distance of $16R_E$. This is interpreted to represent traversal of the magnetic neutral sheet in the earth's magnetic tail and is characteristic of observations of this phenomena by IMP-I (Ness, 1965).

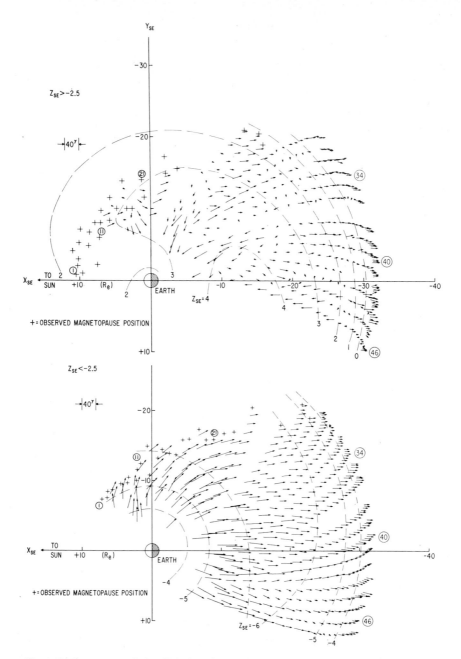

Fig. 13. Summary of the *X-Y* hourly component averaged measurements by the IMP-I satellite while imbedded within the earth's magnetic tail. The lower portion of the figure corresponds to measurements performed while the satellite was more than 2.5R_E below the ecliptic plane. The upper portion of the figure corresponds to positions of the satellite above this plane. Clearly evident is the distortion of the geomagnetic field forming the extended geomagnetic tail (Ness, 1965).

portions for clearer presentation in which the outbound portion of the orbits is shown in the lower half and the inbound portion in the upper half. It is clear in this presentation that the geomagnetic field is extended by the flow of solar wind on the night side of the earth, forming a geomagnetic tail.

The geomagnetic tail is a permanent feature of the magnetosphere and is a direct result of the interaction of the solar wind with the geomagnetic field. Shown in Fig. 14 is a recent theoretical schematic diagram of the magnetic field topology in the noon midnight meridian plane

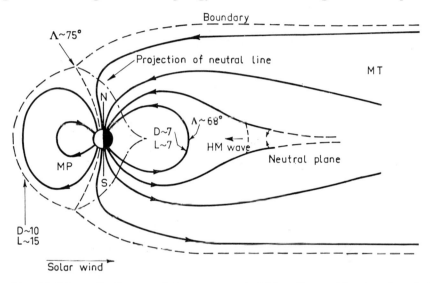

FIG. 14. Schematic diagram of the geomagnetic field as distorted by the solar wind showing lines of force in the noon midnight meridian plane. The open tail comprises two separate bundles of field lines emerging from the polar caps centered at a geomagnetic latitude of approximately 87° on the midnight meridian (after Piddington, 1965).

by Piddington (1965). Additional studies of the geomagnetic tail phenomenon have been conducted by Axford *et al.* (1965), Dessler (1964), Dessler and Juday (1965), and others. The unique feature of an extended magnetic tail, as shown in this figure, is formed with a magnetically neutral sheet containing the current flow leading to the field reversal previously discussed. A strong day-night asymmetry is seen to exist in the field lines that close approximately in a dipole fashion. Direct measurements by satellites of the characteristics of the radiation belts show that indeed there is an appreciable permanent day-night asymmetry associated with the geomagnetic field.

The importance of the geomagnetic tail in various geophysical phenomena has already been suggested in the literature.   The phenomena of aurorae, the geomagnetic storm, and related ionospheric characteristics may well be explicable in terms of this unique feature of the geomagnetic field.   Within the tail, observations of correlated particle and field variations have been observed.   These and the neutral sheet suggest generally a region where $\beta \approx 1$.

V. SUMMARY

Direct measurement of the magnetic field environment surrounding the earth has shown the existence of a confined geomagnetic field as formed by the continual flow of plasma from the sun.   The presence of

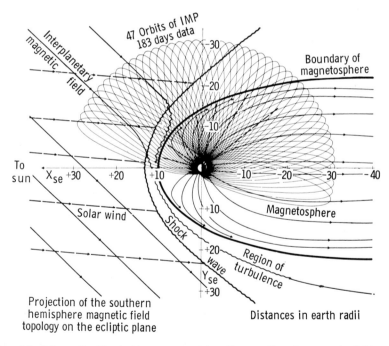

FIG. 15. Schematic illustration summarizing the results of magnetic field experiments mapping the cislunar magnetic field projected on the ecliptic plane.   The direction of the interplanetary field has been observed to be approximately 45° to the directed flow of the solar wind.   Indicated are the relative positions of the IMP-I satellite during the six-month period during which these measurements were performed (Ness, 1965).

an interplanetary magnetic field in the plasma and the average flow velocity lead to the development of a detached bow shock wave encompassing the magnetosphere in the super Alfvénic flow of the solar wind. An important feature in the interaction of the solar wind flow is the development of an extended magnetic tail of the earth in which lines of force originating in the polar cap regions are extended either by interconnection with the interplanetary magnetic field or by viscous drag of

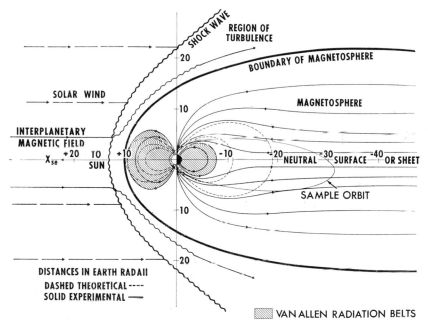

Fig. 16. Illustration of the interpretation of the magnetic field topology within the magnetosphere in the noon midnight meridian plane. Relative position of the neutral surface or sheet in the earth's magnetic tail and the corotating magnetic field lines supporting trapped particle motion is indicated. These include the classical Van Allen radiation belts. Cylindrical symmetry about the earth-sun line has been assumed for the magnetosphere boundary in this presentation.

the solar wind flow on the boundary of the magnetosphere to form the geomagnetic tail.

A summary interpretation of the entire cislunar magnetic field environment is shown in Fig. 15. Here the interplanetary magnetic field is shown to be directed approximately 45° to the solar wind flow. The earth's magnetic field is shown trailing out far behind, forming a magnetic tail. Figure 16 suggests that the earth may be compared to a magnetic

comet in which the nucleus of a comet corresponds to the earth, the coma to the magnetosphere and radiation belts, and the earth's magnetic tail to the ionized gas tail of the comet. An important element in the analogy is the existence of the imbedded neutral sheet in the earth's magnetic tail which may correspond to the observed increase in ionization intensities in the tails of comets. Although it is not expected that comets will possess inherent magnetic fields, it is possible that capture of the interplanetary magnetic field, as suggested by Alfvén (1957), will lead to the development of magnetically neutral regions confining plasmas within the tails of comets (Ness and Donn, 1965).

This research in the measurement of the earth's environment in space has led to insight on a number of classical geophysical problems. It also demonstrates the natural existence of a unique plasma laboratory in which to study collisionless phenomenon. The existence of the solar wind flow interacting with the geomagnetic field as well as other planetary objects permits the direct study of collisionless phenomena that are currently impossible to simulate in the laboratory. It may be expected that in the next few years considerable interest in the field of geophysical plasmas will be generated as a result of these satellite experiments.

REFERENCES

ALFVÉN, H. (1957), *Tellus* **9**, 92.

AXFORD, W. I. (1962), *J. Geophys. Res.* **67**, 3791.

AXFORD, W. I., PETSCHEK, H., and SISCOE, G. L. (1965), *J. Geophys. Res.* **70**, 1231.

BIERMANN, L. (1951), *Z. Astrophys.* **29**, 274.

BRIDGE, H., EGIDI, A., LAZARUS, A., LYON, E. F., and JACOBSON, L. (1965), *Space Res.* **5**, 969.

CAHILL, L. J. (1964), *IG Bull.* **79**, 231.

CAHILL, L. J. and AMAZEEN, P. J. (1963), *J. Geophys. Res.* **68**, 1835.

CHAMBERLAIN, J. W. (1960), *Astrophys. J.* **131**, 47.

CHAPMAN, S. (1963), in "Geophysics: The Earth's Environment." (C. Dewitt *et al.*, eds.). Gordon and Breach, New York.

DESSLER, A. J., (1964), *J. Geophys. Res.* **69**, 3913.

DESSLER, A. J. and JUDAY, R. D. (1965), *Planetary Space Sci.* **13**, 63.

HIDA, K. (1953), *J. Phys. Soc. Japan* **8**, 740.

KELLOGG, P. J. (1962), *J. Geophys. Res.* **67**, 3805.

LEVY, R., PETSCHEK, H. E., and SISCOE, G. L. (1964), *AIAA J.* **2**, 2065.

MEAD, G. D. (1964), *J. Geophys. Res.* **69**, 1181.

NESS, N. F. (1965), *J. Geophys. Res.* **70**, 2989.

NESS, N. F. and DONN, B. (1965), Goddard Space Flight Center Rept. X612-65-272.

PARKER, E. N. (1958), *Astrophys. J.* **128**, 664.

PIDDINGTON, J. H. (1965), *Planetary Space Sci.*, **13**, 363.

SNYDER, C. W. and NEUGEBAUER, M. (1964), *Space Res.* **4**, 89.

SPREITER, J. R. and JONES, W. P. (1962), *J. Geophys. Res.* **68**, 3555.

WILCOX, J. M. (1966). This volume, pp. 433–450.

Nonlinear Mechanics of

Plasma-Like Distributed Media

HERBERT LASHINSKY

INSTITUTE FOR FLUID DYNAMICS AND APPLIED MATHEMATICS
UNIVERSITY OF MARYLAND
COLLEGE PARK, MARYLAND

The finite-amplitude, controlled oscillations produced in a thermal-plasma device (Q-machine) as a result of the universal instability provide a useful tool for experimental research in the nonlinear mechanics of plasma-like distributed systems, i.e., systems in which the pertinent physical parameters are distributed in one or more of the coordinate variables (position and velocity) used to describe the system, rather than lumped, as in more familiar vacuum-tube or mechanical configurations. Results obtained in such experiments have been analyzed by extending techniques of nonlinear mechanics to distributed systems. In particular, nonlinear phenomena such as mode competition and mode locking have been examined, and the relation between these phenomena in plasmas and in related systems such as the gaseous optical maser has been delineated. The current status of this work is reviewed, with particular emphasis being given to the analysis of mode locking and the implications of this effect for turbulence in plasmas.

Although physical systems are always nonlinear to a greater or lesser degree, because of the complexities that arise in the mathematical analysis of a nonlinear system one frequently simplifies the problem by resorting to linear approximations. In many cases of physical interest, the linear representation of a system provides a reasonable description of its behavior and yields reasonable answers to a number of important questions. However, there are a number of basic phenomena whose existence derives specifically from the fact that the system is nonlinear, and such features of the physical behavior will obviously be lost in any linear description. In this case, one can proceed by assuming that the system is weakly nonlinear or "quasilinear," i.e., that the nonlinear features can be treated in terms of a weak departure or perturbation about the linear behavior. This approach has been found to be adequate for the description of a wide variety of problems of physical and engineer-

ing interest, and in the course of the past 20 or 30 years the analysis of nonlinear physical systems (primarily nonlinear oscillators) in terms of a quasilinear representation has come to be known as "nonlinear mechanics" [1]. Until recently, nonlinear mechanics has been concerned principally with so-called lumped-parameter systems, that is to say, systems such as vacuum-tube oscillators, in which the various energy-storage elements such as capacities and inductances, the dissipative elements, and the energy sources are highly localized and easily identified. In the present communication, it will be our purpose to explore the possibility of extending some of the methods of nonlinear mechanics to the analysis of so-called distributed-parameter systems. In distributed-parameter systems, the equivalent capacities, inductances, dissipative elements, and energy sources are distributed throughout the volume of the system, and it is usually difficult to isolate the various functions just indicated. For instance, a given volume element of the system can contain the energy source, the dissipative mechanism, and the equivalent inductance and capacity, all inextricably mixed together. For this reason, the typical distributed-parameter system is much more of a challenge to analysis than the usual lumped-parameter system.

The physical system in which we shall be primarily interested will be a plasma in a magnetic field. This interest has been stimulated by recent experimental developments in investigations of the so-called universal instability in the plasma produced in a thermal plasma device or "Q-machine [2, 3], which will be discussed in greater detail below. It has also become evident recently that these same considerations pertain to the analysis of the gaseous optical maser [4], and some of the relations between these systems will also be considered. Before treating these questions in detail, however, it might be instructive to point out one reason that nonlinear behavior is especially important in these distributed systems. In general, a bounded distributed-parameter system of finite dimensions, such as an experimental laboratory device, will exhibit normal modes of oscillation in the linear representation. However, any question involving the interaction between such modes cannot be treated by a purely linear analysis. Using the approach indicated previously, we assume that the system is weakly nonlinear. The analysis then proceeds by assuming that the normal modes remain the same as in the linear approximation, but that the interaction between modes can be described by a quasilinear coupling term. It will be shown below that this approach to the problem is, in fact, capable of describing almost all of the laboratory phenomena that have been observed in Q-machine experiments reported to date [5, 6].

Because this paper consists of a number of diverse elements, it might

be worthwhile to outline the presentation.   We first describe briefly the
Q-machine and the plasma that it produces.   We then discuss some of
the important differences between linear and nonlinear descriptions of
physical systems which pertain to the particular nonlinear effects of
interest here.   Although they are well known, these differences are not
always kept in mind in the analysis of plasma problems.   We then group
distributed-parameter systems into two broad classes and compare the
behavior of these classes with that of the more familiar lumped-parameter
systems.   Two phenomena that are characteristic of plasma-like distributed systems are then considered; these are called mode competition
and mode locking.   To conclude, we investigate the implications of these
effects in turbulence in laboratory plasmas of finite size and appropriate
symmetry.

It might also be worthwhile to emphasize the basic philosophy underic-
lying the present paper.   Instead of starting with the analysis of a plasma
as an ensemble of charged particle described by the Boltzmann equation
or various macroscopic moments of this equation, our approach is first to
understand the characteristics of nonlinear distributed systems in general
and then to see how our particular physical system, namely, a plasma
confined by a magnetic field, is related to general nonlinear systems and
to see what distinguishing features, if any, are exhibited by the plasma.

In a Q-machine, a quiescent plasma column, about 100 cm long and
3 cm in diameter, is produced by thermal ionization of atomic cesium on
hot tungsten plates [7] as shown in Fig. 1.   The cesium beam is produced
by atomic beam ovens, and the hot tungsten plates are hot enough to
emit thermionic electrons, which, together with the cesium ions, then
form the plasma that is confined by an axial magnetic field.   The plasma
is essentially isothermal, with usual temperatures (kT) being of the order
of 0.2 eV.   Typically, the experiments are carried out in a magnetic field
that varies from 1000 to 8000 G, and the plasma may be regarded as completely ionized for all practical purposes.

If a probe is inserted into the "quiescent" plasma shown in Fig. 1, it is
found that, in fact, the plasma column exhibits regular oscillations in
density and potential.   The column oscillates as a bounded structure,
with traveling waves propagating in the azimuthal direction, corresponding to ascending values of the azimuthal mode number $l = 1, 2, \ldots$ and
standing waves in the axial direction corresponding to $\lambda = 2L$ (L is the
column length).   These oscillations are a manifestation of the so-called
universal instability due to the existence of the density gradient perpendicular to the magnetic field and have been predicted by theory
[8–10].   The possibility then suggests itself that the plasma column can
be regarded as a bounded spatially distributed oscillator in which the

constituent elements (plasma particles) are also distributed in velocity. Perhaps one of the most interesting features of the plasma oscillations produced by the universal instability in the Q-machine is the fact that the oscillation amplitude can be controlled by appropriate adjustment of the sheath conditions. The details of this procedure are explained elsewhere [11]. In this work, the oscillation amplitude is adjusted at levels

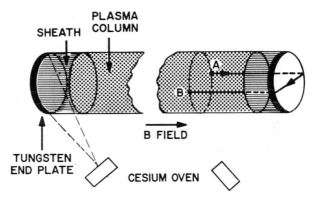

FIG. 1. Schematic diagram showing the formation of a thermal plasma column made up of alkali ions and electrons in a Q-device. The tungsten plates produce ions by contact ionization of the neutral beam of cesium atoms and also provide the required electrons by thermionic emission. (Courtesy 2nd International Conference on Plasma Physics and Controlled Nuclear Fusion Research, Culham, 1965.)

such that oscillation energy is much smaller than the thermal energy of the plasma, and the plasma oscillations are characterized by a stable, narrow-line mode spectrum as shown in Fig. 2. This system is then the object of experimental investigations, and we shall refer to various experimental results obtained with the Q-machine as a basis for the analysis presented in the remainder of the paper.

To begin our comparison of linear and nonlinear representations of physical systems, let us consider the following two equations:

$$\frac{d^2x}{dt^2} + 2b\,\frac{dx}{dt} + \omega_0^2 x = 0 \tag{1}$$

$$\frac{d^2x}{dt^2} + \epsilon(x^2 - 1)\omega_0\,\frac{dx}{dt} + \omega_0^2 x = 0\,, \qquad \epsilon \ll 1 \tag{2}$$

The first equation is, of course, that of a simple harmonic oscillator characterized by a natural oscillation frequency ω_o and a damping term $2b\,dx/dt$. We note, however, that the oscillation amplitude is free to take on any arbitrary value. In order to provide a mathematical

representation of steady-state oscillations, which are known to be realizable physically, it is necessary to omit the dissipation term, thereby implying that the system is lossless. This implication, however, does not correspond to physical reality, and we shall see below that it is, in fact, responsible for a number of the paradoxical results that appear in the linear analysis.

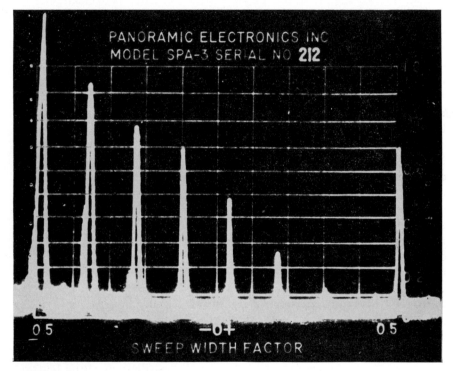

Fig. 2. Typical spectrum-analyzer presentation of the mode spectrum of the universal instability in a Q-device. The signal is derived from a probe that records the variations in density at a given point in the column. (Courtesy 2nd International Conference on Plasma Physics and Controlled Nuclear Fusion Research, Culham, 1965.)

Now let us consider the second equation, which is the celebrated equation of van der Pol [1]. When $x < 1$, the van der Pol oscillator exhibits growing oscillations described by a solution of the form

$$x = \frac{C_1 \cos \omega_0 t}{[1 + C_2 e^{-\epsilon \omega_0 t}]^{1/2}} \tag{3}$$

where C_1 and C_2 are constants.

These oscillations continue to grow until $x = 1$, at which point Eq. (2) becomes equivalent to Eq. (1) with $b = 0$. However, there are some significant differences between the two cases. The van der Pol oscillator reaches a so-called limit cycle, which corresponds to a *stable* amplitude. Under these conditions, the average energy dissipated per cycle is exactly equal to average energy gained per cycle from whatever source is providing this energy, and the physical situation and the mathematical description are compatible. In effect, the van der Pol oscillator conserves energy on a slow time scale of order $\tau = \epsilon\omega_0 t$.

Although this difference between the linear oscillator and nonlinear oscillator might appear to be trivial, we shall see below that the unique-amplitude feature of the nonlinear oscillator is crucial when one considers the response of these oscillators to an external forcing function. This feature is responsible for mode locking, which, in turn, is pertinent to the problem of plasma turbulence.

Another important difference between these two representations centers around the question of whether a self-excited physical system can oscillate in more than one mode simultaneously. If a linear system contains two harmonic oscillators, then, by definition, each oscillator behaves as though the other were not present. This situation is entirely different in the nonlinear case. Here, in general, the different oscillators (modes) must compete for the available energy, and, in fact, in many cases the existence of one mode tends to suppress the growth of any other. This result was obtained many years ago by van der Pol in the analysis of a vacuum-tube oscillator containing two tuned circuits [12].

It is at this point that one of the fundamentally new features of the plasma oscillator emerges. It enjoys the capability of multimode oscillation even with a nonlinear dissipation and in a real sense is a member of a fundamentally different kind of system. Another member of this class of systems is the gas laser [4]. Some of these distinguishing features will become clear from the system of classification of nonlinear oscillators which we suggest below.

In order to systemize our discussion, it will be found useful to classify nonlinear oscillators into the following general classes:

(1) Lumped parameter.
(2) Distributed parameter: (a) distributed resonator (macroscopic fluid); and (b) distributed generator (microscopic gas).

The lumped-parameter system is the easiest to describe and is the most familiar. Here all the physical parameters are highly localized, and the effective energy source, the effective inductance, the effective capacity, and the effective resistance are clearly definable. The familiar

vacuum-tube oscillator is the best example of this kind. The distributed-parameter case is more complicated. The physical parameters of a system can be distributed in more than one way. First, the system can be distributed in space over regions that are comparable with the wavelengths of interest. At any spatial point, however, it is assumed that the system's physical parameters are specified by unique values of the system variables. This is essentially the kind of description which is traditionally used to describe a fluid. A typical example is the microwave cavity oscillator. Although such an oscillator is capable of oscillating in many modes, it is generally excited by an electron beam or current, which is single-valued in velocity, and, in general, such a beam will interact only with those modes that exhibit a phase velocity approximately equal to the beam velocity. However, when the nonlinear representation is used, we find that in such cases these modes will have to compete for the energy available from the beam so that, in general, multimode oscillation is not possible. There are a number of important exceptions to this general rule, and these are discussed in another paper [13]. Thus, we have chosen to call this a distributed resonator to indicate that, although the effective resonator is capable of oscillating in many modes, the effective driving agency is generally single-valued in some sense, and, in general, only a single-mode oscillation is possible.

Now let us consider the case of a plasma in which the particles exhibit a distribution in velocity. Referring to the microwave resonator case, we might say that this is a system with an ensemble of beams. The picture here is very similar to that used by Dawson in analyzing Landau damping [14]. Specifically, out of the entire distribution of particle (electrons) we isolate small delta functions at velocities corresponding to phase velocities of the various modes. These "delta-function" beams interact with individual modes and provide the energy required to drive the modes themselves; however, there is very little interaction between these different beam-mode systems. The oscillation modes are characteristic of the gross properties of the plasma as represented by the collective effects of all of the particles. This situation is a familiar one in plasma physics. One frequently finds that various modes of oscillation of a plasma can be derived from an analysis of the bulk or gross properties but that the question of stability, i.e., the question of whether these modes will in fact be excited, requires a microscopic or kinetic theory analysis of the plasma which, in turn, depends on the form of various distributions functions, etc. It is this feature that distinguishes what we shall call "plasma-like" systems from other more familiar systems. It was first pointed out by Lamb [4] that the helium-neon gas laser is another system that exhibits these properties. In both cases, the fact

being synchronized, and the harmonic $n\omega_1$ plays the role of the synchronizing signal. We assume, as a reasonable approximation, that the frequency of the low-frequency mode is not changed significantly by the mode interaction. This assumption is based on the fact that the relative energy in the low-frequency mode is much higher than that of the high-frequency mode, as is evident from Fig. 2, in which the mode amplitudes are given on a logarithmic scale.

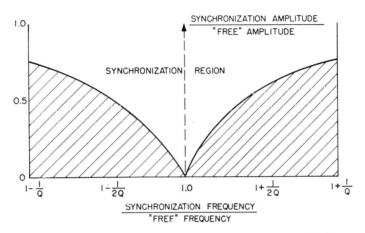

FIG. 3. Synchronization diagram showing the relation between the frequency and amplitude of the synchronizing signal required to achieve locking (both quantities referred to the corresponding quantities for the free-running oscillator). Locking cannot be achieved if the synchronizing signal falls in the cross-hatched region.

The relation between the required synchronizing amplitude and the frequency deviation at the synchronization limit is shown in Fig. 3, which is a curve of the more accurate synchronization criterion:

$$\frac{A_1}{A_0} = \frac{2Q\Delta\omega}{\omega_0}\left[1 + \left(\frac{2Q\Delta\omega}{\omega_0}\right)^2\right]^{-1/2}$$

The high-frequency mode will not be locked if the line representing the amplitude and frequency of the synchronizing signal falls in the cross-hatched region because the deviation is too large for a given synchronizing amplitude. Instead, the frequency of the high-frequency mode varies periodically in a rather complicated fashion, giving rise to a complex "combination tone." If the deviation is relatively large, this complex combination tone becomes a simple "beat" between the injected frequency and the free-running frequency of the mode. In the analysis that follows, we shall be interested primarily in the conditions under which loss of synchronization can occur.

First, however, it is instructive to consider the physical picture behind the entrainment mechanism. Our picture of the limit cycle reached by the van der Pol oscillator implies that a stable equilibrium obtains under steady-state conditions. In the approximation being used here, it is assumed that the ratio A_i/A_o is so small that the injected signal does not contribute to the energy amplitude of the synchronized mode. However, it can affect the *instantaneous* rate at which this mode exchanges energy

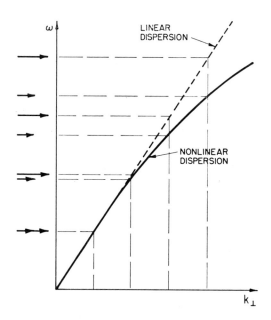

FIG. 4. Dispersion diagram showing the nonlinear correction effect of the finite Larmor radius term in Eq. (4). The abscissa is plotted in units of the aximuthal mode number of the universal instability; the long arrows denote a linear frequency spectrum, whereas the short arrows indicate the actual nonlinear spectrum with the correction included.

with the energy source; in turn, this can result in a change in the phase-balance relations with consequent modification of the frequency at which oscillation takes place. Unless the oscillation frequency is locked to the injected signal, the instantaneous energy exchange rate is continually being perturbed. Since the injected signal is assumed to be fixed, a necessary condition for steady-state oscillation with fixed amplitude and frequency is that the oscillator be locked to the injected signal.

In considering the plasma case, we are now interested in possible mechanisms that might introduce frequency deviations between the harmonics of the low-order modes and the free-running frequencies of

higher-order modes, thus preventing mode locking from occuring.　Such a mechanism is available in the correction factor due to the finite Larmor radius term in the dispersion relation in (4); it will be evident that the mode frequencies are given by a nonlinear dispersion relation of the form

$$\omega_l = \frac{l\omega_*}{1 + (k_\perp r_L)^2} = \frac{l\omega_*}{1 + l^2(k_\perp{}^0 r_L)^2}$$

where $l = 1, 2, 3, \ldots$ as indicated earlier.　The value of $(k_\perp{}^0 r_L)$ in typical Q-machine experiments is of the order of 0.2, so that when $l > 5$ the frequency deviation due to this effect becomes large enough to represent a significant fraction of the frequency spacing between two successive modes; at this point, one might expect the mode-locking mechanism to become inoperative.　This situation is shown graphically in Fig. 4, in which we compare the frequency relations for a linear dispersion relation and a nonlinear dispersion relation.　This picture would indicate that the mode locking should be operative as long as only a few modes are excited; however, as the system becomes more and more unstable, and modes characterized by higher l become excited, a point is reached at which the interlocking mode structure can no longer be maintained, and a transition to a turbulent situation should occur rather suddenly.　An abrupt transition from a coherent locked-mode spectrum to a turbulent state is observed experimentally in the Q-machine under appropriate conditions [11] and appears to be compatible with the model proposed here.　It is hoped to check this point in future experiments, since alternative explanations have not been ruled out [11].

ACKNOWLEDGMENT

This work was supported in part by the Air Force Office of Scientific Research and the Atomic Energy Commission.

REFERENCES

1. Minorsky, N., "Nonlinear Oscillations." Van Nostrand, Princeton, New Jersey, 1962.
2. Lashinsky, H., *Phys. Rev. Letters* **12**, 121 (1964).
3. Buchel'nikova, N. S., *Zh. Eksperim. i Teor. Fiz.* **46**, 1147 (1964).
4. Lamb, W. E., Jr., *Phys. Rev.* **A134**, 1429 (1964).
5. Lashinsky, H., *Phys. Rev. Letters* **13**, 47 (1964).
6. Lashinsky, H., *Phys. Rev. Letters* **14**, 1064 (1965).
7. Rynn, N. and D'Angelo, N., *Rev. Sci. Instr.* **31**, 1326 (1960).
8. Kadomtsev, B. B. and Timofeev, A. V., *Dokl. Akad. Nauk SSSR* **146**, 581 (1962).
9. Silin, V. P., *Zh. Eksperim. i Teor. Fiz.* **44**, 1271 (1963).
10. Mikhailovskii, A. B., *Nucl. Fusion* **2**, 162 (1962).
11. Lashinsky, H., Proc. 2nd Intern. Conf. Plasma Phys. Controlled Nucl. Fusion Res. Culham (1965).
12. van der Pol, B., *Phil. Mag.* **43**, 700 (1922).

13. Lashinsky, H., Proc. 7th Intern. Conf. Phenomena Ionized Gases, Belgrade (1965).
14. Dawson, J., *Phys. Rev.* **118,** 381 (1960).
15. Rayleigh, Lord, "Theory of Sound," Vol. 2, p. 221. Dover, New York, 1945.
16. Kadomtsev, B. B., *Zh. Eksperim. i Teor. Fiz.* **43,** 1688 (1962).
17. Edson, W., "Vacuum Tube Oscillators." Wiley, New York, 1953.
18. Adler, R., *Proc. IRE* **34,** 351 (1946).
19. Stoker, J. J., "Nonlinear Vibrations in Mechanical and Electrical Systems." Wiley (Interscience), New York, 1950.

Atomic Processes in Plasmas

T. D. WILKERSON

INSTITUTE FOR FLUID DYNAMICS AND APPLIED MATHEMATICS
UNIVERSITY OF MARYLAND
COLLEGE PARK, MARYLAND

Experimental plasma physics deals with both atomic and collective processes, i.e., with two- and three-body interactions of particles and photons versus many-body interactions over distances of order of a Debye length or cyclotron radius. Two of the Institute's laboratories are engaged in measuring atomic radiation and collision coefficients that are important in stellar atmospheres, dilute plasmas in space, and high-temperature plasmas on earth. Radiative transition probabilities will be measured for spectral lines of several light elements, e.g., CI, CII, SI, SII, NeI, AI, AII, between 2000 and 12,000 Å. Other elements and shorter wavelengths will follow this initial program. The spectroscopic source is a gas-driven shock tube that operates up to 15,000°K with at least 100 μsec of steady conditions behind the reflected shock. Particular attention has been paid to direct measurement of the gas properties, rather than relying on shock-wave theory alone. Data are presented on excitation temperature, measured by the line-reversal technique. The flash lamp and fiber-optics employed for this and other purposes are also described.

Collision cross sections will be measured for ion-molecule, ion-atom, and electron-molecule reactions in the energy range 5 eV–5 keV. Techniques of mass and energy analysis and single-particle detection are adapted from plasma analyzers used both in the laboratory and in space. Initial efforts have been concentrated on focusing of ion beams and efficient delivery to scattering chambers. Data are presented on electron pickup by protons in atomic and molecular gases between 100 and 1000 eV.

Institute research on atomic processes covers topics which Professor J. M. Burgers has studied during his career. The faculty, staff, and students working in these fields are indebted to Professor Burgers for his encouragement to pursue these experiments.

I. INTRODUCTION

Events taking place at the atomic level of matter are not only of great interest in themselves but are also important on a larger scale where they

can both influence the behavior of many-particle systems and often tell us what is going on in these systems. This is particularly true in plasmas, where the *light* emitted by constituent atoms, ions, and electrons contains a great deal of information about the plasma state, and this state is governed by *collision interactions* of particles that may have been accelerated by plasma waves or other large-scale events. This interplay between few-particle and many-particle phenomena is important in space plasmas, such as the earth's ionosphere, comet tails, and, as far as we know, all zones of the atmospheres of the sun and other stars. In earthbound plasmas and high-temperature gases generally, we can find examples in controlled or uncontrolled fusion devices, rocket exhausts, MHD power generators, and the plasmas used for basic research such as those described by Dr. Lashinsky and by Dr. Kolb.

A specific case of great interest is the stellar plasma, which sends its light to us over great distances—an elaborate code describing what elements are present and how much of each, the density of electrons, the temperature (if it can be defined), and variations of all these quantities in space and time. Reading this code requires that we know the atomic constants governing both *radiation* and *collision;* the better one can read it, the more can be said about the abundances of the elements on a universal scale and the probable evolution of the universe.

Two of the Institute's laboratories are studying atomic processes of interest in plasma physics. The first category I shall discuss in Section II is heavy-particle collisions, currently between 100 and 1000 eV and later on as low as we can achieve, hopefully in the 1 to 10 eV range. Several topics are currently under study, but the furthest advanced is the measurement of electron capture by hydrogen ions in various gases. The bulk of this work has been done by Dr. D. W. Koopman, Mr. P. G. Cable, and Mr. M. Kato, with the assistance of Dr. K. W. Ogilvie (Goddard Space Flight Center), Mr. H. J. Zwally, Mr. J. Brecht, and myself.

Section III will treat the current state of research on transition probabilities for atomic line radiation or, more precisely, the first results of the plasma-diagnostic procedures being applied to the shock tube that is our spectroscopic source. This gas-driven shock tube easily achieves temperatures up to 15,000°K and electron densities up to 10^{17} cm^{-3}, so that many lines of light elements can be observed both in emission and absorption under known conditions. The principal researchers have been Dr. G. Charatis, Mr. M. H. Miller, and Mr. G. Mabry, and assistance has come from Dr. D. W. Koopman and myself, Mr. P. W. Murphy, Mr. J. R. W. Hunter, and Mr. S. McPhillips.

II. COLLISION CROSS SECTIONS

Heavy-particle interactions form an important, and sometimes dominant, class of events in plasmas and are very hard to treat theoretically. One realizes at the outset that a complete description of two atomic systems in collision must, at least in some ranges of energy, reckon with molecular properties, namely, the properties of the molecule capable of even a transient existence in the collision. Moreover, the generally high rate of approach of the collision partners makes it unclear what molecular problem to solve. Since the customary hierarchy of energy level types (Born-Oppenheimer approximation) is turned over, one is left with only rough ideas as to what to expect [1–3]. An early attempt at an overall view was Massey's "adiabatic criterion" [4], which predicts maximum charge-exchange cross sections for that energy which makes the collision duration comparable to a quantum-mechanical transition time, $h/\Delta E$, where h is Planck's constant and ΔE is the energy change or extent of inelasticity in the collision process. This idea is borne out by a striking number of cases of charge-exchange [4].

The experiments reported below are in the transition region between nonadiabatic and adiabatic (sufficiently slow collisions that atoms smoothly adjust to each other's presence). This energy range is most important to understand well, although it falls below many cross-sectional maxima because (i) reaction rates between species in a plasma are integrals of cross sections weighted by particle distribution functions, and (ii) most plasmas have distribution functions that peak in or below this energy range.

We have begun to study several types of heavy-particle collisions (single ion-atom, single ion-molecule, multiple ion-atom) while pursuing one type to the place where the results can be compared with previous work. We report here the latter results on electron capture by H^+ and H_2^+ in argon in the energy range 100–1000 eV, while indicating some of the developmental work that has gone before [5].

Figure 1 shows a typical system in which an ion beam can be generated, analyzed, controlled, and detected. This top view shows two diffusion pumps and a bell-jar as the main vacuum components. From left to right, we have an electron-bombardment ion source [6, 7], a "Wien filter" or $E \times B$ velocity selector, an electrostatic energy analyzer [8], and a detector [9] capable of recording single ions even at energies of 1 eV.

This system has proved very useful for learning how to carry out beam

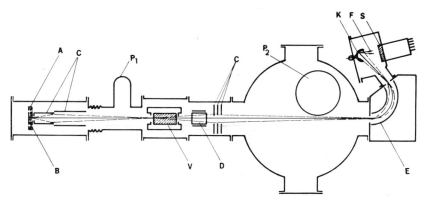

FIG. 1. Apparatus for producing and analyzing ion beams. From left to right, A and B show the electron-bombardment ion source, C a compound lens, P_1 a pump-port, V a crossed-field velocity selector ($\mathbf{E} \times \mathbf{B}$), D two pairs of deflection plates, C another lens, P_2 the main pumping port, E a cylindrical electrostatic energy analyzer, and K, F, S components of a single-ion detector. This apparatus was very useful for energy and mass analysis of beams and for systematic studies of beam current and geometry.

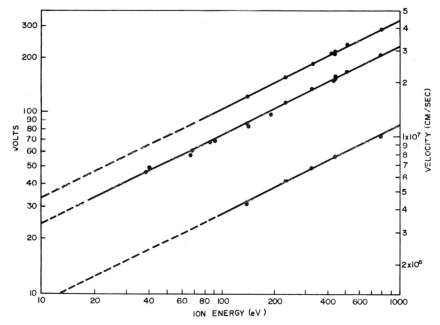

FIG. 2. Simultaneous energy-velocity analysis of ions emitted by electron-bombard-ment source running on hydrogen gas. Data collected by setting repeller voltage in ion source, finding the roughly equivalent energy analyzer voltage, and then tuning the potential drop in the velocity selector (left-hand ordinate) to the peaks in observed ion current. The ion groups shown here are, in descending order, H^+, H_2^+, and $O_2^+-N_2^+$. The minimum observable ion energies were about 40 eV for H_2^+ and 140 eV for H^+. Ion beam width at entrance to energy analyzer roughly 1 cm.

operations properly and for testing various components. Several modifications stand between it and the hydrogen-argon measurements, but not such drastic ones as to vitiate the experience gained here.

Figure 2 shows the combined energy-velocity analysis of the ion beam in the prototype system, where the data points correspond to simultaneous settings of the energy analyzer and velocity selector. The three mass groups evident here are H^+, H_2^+, and heavy particles such as N_2^+; each follows the expected relation between particle energy and velocity-squared. This graph shows that we could, in principle, use either the proton or H_2^+ beams for meaningful collision experiments over the indicated energy range.

As a practical matter, however, the ion currents here were too low for the type of scattering geometry to be used first, so that a higher-current, rf ion source (ORTEC) was used. Radio-frequency ion sources are commonly employed in van de Graaf accelerators and typically consume tens of watts of rf power in the frequency range of tens of megacycles. In the energy range of interest to us, typical total ion-output currents were in the range 1–10 μA; the source has magnetic focussing and is electrically isolated for greater control over the mean particle energy. Careful shielding is required to keep rectified rf out of oscilloscopes and sensitive electrometer circuits.

Electrometers are used for measuring currents in the scattering chamber shown in Fig. 3. This chamber [10, 11] takes the place of the single-ion detector on the right of the bell-jar in Fig. 1. Its purpose is to provide a low-pressure gas target for the main beam in such a way that cross-currents due to scattering can be collected while the rest of the vacuum system is at a sufficiently low pressure as not to perturb the ion beam. Typically, we would have a 500-eV proton beam entering this chamber through the slit below, and the internal chamber pressure would be about 1 μ (10^{-3} torr) of argon. Two principal reactions ensue: the one of interest here is *electron capture* by the proton, yielding a fast neutral hydrogen atom, plus a slow argon ion that is easily swept up by the weak electric field put across the chamber. The electron capture cross section is given by the ratio of scattered-to-incident currents, divided by the number of argon scattering centers per square centimeter in the "line of sight" of a typical proton. The other important reaction to consider is *ionization,* which could contribute spurious effects to electron capture measurements; however, an ionizing proton will simply create an electron-argon ion pair and continue on through the chamber with slightly reduced energy. Both the electron and ion will be collected, so that neither will contribute to the *net* positive current observed flowing to the collection plates. In other words, we are using the chamber in a mode that

balances out ionization currents, leaving only the electron-capture contribution.   Almost needless to say, this mode of operation requires great
caution about collection of charged particles, production of secondary
electrons, etc.   The scatter in our results probably reflects our degree of
control over these effects at the time the data were collected.

At a given proton or H_2^+ energy, the electron-capture current I_c and
the main beam current I_0 are measured as functions of chamber pressure,

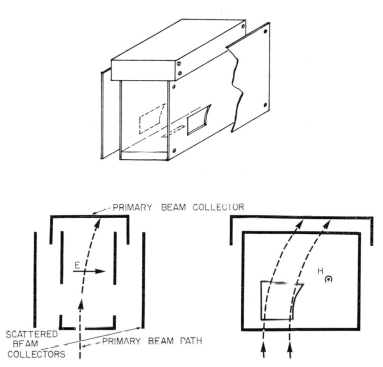

FIG. 3. Gas cell for observing ionization and electron-capture currents due to primary ion beam passing through the gas.   Cross-currents are measured as functions of
primary beam type, current, energy, and gas pressure.

so that zero levels can be subtracted away (due to leakage current in the
scattering chamber) and the thinness of the gas target can be verified.
Figure 4 shows data for H^+ and H_2^+ over a range of incident ion energies,
and illustrates the method of data reduction already alluded to.   Each of
our data boxes contains four to eight different pressure runs by various
operators.   The widths of the boxes are not due to uncertainties in
energy, but indicate rather the energy spread in groups of results chosen

for averaging together; the scatter of results even at one energy was comparable to what is shown here (20–25%).

The proton data are similar to earlier results [11–13] but suggest a stronger dependence of the cross section on energy than has been seen before. The matter is clouded by a degree of scatter which is quite common in cross section experiments. Probable error is often not clearly specified in the literature, but the scatter of all these measurements

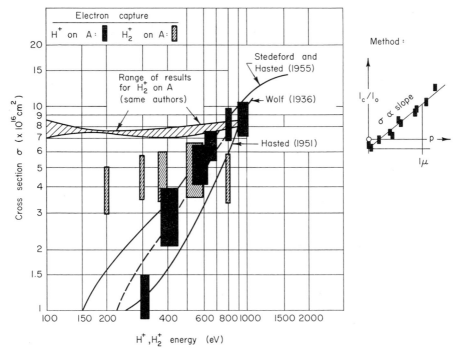

FIG. 4. Absolute electron-capture cross sections for H^+ and H_2^+ in argon, measured as indicated in text and in figure on right. Proton results suggest steeper energy dependence than observed in earlier work. Reliability of H_2^+ results in doubt, because of possibilities of beam contamination and unaccounted-for secondary electron emission.

seems to be comparable to ours. Our immediate plans are to reduce the random errors due to background gas and leakage currents and to examine several rare gases for significantly steeper cross section curves than have been measured before. As implied early in this section, such results would seriously affect calculated reaction rates for charge exchange in plasmas having most of their particles in the lower energy range under discussion.

As for the H_2^+ results, we cannot yet make a clear comparison because of the possibilities of beam contamination due to H_3^+ or excited states of H_2^+; the latter feature may also affect the earlier work. It is now fairly widely realized that many absolute cross section measurements have been influenced to an uncertain degree by atomic excitation, so that redeterminations by factors of 2 and 3 would not be surprising. We expect to return to the study of molecular hydrogen ions after completing beam-manipulation sections for higher H_2^+ purity and longer times of flight. Our present data on H_2^+ may be affected by the production of secondary electrons [14] to a degree that may require more elaborate precautions.

In this section, we have seen that there is a great practical need for good cross section data, particularly at low energy, and that there is an intrinsic physical interest, particularly for heavy-particle interactions. That charge-exchange cross sections rise rapidly to maxima in the kilovolt range seems to be due to the mutual interaction of many particles that, so to speak, do not have time to adjust to the rapid onset of perturbation. To pass beyond a picturesque description to a grasp of the simultaneous quantum processes involved has proved to be very difficult. Further experimental work, particularly at low energy, seems mandatory in view of the theoretical difficulties and experimental disagreements.

III. ATOMIC TRANSITION PROBABILITIES

We are measuring atomic transition probabilities, using a gas-driven shock tube as a spectroscopic source. Since such instruments can generate a plasma of known conditions and composition and our observing instruments record atomic line intensities, one has only to divide the line intensity by the number of atoms in the upper energy level in order to find the inherent probability (per atom in the excited state) for the line to be emitted. Once in possession of such atomic constants for a given element, an astrophysicist can use the line intensity seen in a distant source as a measure of the elemental abundance in that source. Reliable calculation of line strengths is still difficult in general, and so empirical determination of them is desirable, at the very least, and mandatory in many cases.

General accounts of this type of experimental astrophysics have appeared in recent years [15–19], and the shock tube has played a prominent role in this field [20–24]. Our present emphasis is on the spectra of the light elements (e.g., neutral and singly ionized carbon and sulphur)

between 2500 and 10,000 Å, on new diagnostic techniques and instrumentation, and on preparations for future work in the vacuum ultraviolet. We report here the first results of experiments to check on plasma conditions in the shock tube. In refined form, these will be coupled with line-intensity measurements to give the final data on atomic transition probabilities. For this purpose, the shock tube has two great advantages

Fig. 5. Test section of spectroscopic shock tube with 1-ft scale. Tube is 3×4 in. welded tube with inside seam removed; wall thickness $\frac{3}{16}$ in. Reinforcement with bars and jigs prevents elastic deformations due both to shock pressures and to static pressures (500–1000 psi) following each experiment. Mountings for side windows and transducers are shown. "Driver gas" chamber (4 meters upstream) not shown.

over many other light sources: the plasma possesses a high degree of uniformity along a line of sight perpendicular to the tube axis, and there exists a well-defined and extensive theory for the plasma state to be achieved as a function of shock velocity.

Figure 5 shows the shock-reflection end, or "test-section," of our shock tube. When the tube is fired by release of the high-pressure "driver gas" several meters upstream, a shock wave runs through the test gas into this chamber and reflects from the end wall. Having thus been twice com-

pressed by strong shock waves, the test gas is elevated in temperature to 10,000°–15,000°K and rendered highly luminous. It is stationary at these conditions for about 100 μsec. Subsequent wave interactions further increase the gas temperature, so that one would see here a suc-

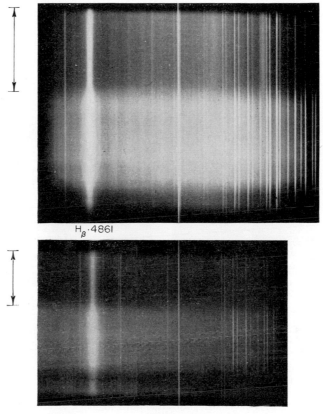

$H_\beta \cdot 4861$

FIG. 6. Time-resolved emission spectra recorded near end of shock tube, using $f/6.3$ spectrograph and rotating-drum camera. Shock-tube test gas is neon plus "spectroscopic additive"; additive was H_2S in upper picture and CH_4 in lower. Direction and extent of arrows show the time direction and duration of the state behind the first reflected shock. Hydrogen and red neon lines appear in both films, whereas the upper shows one of the strong lines of neutral sulphur (4695 Å), the lower several lines of neutral carbon and molecular bands of C_2. Hotter gases at later times yield brighter and wider lines and an enhanced recombination continuum.

cession of thermodynamic states that must be time-resolved in order for us to have a well-defined state for spectroscopic analysis.

Typical time-resolved emission spectra are shown in Fig. 6, with time increasing downward and wavelength increasing from the blue (left) to

the red (right). The bulk of the test gas is neon in both cases, whereas we have added of order 1% H_2S and CH_4 in the upper and lower experiments, respectively. In both, then, we naturally see the blue-green Balmer line H_β (4861 Å) and the familiar red lines of neon. There is an evident time-development toward brighter spectra and hotter states, as multiply reflected shocks compress the gas behind the first reflected shock wave. The quenching of luminosity is due to mixing with the cold driver gas, which finally expands down the entire length of the shock tube. Prior to any atomic emission, one sees the Swan bands of C_2 at the primary and reflected shock waves [25] when methane is used as the spectroscopic additive.

Behind the first reflected shock in the methane case, we see character-istic lines of atomic carbon at 5380 Å, 5052 Å, etc. They are absent when hydrogen sulphide is used; instead, we then see strong lines of neutral sulphur, such as 4695 Å and more diffuse members of the same multiplet.

We have made a great number of *hydrodynamic* measurements that verify that the gas behind the first reflected shock is close to the thermal state predicted by shock-wave theory. These include reflected shock velocity and absolute pressure, and extend the range of previous checks of this type [16]. The absolute pressure in question is usually about 10 atm and the temperature above 10,000°K, conditions that, together with the amount of spectroscopic additive, usually guarantee a steady state in local thermodynamic equilibrium, even though the available times are in the 100-µsec range.

Passing to *spectroscopic* measurements of the plasma state, already one such is implicit in the diffuse character of the H_β lines which is evident in Fig. 6. The hydrogen atom, being a one-electron system, is particularly susceptible to the Stark effect, which manifests itself here as a broadening related directly to the density of charged particles in the gas [19]. Toward the end of this section, I shall discuss the methods we are using to measure electron density from the H_β profile. For now, it should suffice to point out that such measurements do indeed provide a check on the ionization temperature of the shock-tube plasma.

A direct measurement of excitation temperature is provided by the method of spectral line-reversal [26]. Imagine that a very bright (and variable) source of continuous radiation be placed behind the shock-tube test section in Fig. 5. Given the appropriate windows, a spectroscop-ically equipped observer on the near side of the tube would see emission spectra of the type shown in Fig. 6 only if the background radiation were held down to a low level. If the background continuum were then turned up, so to speak, so that its brightness exceeded the Planck (blackbody)

function appropriate to the shock-tube temperature, our observer would then see the shock-tube spectra in absorption against the intense background. By so adjusting the external source that one finds the reversal point from bright-line to dark-line spectra, one puts in evidence the shock tube's Planck function, which is to say its temperature, without recourse to any atomic constants save the velocity of light and Planck's constant.

This is accomplished with our shock tube by means of a very bright, pulsed flash lamp [27, 28], whose continuum intensity varies in times suitably short that reversal can be clearly observed once or several times during the 100-μsec interval of interest. Essentially, what one measures is the population ratio of the two atomic energy levels associated with the given spectral line. A good test of the customary equilibrium assumptions is that all lines of all elements shall demonstrate reversal at the same temperature and that this temperature shall correspond to the ionization and gas-kinetic temperatures found by other means.

The first line-reversal results in the present program are shown in Fig. 7. In the lower graph, reversal temperatures for neon lines behind the first reflected shock are compared to the temperatures predicted from shock-tube theory and the primary shock Mach number. Although the method is not precise, owing to low optical depth in the lines studied, the results are definitely in the range hoped for. Much more precise measurements are now underway, in conjunction with definitive hydrodynamic calculations of real gas effects. As far as we are aware, these reversal measurements in the range 10,000°–15,000°K are pioneering ones; we expect them to yield many valuable data in this and other laboratories. Given sufficient precision, they may offer the possibility of cross-checking the radiative and thermal temperature scales in this range.

Furthermore, the upper graph of Fig. 7 suggests that useful gaseous states well above 15,000°K may be attained, in the same experiments, behind multiply reflected shock waves. Of course it remains to be shown that this region is so free of inhomogeneities as the well-formed plasma behind the reflected shock. This, too, will be looked into further.

The present data on line-reversal also exemplify a trend in our work, namely, to augment photographic procedures with multichannel photoelectric recording. With conventional shock tubes, which cannot profitably be fired at 1-min intervals, photographic spectroscopy is practically essential for recording wide spectral ranges; its main drawback is the requirement of absolute, heterochromatic photodensitometry of films, which is tedious and gives intensity precisions of 5% at best. With several photoelectric channels, one can easily record a chosen subset of the data under higher precision without, however, depending solely on

wavelength scans over a long series of experiments. The reversal measurements were made by means of slitted "light pipes" in the spectrographic image plane, each feeding its own photomultiplier. Some of the fiber bundles were located on spectral lines and others in the line-free continuum between.

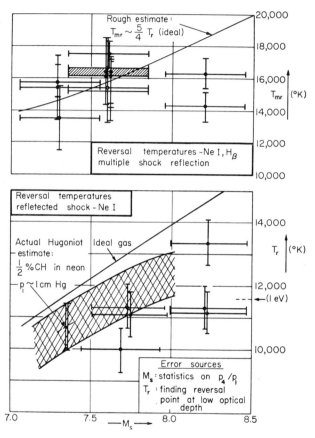

Fig. 7. Comparison of predicted and observed line-reversal temperatures, demonstrating agreement to better than 20%. The case of principal interest is shown in the lower graph, behind the first reflected shock where most of the present spectroscopic work is done. Refined calculations and measurements will enable much more precise comparisons, both here and in upper graph where predicted temperature is rough approximation.

Spectral line profiles are also recorded with a multichannel photoelectric device (called a SQUID, for sequential image dissector) shown in Fig. 8. The essential feature of this device is that the clean geometry of a microscope cover-glass is combined with light pipe flexibility, so that

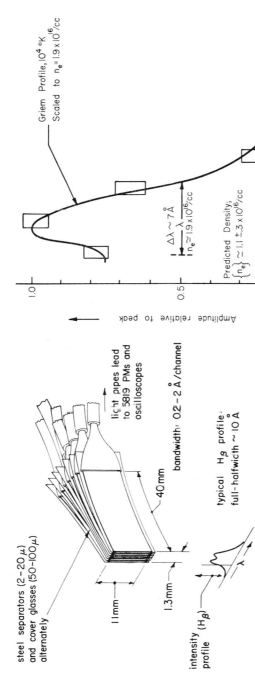

steel separators (2–20μ)
and cover glasses (50–100μ)
alternately

light pipes lead
to 5819 PMs and
oscilloscopes

11mm

40mm

1.3mm

bandwidth: 0.2–2 Å/channel

typical Hβ profile
full-halfwidth ~10 Å

intensity
profile (Hβ)

Griem Profile, 10^4 °K
Scaled to $n_e = 1.9 \times 10^{16}$/cc

$\Delta\lambda \sim 7$Å
λ
$n_e \simeq 1.9 \times 10^{16}$/cc

Predicted Density;
$\{n_e\} \simeq 1.1 \pm .3 \times 10^{16}$/cc

Slit width ~0.7Å

4860   4870   4880

— λ (Å) —

Amplitude relative to peak

1.0

0.5

0.0

FIG. 8 (above). Sequential image dissector (squid) for precise partition of spectral line profiles into narrow wavelength bands. Particular use for Hβ profiles is indicated schematically. This method of joining glasses to light pipes used in second model of squid.

FIG. 9 (right). Wavelength (single-channel) scan over Hβ profile in a set of eight similar experiments, using only one squid channel for preliminary tests. Theoretical profile shows expected nature of result.

many narrowly spaced wavelength bands can be observed by a set of photomultipliers. Figure 8 shows the squid model now in use; the data given here were taken with a prototype that required considerable compensation for differing angular properties of the channels.

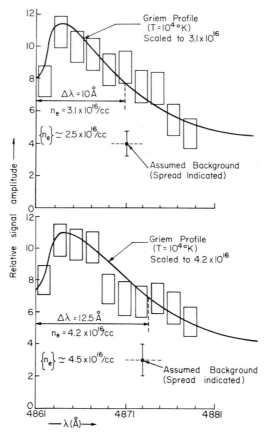

FIG. 10. Typical H_β profiles from two shock-tube experiments, using first model of multichannel squid. Scaling the observations to the theoretical shapes as indicated gives agreement in electron densities to 20% or better. The error bars shown here arise from calibration difficulties, due in turn to details of light-pipe termination and consequent sensitivity to angular properties of illumination. Second model of squid (Fig. 8) superior in many respects.

To check the operating principle of the squid, one channel was studied with the usual laboratory light sources and then tuned over the H_β profile during the course of several similar shock-tube runs. The results are shown in Fig. 9. Then the first multichannel squid was assembled and used in many experiments; two typical runs are given in Fig. 10. In all

cases, one can fit the data to expected profiles and thereby estimate the electron densities from the halfwidths [29]. These estimates are indeed comparable to calculated electron densities for shock-tube runs of this type, and so we have confirmed the expected range of conditions from yet another point of view. Further observations and developments with squid devices will soon be reported [30].

In this section, we have seen that the conventional shock tube gives high-temperature results for electron density and temperature which are within 20% of expectations. Thus, an important step is made toward the study of light elements and their ions under those conditions. The necessary improvements of instruments are clear and are underway, so that new line-strength data will soon be available on such elements as sulphur, carbon, and the halogens. We expect that these data will be useful for checking approximate methods of calculating line strengths and for measuring plasma conditions and elemental abundances in a variety of light sources.

IV. CONCLUSION

The Institute's experimental studies of collisional and radiative processes at the atomic level will continue along those lines of importance in understanding laboratory and astrophysical plasmas. Ample evidence exists for the dual character of plasma physics as a scientific discipline. It is generally true that both two-body and collective particle interactions must be understood in order to have a complete picture, whereas one type of process or the other may dominate in any particular case. Together with the Institute's theoretical and experimental studies of collective processes, we expect the atomic experiments introduced here to contribute valuable data for future developments in plasma physics.

ACKNOWLEDGMENT

This research was initially supported by the U.S. Air Force Office of Scientific Research and is now supported by the NASA Office of Space Science and Applications through Grants NsG-283 and NsG-359.

REFERENCES

1. McDaniel, E. W., "Collision Phenomena in Ionized Gases," particularly Chapter 6. Wiley, New York, 1964.
2. Hasted, J. B., "Physics of Atomic Collisions," particularly Chapter 12. Butterworth, London and Washington, D.C., 1964.
3. Bond, J. W., Watson, K. M., and Welch, J. A., "Atomic Theory of Gas Dynamics," particularly Chapter 4. Addison-Wesley, Reading, Massachusetts, 1965.

4. Massey, H. S. W., *Rept. Progr. Phys.* **12**, 248 (1949); Hasted, J. B., *Advan. Electron. Electron Phys.* **13**, 1 (1960).
5. Cable, P. G., for the Atomic Collision Group, Atomic Collision Research. Univ. of Maryland Tech. Note BN-404 (June 1965).
6. Coggeshall, N. D. and Jordan, E. B., *Rev. Sci. Instr.* **14**, 125 (1943).
7. Hagstrum, H. D., *Rev. Sci. Instr.* **24**, 1122 (1953).
8. Hughes, A. L. and Rojansky, V., *Phys. Rev.* **34**, 284 (1929).
9. Schütze, W. and Bernhard, F., *Z. Physik* **145**, 44 (1956); Daly, N. R., *Rev. Sci. Instr.* **31**, 264, 720 (1960); Afrosimov, V. V., Gladkovskii, I. P., Gordeev, Yu S., Kalinkevich, I. F., and Fedorenko, N. V., *Soviet Phys. Tech. Phys. English Transl.* **5**, 1378, 1389 (1961); Eubank, H. P. and Wilkerson, T. D., *Rev. Sci. Instr.* **34**, 12 (1963); Ogilvie, K. W., McIlwraith, N., Zwally, H. J., and Wilkerson, T. D., NASA Tech. Note, TN D-2111 (1964).
10. Hasted, J. B., *Proc. Roy. Soc. (London)* **A205**, 421 (1951).
11. Hasted, J. B., *Proc. Roy. Soc. (London)* **A212**, 235 (1952).
12. Wolf, F., *Ann. Physik* **23**, 185, 627 (1936); **25**, 527, 737 (1936).
13. Hasted, J. B. and Steddeford, J. B. H., *Proc. Roy. Soc. (London)* **A277**, 466 (1955).
14. Ghosh, S. N. and Sheridan, W. F., *J. Chem. Phys.* **26**, 480 (1957).
15. Petschek, H. E., Rose, P. H., Glick, H. S., Kane, A., and Kantrowitz, A., *J. Appl. Phys.* **26**, 83 (1955).
16. Laporte, O. and Wilkerson, T. D., *J. Opt. Soc. Am.* **50**, 1293 (1960).
17. Kolb, A. C. and Griem, H. R., High Temperature Shock Waves, *in* "Atomic and Molecular Processes" (D. R. Bates, ed.), Chapter 12. Academic Press, New York, 1961.
18. Wiese, W. L., "Proceedings of the Tenth Colloquium Spectroscopicum Internationale" (E. R. Lippincott and M. Margoshes, eds.), p. 37. Spartan Books, Washington, D. C., 1963.
19. Griem, H. R., "Plasma Spectroscopy." McGraw-Hill, New York, 1964.
20. Charatis, G. and Wilkerson, T. D., *Phys. Fluids* **5**, 1661 (1962); "Proceedings of the Sixth International Conference on Ionization in Gases," Vol. III, p. 401. SERMA, Paris, 1963.
21. Bauer, S. H., Kiefer, J. H., and Loader, B. E., *Can. J. Chem.* **39**, 1113 (1961).
22. Koopman, D. W., *Phys. Fluids* **7**, 1951 (1964); *J. Opt. Soc. Am.* **54**, 1354 (1964).
23. Elton, R. C. and Griem, H. R., *Phys. Rev.* **135**, A1550 (1964); Day, R. A. and Griem, H. R., *Phys. Rev.* **140**, A1129 (1965).
24. Garton, W. R. S., Parkinson, W. H., and Reeves, E. M., *Astrophys. J.* **140**, 1269 (1964); Goldberg, L., Parkinson, W. H., and Reeves, E. M., *Astrophys. J.* **141**, 1293 (1965).
25. Charatis, G., Doherty, L. R., and Wilkerson, T. D., *J. Chem. Phys.* **27**, 1415 (1957).
26. Kurlbaum, F., *Z. Physik* **3**, 189 (1902); Fery, L. *Compt. Rend.* **13**, 909 (1903); Kohn. H., *Z. Physik* **33**, 957 (1932).
27. Garton, W. R. S., *J. Sci. Instr.* **30**, 119 (1953); Garton, W. R. S. and Rajaratnam, A., *Proc. Roy. Soc. (London)* **A70**, 815 (1957); Garton, W. R. S., *J. Sci. Instr.* **36**, 1 (1959).
28. Charatis, G. and Hershey, T. L., A Flash-Lamp Source of High Intensity Continuous Spectra. Univ. of Maryland Tech. Note BN-361 (July 1964).
29. Mabry, G. and Charatis, G., to be published.
30. Miller, M. H., Wilkerson, T. D., and Hunter, J. R. W., "Proceedings of the Culham Conference on UV and X-Ray Spectroscopy of Plasmas." Inst. of Physics, London, 1965.

High-Current Gas Discharges

ALAN C. KOLB

U.S. NAVAL RESEARCH LABORATORY
WASHINGTON, D.C.

High-current, pulsed gas discharges in single-turn coils provide a simple means for the generation of temperatures in the 50–1000 eV range. Because of the high electron densities (typically 10^{16}–10^{17} cm^{-3}) in the magnetically compressed plasma, the kinetic degrees of freedom are rapidly thermalized. Thus, spectroscopic techniques are particularly useful for temperature and density determinations. The quantitative results show that energetic plasmas can be contained for times of the order 10 μsec. There are various factors that presently limit the temperature and confinement time. These limitations and the historical development of this line of research were discussed.

Subject Index